RHYME
VERSES
REASON

ACKNOWLEDGEMENTS

The publishers and editors are grateful for the efforts of the following individuals in making this anthology possible:

Thelma McGrath, Thomas McGrath, Sandra Richards,
Joanne Sydenham, and Roger Thomas of Prontaprint, Paignton

RHYME
VERSES
REASON

An Anthology
of verse from the
younger generation

Vanessa Sydenham
Editor

Steve Sydenham
Publisher and Managing Editor

ISBN 0-9528964-8-6

Published by
Poetry In Print
PO Box 141
Paignton
TQ3 1YY

Printed In Scotland
by Bell & Bain Ltd., Glasgow

INTRODUCTION

Welcome to our third anthology of verse specifically for children and young adults. This came about as a direct result of a competition open to schools and we sincerely thank teachers and parents for their enthusiasm and for helping to make the competition and the anthology such a success.

Congratulations to the winners of the competition and to all of our young contributors, well done, a superb effort by all concerned. Most of the poems that appear within these pages are from young poets whose work is appearing in print for the first time and for many we are sure it will not be the last.

The competition was open to all ages and abilities and for some of the contributors an extraordinary effort was required simply to submit an entry. To these children in particular the excitement of seeing their work published means so much and we sincerely hope this will help to encourage them to write even more in the future. The comments made by their teachers and parents has been most rewarding to all concerned at Poetry In Print.

Theories of what a poem should be are only of minor importance here. It is more important that the student has taken the time to write something, perhaps loosely poetic, but interesting and often unique. The editors have truly enjoyed putting this anthology together. The poems are written with such honesty and openness, coupled with a lively imagination and expression that can only come from young minds.

We wish all of our young contributors much success for the future and hope all of their dreams and aspirations come true and we thank them very sincerely for their efforts.

CONTENTS

Introduction	v
Contest winners	vi
The poems	7
Biographies of poets	457
Index of poets	490

Prizewinners
Open Poetry Competition for Schools

15-18 Years

1st: **Caroline Anderson** / Walton, Essex   **Tendring Technology College**
2nd: **Leah Bulloch** / Great Yarmouth, Norfolk   **Lynn Grove High**

Runners-up:

Holly Barker (St Hilda's R.C. Girls High)
Jenna Biddell (Swanmore Secondary)
Gemma Breakwell (Loughborough Girls High)
Kelly Savile (Bishopsford Community School)
Beverley Willbourne (Milham Ford)

Becky Barton (St. Bedes)
Bryony Boutell (St. Hilda's RC Girls High)
Harriet Pinel (All Hallows R.C.)
Anna Wakefield (The Corsham School)
Amber Wilson (Swanmore Secondary)

11-14 years

1st: **Danielle Ward** / Lockington, Derbys   **Loughborough Girls High**
2nd: **Hannah Aspin** / Higher Ford, Lancs   **St. Hilda's R.C. Girls High**

Runners-up:

David Breakell (Borden Grammar)
Emily Burns (Lynn Grove High)
Natasha Goldup (The North School)
Rachel Kett (Rainsford High)
Imogen Stoddart (Rank House Middle)

Rachel Brennan (Sweyne Park)
Laura Easton (Sladen Middle)
Erika Gulbrandson (The Magna Carta School)
Zoey Seaton (Bishopsford Community)
Lula Teunissen (Oxford High)

8-11 years

1st: **Natalie Titmus** / Singleton, Kent   **Great Chart Primary School**
2nd: **Rachel Reynolds** / Norbury, London   **St. James The Great Primary**

Runners-up:

Chynalouise Atherton (Manor Beach Primary)
Jonathan Craig (Christ Church CE Primary)
Jack Gould (Theydon Bois Primary)
Charlotte Lander (Crockenhill Primary)
Alastair Prince (Aston Fields Middle School)

Sophie Bowsher (Zouch Primary)
Luke Donovan (Springfield Primary)
Sam Grant (Two Waters Primary)
Harriet Lockyear (John Hampden Primary)
Chelsea Wood (Zouch Primary)

7 & under

1st: **Charlotte Anderson** / Swadlincote, Derbys **Belmont Primary School**
2nd: **Kieran Brownfield** / Heamoor, Cornwall   **Heamoor County Primary**

Runners-up:

Hannah Boukhobza (Fleet Infant)
George Daniel (Chilworth CE Primary)
Rachel Horner (Whitehill Junior)
Catherine Rhodes (St Marys Catholic Primary)
Julia Ryrie (Aycliffe Drive Primary)

Susannah Cohen (Dr. South's Primary)
Jordan Dormer (Aycliffe Drive Primary)
James Montague (Aycliffe Drive Primary)
Emma Rogers (Little Chalfont Combined)
Shanise Webster (Cliff Park First School)

Congratulations to <u>ALL</u> entrants for such a magnificent effort - Well Done

First Prize Winners

Untitled

I am the eldest of my parent's children,
I am the youngest of my parent's children,
But I can never be the middle child for I am the only one.
When I was two years, one month, one day,
A car hit my father's and took him away,
Did he die with ease? Did he die in pain?
These are the questions I torment myself with, again and again.
How could he not make it? Was our love not enough?
How dare he leave this world without us?
I did not know him but I miss him so much.
Feelings of anger, bitterness and fear,
This is why I shed tear after tear.
Day by day, I change from the little girl he knew,
As I struggle to become what he would have wanted me to.
That starts feelings I do not want to feel,
How am I supposed to be normal,
When this wound will not heal?
I am the eldest of my parent's children,
I am the youngest of my parent's children,
I can never be the middle, for I am the only one.

Caroline Anderson (Age 15)

Orphaned

Watching the world go crawling by
Tears of torture envelop my eye
My mouth is dry, like crinkled leaves
My limp arms surrounded by ripped, ragged sleeves.

My insides are shrinking with a crippling pain
And my back is feeling like lead again
Feeble coughs are seeping away
From my arid mouth, as they do every day.

My stomach is engulfed with an anguishing cloud
And ravenous feelings almost scream out loud
The dusty street is like the Devil's hell
As it haunts my day, and my night as well.

My body is stinging like a nest of bees
And aches and grazes are piercing my knees
Looks of venom are hurled at me by people passing by
But my skin's too shrivelled and painful for me to move, however I try.

I'm seen as dirt, to be brushed away
In another agonising, harrowing day
An orphan since the age of three
The dusty streets are home for me.

Danielle Ward (Age 12)

Anne Frank

Hopelessly I write with the faint branches on my window,
Wondering sadly if I will see my friends,
Dreamy clouds floating with a deadly stream of blood,
Soundless rain tapping on my window,
Lying there my secrets drift,
As the fear of death comes to me,
My circulation suddenly disappears,
Fearing the Germans, I have an uneasy sleep,
Imprisoned in this box,
A hushed silent wind,
I feel lifeless from blood shots and frozen from the suffering
Will it ever end?
I soon was in pain,
Then everything was a blur of horror.

Natalie Titmus (Age 10)

Marshmallow Sky

Lying alone in a summer meadow,
I feel the winds warm breeze on my face
I hear the buzz of a bumble bee nearby
Then I glance up at the sky
What are these shapes of fluffy white?
Like cotton wool in a bed of blue
A flurry of snow that's brand new
Baby polar bears snuggled in soft fur
To smother me in a fleece of velvet white
What are these shapes pure and bright in a pool of brilliant light
Candyfloss cushions to sink into
Deep and woolly fuzzy and warm
I wish I could reach my marshmallow sky
To touch and taste before it floats on by

Charlotte Anderson (Age 7)

Second Prize Winners

Life's Mystery

Is life a dream? Are we dreaming?
What is life? Has life got a meaning?
Day by day we go our own way
Not knowing what's round the corner or what people might say.

Life is not perfect as we full well know
Questions that are asked, like where will we go?
We travel places and what do we see?
Just life as it was planned out to be.

Love revolves around everyone's life
People get married to become husband and wife
Why is there good? And why is there bad?
Nobody knows why people get sad.

People laugh and people cry
People live and sadly they die
Why are we here if life is so cruel?
Why does this dream end so small?

One day this world will be gone
Then where do we go? Will things still go wrong?
If this life is a dream, then we are dreaming
If this is real then life has real meaning.

Leah Bulloch (Age 15)

The Photograph

Dust will gather on me,
But my face will stay the same.
I was once red-blooded woman,
But now dwell within a frame.
He was once my one true soul mate,
But has now found someone else.
And it pains me to sit back and watch,
From this old dusty shelf.
Yet it's me who made his memories,
And I who filled his heart.
And 'twas me who gave him butterflies,
Right from the very start.
It's my voice that he will hear at night,
My face that he will miss.
When he leans towards his second best,
To pout his goodnight kiss.
Oh love I vow I'll wait for you,
Though dead I'm still your wife.
But for now I'll have to just accept,
You're getting on with life.

Hannah Aspin (Age 12)

Alone

When it's playtime, sitting all alone,
Or sitting at home yapping on the phone,
Remember the times when you were happy.
Crawling around in a babies nappy,
You'll remember what it's like to be . . .
Wandering around feeling free!

Maybe life won't always be kind,
Some people are deaf, some people are blind,
It doesn't matter if you look good or not,
It doesn't matter if you have a lump or a spot,
The main thing is that you always feel fine,
And life feels good all the time!

Don't take life for granted,
With all your friends never be parted,
You never know when you'll need someone,
To chat, to play and have some fun,
Sometimes you might feel lonely,
And sometimes you'll feel that time goes slowly.

Rachel Reynolds (Age 10)

My Pet Dragon

I have a pet dragon who lives with me
He lives in cave not a house or a tree
With his big belly, little arms and big feet
He is rather scary but the smell is not sweet
There is his big snout where out comes smoke
It smells like a barbecue with chips of oak
His teeth are enormous so long and so sharp
It doesn't take him long to eat a big carp
He has a shiny body with scales all over
They are the colour of finest clover
He soars through the sky with the ease of an eagle
Flaps his big wings and chases next door's beagle
He breathes fire and scorches the land
You have to keep a bucket of sand to hand
Well now is the end and I'll finish with this
To have such a monster oh such a wish.

Kieran Brownfield (Age 7)

Silence

Silence is a lonely sea hitting the shore
Silence is a dream about a mysterious place
Silence is the breeze running through the trees
Silence is a candle glowing gently
Silence is a leaf fluttering down
Silence is a baby sleeping

Sophie Astles (Age 6)

Spring

Spring spring lots of fun
Easter eggs and hot cross buns
Daffodils out and tulips too
We could take a trip to the zoo
April brings a birthday for me
Lots of fun at my party
Family and friends all together
Makes me want Spring to last forever

Amy Ashmead (Age 7)

Time

Time is a dark and mysterious element of
A thought provoking existence that we call the 'universe'
Time is a man made matter that helps us count the
Endless 'days' of eternity
But I ask you this,
What is time?
If you look it up in a dictionary, what would it say?
'All the years of past, present and future'
Or
'The continuous existence of the universe'
Perhaps even
'To measure how long something takes'
But how can we define time when it is something
That was not created but just exists?

Becky Barton (Age 16)

Wish Wish Wish

I wish I was taller
I wish my freckles would go
I wish the bully was smaller
I wish my mum wouldn't always say no

I wish I could fly
I wish I had curly hair
I wish the cars wouldn't go by
I wish I was the mayor

I wish I had a doggy
I wish I had a new pencil case
I wish it wouldn't be foggy
I wish I had a different face

I wish I wasn't poor
I wish I had a new hat
I wish my bed wasn't on the floor
I wish I lived in a bigger flat

Oliver Alexander (Age 8)

Please Mrs Ramsden

Please Mrs Ramsden
Charlie's not in today,
He fell off his chair
And now he can't play.

Please Mrs Ramsden
I'm sorry I can't write,
But Daniel has tied my hands
Far too tight.

Please Mrs Ramsden
It's just not fair
Natasha has just trimmed the
Back of my hair.

For goodness sake
Just leave me alone
I don't know the answers
And I want to go home!

I don't know it all
Oh why can't you see!
I'm only a teacher
So DON'T ASK ME!

Nicholas Atkinson (Age 7)

The Witches Spell

Frog breath potion and snail slime lotion,
What a wonderful notion

Witches nails and all things sweet,
And things you know you'll never eat

Horses guts and leeches liver
Things so gross they make you shiver

Dead rats whiskers and fat cats eyes
Cows bladder and wolf meat pies

Vampires fangs and sickly manure,
And bubble gum from the corner store

Frog breath potion and snail slime lotion
What a wonderful notion

Emily Allen (Age 10)

My Favourite Time

What a wonderful world it is
Especially in the spring
With pretty flowers, leaves on the trees
And beautiful birds that sing
You see lambs in the fields, chicks in their nest
It is the season I like best

There's wonderful blossom in pink and white
There's crocus and snowdrops
What a delight
The mowers are busy on the lawn
The showers are watering the farmers corn

The daffodils sway in the breeze
The gardens are visited by butterflies and bees

This is the end of my little rhyme
To show that spring is my favourite time

Stephen Angood (Age 10)

Foot And Mouth

Deathly Foot and Mouth is a spreading murderer,
Foul Foot and Mouth is a creeping predator waiting for its prey,
Gruesome Foot and Mouth is a horrid verse from the song 'Tragedy',
Killing disease is the opposite of a beautiful birth,
Vile Foot and Mouth is an octopus spreading out its tentacles,
Awful Foot and Mouth is a dead night.

Emma Arnold (Age 10)

The Teacher Creatures

Teachers teachers,
They're the worst ever creatures
Some are ugly and some try to be sweet
But none are better than your rare parakeet

The school the school is a place for work
It's also the place where teacher creatures lurk
The headmaster teacher, he rules the lot,
Beware! Beware! of his cauldron pot!

Teacher creatures are from the outer space
They came to earth to destroy the human race
There's no escape! I tell you now!
Don't ever choose to have a row

They have some powers I've never seen
To have a conversation, I'm not very keen
Their breath their breath will wake the dead,
But I'm not coming out of my cosy bed!

Seretse Alleyne (Age 10)

The Sea

As I rush up onto the open shore,
I crash upon the rocks,
And bring up shells, more and more,
Boats come out of their docks,
And make waves for the children to play in,
What fun.

Lifeboats wizz around, saving people,
Who can't swim, who are about to take a
Deadly drown

My sea life swim amongst me,
They are my pets, my people, my family,
My friends
And oh, how I wish people would not catch
Them in nets.

Sophie Ashton (Age 9)

Mosi - au-Tunya

The Mosi-au-Tunya's noise is deafening
Its spray is like glistening teardrops in the sun
Smoke spreading out and sliding
Rainbows like a sparkling prism
Waters crashing over the edge like a puddle
Splashing over the kerb
It's splashing violently over the edge
Gorges deep as a full length football pitch
I'm looking down at the bottom of the pitch
It's shouting like a roaring ocean

The smoke is thundering which resembles its name
Rocks slimy from gallons of water
Rocks feel like newts bodies
Feet disappearing in spreading fog

The smoke is thundering which resembles its name
Rocks slimy from gallons of water
Rocks feel like newts bodies
Feet disappearing in spreading fog

Holly Aucutt (Age 11)

Untitled

There are many ways to travel
Would you like to go to Spain?
Then zoom down to the airport
And get on an aeroplane.

There are many ways to travel
Would you like to drift and float?
Make up your mind and come along
Let's go and get a boat.

Sophie Aggar (Age 7)

The Shining Sun

The sun is like a queen's palace,
Glittering with all the gold,
The sun is like a diamond's eye,
Shining down from high above,
The sun is like a beautiful sunset,
Shining down on the prince of sleep,
The sun is like a crystal ball
So pretty and bright,
The sun is like the lord of knights,
Ruling people in heaven,
The sun is like a touch of heaven

Jade Ackroyd (Age 11)

Secrets Of The Savannah

As the sun rose hot in the breeze
The green of the leaves on trees
Went brown and fell to the ground
The river was cool but warm
And reflections were there at the crack of dawn
Birds and butterflies in the air
Weeds, water everywhere
As I walked by a herd of animals
I saw some people on the back of camels.

Hunters ran by and shot elephants passing by
As the sun went down and up came the night sky
Peaceful and calm everywhere felt
A beautiful scent in the air was smelt
At the end of another perfect day
Animals, people plodding in their own way
They can feel the breeze upon their faces
It came from the poshest and poorest places
Whilst there in the distance, elephants lay
And lions and tigers stood, stalking their prey
Everyone's waiting for another day

Chynalouise Atherton (Age 11)

Spring Time

Spring - my favourite season.
Pink blossom, animal babies and birds starting to sing.
Rare snowdrops, butterflies and lambs being born.
In your garden, buds on plants appear.
New leaves, longer days and Easter is here.
Getting warmer, daffodils and tulips by my garden shed.

Claire Atkins (Age 7)

Secondary Transfer - New School, New Life

This is where my life begins
Set your goals and achieve many wins
Start your year without any fear
Give your achievements a great big cheer
Achieve your best in the test
Then lay back and leave the rest

This is where my life begins to settle
Sitting there like a boiled kettle
Twists and turns and many bends
Soon I will be moving on
This was where the sun had shone

This is where my old life begins to end
Say goodbye to my best friend
Start to say all your bye's
Then forget all your white lies

Dean Anderson (Age 11)

Underneath The Silence

Underneath the silence I can hear. . . .

The lions breath from a mile away as it crawls nearer to me
The screams from children that are being tortured
The sizzling sausages in a hot pan
The fizz from a coke can opened at a disco
The pop of a champagne bottle at a wedding

Underneath the silence I can feel . . . . .

The lions claws gripping my skin, tearing my flesh with anger
The soft lions mane brushing against my skin in a forest
The rough surface underneath me as I try to save my friend from the war
The cool water flowing through my toes as I paddle in a tropical ocean
The breeze of a ghost walking straight through me

Kirie-Lea Ashley (Age 11)

Yellow

Yellow is the bright sun
Yellow is the colour of a flamey fire
Yellow is a bright Yellow daffodil
Yellow is a curly banana
Yellow is the colour of happiness

Emily Andrews (Age 6)

The Singing Meadow

In the singing meadow
Flowers, lambs, sheep and grass
It's so peaceful when you get there
You will never want to leave
Sticky grass, mud and swamps
Lambs leaping in the the grass
Swallows swiftly gracefully
Flying high above in the sky

You will hear the meadow singing
What a noisy place it is

In the singing meadow
Birds singing, fairies having parties
Dancing gracefully sparkling in the night
All is quiet badgers snoring rabbits munching
Foxes creeping, running spiders,
Animals are running wildly
Night has fallen in the singing meadow

You will hear the meadow singing
What a noisy place it is

All is quiet not a peep

Natasha Alison (Age 8)

The Storm

The wind was flashing
And the leaves are rushing
In the sky it is flashing
And the windows are smashing
And houses are burning
Rain is pounding
Cars are crashing
Trees are breaking
People are crying

Jake Adams (Age 8)

Forever

I feel I need to
Protect me from
A tall white vampire
It shouts!
It's got blood on
It's teeth!
It is disgusting
From inside it sucks our blood
Takes us forever

Mobeen Akhtar (Age 10)

Leeds United

Marching on together
We're gong to see you win
Tra la la la la
We are the best
Better than the rest,
LEEDS, LEEDS, LEEDS.

When Leeds play a team
They look really mean
Viduka, Smith, they rule,
Bowyer, Radabe, they're cool.

Marching on together
We're going to see you win,
Tra la la la la la
We are the best
Better than the rest
LEEDS LEEDS LEEDS

Go on LEEDS don't stop
Until you get to the top

Danny Austin (Age 11)

The Writer Of This Poem

The writer of this poem
Is as foolish as a lemming
Total rubbbish at science
But invents like Ian Flemming!

As witty as a boffin
When he puts his mind to it
But uses on his worst days
A ketchup rinse on his footy kit!

As comical as a monkey
As loud as a bell's ring
But one bad thing about him
Is he listens to music by Sting!

He watches Coronation Street
He always picks his nose
He listens to rubbish music
He has filth between his toes!

James Anderson (Age 10)

Bomb

Ten seconds to go
What will I do
Nine seconds to go
It's nearly there
Eight seconds to go
Even closer
Seven seconds to go
What will happen?
Six seconds to go
I'm going to die
Five seconds to go
Four seconds to go
Three seconds to go
Two seconds to go
One second to go

BOOM!!!

Joshua Atkinson (Age 10)

I'll Follow You

I'll follow you through
The automatic doors
I'll follow you where ever you go
Over trolleys under trolleys
Where the fruit goes
I'll hear what you say
I'll follow you foot by foot.

I'll go to bed with you
I'll bump my head with you
And I'll never stop following you
And I'm never going away

I'll follow you
And I mean it
I'll follow you

Day by day, night by night

I will see you
You will see me
I'll never take my eyes off you
Even if you go away
I'll follow you, I really mean it.

Zoe Attrill (Age 8)

Aliens

A ll of them kill,
L ust for death,
I n secret they hide,
E very brother is one,
N ever let them touch you,
S lipping into shadows with victims.

Jonathan Abbott (Age 10)

Horses

Horses are high,
Horses are small
Horses are fast,
Horses are magnificent.

Tasia Assimakopoulos (Age 6)

My Poem

My poem, what is a poem
A set of words
A feeling
Or just a meaningless sentence
But for me a poem is a release
Of a desire,
Of a life
I will never see

Murray Aldrich (Age 12)

Spring

In Spring it's nice to play
But it is especially nice in May
Because lots of baby animals are born
My favourite is a little fawn

The opening of all the buds
And in the fields the cows chew their cuds
Birds in the garden building nests
And feeding chicks on small insect pests

Also we musn't forget the buzzing bees
And the gentle rustling of the trees
And there is the wonderful sun
In which we have a lot of fun

Lauren Ashford (Age 9)

Jupiter!

You are orange and yellow
And a very good fellow,
You are the 5th away from the sun
You probably weigh more than 15 tonnes
You are the one made up of gasses
When you orbit the sun, you make your axis,
Do you play nonsense games?
Sometimes called fiercy flames
Are you alone?
Do you moan?
You need a friend
Or else you'll end.

Kiran Abbas (Age 9)

It Was So Noisy

It was so noisy
I couldn't hear the fire alarm buzzing loudly

It was so noisy
I couldn't hear a grizzly bear's growling echoing

It was so noisy
I couldn't hear a twisting twister twisting

It was so noisy
I couldn't hear the rugby players proudly sing the national anthem

It was so noisy
I couldn't hear a robber crashing through the window

Jonathan Ashfield (Age 7)

The Shark

Deadly and smart
Never been seen
Deadly and keen
Never been seen!

The mother protects her baby
The shark swimming for his life
The shark kills man!

Never been seen
Never been seen
Never been seen

NEVER BEEN SEEN!

Jack Annison (Age 9)

Class Time

Teacher Teacher they're so boring
I don't know why I keep on snoring
I sit at my desk and threw a stress
And that was the end of me

Beverley Arnold-Harman (Age 11)

The Rock

There was a wrestler called Rock
And he lived in a stone Block
His Block fell down
He moved to the town
And decided to live in a sock

Bradley Asquith-Briggs (Age 9)

The Trench!

The trench! worst place you could be
The smell of rotting flesh,
Bits of bodies floating in the trench
When full of water

No man's land full of bodies (decapitated that is)
Massive craters where the shells have landed
Barbed wire at the front of both trenches
And pools of bloody water

Dressing quarters the smelliest place
Men with wounds to their arms, legs and heads
Different quarters for different wounds
Men are dying all the time from the infections going around

Matthew Aldridge (Age 14)

Friends And Bullies

Friendship is important
Everyone has friends,
Friends don't bully you,
Friends understand that,
Friendship is important.

Bullying is cruel,
Bullies are horrible,
Bullies hurt your feelings,
Bullies don't understand,
Bullying is cruel.

And just remember,
To be a good friend,
And not a bully.

Shahanaz Ahmed (Age 9)

The Sea

The sea always seemed so beautiful to me,
A place of peace, thought and tranquillity,
The sun gleaming on the still calm water
Nature's so lovely I said without any falter.

I saw children running around on the beach,
Golden sand supporting their feet,
Building sandcastles used to seem such fun,
Oh I wish I could build one, just one.

I used to be able to make a good fort
My brother would always chant and taunt,
I'll kick it down, I will I mean it,
I'm not being silly it's not a trick.

I looked down towards the sea
I could see all the families having picnics for tea,
It reminded me of my old holidays,
And how they used to be.

Suddenly my thoughts got lost,
A figure ran down the beach,
In to the water and jumped in,
My silence had vanished into ripples in the sea.

Emily Alton (Age 12)

Rat

A Rat Began

He stole a wriggling worm from the ground,
He stole a pink hair from a bird
And made his tail.

He took black coal from a coalmine,
He took the darkness from the sky,
And made his demon eyes.

He snatched the grease from a frying pan,
He snatched a fluffy black coat,
And added grease to make his greasy fur.

He pinched the sharp lead from a pencil,
He pinched the sharpness from a pin,
And formed his teeth.

He gathered the shape from a crescent moon,
He gathered a spike from a hedgehog,
And made his scratching nails.

Finally the rat was complete,
Now it had the five precious things it needed,
So the rat was born.

Sarah Allen (Age 10)

My Mad Family

My house is a mad house
In the morning all the alarms are going off
My mum's shouting "shut up,"
And my dad's downstairs swigging beer

Just before we set off to my grandma's,
I hear the bussing of the electric toothbrush
My brothers are shouting "why do we have to go to grandma's?"
And my dad's downstairs swigging beer

At my grandma's my mum's shouting "stop drinking beer",
My grandad's fixing on his false leg,
My grandma's putting in her false teeth
And my dad's downstairs swigging beer

We get home at 9 o'clock
My brothers are shouting "why do we have to go to bed?"
My mum's shouting "shut up and go to bed",
And my dad's so drunk he can't get up the stairs to bed

Elizabeth Allan (Age 11)

Birthdays

Oh when will they get here?
When will they come?
They should be here now
It's half past one!

Why's no-one here yet?
Why are they all late?
Is it my watch that is fast?
Or have they the wrong date?

I'm sure I said it's today,
And at half-one,
Why is no-one here yet?
Why has no-one come?

Did I say it's tomorrow?
Did I say it's next week?
Or maybe I said . . . . .
Or maybe . . . . . .
Or maybe . . . . . .
HERE THEY COME

Emily Anstis (Age 10)

After The Storm

Alone, standing bent with a small, nut fruit,
Red stems, smooth hands clapping the wind.
Raindrops flow in its channels,
And soggy forts are washed away
To house the grounded dead.

Cupped hands sieve the beams,
A trickling sunlight potion,
With golden drops that dance away.

As dawn spreads, the fallen leaves
Cover terrible work with a brilliant finish.
Layers of spent evil, shaded that no light
May creep beneath the blanket of dry tears.

The tree weeps with desperate loss,
But cradles in furrows new life near its heart.
All is forgiven but never forgotten,
A thousand stories flow in veins,
Riding the rings, stretching fingers.
The night's spoils: blood-milk sap,
To feed the next infant.

Harriet Boulding (Age 16)

Dear Mum

I went for a run
I eat a bun
My sister eats some crisps
Crisps are lovely for a snack
I went to the meadow to play
And a bird got in my way
And we started to play

Sabrina Akhter (Age 10)

My Poem

There once was a number named pi
Who frequently liked to get high
All he did every day
Was sit in his room and play
With his imaginary friend named i.

There once was a letter named e
Who took way too much LSD
She thought she was great
But that fact we must debate;
We know she wasn't greater than three (3)

There once was a log named Ln
Whose life was devoted to Sin
She came from a tree
Whose base was shaped like an e
She is the most natural log I've seen

Suki Alalasundralingam (Age 16)

Love Poem!

Love is a dove gliding and swooping
High and low with no place to go.

Love is like a bird, I want to fly away,
Don't know where my soul is,
Don't know where my home is.

Love is like a candle burning out
And it's now burning my snout.

Love is like a caramel cream,
Love is like a dream,
But suddenly turns into a nightmare.

Love is like the story,
The hare and the tortoise race,
Sometimes it's fast, sometimes it's slow

You really don't know!

Timaisha Masomi Abbott (Age 12)

Anger

Anger is a flamey red,
It tastes like burnt paper,
And smells like dull burning rubber,
Anger looks like a volcano erupting,
It sounds like grinding teeth,
And feels like a disease spreading.

Peter Auton (Age 11)

Peter And The Wolf!

There was a boy called Peter
His grandfathers name was Grumpy Cheater
He was playing in the garden
When he saw his friend bird
Who came from his holidays in harder

When he saw a duck in the pond
Quack Quack
I knew you would hop along
While they were sitting
The bird was singing

Along came a sneaky cat
Who was really fat
And sat next to Peter
Who was acting like a scary creature

Thump! thump! thump!
Along came a wolf
Climb! climb! climb!
Up the tree they ran
As quick as they can

Sabihah Afshan (Age 10)

I Know

I know a person who lives in West Bridgford,
Who lives in a house quite near a new farm.

I know a person who has quite nice neighbours,
Who come round quite often with fresh cakes and pies.

I know a person who has a grey pony,
Who can be quite naughty but is sweet at heart.

I know a person who's really quite tiny,
Who's got brown hair and eyes and feet at size five.

I know a person who really likes English,
Who likes reading stories and writing them too.

I know a person who really likes flying,
Who enjoys taking off and especially loves landings.

I know a person who loves playing games,
Who really loves winning but really hates losing.

I know a person who does enjoy skiing,
Who loves going fast but only when she can stop!

I know a person who does know this person,
I know a person and that person is me!

Lizzie Allcock (Age 12)

Forest Animals

All the forest animals love to play
All the way throughout the day
All the forest animals like the mice
As they are very kind and nice

All the forest animals are very sweet
Always scavenging for something to eat
When the winter is bleak
They shall seek some peace for sleep

The rabbits hop around
Bound, bound, bound!
Then in the Spring the little fawn
Shall be born

Felicity Allmand (Age 10)

Cupboard Love

Deep, dark, brown eyes,
Looking longingly at me,
Looking adoringly at me,
Pleading with me,
Begging me to notice him,
Assuring me of his love.
His whole body leans towards me,
I am the only one who matters . . .
Until I give him my last piece of toast -
Who'd have a dog!!

Caroline Amos (Age 12)

Communication

E-mails are exceedingly fast.
Telegrams are a thing of the past.
Will communication change in time?
It may never change in time.

It will be a part of me,
If it changes this century.
Although the seasons change many times,
Communication will never change from lines.

It may be smaller, more hi-tech or weightless,
It will never be pointless.
Communication keeps people in society,
Without it they would be solitary.

Maybe you will see
What communication will be
In your century.
Communication will be,
Communication will be . . .

Stephen Adams (Age 15)

The Jaguar

I am sleek and black
Most of my kind are spotted
But I was born as black as the darkest night
I am a creature of strength and rage
I can kill you with one swipe of my paw
Yet you hunt me for my fur
I can climb the tallest tree
And swim a mile across the river
I can kill anything in this jungle
I live in the forests of the Amazon
But you chop down all my trees
Soon there will be nothing
I am a bolt of lightening
When I catch my prey
My roar is as loud as the bang of a bomb
You are a meal for me
I will rip you apart
With my claws
But only if you harm me

Nick Albrow (Age 11)

Through The Door

Open the door and you will see
Lions and tigers and bumble bees

Open the door and you will see
Dragons and wizards and prophecy

Open the door and you might see
Spells and swords and sorcery

Open the door and you might sight,
Winding corridors and a lot of fright

Open the door and you might meet
A really cold day and a lot of sleet

Open the door and you will see
People and reality and maybe me!

Sâm Alamdary (Age 11)

Lightning

I illuminated the Taj Mahal
I set an oak tree alight
I destroyed everything in my path
I made people scatter like racing horses
I forced dogs all over the town to run into their baskets
I zapped an old man with a walking stick
I slowly disintegrated in to the fluffy white clouds

Andrew Allcock (Age 8)

My Cousin's A Venusian

My cousin's a Venusian
He comes from that fiery planet
For some odd reason he can't abide
The smell and look of granite.

My cousin's a Venusian
I think he's here to stay
On our cosy little planet
Not just for today.

I wish I could be a Venusian
I could run around all day
Shooting other aliens
With my powerful death ray!

Marcus Barnett (Age 9)

The Polar Bear

I look so cute and cuddly
Well that's what people say!
Can I just tell you
"Don't be deceived when you see me
I'm as fierce as a raging bull!"

My teeth are as sharp as razors
My feet are large and padded
My fur is as white as snow
I camouflage quite easily
I hunt patiently for my favourite meal
    "The Seal!"

I love my world
Snow and all
I'm king of the Arctic!!!

Rachael Atkinson (Age 10)

In The Queen's Pocket

In the Queen's pocket I found
A £1,000,0000,0000 note,
A crown,
A silver sword
A pot of wrinkle cream (to stop wrinkles)
A football boot
A baseball bat and
A mini toilet

Zeke Africa (Age 10)

Distracted By A Sunbeam

Alert,
Ears twitching,
Sharp-eyed and vigilant,
Tail thumping and flicking,
She quivers with excitement.

Whistling,
The tiny sparrow,
Only inches away,
Is oblivious to the danger
Which lurks behind the glass.

Distracted,
By the sunbeam
She can never resist,
The contented rumble begins,
Glazed eyes
No longer see,

The
Cat
Sleeps zzzz

Robert Ainsworth (Age 12)

Who Shot Phil?

Who shot Phil?
Did he leave a will
Is he dead or alive
Only the director can decide
Was it Mark or maybe Lisa
They had plenty of reason to pull the trigger,
And see poor Phil dead,
Or could it be Ian or Dan
He took the cafe and the Vic
From right under their noses
They'd like to see him dead
Maybe it was Steve or Mel
They had the best reasons
To kill bad boy Phil
They'll keep us in suspense
For weeks on end
Who shot Phil?

Daniel Atkinson (Age 13)

Equine Glory

As sleek as a greyhound
Swift as a deer
There is nothing that she can't climb and clear
With long slender legs
So sturdy and strong
This is the mare that I bought for a song
She's a little too large
But my, is she pretty
The finest bred horse in the whole of the city
Her eyes shine with spirit
She holds her head with courage and pride
In all of her days she will not leave my side!

Amber Allen (Age 12)

Al The Bus Driver

You all get on my bus every day and every night.
With all your grey, dull faces, thinking I'm really boring
You think I do nothing but drive this bus around the same old route
You carry your little world around in your black briefcase.
Thinking you're the important ones and I'm just the bus driver
But you don't know do you?
You don't have any idea do you?
How do you know what I am?
What I think?
What I feel?

JUST THINK ABOUT IT!

Richard Andrews (Age 12)

In The Cold Dark Depths Of Space

In the cold dark depths of space
Cruises an ancient battle barge,
A lonely place.

Supposed to be empty
Since years gone past
But inside lurks a creature,
Swift, small and fast.

So in space it floats,
It is its home
On a pile of bodies
Turned into its throne . . .

Chris Adams-Salmon (Age 13)

Blue

Blue, bluer than the sky
Whispering, breathing softly
Sparkling in the sun
Shimmering echoes of light.

Crashing, smashing against the cliff
Surrounding, enclosing the land
Protecting, carrying it's vessels
Gently along their paths.

Full of mysteries, secrets we will never know
Brightness, darkness we will never see
Full of life, movement, never understood
Layers of the past in the depths lay buried.

Jemma Appleby (Age 13)

The Owl

I am a snowy owl,
As white as a vanilla ice-cream,
My claws help me catch my food,
As sharp as knives,
My eyes are bigger than a bouncy ball,
Looking for small animals.

Hiding like bugs,
I don't go out in light
But I do go out at night,
When you're all in dream land.

Louise Ashenden (Age 9)

What Is It?

It's crawling on the floor,
It's gone out the back door,
It's eating worms,
It's turned around,
Hide here it comes,
It's in the living room,
It's going to my mum,
Wait it stopped,
It's making a sound,
It's rattling,
Ouch! biting my leg,
It's hit me with a peg,
I slowly pick it up,
And I gave it a bottle,
Because baby boys like that.

Ben Austen (Age 12)

Friends

I have a best friend called Shannon,
She mostly is a pain,
She isn't very tidy,
She also is insane!

I have a friend called Amber,
She always likes to smile,
She also is quite funny
When she tries to run a mile!

Hazel Austen (Age 10)

Football

Football, football
Is so great
I like to play it
With my mate

Football, football
Is so rough
If you are good
You must be tough

Football, football
Needs some balls
To play the game
By its rules

Football, football
Needs a shot
Or it's pointless
Without a plot

Matthew Alps (Age 9)

Sea And Sand

The sun shines brightly
Big waves splash against the shore
The sea creatures stir

Sand castles being made
Shells lie broken on the sand
The tide has gone out
Dolphins jump about
Fish swim all day happily
Whales blow big fountains

Laura Atkinson (Age 10)

Little Sisters

What I hate about little sisters
Is when they scream and squeal
What I like about little sisters
Is when they're asleep and silent
What I hate about little sisters
Is when they scratch and bite
And run off and tell mum that you did it
What I like about little sisters
Is how they play and pretend
And be all sweet and all of that

Jake Aubrey (Age 8)

Sunshine

I shone down at an old lady and made her weep!
I forced a packet of matches to crumple up and set
alight
I helped a magnifying glass burn through a newspaper
Like a hot knife through butter!
I skimmed the grass and it turned to ash!
I slowly started to disappear
The moon covered me fully and I went to bed

David Adams (Age 8)

My Wicked Teacher!

My wicked teacher is so strict
That she smacked me on the bum

My wicked teacher is so strict
That she shouts and bursts my ear drum

My wicked teacher is so strict
That she gave us detention for nothing

So how can we make her stop . . .
LETS EXCLUDE HER!

Jodie Attack (Age 8)

Tiger, Tiger!

Tiger, tiger running through the jungle,
Trying to catch its prey,
The sun is gleaming,
And the tiger sleeps as it is dreaming,
The tiger just sits in the tree,
Waiting to catch a fly or maybe a bee.
In the stream is the reflection of the moonlight,
But the tiger is still running free at night.

Maddie Amor (Age 10)

Whales

Wandering and weaving,
Howling and hurrying,
Acting and acrobatics,
Laying and leaping,
Eating and echoing,
Snoring and sleeping

WHALES

Daniel Allen (Age 8)

Night

As the sun sets in the west,
A strange figure appeared in the east,
Night has appeared sending shadows over the land
As people turn out their lights
The stranger gets bigger and bigger
Everyone's sleeping now
Waving his black cloak over the villages
Clocks strike midnight, ending the silence
Night is sweeping over villages and towns
The sun is rising in the east
And night is returning to his gloomy mountains in the west.

Bethany Allen (Age 11)

Funny Ferocious Finch

My skinny shiny lizard turned into a wizard
While riding a hunky, horrifying hairy horse
I saw a nutty monkey and my friend though that he was funky
When it wrestled with a small, slimy, silky snake
As she looked at my dove my mum fell in love
But did not know he had a pecking, powerful, pretty parrot
Amy's cute fancy fish eats out of a doggy dish
That belongs to her funny ferocious finch

Nicky Ashbrook (Age 10)

Coconut

In Tobago is Gregory Cool
Far from home is Gregory Cool
Hut to live in is Gregory Cool
Scrambled eggs is Gregory Cool
Fried fish is Gregory Cool
Climbing trees is Gregory cool
Coconut milk is Gregory Cool
Swimming with dolphins
That is Cool

Rizwan Ashraf (Age 8)

Red Nose Day

Red nose day is fun
Look out here comes the sun

A boy called Roy
Jumping with joy

Oh no here comes a dragon
Yippee! Mr Red Nose saves the day again

Sam Abbott (Age 8)

Teachers

Grown ups say things like:
Speak up
Less noise
Don't be lazy
Say thank you
Say please
Stand up straight
Put a sock in it
Sit up straight
Take your elbows off the table
Haven't you got a hankie?

Abigail Ayrton (Age 9)

Owl

It swoops around and around
Like spinning hoops off the ground
It looks at you like a cat
And when it moves it's like a bat
It rests high up in the trees
Where it is always free
When it suddenly grabs its prey
The other animals fly away

Joe Avery (Age 9)

Christmas

The snow piles, the wind blows
The clouds gather to form rain.
The moon has risen, showing its glow
The air is crisp and cool
Everyone is sound asleep
The night before Christmas
Dawn awakes
Sunshine and warm air
Everyone's excited
Christmas day is here
Presents, presents piled high
Waiting to be opened
Christmas dinner cooking in the oven.
Christmas pudding bubbling in a pot.
Everyone's eating
Chomping every piece.
It's time to open the presents
Everyone's ripping the Christmas paper
Everyone's enjoying it, having fun
It's a time to remember,
Christmas Day has come.

Kelly Arscott (Age 11)

The Kitten

I'm playful when you get to know m
But I'm sleepy and weary at night
I wrap myself up in a blanket
You can turn off the night light
I'm tiny, sweet and loveable
I'm small and as furry as a ted
I am nervous and I am shy
But I'm still wild and frisky inside
You see that I like to eat
And my favourite dish is meat
I clean myself neatly
I won't make a mess
My family are all bigger than me
They prowl around the jungle
But as for me
I don't, I just want to be your pet

Bethany Atack (Age 8)

That Is The Question

To be or not to be,
That is the question Shakespeare put to us.
I myself would rather have been than not to have been
If you have never been then you wouldn't know what being was like
            and therefore wouldn't miss it.
Because we have been, comprehending never being is impossible.
One day everyone will cease to be and will shortly be forgotten
            as will I and this poem
So in the end we will never know if we've been or if we haven't
Which leaves the question,
Have we actually been at all?

Luke Avron-Cotton (Age 16)

War

Kosovo, Falklands, The Civil War too
They spread diseases not just the flu,
It's evil it's horrible the war is sick
It could have been better if it had been quick
World War II took over five years
That's five years of death and five years of tears
Those poor innocent men fighting for their countries
It should never have happened,
It just wasn't worth it.

Craig Ashworth (Age 14)

My Brother

My brother is stupid, violent, horrible
When we play games he's bad tempered, slightly

He is ugly, stinky, nasty, smelly
When it's dinner he is messy, fat, chubby.

He likes stupid, annoying football
He doesn't like pretty, nice dolls.

Eleanor Andrews (Age 9)

Best Friends

I have three best friends not just one
Every day at playtime we have lots of fun
We greet each other every day
And then we start to play
We always are in loads of trouble
Since there's four of us we're in double
We're running around every day
Or we like to sit and lay
So in the future we won't see each other
But I know we'll be friends forever

Craig Alexander (Age 10)

Fireworks

Crackle crackle pop pop
Wee wee right to the top
Rattle rattle whiz whiz
Boom boom watch them fizz
Come and see the fireworks sizzle
Cover your eyes because they whistle
Zoom zoom boom boom
Sparkles glow watch the show
At the firework display

Edward Adams (Age 10)

Floppy Fish

There was a floppy fish
And he ate a dish
And as he died
He got fried
Then he got took to a shop
And then pop
And that was the end of him!

George Barton (Age 5)

The Family And the Parked Car

The boy got knocked over by the parked car
And landed a mile far
His mum screamed aaah
And landed two miles far
His dad screamed oooh
And landed three miles far
His pet screamed oooh
And landed four miles far
The house which screamed oooh
Aaah, eeeeh
And landed five miles far

Sabah Arqum (Age 10)

If You Want To See A Golden Goose

If you want to see a Golden Goose,
You must go down to the old cave
I know a goose who lives down there
He's got lovely feathers but he's not well mannered
Yes! if you want to see a golden goose
You must go down to the old cave
Then say "Golden Goose come to me"
Then when you see him
Don't stick around or he will bite!

Jodie Atkins (Age 8)

The Zoo

There are lots of animals in the zoo
Elephants, circuses, monkeys too
People laugh while the monkeys swing
And turn to see the birds sing.

The children smile all one day
As they watch the animals play
We all love to go to the zoo
With so many things to do.

Thomas Absalom (Age 8)

From A White Plastic Bag

A soldier gives children sweets
They hold out their hands
They smile through the wire fence.

Jessica Bristow-Jones (Age 15)

My First Flight

Once when I was eight years old,
We went to the airport when it was cold.
We showed our passports what a sight,
I'm surprised they let us on the flight.
We walked onto a really big plane,
My brother must be going insane.
We started going really high,
We broke the limit in the sky.
When we were landing it was bumpy,
But no one was ever, ever grumpy.
When we had reached where we were staying,
My mum and dad at the desk they were paying.
My brother and I were in the pool,
While my mum and dad were keeping it cool.

Leah Allen (Age 11)

The Lion Pride

They slink through the grass,
They're closing in.
Shoulders moving up and down,
Camouflaged in the grass.

Sneaking up on the prey,
Hardly making a sound.
They start to move,
Their prey doesn't budge.

Suddenly they charge,
The prey jerks into life.
The chase is on,
The lions triumph.

Rachel Brock (Age 12)

Winter Wind

Whirling, howling, winter wind
People shivering outside
Howl winter wind.

Cold, shivering wind
Blowing trees down
Howl winter wind.

Across the meadow
Through the trees
Howl winter wind.

Emma Bellerby (Age 7)

Foot And Mouth

F armers closely watch their flock
O nly to expect the worst,
O ne sheep spreads it to the next,
T rails of smoke litter the sky

A nd corpses clutter the ground.
N o one really cares;
D isinfectant cleanses the ground.

M outh Ulcers appear
O ut comes the gun!
U nfortunate sheep are killed.
T hey are killed to prevent the disease.
H ow can such a disease spread?

C arried by birds,
R ats spread it too.
I t's even airborne
S o will the disease ever cease?
I hope so for the farmers' sake.
S hould so many animals die?

Richard Barling (Age 15)

I Shall Tuck Away

I shall tuck away
A teddy bear with no hair
A car, some tar, and a jar
I shall tuck away
A man, a van, a plan and a can
I shall tuck away
A pen, a howling hen, a barking mouse,
An ugly wood louse
I shall tuck away
A bay from a long way away

I shall tuck this all away and run away

Craig Askew (Age 10)

My Dad

The skies light up like fireworks
Before I go to sleep
I think of my dad
And begin to weep.
I think of the good times we had before
He passed away
And I realise he will never come back to me
Forever and a day
But I know, that where he is now
He will be
Looking down on me.

Alec Burgess (Age 16)

The Future

Robotic arms
Electronic children
Bionic slaves
The future comes in waves

The world goes round
But the people stand
Or perch upon lazy planets
Surrounded by computer gadgets

Mothers, fathers, uncles, aunts
Don't exist
All are metal fascists

Destruction looms
Love has vanished
Havoc comes
Peace is banished

Hannah Brownlee (Age 16)

Thoughts

The velvety darkness, of the star-studded sky,
Envelopes me in my thoughts.
The evening wind, circles around me,
And still my thoughts spiral on.
The nothingness that everyone sees,
Is everything to me.
I stand, isolated, alone,
And yet, I am with everyone.
There is silence, but I hear their voices,
There is darkness, but I see a light
A strange calmness washes over me,
And in that one instant
I am truly content.

Bryony Boutell (Age 15)

What Is Yellow?

Yellow is a star
Like a ball of fire
Yellow is a buttercup
Flickering by some wire
Yellow is a teddy
Like my real friend Percy
Yellow is a sunset
Like burning mercy
Yellow is the sand
With a couple of waves
Yellow is Africa
With a great big cave
Yellow is the sun
Which is blazing bright
Yellow is your T-shirt
That shines when you're in the light
Yellow is a butterfly
With bright bright wings
Yellow is Winnie the Pooh
Who loves all my rings.

Annabel Sarah Beese (Age 7)

It Was So Noisy!

It was so noisy that
The walls of the class smashed on the floor with a tumble and crash
It was so noisy that
The children tried to escape out of the classroom
It was so noisy that
The class teacher screeched his head off
It was so noisy that
The book boxes fell on the floor with a CRASH!
It was so noisy that
The people in Africa could hear!

Caitlin Baglow (Age 7)

Spring

Spring is good
Yellow sun shines
Flowers dance in the sun
Green grass blowing
Chicks start hatching
Trees blow in the breeze
Buds start shooting
Spring is good.

Liam Berryman (Age 7)

Number Poem

Ten tall tigers all in love
Nine naughty nannies knitting all the toys
Eight elephants eye to eye eating all the grapes
Seven shivering snakes shuffling around
Six sickly bugs staying in the bathroom
Five fire fighters squirting all the dogs
Four fit frogs flicking all the grass
Three tired turtles thinking about each other
Two tiny tigers playing a nice game
One octopus crawling all about.

Amelia Barnett (Age 6)

Storm At Sea

"Wake up! Wake up! The storm's at sea!
Wake up! Wake up! Please help me!
We're sinking! We're drowning!
Wake up! Wake up! Please help me!"

"Gently gently storm at sea
You're making my best friends scared"

"How did you do it Jesus our friend
It's a miracle, it's a wonder
You just calmed the fiercest thunder"

Nicki Biggs (Age 7)

Pencils

Blue marks on the page
Long and slender, while it moves
In an artist's hand.

Red marks come to play
Entwined between the blue mark,
Mixing as they go.

Black marks come along
To stop the red and blue's play
Blocking them from fun.

Rubber the leader
Has seen what black mark has done
So he rubs black out.

The red and blue mark
Laughed at the black mark's mishap
So they got rubbed ou.!

Philip Broadbridge (Age 15)

The Seal

Small, grey body
Little, tiny tail
Huge, big, round eyes
Teeny weeny, fishy mouth
Soft, beautiful flippers.

Isi Bogod (Age 6)

My Four Seasons Poem

The flowers come out of their house to play
The sky has been freshly painted
A bright green rug the soil puts on
And the trees grow their hair.

Like a flaming fire the sun burns
And back from holiday the birds come
Like a candle stick the ice creams melt
And the hose is a slithering snake.

The trees have a hair cut again
And the grass gets a golden hat
Their nice green coats the bushes take off
And on the road the leaves race.

Trees pull on their white hat and scarf
In a shiny white blanket the grass sleeps
A hard silver rug spreads over the lake
As to the south the sun's warmth flies.

Stephanie Biggs (Age 9)

The Unspoilt Wilds

Everywhere is clean;
There are leaves of gold and green,
Lying on the ground.

Animals are here;
Searching, snuffling, here and there;
Gobbling down all things.

Mountains tall and black;
Shards of black ice in the sky;
With high eerie birds.

Blue glistening lake;
Salmon up a waterfall,
And the flashing sun.

Colin Broadbridge (Age 15)

The Storm

The thunder monster gently awakes
He starts the storm
The clouds begin to cry
Each time the clouds tears get heavier
The sky darkens
The thunder monster gradually pads away.

Ashika Bhatt (Age 7)

A Football

Is this ball so consequential, so solitary?
For this ball will resolve ascendancy for him,
If played with profound hands.
The overlooking silhouettes from the crowd,
Shower the pitch only with twilight,
Nothing with just this ball, he stands in isolation.

His eyes fixate, obstructing vision, intellect,
Only to this innocuous looking prop,
It destroys emotions with its black and white pattern
Maybe black for evil, maybe white for virtuality,
But how can this . . . thing possess so much?

A thousand cries for exultation,
A thousand more for anguish,
With just this one petite commodity,
As empty as those who weep,
When overcome with this possessive instrument,
How does this ball control emotions?
Inside this indistinct ball has feelings,
Has sorrow, has joy but from those
Of which are you?

Yasser Baghdadi (Age 15)

Will Store At The Back Of My Memory

In my memory box I keep . . . .

My long lost Uncle Brendan
The sound of my cousin crying
And the bark of my dog Bella.

In my memory box I keep . . . .

My loving dad acting as if he was the mother
My loving mum picking me up with a big smile
The sound of my sisters arguing.

In my memory box I keep . . . .

The squeaking from my long lost guinea pigs
The love of my Auntie squeezing tightly
The friendship I get from my kind friends.

In my memory box I keep . . . .

The scratching of the hamster
The smell from my Nana and Grandad's cooking
And the smoke from my Grandpa's cigarettes.

Charlotte Butters (Age 10)

Use Your Senses!

Touching the paw of my icy Aunt's dog
Touching the burning green grass on a fresh summer's day
Touching the smooth glass on a silver night.

Listening to the beautiful birds singing across the shiny sky
Listening to the cars zoom like a speed boat
Listening to the chewing of bubble gum and then BANG!

Smelling the lions tangled fur a mile away
Smelling the delicious food from the kitchen
Smelling the rough beds you sleep on.

Tasting the chips that have come out of the fiery oven
Tasting the fiery wood at night
Tasting the marshmallows at night and squeezing them.

Looking at the shadowing beetles
Looking at the glazing sun
Looking at the glittering moon.

Francis Beechinor (Age 6)

Hey, Ape

Through the jungle the ape goes
Stomping and stamping looking for his tea
Fighting, scaring off other apes
Hairy, black, big, frightening
Hey, ape, don't behave like that.

Michael Buck (Age 7)

The Inside Instinct

Whispering keenness, deep breaths and snarling -
The scenes from a snow tight, blanketed battlefield.
For solely one victor will exit it proudly.
Could it be the gruesome and sluggish?
Or could fate have its way for the devil-minded and ruthless?

Both of the hounds are remorseless and savage but the survivor must be the heartless inhuman.
As domesticated Buck, gleams over the horizon, his devilish tricks, win him Spitz's leg.
But alas as the practiced ill-bound fighter screeches in pain the meddlesome Buck strikes strangely again!

His Canadian bitterness, adds to his ongoing rage.
To rend and destroy, became Spitz's main aim.
Buck's molars compressed, they enter Spitz's neck but the Spitzbergen monster made a save with his fangs.

A whirlwind of rushes, was shown by our Buck, but the agile old hound, seemed full of pure luck!
Whoever came last, was dinner for sixty!
Buck took a leap and was over huge Spitz, where his instincts spoke for him as thrice he dug in.
Lolling tongues waiting, the dogs seemed to glow.
Moon-flooded spitz didn't know where to go,
His heart just collapsed - into the snow . . . .

Irwin-Malek Chaïr (Age 11)

Disease

There is no way out, where will I go?
Pressure, tension the adrenaline rush is constant
Stuck in a wondrous commotion
Deep breathing, keep focused, the pain is slow
Exposed to everything the dimness, the brightness
Silence, horror!
Calm, anger, happiness, sorrow and regret
Freedom soft and spiritually meanders away from my grasp.
Helpless and useless, enclosed away from what I once had
There is no way out, where will I go!
No one acknowledges my suffering.
But soon the playful grey shadow will absorb me forever .....

Holly Barker (Age 15)

Looking To History

Kicked, pummelled, worn away,
Disregarded as importance,
Toppling, then tumbling about the feet of towering giants.
Disagreeing with jagged stacks,
Blistered with age, soothed by moss,
As they grow, I shrivel, into nothing more than dirt.
That is what I am, dirt,
Now embedded in the roots of History.

From my life as a rock,
I have learnt that time never stands,
There's always sights, sounds, existence.
What I don't know, is not nature,
My friend, the shining sky,
The one I look up to,
The one who has been here,
The one who *is* History.

Jenna Biddell (Age 15)

Today's Youth (The Difference)

Today it's not all boys, fashion and make-up
Today's youth have something different, technology!
Forget the occasional phone call and snail mail,
Mobile phones, text, internet and E-mail
That's where it's at!

Alot has changed,
Including music,
So long flower power lyrics
Hello, new rebellious types
The new range taking us to new heights.

No longer are the streets safe to roam,
(So the adults say),
Not much happened back in their day,
Our lives have become more confusing in every way,
No matter what my parents say!

Lisa Burton (Age 16)

Swish, Swish, Sea

Woosh, woosh, the swishing sea
The waves the sand
In the sand lots of shells
Listen to the waves
Crashing against the rocks
The lighthouses
Flashing at the boats
Little fish in the sea
And the big whales
Splashing about
In the deep blue sea.

Jack Beard (Age 6)

Springtime

Spring is when the sun comes out
There is also lots of rain
Flowers bloom
Lambs are born
Leaves on trees appear again
I'm happy when spring comes
Around again.

Liam Bateman (Age 7)

Needs

What is there in this world
That you can't live with
And definitively without?
You've got to know
And soon you will
Sooner that you will ever know
You can live without
Anything that seems to you
To rule your life throughout
The new sports car, that
Can out run the old - for now
The television and the
Show you never miss.
The solution to this problem
Is none other than the cause
All you need is me!

Leigh-Anne Buse (Age 15)

My Angel

...1 your world up in the sky,
...'ou sit and watch my world go by.
...'ou watch the silly things I do,
...ven though I can't watch you.
...Vhilst you can see my every smile,
...won't see you for a while.
...ut I won't wish my life away,
...ll always live for the day.
...ll enjoy the sunshine and the rain,
...ntil I can hold you again.
...ntil we will each other find,
...ou'll never really leave my mind,
...s I sit down here and watch you float by,
...n a cloud, up in the sky.

emma Breakwell (Age 16)

Desert

...he scorching heat
...he stifling air
...nd on my feet
...weat in my hair.

...ack of water
...arth parched and dry
...un above me
...urning the sky.

...ight time arrives
...nd all is calm
...t the oasis
...eneath the palms.

...amel train marches
...eyond the dunes
...hrough night's darkness
...houettes by the moon.

artin Baker (Age 15)

Silence

Silence is when you can hear things
A tiger prowling through the grass
A cat purring in its basket
A mouse twitching its whiskers
The sun rising
A bird twittering in the trees
A deer leaping in the air
Children playing Chinese whispers
Stars twinkling in the sky.

Hannah Boukhobza (Age 7)

Lost And Alone

Walking all alone I wonder
Running by myself I think
Jogging on my own I ponder
In my heart my hopes all sink.

I sat in the dark with no one to talk to
I stood in the light with nobody there
And even though deep down I knew
I honestly thought I did not care.

I always assumed no one would listen
I realised I was left and lost on my own
That is why I connected paper and pen
Now I know the real truth that I'm lost and alone
Left on my own
Lost and alone .....

Amanda Bateson (Age 15)

Lovely Poems

L ots of poems
O h wow a book of poems
V erse upon verse in one whole book
L ots of lovely poems
E very day after school I read poems
Y ou'd better get a book of poems

P oems upon poems, oh what wonderful poems
O h short poems are the best
E ntertaining me and you when we are bored
M orning and afternoon, yes PLEASE
S uddenly poems have gone!

Elissa Blankley (Age 7)

Winter Poem

Winter, winter lovely winter
All lovely sparkly snow
We go outside and play snowy games
When the sun starts to shine, the snow
Starts to sparkle and melt silently
But it doesn't mean the winter has gone.

I love winter very much
It's so lovely to touch
I love it when the robins come out and
Sing down the end of the spout
I wish winter never ends
But it has
Good bye.

Melissa Baines (Age 7)

Waiting

Crashing, tumbling, floating, falling,
Racing to my mother, the sea,
Rocks and stones
Fill my darkest depths,
Waiting patiently.

My clear, blue waters,
Sparkling silently in the sun,
Fish darting -
Beneath the dappled shadow of the trees,
Waiting patiently.

My race has begun,
To reach the valley of clarity,
Where, my streams bubble
And children play,
Free from all their troubles and cares.

Ria Bullard (Age 15)

Standing In The Hurricane

First there starts a hurricane
You find yourself standing in the rain

When you come in all cold and wet
Try not to fret you'll soon be warm and dry
And eating apple pie
While feeling as blue as the sky

Next you're sitting in a chair trying to put
Socks in a symmetrical pair

A tremendous rumble and then a tumble
I grab a candle and turn the handle

What I see is quite a SHOCK!
A bear is trying to shift a rock.

Matthew Blenkinsop (Age 6)

The Wind Poem

The wind sounds like
People running
Through thick green grass
Swimming in the waves at
Night and walking through
Soft white snow.

On a windy day
I feel like I am being
Pushed back by a train
Swirling through trees.

The wind makes people's
Wigs come off
Blow down houses.

The wind is like a ship
Which has just crashed
A tornado hurling in the sky.

Chloe Brown (Age 7)

Lonely

If I am lonely
What can I do?
Play on the seesaw
Or go to the zoo.

If I am lonely
I will read a book
If you like it
I'll let you have a look.

If I am lonely
I will phone my friend
But she doesn't like me
BOO, BOO, BOO.

If I am lonely
And there is nothing to do
I will sit all alone
Or can I play with you?

Laura Amy Browning (Age 7)

Cats

Creeping in the night
Rustling behind the trees
Cats are coming
Cloaked like queens

Crawling, purring
Hear no sound
Cats are coming
Clawing the ground

Green eyes glowing
Through the moonless sky
Cats are coming
Hunting up high

Paws pattering
Tails dancing
Cats are here
Prepare to die.

Sarah Bamber (Age 11)

Reading

R eading is meant to be quiet
E veryone likes to read
A ll books are good
D readful people hate to read
I n a book it describes things
N othing like T.V.
G randma loves books and so do you and me.

Zoe Batchelor (Age 9)

Snow

I buried the gardens
I let children play snowball fights with me
I forced everyone to stay at home
I made gates freeze
I make the temperature go beyond freezing
I froze the car doors
I suddenly started to melt
Soon I was slush ... then puddles.

George Bishop-Green (Age 9)

Genie Chant

Sister lamp
Brother lamp
Mother lamp
Father lamp
Oh home giver
Oh prison
Oh friend lamp
What have you in store for a wealthy
Genie today?

Oh this lamp holds my soul. I cast my spell to help me be free.
We give wishes. I hope someone rubs the lamp to set me free.

Sister lamp
Brother lamp
Mother lamp
Father lamp
Oh home giver
Oh prison
Oh friend lamp
What have you in store for a wealthy
Genie today?

Harriet Bradford (Age 7)

Oh Running River

Oh running river
Where do you run to?

I run to my mother who
Lives in the blue

Do you like people
Making your drops lift?

Oh yeah, as if

Oh beautiful river
Liquid glass
What are you full of?

Watery mass

Oh splashing river
When should I go?

Now would be nice
I just have to flow.

Christine Beardsworth (Age 10)

Colours

A stranger came to town today and took all of the colours away
The sweet tasting red of the strawberry lolly
The shiny, silver Tesco's trolley
The yellow of my Arsenal football strip
The pink colour of my new lipstick
He took away every one
Even the golden, yellow sun
My dazzling shiny, bright, blue eyes
The stranger must think that he is wise
The lime, lime green on my wall
He left us with black and grey that's all.

Abigail Bartlett (Age 11)

My School

I like school it's got a mole

I've got a friend called Paul, he is really cool

We play it and we have a football kit

We have literacy and numeracy.

Chloe Bullworthy (Age 7)

Changes

You walk, in a hippy way down the street
With those cool trainers on your feet ...
But then, when you come to school
Everybody laughs at you like a fool
For you have glasses on your face
And round your teeth you have a brace
For no more earring upon your ear
And a kick me sticker upon your rear.

Sam Bickerstaff (Age 11)

An Unusual World

A diving, dipping dolphin
A big, baking banger
What an unusual world.

A glimmery pair of green glasses
A gliding, graceful glacier
What an unusual world.

A pretty, pink pig
A mad, moving monkey
What an unusual world.

A cheeky, Charlie chimp
A swimming, Sammy seal
What an unusual world.

Jade Balmayer (Age 8)

Sitting In My Cabin

Oh dear oh dear it's time to go
We are leaving land and going away
We are sailing the ocean blue
Danger is ahead of us I know it I can tell
Here I am sitting in my cabin; dubious
Just behind the horizon there is a mystery to solve
What if we perish and die?
No one will hear our cries.
Will the Golden Hind be able to carry our men?
We are of will, we come back?
Hooray hooray land is in sight
People are there in Plymouth welcoming us home
It is a victory
I am proud of my Golden Hind it has carried my men
And made me money
It's been my dream now and I have done it.

Lauran Bailey (Age 10)

Fantastic Mr Parrot

I saw a parrot in a tree
Doing what it shouldn't be
Eating grapes, oranges, nuts too
Which were hard to crack straight
through.
Smashing grapes into eights
Splashing bits everywhere.

Michael Barton (Age 9)

Peregrine

The king of the skies
Uses its sharp eyes
To plumage and blast its prey.

Its razor sharp talons
Execute its prey.
In its castle nest it lies.

Adrian Ball (Age 8)

Red Nose Day

It is Red Nose day when people
Spend money for Comic Relief
And if you spend money
You can have a Red Nose
Hurray, hurray!

Aysha Bi (Age 9)

Winter Poem

Flashing globe moon
Gloomy soundless sky

Owl gliding through ghostly darkness
Seeking out prey

Mouse scuttering under the chilliness
Squeaking for a home

Milky snowman standing outside in the fresh air
With a cloak around its neck

Frozen bare trees alone in the snowy weather
Without even one single leaf
The purring wind hitting the blizzard
Like two fighting men.

Bardia Barimani (Age 10)

Peter And The Wolf

Peter was played by the strings
That made lots of dings

The Bird was played by the flute
That made him sound quite cute
The oboe played the Duck that gave
Him bad luck

The Grandad was played by the bassoon
That sounded very bloon

The Wolf was played by the horns
Than sounded like corns
The Cat was played by the clarinet
That sounded like a threat.

Mercedes Baker (Age 9)

The Dragon

A long time ago,
When myths ruled the land,
There lived a rich king,
Who thought he was grand.

Oh look at me, I know everything,
I know how to dance, I know how to sing,
I know how to act, I know how to play,
Hey there! You loser! Get out of my way!

I've made all the rules,
And I know them all fine.
Stop that! You stepped out!
Now get back in line!

But, over the mountains,
A short way away.
There lived a small dragon,
Who slept through the day.

This dragon flew out,
And burnt the king's land.
So that was the end,
Of the king who was grand.

Sylvia Barnett (Age 11)

The Princess

Once upon a time
In a land long ago
There lived a princess
Whose skin was as white as snow.

The princess was a nice girl
She even had a white floor
But the princess had a bad spot
She always wanted more.

The princess had lots of money
She had a nice car
She even had the money
To have a full sized bar.

She also had a bad spot
She loved eating sweets
But they were disgusting
They tasted like her feet.

On the fourth of July
The old king said
That girl is a pest
So she got shot dead.

Mitchell Barker (Age 9)

The Little Boy Called Bill

There was a little boy called Bill
Who lived in a house on a hill
In the house lived a mouse and a big fat cat
And they all sat on the mat together and made
A pledge to be friends forever.

Calli Banks (Age 8)

Husky

He's king of the snow
He looks so cute and cuddly
He's warm and fluffy
Camouflage in the snow
Speeds through the chilly Arctic.

Adam Batchelor (Age 10)

Fire

It starts with a spark of a golden flicker
Bright orange, sparkly maroon and a golden yellow light
The brilliant smoke grows ferociously fast and bold
The wood sparkles greatly as it burns
Dancing flames tremendous and strong
Flashing fluorescent yellow, sparkling silver and brilliant blue,
The fire is crackling madly like sparklers burning
The air is grey so grey almost pitch black
Clouds puffing up brilliant into the once was blue sky.

Keren Louise Beddoe (Age 9)

Peter And The Wolf

Peter opened the gate
He saw his best mate
He went to play
He got smashed with clay
Along came a duck
Reading his busy book
The cat came creepy
Peter was really sleepy
The cat was wandering around
Until he found his golden pound
Along came Father Grumpy
His head was sore and bumpy.

Aaliya Bibi (Age 10)

Water

The trickle of rain falling down the window
The crash of rocks crashing together
The plop of water falling on the ground
The gurgle of water going down the drain
The swirl of bathwater as I pull out the plug
The drizzle of sweat falling down my face
The fall of raindrops falling on the ground
The showers of rain at the North Pole
I pour some water in a see through cup
The drip of raindrops on a summer's day
The splash of tap water as it splashes on the sink
The squirt of a water gun as kids squirt each other
The sprinkle of rain as I shake my umbrella

Rukhsana Bibi (Age 10)

Dolphins

Dolphins swim in water
Mother with her daughter
In and out the waves
Playing games in caves.

Sarah Brick (Age 9)

Food

My favourite food is pizza
Glistening with golden cheese
Spotted with pepperoni
I can eat this with ease

But please, please, don't give me peas
Green and round and fat

I quite like Indian
That's a first for me
Some people don't
Can't you see?

But please , please, don't give me peas
Green and round and fat

Steaming pots of casserole
Potatoes in a mound
I hate the taste of the gravy
As I chase the meat around

But please, please, don't give me peas
Green and round and fat

Another thing I hate
Is spaghetti Bolognese
The lumps I cannot stand
No matter what my mother says

But please, please, don't give me peas
Green and round and fat.

Jessica Bensted (Age 9)

The Bee That Could Not See

There was a bee
He could not see
He could not make a cup of tea
So he flew around his kitchen
And bashed into the wall
On the floor he landed
And laid there for a while
And dreamt about the days he was
Cruising down the Nile
When the dream was over
He flew up in the air
What a poor little bee
Who could not see
He never had that cup of tea.

Katie Brierley (Age 8)

What Is It?

Shaggy golden coat
Slowly creeping sharp claws
Razor sharp teeth
Slowly approaching its prey
Ears twitching like radar scanners.

Henry Brittain (Age 8)

Lightning At Its Fiercest

You're lying in bed
Not a worry in your head
Time to sleep
Nothing will creep
Or so you think!

Smash, crash, lightning flash
Thunder roar, the swinging door
You'd better hide!

Thunder and lightning collide
The door swings to the side
Nothing is there, look if you dare
But prepare for a scare!

You jump out of bed and cover your head
Mummy says there are lots of ways
To conquer fear.

And that's why I'm here

Shaking in fright, not wanting to hear
The lightning strike the roaring thunder

And me ... the withering blunder

Sophie Bowsher (Age 10)

Alarm Clock

Tick tock, bring bring bring
Stop the alarm clock
I have an alarm clock

Tick tock, tick tock, bring bring bring
Stop the alarm clock

Stop it at 8 o'clock

Tick tock, tick tock, bring bring bring
Stop the alarm clock

I need my alarm clock so much

Tick tock, tick tock, bring bring bring
Stop the clock
I have a blue alarm clock
And it goes tick tock, tick tock
Bring bring bring, stop the
Alarm clock at 8 o'clock

Tick tock, tick tock, bring bring bring
I have a little alarm clock
Tick tock, tick tock, bring bring bring
I have an alarm clock
Tick tock
Tick tock.

Jodi Bolton (Age 8)

Netball

N asty opponents
E veryone cheering
T eams are ready, the
B lues have won
A nd the
L ilacs have
L ost

Laura Brown (Age 11)

The Ocean Lives Again

The sea has never had so much tranquillity
Darkness, never fading, everlasting
The inky black sky's reflection shimmers gracefully
The lapping of the waves soothe every living creature
Lulling them to sleep

The darkness cannot fight the silvery white moonlight
Stillness envelopes the world
The break of day penetrates the darkness
The world stirs from its sleep
The ocean lives again

Kelly Burchmore (Age 9)

The Snow

Snow falls to the ground
Like icing sugar sprinkled
On a bun.
In the morning
When you step outside
The ground is covered
In snow
It's like a crunching crackly
Carpet.
People play in the snow
Building snowmen
And throw snow
At each over.
Then they return home
With snow covered
On coats which melts
And turns to
Water.
The children go near the
Fire and fall asleep
When the warm sun
Comes and the snow
Disappears.
Like it was never here.

Christina Burnside (Age 9)

Battle Of Bosworth Senses Poem

I see blood thirsty opposition
Charging at us
I hear the wailing noise from the opposing army
I want to run home like mad
I see the blood pouring out,
Of my legs
I think I will have a terrible death
I touch the disgusting blood on my sword
I trudge along the ground extremely slowly.

Joe Burgess (Age 9)

The Friend Factory

School is a friend factory
You go to make friends
Friends are like a chain of people
Learning about one another. I have
Lots of friends. We have fun
And play games.
We all have the same interests and hobbies,
We are all fast
We are all friendly and we are all happy.
I have made lots of friends at
The friend factory.

Robert Bradford (Age 10)

37

The End

How did the world begin?
No-body knows.
We only have ideas,
That blossom and grow.
The world was peaceful, green and quiet,
But look who moved in,
Man and his gun
And made the earth grim.
Now there are buildings, factories and cars,
Burglars and murderers
Who are still not behind bars.
With all this badness in the world today,
Who knows how long it will last,
Or are we nearing the end.

Laura Bracey (Age 12)

Boring School

Boring school doing work all day
Over and over never any play.
Writing lines, doing work
I am not very sure how you spell lurk!
No PE or Games
Getting just the cane.

Science today, work all day
Chris wants some enjoying play.
History, English Language and French
I look outside I'm going to get drenched.
Oh yes it's time to go home
Later on there will be more moan!

Oliver Bolton (Age 9)

The Engine Driver

The whistling loud train doors go...
Slam! Slam! Slam!
Trains go clatter, clatter, clatter.
Trains go jickety can, jickety can.
The train driver goes, "All aboard!"
Trains like massive monsters!
Crash, bang, wallop!
Clatter, clatter, clatter.
Trains like whooshing wind,
Sh! Sh! Sh!
Slower, slower, slow,
Trains like hissing snakes,
Under the bridge.

Siân Brown (Age 6)

A Literative Poem

One waddling wasp watched weary wasps wallpapering walls
Two terrified tortoises talked to terrific tigers
Three tamed tigers tackled their tails
Four fat ferrets fixed fireplaces
Five ferocious fishes fought for food
Six screeching swallows scratched smirking sailors
Seven slithering snakes slide slowly
Eight elderly elephants electricuted Easter eggs
Nine naughty newts nibbled nan's necklace
Ten tiny tarantulas tip toed to the toilet

Jade Berry (Age 10)

If Dogs Could Fly

If dogs could fly,
I'd fly my dog,
All the way to America,
To visit the President,
And have some tea.

If dogs could fly,
I'd fly my dog,
All the way to Australia,
To visit the kangaroos
And maybe even try their food.

If dogs could fly,
I'd fly my dog,
All the way home,
To play fetch and ball,
And go for long walks.

I love my dog,
He's my best friend.

Victoria Bysh (Age 11)

Sand

Sand in your apples
Sand in your pears
Sand in your pants
Sand on your stairs

Sand in your garden
Sand on your clothes
Sand on your stove
Sand on your toes

Sand in your fingers
Sand in your hair
Sand in your armpits
Sand everywhere!

Claire Burgess (Age 10)

Super Heroes

I like lots of super heroes,
Like Super Ted
He cuddles me in bed
And Radical Rhino
He protects me from the evil Dino
Not forgetting Merlin,
He's old and almost dead,
The problem is these super heroes
All come from my head

Neil Brown (Age 10)

Spring

I woke up in the morning and started to yawn
I looked outside the window and saw a spring lamb being born
The blossom on the trees was pink and white
I looked through the clouds and saw the sunlight
I went down stairs to breath in some air
And the little bit of breeze flowed through my hair
I saw the little flowers and the buds on the trees
And heard the sound of buzzing bumble bees
I like Spring! I like Spring! Spring is cool!

Charlie-Ann Bryant (Age 7)

Monsters

M onsters are scary!
O range ones kill
N ever talk to monsters
S ome are invisible
T hey are very ugly!
E very one of them are scum.
R un when you see them
S ome are pleasant but bad

Dan Bridgewater-Bagnall (Age 10)

The Sahara Desert

The Sahara Desert's like a dragon's flaming breath,
The blazing heat the sign of death.
You feel the heat and try to survive
But with no water you know you will die.
You cry for help with sand on your face
But then you think you're the last of the human race.

Josephson Bowling (Age 12)

The Game Of Life

Life's a game of chess,
A wrong move could cost your death
A piece is vital,
To the serious game of life
Beware of the game's dangers

Joshua Brocklesby (Age 11)

Alone

As I sit in my home
All on my own
Tired and scared
I hear tapping on the window

I hear one of the doors slam
Could it be the heavy wind
Or could it be a man

I hear a rustling from outside
I draw the curtains
And run behind the sofa to hide

It begins to rain outside
Hail and sleet follow
When all of a sudden thunder
And lightening appears
I cover my ears

As I creep up the stairs
As quiet as a mouse
I wonder if I am alone in my house
So I motion into a run
And hide under my covers

Simone Barchard (Age 12)

The Earth's Moon

The Earth is not alone
In the darkness and the gloom
It has a special partner
That partner is the Moon.

It rotates around our planet
Making sure that we have night
Some people say it will always be there
In the darkness, still in flight.

Some scientists do believe
That the Moon will move away
Making the Earth's rotation change
And give us continuous day.

And if the Moon should disappear
And leave our starry skies
Many creatures may become extinct
From the floods that will arise.

But hopefully the Moon will stay
Still visible through the night
And it will orbit our planet
In the darkness, still in flight.

Claire Bayley (Age 13)

Shoreline

The shoreline sings
a fading melody,
with little care to achieve perfection, but
with its natural sweetness
echoing those tragic moments,
and drowning the thump of the murderous waves
which took you to the earth and didn't bring you back.

Sing, shoreline, sing this fading melody,
and sing although the wind is keeping you.
Strive to break free
and dance to the rain's distant rhythm,
forgetting the storm
which took your sweetened voice and didn't give it back.

I'll carry you when you are tired.
I'll pick you up when you have fallen.
I'll sing when you cannot.
But I cannot do what cannot be done.

Forgive me, shoreline.
Keep singing from your heart,
and touch the drowning eyes upon the shore, to dry them,
and to tell just how to keep them dry.

Christopher Berry (Age 15)

Hamsters

Hamsters run like greased lightning
Like they've just had an injection in their foot
Hamsters scutter in their sawdust
And sometimes nibble your finger
They sniff for food with their tiny, pink noses
Hamsters nibble their food with their little blunt teeth

Kimberley Jayne Bradbury (Age 10)

On The Motorway

Cars here cars there driving on the motorway
Driving fast driving slow on the motorway
Indicating on each line on the motorway

In April seeing lorries driving on the motorway
Trying to count it's just too hard
There are too many to remember

Seeing the scenery is nice
Especially when you're sat in the back of a car
The hills are all big and sometimes you would stop off
So that you can see around
Especially Blackpool where you see the illuminations.

Andrew Bullock (Age 10)

Wolf-Woods

I was running very fast,
With a crazy wolf behind me.
He wanted me for lunch
So I ran from him, behind me -
Crack, crack, crack went the leaves,
Crack, crick, crack went the twigs.
As I was storming on
The wolf was desperately starving,
He was about to chomp me.
Crunch, crack, crick
Went the twigs and leaves.
Crunch, crack, crick
Crunch, crack, crick
Crunch, crack, crick
Still I ran,
As fast as I can,
Crack, crack, crack,
Crick, crick, crick
Still I ran,
As fast as I can
Crack, crack, crack,
Crick, crick, crick,
Crunch, crick, crack.
He was ready for attack!

Sam Backhouse (Age 9)

Playing In The Playground

Playing in the playground, one, two, three,
Here comes a girl, will you play with me?
In the playground I am skipping
And you are kicking!

Harrisah Bibi (Age 9)

Field Of War

Troops lined up with fear inside,
Believing they must die with pride.
The whistle blows, an almighty sound,
And hearts and blood begin to pound.

They pray to God to now stay near,
To those they love and find most dear.
Then they run, over the hill,
Gun shots sound, then all is still.

So many died in that long fight,
From light of dawn to dead of night.
But poppies bow forever more,
Where once there was a field of war.

Hannah Baker (Age 12)

Genie Has A Wish

Genie wishes to be so big and not so small
But he can't help himself
If only someone could rub his lamp
He could be his Master because
If he was ever so nice he would imprison Genie
So Genie could be a normal boy
And grow to be a handsome man
And that is Genies wish

Genies wish becomes so true

Genies wish has come today for Genie has a Master
Genies Master gave him his biggest dream
Genie are you ready to become a real boy asked his Master
Yeah! I'm ready to be a real boy said Genie
Then I wish Genie to be a real boy
        Now Genie is a real boy!

Stephen Brewster (Age 13)

Hope And Peace

Hope and peace have no colour because it is so pure
It smells like roses blossoming in a garden
It tastes of fresh fruit all nice and new
It sounds like water trickling down a stream
Hope and peace live in your heart

Emily Batchelor (Age 10)

God Help Me!

I pray to you God
Will you help me in this bad nightmare?
I'm being controlled by strange creatures.

I can't, I can't do it!
Wherever I go there are people
I can't think properly
Please God they're doing it still
You didn't do anything, did you God?

I'm still praying, please help me
I'll do anything. I know I've done a
Lot of bad things in my life but
I regret doing them
Just please help me, just this once

They're still controlling me
God HELP, HELP HELP
They're still there, controlling my mind
God just stop it!
Send me out of this nightmare
Just STOP, STOP, STOP!

Ricky Bowers (Age 12)

The Battle Of Moo

I once heard of a battle
Which was for some cattle
The cattle mooed and mooed
As gun shells flew and flew
When the cattle were hit
The troops had a fit
They called a vet
He said "They aren't unusual pets"
When he came
He said "What happened here was no game"
They asked if they would be OK
He said "I'm sorry but no way"
When they all died
They cried and cried
Since the cattle were dead
They cut off their heads
They put them into a cart
And pushed them to a mart
That was all I heard
I must find the rest somewhere in the world

Jamie Blitz (Age 11)

Soldiers

They are waiting for the drill
They are waiting for the fighting to begin.
They are not scared at all
They are still waiting.
They are saying we are going to win
We are going to live
But they want to go home.

Laura Butcher (Age 14)

Colours

Yellow is a field of sunflowers
or the sun shining
or sand on a beach
or a lion crawling in the shade of a tree

Red is the blood dripping from vampires teeth
or the red sun setting in a dusky sky
or a prickly rose swaying in the breeze
or Hannah's warm woolly jumper

Blue is my favourite colour
or the sea crashing against the cliffs
or the sky on a clear day
or a ball rolling across the playground

Jeremy Browne (Age 9)

The Seasons

Daffodils, tulips, grass that's green
Are some of the things that can be seen
Spring is a pretty time of the year
The baby birds in the morning I hear.

The hot summer days are the best
Our school holidays is a nice long rest!
I enjoy my holidays in the sun
Me and my friends have lots of fun.

In Autumn, the leaves turn from green to gold
The nights are longer and going cold
There are no children playing outside
All baby animals hibernate and hide

In winter the mornings are frosty and cold
To get out of bed I have to be told
Hot chocolate by the fire warms my toes
Oh how I love it when it snows.

Hayley Blackbrough (Age 11)

Nanny's Pudd

I like the taste of Nanny's pudd
Its creamy sauce a pure delight
I'd eat it with relish if I could
A second helping in one night!

Hannah Bridger (Age 11)

My Friends

Annabel, Laura and Julia are my best friends
I have known Laura since
I was two and a half
I have known Annabel since
I was seven and a half

But I have known Julia
Since I was eight
They are all my best friends
They always have been, and
They always will be

I sometimes fall out with them
But I still like them
Sometimes I have them
Round for tea
Or I phone them up after school

I eat lunch with them
I sit with them
We help each other when we have
Had a bad fall or a cut knee
I love my friends.

Abigail Bailey (Age 8)

Death

I feel angry
I feel as if it's all my fault
I wish I didn't say those nasty
Things to her
I wish I said I'd always be there
I don't want to do anything
I want to stay at home
All I think about is her
I can't concentrate at school
The teachers get angry with me
I know I'll never see her again.

Although it's hard, I think about
The good times I had with her
I can still remember her smile
Her pearl white teeth glistening in the sun
Her rosy cheeks
Her golden curly hair
The jokes she use to tell me
The way she taught me how to tie my shoelaces

I know she will always be here for me
And I will always be there for her
Wherever she is.

Rachel Berry (Age 12)

I Dream

I dream that I could fly
So that I could touch the sky

I dream that I could sing
Then I'd have everything

I dream I was magic
Then my life wouldn't be so tragic

I dream I could make a curse
To have as much money as the Queen's purse

I dream I could be a footballer
Then I'd be popular

I dream I could make my sisters disappear
Then my world could be bright and clear

I dream there wouldn't be any rules
Then I wouldn't get called a fool

I dream that Foot and Mouth would go away
Then animals wouldn't get slaughtered every day

I wish everyone was proud and glad
Then the world wouldn't be so sad.

Sam Bellingham (Age 13)

A Snake

A snake is a patterned shoelace,
Wrapped tightly around its contracted, helpless prey.
Patchwork patterns running down its back,
It opens its mouth bigger than a black hole.

A snake is a skeleton covered in quilted, patterned material,
Its tongue is a flickering flame,
Its body is a sleek car,
It frequently changes its attire and
Is awarded some brand new garments

James Baker (Age 10)

Easter

Chocolate eggs are yummy
Easter is funny
Easter is fun
When you run

Hannah Brown (Age 9)

The Hippo

The hippo is the king of the African river
When you see him sat there you will begin to quiver
He's big and fat, he will fill you with fright
You will feel even worse if you saw him at night
When the crocodiles pass they try to attack
But the hippo's too clever and fights right back
When the hippo's asleep you will hear him snore
It is even louder than a lion's roar.

Kerry Beddow (Age 9)

Teachers

What can you see when you look at a teacher?
You see someone who would like to teach ya!
Most of us think that teachers are mad,
But acually they feel quite glad.
Glad about what?
That leaves us in a spot!
Most of the kids don't listen at all,
Some of us sit and watch the clock in the hall,
Some of us sit around and stare
But the rest of us listen, which is only fair.
Some teachers are strict,
And some aren't fair,
But actually
They do really care.
They set us homework
And they give us detentions,
All they want you to do
Is learn and pay attention.

Amy Barnes (Age 11)

My Dustbin

When I went to put my dustbin out
Someone made me jump with a shout.
I went flying but the dustbin stayed on the spot.
This boy called Justin.
He was the one who did it
He didn't care one little bit
Mean Justin he put rubbish on my hair
I wish he was a attacked by an ugly bear!

Helena Byrne Stevens (Age 8)

Poppy

My dog Poppy has a furry back
My dog Poppy has a lovely happy spirit
She's really fast and quick and smelly
She has a wobble belly
She eats moths and spiders too
I think she is really gruesome.

Charlotte Barwick (Age 9)

Mum

This poem doesn't have to be long,
A few lines says it all,
I love you Mum and I always will.
Thank you for always being there for me,
When I need you the most!

Jade Babet (Age 10)

Liberty And Livelihood

Liberty and livelihood across the Downs
The life of the farmer can be seen in the fields
Years of breeding to make the best fleece
And hours of milking to make ends meet

Foot and Mouth is the name of the beast
That blisters the face and blisters the feet
You shut the farm and let no one in
But as it moves on the wind no one can win

But when the call comes and you know it is true
Your life's work is over but it's not down to you
The livestock are ill or maybe they're not
But the Ministry will come to slaughter the lot

The countryside is closed until further notice
Everything is dead so said the notice
Liberty and livelihood across the Downs
Has come to an end and burns in the fields.

David Breakell (Age 14)

The Worst Sound

The baby fox cried
Like it was waiting for its mother
The baby fox's cry was
Like an emptiness in my life

There was a sound of thunder
Like a drum banging repeatedly
The sound echoed

I had never heard a worse sound
Than a gun shot
That had gone through my heart

The quietness after the shooting
Like a pin dropping
On the floor

Gemma Bullock (Age 12)

Different Things

All different names like Laura, Sophia and Esmeralda.
All different languages like French, German and Dutch.
All different colour skins like black, brown and pink
All different ages like 2, 5 and 8.
All different clothes like animal skin, thin cloth and silk.
All different houses like igloos, wood, mud huts, straw house and brick.

All different

Children!

Laura Binnee (Age 8)

Watch Out

When I am old, I shall sit in my rocking chair, all day
Squeaking it backwards and forwards
Getting on everybody's nerves
I shall knit with my knitting needles
Going click clack, click clack
Getting on everybody's nerves
I shall rattle on telling people stories about when I was young
Getting on everybody's nerves
While knitting them old fashioned hats and making them wear them
I shall offer people cups of tea, and then tell them my back's hurting
So they make the tea for me
Getting on everybody's nerves
I shall invite myself around my children's homes
Getting them to make my favourite food
I shall really annoy people by ignoring them
And pretend that I am deaf
Getting on everybody's nerves
But now I'm young, I have to obey my parent's orders
Eat what I am given, mind my language, and behave myself
Not being able to get on people's nerves
Without being shouted at and put to bed by my parents
But it would be fun to get on people's nerves sometimes.

Leah Burrell (Age 12)

A Trip To Memory Lane

On the way to memory lane
A sign post with a picture
Of our old dog Eddie
On the way to memory lane
The first tooth of our new dog Tiny

At memory lane
Memories of my old cat Gina
At memory lane
Memories of holding a python

On the way back from memory lane
Pictures of the Albino squirrel in our garden
On the way back from memory lane
Playing with my first airfix kit.

Joseph Bond (Age 10)

War

The soldier is kicking
He wears a mask
Another soldier is shooting
His face is covered too
Others watch
They prepare for war

Sarah Bell (Age 15)

Nightmare

I once had a nightmare
That gave me a scare
I had it twice
Which wasn't nice
But nothing is fair

It was about my brother
Who gave me a shudder
When he locked me out
I started to shout
There was no one other

Apart from a bird
Who was absurd
He had a head
Like someone dead
And I could not be heard

He started talking
About something boring
He then started to chase me
Maybe to taste me?
I was running not walking.

Joe Blayer (Age 12)

The Seasons

Seasons why do you only come once a year?
Is it because you need a break?
Or is it because it's too cold over here?
"No it's because you travel round the world."

Why does it hardly snow in winter?
Is it because it's too warm
Or is it because it's not cold enough?
"No it's because it's too wet over here."

Why is it always cold in summer?
Is it because you hate this country?
Or is it because you can't be bothered?
"No it's because you hate your job."

Spring why are you fresh?
Is it because you like to be new?
Or is it because you hate winter?
"No it's because you need to be
Fresh for the new baby animals."

Alexandra Bolland (Age 10)

Tidal Wave

Coming
Towering over me
Like a wall of water
I'm thrashing
And screaming
But it just crashed over me
Smothering me
Gasping and screaming
But then it's gone
Almost as quickly as it came
But taking me with it.

Eve Blumson (Age 10)

Knights

The knights of the old were often told
The battle they would win
Upon their horses gallant they rode
Of course the day they'd win!

The bowmen drew
The arrows flew
Into the battle they went
A mighty cry rose to the sky
As down the arrows were sent.

Proud knights and bowmen cheered alike
Triumphant - they had won
Another day when all could say
"We truly deserved to win".

Adam Bryant (Age 8)

On A Cold Winter's Night

On a cold winter's night
When the snow was falling
All the lakes were frozen
Mostly for the morning.

When all the children lay fast asleep;
In their bed
With their feet all pleasant and warm
Dreaming in their head.

Suddenly something cried,
"Help, help! it yelled,
(A very deep yell)
"I'm being held."

Everyone awoke at such an astonishing sight
The man had been held by the light
All the children were scared and amazed
But the older people just laughed at the sight.

Heather Bradley (Age 11)

Spring And Summer

Spring is just the start of flowers starting to shoot
Trees starting to grow and animals starting to wake up
To eat their food after hibernating in their warm beds.

Summer is great!
Summer is hot!
Summer is full of beautiful flowers
Like roses, blue bells and daisies
They are beautiful colours!
Like red, yellow and purple!
I love summer with all the flowers and colours.

Ellie Blackmore (Age 9)

Darkness

When I think of darkness I think of evil things
Like demons and devils
The gloominess takes over and everything becomes sad.
Thunderclouds cover the sky
While children are asleep having nightmares.
Miserable and murky
Nobody wants to do anything.
Winter comes and everything goes white
Which is supposed to be the colour of light.
Or maybe not?
Owls hoot then everything goes quiet.
Another night is over.

Bethany Bulow (Age 10)

If You Want To See A Witch

If you want to see a witch
You must go down to the deep, dark forest of doom
I know a witch
Who is living down there.

She's ugly, she's wicked, she's green and mean
Yes, if you really want to see a witch you
Must go down to the forest of doom
And say,

"Witch, witch
Where are youuuuuu?"

And up she'll pop
But don't stick around
Run for your life!

Daniel Brown (Age 8)

Sunshine

I made an old man take off his coat
I singed the grass as if I was fire
I made the river into a stream
I made the colourful flowers into black
Silhouettes
I evaporated the water from the plant pots
And garden toys
The wind blew the clouds and the rain away
I took over the skies once again.

Richard James Barnes (Age 8)

The Magic Box

I will put in the box
Huge flames from a bonfire with a dummy of Guy Fawkes burning
A ray of the red hot sun, roses appearing out of the ground in summer.

I will put in the box:
A frozen icicle hanging over a dark cave
The Yeti thundering down a hill looking for food, and Santa Claus flying in the dark wintry sky.

I will put in the box
The first laugh of a baby, the 100th birthday of my mum
The last hug of mopsy before I go on holiday.

I will put in the box:
A 13th month in the year and a red moon, people in space exploring planets
Collosal round eyes of glowing aliens visiting earth.

My box is fashioned from snow, gold and silver with furry penguins on the
Lid waiting for food from their slave of a mother and vampire breath in the
Corners, the hinges are swayed over palm trees shining in the sun.

I shall fly in my box visiting interesting jungles with fierce tigers, slithery
Snakes and luxurious exotic golden beaches, with the sparkling sky blue sea
Washing away the sand.

Craig Burman (Age 9)

Mum

Mum you mean so much to me
Although you may not agree
You may shout
But no doubt
Mum you mean so much to me!

Mum you make me so happy
When I was a baby you changed my nappy
When you get mad
I get very sad
Mum you mean so much to me!

When I was little
You showed me how to play skittles
When you make my tea
My face shines with glee
Mum you mean so much to me!

Anum Butt (Age 10)

Friends

I would like a friend to be
Loving and caring always to me
It doesn't matter what they say
I just want them to always stay
Together, forever no matter what
Our friendship should never stop
We can share our secrets and I'll guarantee
Forever, together, we will always be.

Emma Bateman (Age 11)

Slimy Slugs

What I hate about slimy slugs is
Their skins are slimier than worms

What I like about slimy slugs is the way
They crawl up people's backs and give them germs

What I hate about slimy slugs is the way
People scream when you shove them in
Their faces and when they eat all your mum's petunias

What I like about slimy slugs is how they
Are so disgusting!

Jessica Beard (Age 8)

You And Me

When I'm with you
And you're with me
There will be no fears cause
You've got big ears
I like it when you're around
I think you're really sound.

You think we're free
You're my friend, I see
There will be no fears
There will be no tears
Just you wait and see!

Stephanie Ball (Age 14)

Animal Testing

Then they shot me in the leg
The dart came and I fled
But rapidly grew weaker and weaker
And in that next metre
I collapsed into the poacher's arms
He took me to a beauty centre
And when I entered
Woke up to my future destiny
Next time I would be dead
He took me to a long dissection table
And I was no longer able
To move my paralysed body
I looked up with feared eyes
And saw a sharp syringe plunge into my tail
And then another impaled
Into my soft stomach tissue
I prayed for my innocent life
Then just after my death
I had a hard punch to my chest
My last thought was why?

James Briggs (Age 11)

Love

Love is as white as a dove
As pure as the purest waters
And as bright as the sun

Love makes the world go round
It is always to be found
In everyone, in every part
Hidden away inside the heart

Love is as light as a snowdrop
Like a breath of fresh air on a
Summer's morning
And as strong as the strongest rock.

Danielle Barber (Age 9)

Tiger Eyes

Tiger eyes, charging spies
Legs the strength of human fear
Kills as quick as stealth
Passing by

Takes a deer by the spine
Kills as quick as speed and light
Tiger teeth glare like blood
Stripes of death
Claws of fire
Signs in the night.

Andrew Browes (Age 14)

Home Alone

I looked out of the window and what did I see?
A man looking over the wall at me
I screamed AHH! But he just smiled
I called down for Emma
She came running
We ran back upstairs with a mobile phone
We were as quiet as mice
But then bang, bang, bang at the door
He was coming back for more
We screamed, we couldn't help ourselves
Bang, bang, bang even louder this time
We wanted to climb up into the loft
But we couldn't, the ladder was not out
And we were too small to get it
The knocks suddenly stopped
No noise could be heard
But then suddenly the front door opened ...
My mum was home, we sighed with relief
I told my mum what happened
And I never stayed at home on my own again!

Aimee Burrows (Age 11)

What Is The Moon?

The moon is a silver piece of tinfoil
Shining bright

The moon is a huge silver banana
Flying high in the sky

The moon is a big ball of cheese
Hanging from the sky

The moon is a round sea splashing over
The sun

The moon is a light at night
Flickering quickly

The moon is a cat leaping in and out
Of the stars.

Jamie Bird (Age 11)

The Stars!

I sometimes look up at the stars in the sky,
And it seems like the moon's made of cheese,
Somewhere I bet there's a star made of sausage,
With ketchup and hot mushy peas.

Sophie Brine (Age 10)

The Charge Of The Aunties

Half an inch, half an inch, half an inch they got closer
Here come the Aunties of death ready for the kill
"Give us a kiss, we haven't seen you for a while,"
Said the Aunties in the house of hell.

Half a snog, half a snog, half a snog they gave me
Here come the licking lips ready for the kill
"What am I going to do? These Aunties are deadly."
Said I in the house of hell.

Half a fear, half a fear, half a fear come to me
Here comes my survival ready for I to be free
"I am saved here comes the idea, I smash down this wall,"
So I did in the house of hell.

Half the house, half the house, half the house I ran
Out through the door ready for the long run
"The Aunties can't run, they're old fogies,"
Said I outside the house of hell

Half a mile, half a mile, half a mile I sprinted
Into the Sahara Desert to get away from the Aunties
"I might be in a giant sandpit, but it's better than being with the Aunties,"
Said I in the middle of nowhere.

Darren Burns (Age 12)

At Last They Have Gone!

Make the cauldron bubble high
So they can see it in the sky
Watch it whirl and watch it bubble
Make it swirl and make some trouble.

Put in some rats
To give them a fright, then comes a ghost
To go bump in the night
Add some bats to make them faint
Then some brightly coloured paint
Add some blood to make it red
Like their awful coloured bed.

At last they have gone in a puff of smoke
Now they have gone I have no one to poke.

Naomi Barrett (Age 12)

Dad

Dad, dad is sometimes sad,
because I'm being bad.

He said to me "Stop being bad
and be a nice lad".

I said to dad
"I'll be good if you stop being sad"
and I ended up being a very good lad.

Dustin Charles Burt (Age 9)

I'll Follow You

I'll follow you
To your maths lesson
Where you add up
I'll follow you
To your literacy lesson
Where you think
I'll follow you
To the cloakroom
Where you keep your coats
I'll follow you
Through the class room
Where you try to keep things tidy
I'll follow you
In to the hall
Where we do PE
I'll follow you
In the library
I'll follow you
I'll follow you.

Lauren Bennett (Age 9)

Rabbit

The white running light
The gracefulness of the wind
As if it is itself
The whiteness of a plain shirt
With no crease

The silentness of a war
Which has ended
With red eyes that remind you of
The red poppy fields
Hides in its burrow

Jason Berry (Age 12)

Angels

They flutter softly
Across the sky
Spreading their wings
As they fly

Their sparkling gold halos
Their white, soft wings
Their smiling faces
Of joy they bring

They dance around
On their flight
But you'll never see them
In the night.

Samantha Billingham (Age 12)

The Fearsome Beast

My wings are large, long with green on them
My eyes are red and fiery
My tongue is a long and slimy tongue
My claws are sharp like daggers and knives
My breath is poisonous when I breath out
My voice roars very loud
My tail is strong and thick
I've seen people dying
I've heard the people's cries
In play I mess with my food
In anger I destroy and ruin everything in my way
They call me killer beast.

James Brunning (Age 13)

Love

People say love's a funny thing
But I don't 'agree
I say it's special, it's great, it's lovely!
The meaning of love is the funny thing
'To regard with affection'
Regard and affection are the funny words
Not love, love is a nice word
Not funny, not silly, nor stupid
Not to be laughed at, or to point out
Not to stop and stare at
But love is love
And what more can be said
It's Love!

Alex Bolden (Age 13)

The Haunted House

T rees rustling in the wind
H owling wolves in the graveyard
E veryone scared to go there

H owling dogs upon the hill
A round the house no one goes
U nder the moonlight
N ever to be seen
T errifying noises creep around at night
E very noise makes the living jump
D ead people in the graveyard

H ouse scaring the people away
O ut and about the ghost goes
U nder the ground the bodies lie
S illy noises scare you
E ven the animals are scared.

Kyrie Boreham (Age 14)

The Reflection Of the Waves

I stand alone on a pebbled beach, staring back at charcoal lonely hills,
No children play on the swings, no lovers sit on the wall in Winter,
I walk towards my only companion, the white, whispering waves and I feel the soft sand beneath my feet.
I remember lying under the stars, my hand in his,
I remember listening to the distant hum of the old jazz band,
I remember looking at the sparkling spring colours of the valley's trees.
I remember staring at the gentle sea and hearing its soft lulling,
I remember feeling the damp, warm grass under my body and the soft earth beneath my feet.
But that was just a memory.
I stare out at the open sea and suddenly I catch my reflection,
I regret standing alone by the Liverpool estuary in Autumn
I regret thinking about the past over and over again
I regret staring as the happy people walk past as I stand completely alone,
I regret leaning over the railings and catching my reflection in the waves.
I think of the birth of a love which was soon to die.
I think of mourning alone for the death, but now I do not regret
I am free of keeping hold and free of letting go, contemplating
Once again I remember the feeling of control so I dance over the waves and spin around on the beach.
What have I learnt since being a child ..... that I want to be a child.

Caroline Brindle (Age 13)

Water

The gates were as big as Big Ben
I hid as if I was a hen
The water got in
And surrounded the bin
Which started to spin
At the drop of a pin
I ran up and down
Oh no will I drown?
I had to be quick
Or I would be sick
I closed the front door and
The water was no more.

Nicholas Bennett (Age 12)

Pig And Dog

The pig oinks loudly
With a great big pink body
And a small tail

The dog barks loudly
It has a hairy body
And big fuzzy ears

Matthew Byrne (Age 11)

Zebra

A zebra has the speed of a cheetah,

The colour of a black and white T.V.
Camouflaged skin like a chessboard
Big eyes the size of bowling balls
The stamping feet of a rhino
The wagging of a dog when it has gone
For a walk
The body of a bullet.

Adam Blacker (Age 11)

Sea Memories

I close my eyes, on a rainy day, and dream of a day by the sea
The sun shines bright whilst the waves crash in harmony with the
Cool and gentle breeze.
The sand under my tanned body, gritty to the touch
Suddenly the rain, wind and cold drifts away
I'm back in the bliss of the beach.

Alex Boulton (Age 12)

Dreaming!

Dreaming is like wishing but you don't know what you wished for,
Dreaming is like butterflies on a summer's day
Dreaming is like buttercups at all times of the year, go to sleep wake up,
Dreaming is like walking on clouds
Dreaming is like damaging the unbreakable.

Felicity Beales (Age 12)

oot And Mouth

vil Foot and Mouth is a black cloud casting a shadow over land
icked Foot and Mouth is precious money going down the drain
asty Foot and Mouth is a miserable death spreading far and wide
eadly Foot and Mouth is dark ink absorbing all animals
ysterious Foot and Mouth is a haunting ghost touching everyone
ighty Foot and Mouth is a black bull among the cows
lent Foot and Mouth is a secret whisper being passed on.

iamh Byrne (Age 11)

d Nose Day

d nose day is a day when you can say pants
dless days for people who sit with ants a
ay when you can raise money, for those who really need it
thing ever changes in them worlds that are like pits
ange is not the right colour for your nose on red nose day
ueezed in so many different ways
veryone laughs on this special day
vastating for people who lose family in terrible ways
nazing money collected in the end
ou always remember this day comic relief that sends you around the bend.

assandria Bunker (Age 11)

e Clouds

eir white, soft, silky texture, yet so delicate when observed
u look out of the window, far out of the window
u stare deep and hard, for what seems like hours
en you feel yourself drifting away, the window disappears
d you're left staring up into the sky. Your eyes drift
wards, so slowly, so anxiously.
urs eyes meet the clouds
u wait for something to happen, nothing does
ur brain tells you it's a waste of time
u slowly drift back again
u look hard out of the window, you look upwards into the sky
your amazement you no longer see clouds, you see objects
gantic buildings, animals, cars, bikes ...
u stop, you hear a voice but you can't quite distinguish
nat it's saying
u go cold, you can feel yourself drifting away, the
ndow slides back into focus, you feel as if you're falling
eper and deeper and deeper ...
u gain awareness, you look around, and then you realise;
OU'RE BACK!

y Banister (Age 12)

Colour Blind

Girl walking down the hall
Eyes to the floor
Arms full of heavy books
No one holds the door

Harsh words hit her ears
Stinging like a bee
Other words swim through her head
Including, "Why me?"

The class had art today
They said they used her face
They were using charcoal
It's all because of her race

She trudged along with her books
All alone, by herself
Until the girl came up
And asked if she wanted help

The kids don't see her differently now
They no longer see
The barrier between their two lives
Inside she's you and me.

Emily Burns (Age 12)

I Will Store On My Shelf

I will store on my shelf
The last bark from Bruno
Twenty-four rabbits haring round the garden

My Harry Potter collection
My favourite outfits
My treasure box

My grandad's photo
My grandad's hat
And his last laugh

My family tree
My family photo
Sophia's first laugh

My chinchilla
My mum and dad
My reading lamp
My grandad's ferrets

My shelf completely!

Freddie Broad (Age 10)

I Love You Forever

I love you

L ove you forever
O n my heart I swear
V ery much
E very day I love you

Y ou make me so happy
O ver my heart I swear
U are a beautiful person

F or you I will give my heart
O ver my heart I love you forever
R ewind your lies, love me as much as I love you
E very day I think of you
V ery much
E very day I love you
R ewind yourself and be mine forever.

Daniel Bundock (Age 13)

Growing Up Too Big

Screaming is what babies like to do best
Whining is what babies and kids like to do
Crying is what babies do
If they want something to eat or drink or need a nappy change
They grab and snatch and yawn
Nobody cares when I scream and cry
When I want something to eat or drink

It's not fair!

Lauren Berrett (Age 6)

Indecision

I sat there trying to think of a poem
One that could amaze the judges reading
The fact is I just didn't know where to begin
Should it be funny, should it be not
I could think of the subject but that was my lot
Putting words together, that was my trouble
I was waiting for an idea to come and burst the bubble
Then it hit me
I should write about how I feel
And not make the poem to be such a big deal
I noted down all of my thoughts
Then placed them all together, or so I thought
Then came the problem of how to stop
A funny gimmick or a twist in the plot?
But I thought no, just a simple full stop.

Michael Burton (Age 13)

Penguins Dance

As they slide through the ice
With black jackets and white shirts
They do the penguin's jive
All the ladies wearing skirts

Lots of jolly penguins
Dancing all around
But the baby penguins are not there
Not one can be found

For they are in an igloo
Very fast asleep
Wait! There's a little penguin
Hey! Eyes closed! Don't peep!

Oh! Naughty little penguin
Why won't you rest your head?
You can guess what the baby Pingu said
I WOULD MUCH RATHER PLAY INSTEAD

Olivia Bennett (Age 13)

Alphabet

A is for apple nice and crunchy
L is for lemonade nice and fizzy
P is for plum nice and juicy
H is for hippopotamus big and scary
A is for ant eater with a very long nose
B is for bee black and yellow
E is for elephant with a very long trunk
T is for together I like them all together

Alexander Baker (Age 6)

My T-Rex

I have a T-Rex
I don't know what to do with him.
He's growing so big, he's bigger
Than my mate Billy the Kid
And he's only 8 foot high.

He gobbles his food down like
A tornado sucking up a town.

When he dribbles grab your swimming
Goggles as you're in for a big storm.

He likes playing hide and seek
But when he hides he closes his eyes
And he thinks no one can find him.

Tom Benham (Age 11)

Dreams

Close your eyes and drift away
To a place where pixies dance all day
Close your eyes and fall asleep
To where through the leaves shy fairies peep
Close your eyes and fly away
To a place where there's no night or day
A place where your fears don't exist
Where unicorns run in blue swirling mist
This is a place where it's fun to be
A place where your soul can run free

Open your eyes, it's time to return
To a place where there's things to learn
A place where you don't want to be
A place where you can't be free
At this place you can't wait to:
Close your eyes and drift away!

Joe Bevan (Age 13)

Ghosts And Ghouls

Their screams linger in the air
Like the screams on a scary-ride at the fair
Their chains rattle
Like an old-rusty fishing tackle
They glide through the night
Staring at the moonlight.

Lawrence Bole (Age 8)

Spring

Plants and flowers start to grow
Where once there was a layer of snow
A babbling brook, hear it flow
Spring is here, I'm sure, I know

The new born birds in their nest
The world's looking its finest best
Better than my room, which is a mess
Winter storms grow less and less.

As the sun disappears behind the hill
The frost once more brings a winter chill
The fog rolls in, all is still
Except an owl which is loud and shrill.

As the morning creeps up o're land
The sun rises higher, bigger and grand
I hear the sound of a big brass band
Spring is making a wonderful stand.

Charlotte Bradbury (Age 11)

River

R unning through rocks
I n stillness or movement
V egetation growing
E ver blue and clear
R unning to the end and back.

Laura Baggalley (Age 12)

The Seven Stages Of Woman

First the birth
She comes as a beauty
And the infant in her wise mother's arms.
Second the schoolgirl dolls and little toys
Tumbling about in the playground.
And then the beautiful sleek and image important
Mirrors and lovers reluctantly training for the next stage.
Because next the looking and learning youngster
Beautifully and gracefully walking to her first job.
Children underway, her husband and her admiring the newborn baby
The best thing in the world to her
Her husband now second best in everything.
Now she's middle-aged almost feeble
The hard part's over, no caring for children
Yet she worries about her beloved precious kids -
Where are they? What are they up to?
Finally the old and weak, last and seventh stage of her life
Looking at her old photos, and grandchildren with lives of their own.
Time goes too fast
Until her worries are over and she dies.

Rachel Brennan (Age 12)

Rats

Wild rats are mean
Brown and black
They're found in the compost
In the barn, in a sack.

Their eating habits are appaling
They live in shabby holes
They would kill my pet guinea-pigs
They will kill peacocks and voles.

The sight of them makes people vomit
The smell turns you green
And when you see them scuttle off
They always make you scream!

Their tails are like a slithering snake
The sight would make you shiver
That mean kind of look they shoot at you
Causes you to tremble and quiver.

My pet rats are small and sweet
They answer to their names
They'll sit on my shoulder, watch T.V.
And play innocent, ratty-type games.

Elizabeth Bell (Age 12)

The Crocodile, The African And The Unhygienic Cow

Once there was a crocodile,
Whose teeth gleamed white and green,
He lived along the deadly Nile -
Where he was unable to be seen.

One roasting day, he felt hungry,
As he had swum the whole night through.
He started to act quite angrily
'Cos he wanted to eat a kangjimaboo.

Suddenly old croc spotted and African,
By the name of Zabepidad.
He was a lean and tasty looking man,
And croc was very hungry ..... he wanted the lad. YUM, YUM!

The African carried a saucepan,
Whilst he walked to the edge of the Nile.
He scooped up the murky water,
Not noticing the crafty crocodile!

Croc jumped up, teeth bared, reaching far,
He wouldn't catch Zabepidad now!
Croc lay on the ground, like a broken jar
And found that he'd landed on an unhygienic cow
YUK!

Emily Bond (Age 10)

Cats

Cats are cuddly
Cats are cute
Cats are cool
And cats are very sleepy
But cats love
Creamy milk
Scared mice
Soft pillows
Tickly flees
NO CLAWS!

Lucy Barnett (Age 10)

Colours

Red is a colour of love
Anger can show this too
Indigo a colour of wisdom
New to a world of doom
Blue a colour of peace
Orange a colour of power
With these colours we live

Freya Bardell (Age 9)

Spring

Lambs skipping about
Daffodils swaying
Crocuses dancing in the warm spring breeze
Children playing, children skipping
Children running in the sun
The shops full of Easter eggs, ready to be bought.
At the farms eggs hatching, two every hour
Ducks quacking, farmers dogs are barking
Animals see the world for the first time ever
New life has come in Spring.

Tristen Bronner (Age 8)

The Storm

When I walk upon the cliffs I look up at the powdered black sky
The sea crashing on the rocks
The wash from the waves
Clouds thundering passed like booming drums
If I close my eyes, I see white horses galloping over the waves
Near there is where I like to be, it's where I feel free
In the distance I see fishing boats being kicked about
Like a football, the rocks against the waves
I'm a genie in a bottle, but when I near the sea,
The sea sets me free.

Emily Borton (Age 8)

The Monster

The monster crept, on padding paws,
Up to a high, brown table,
It ran up the stairs, and slipped past doors,
And the townspeople called it Mabel.

It sometimes was told off, it sometimes was loved,
But everyone knew it was there,
Its basket was made from an old wicker bench,
And for food, it had its share.

It purred when it was stroked,
And when angry, it wagged its tail,
It jumped on you in the morning,
And it tried to collect the mail!

It defied the bad things in life,
The good things it took for granted,
It loved being in the garden,
For catnip, its owners planted.

But alas, it didn't scare the townspeople,
When it wailed throughout the house,
Because it was only a cute, little cat,
And it only scared a mouse!

Lui Benjamin (Age 9)

Mothers

"Anya get up!"
My mother would call;
As she stood standing
In the downstairs hall.

"There's no time to waste
There's no time to spare,
And please remember, to brush
Your hair."

Leave me alone
I need time to think.
I've just woken up,
My face - red and pink.

"There's no time to waste
There's no time to spare,
And please remember, to brush your hair."

If only my bed
Could walk to school
I could sleep in class
It would be really cool.

Anya Benton (Age 10)

My Best Friend

Eyes like two shining sapphires
Hair like a cascade of silk
And a face like a jewel
Always fun and playful
Always full of joy
And when I'm with her I can never be bored
She's like a bouncy rubber ball
A tiny green frog
She can never stay still for long
She has a wild imagination
Always playing games
Running like a cheetah
She has an active ginger dog
Who runs and leaps and bounds
Energetic and cute
You can't separate us
We're always seen together
I don't know what I'd do without her
She's been my best friend for four years
And she'll be my best friend forever.

Helen Beaumont (Age 10)

Acrostic Poems

S cience is proof how things work
C lass teachers are relied on to take care of you
H and writing is useful in most occasions
O ffice monitors try their best
O ffice is where help is at hand
L earning is about different things

Jonothon Blain (Age 10)

Aliens

Are there really aliens in space?
If the answer is yes
Then what do they do up there
In such a boring place?
Do they watch T.V.,
Go to school
Or swim in a swimming pool?

Do Aliens live in houses?
Do they have pencils and pens
And garden dens?
Do they eat
Burgers and fries and meat?

Do Aliens have cars
And vans and trucks?
Do they live on the planet Mars?

Who knows the answers to all these questions?
But,
Are there really Aliens in space?

Hannah Baldwin (Age 9)

Teachers

Teacher creatures are from outer space
They're a very well educated race
They came to earth in search of slaves
And hid their ships in a tunnel of caves.

The leader is a gruesome fellow
His head is green and his eyes are yellow
His teeth are brown and smell like heck
His name is terrible, it's Mr Beck!

Second in command is Mrs Vassallo
Her eyes are orange; she's shaped like a marshmallow
She rules 5.1, with an edge of terror
She's only afraid of a large mirror.

As long as they're here
Children aren't safe
From comprehensions and a maths race
They've got powers I've never seen
To meet one, I'm not so keen.

With armies of teachers they're ready to fight
Either that or I'll take flight!
To Ghana or to Nigeria
I never want to run into another teacher!

Anthony Byrne (Age 11)

Spring

Spring is a happy time
With warm sunshine
There is new blossom on the trees
Daffodils and bluebells blowing in the breeze
Children running in the meadow
Listening to the birds singing
Spring is a happy time for me.

Laura Bradley (Age 8)

Earthquake

Rumble
Tumble
Shudder tremble
Crash a quiver
Suddenly a crack in the ground
Buildings collapse
Desperate cries from people
Now, it's all over
A silent town
Here come the rescue teams
To pull the people 100 feet from under the ground
And the Red Cross with supplies
For the survivors
Who were in the Indian Earthquake

Daniel Bryan (Age 9)

Rain

When the rain is a dreadful blizzard, it is a herd of
Elephants stampeding away from being a prey.
When the rain is a tearful sky, it is a broken heart
Of those once loved.
When the rain is a fireful sky, it is a swarm of bees
Protecting their queen.
It is the crying of the clouds which make the glass
Shatter to the ground.

When the rain has turned into a ferocious wind, it has
Only left unendable leaks.
When the drip in the puddles has turned into a splash,
It's the best of the best that wins the great badge.
When the rainstorm has picked up its drenching world
Stirring ahead.

It is the small tears which make the most fears.
When the raging storm is slamming on the windows,
It is a beam of light from the burning star.
When the dangerous blizzard has done what it's done,
It's the end of a century!

Emily Bruder (Age 11)

Lions

Lions
They eat people
Big yellow teeth and claws
Not friendly
Chase people
Roam noisily and loudly
Teeth like knives
Claws like forks
Cubs bounce
Lick babies
Jump on animals

Terry Bowtle (Age 11)

The Witch's Kitchen

In the witch's kitchen
There is a cupboard all rusty and broken
A chair with one side bent
Just like a golf club
A massive table all smashed and dusty
Sounded like a plain field
Just quite but only the crawl of a mouse
Spider's web crawl over the black cat
No one enters but only the witch
In her black cat
Hat
Just silent and still
If you enter you will never get out
Even if you shouted!

Lara Boucher (Age 8)

In Surgery

I slipped on my mask, the elastic snapped around my head
My surgery clothes rustled as I walked through the doorway,
Where I slid on my gloves and clapped them to my hands
My patients heart being pumped, pumped through a machine
The whirring, buzzing, clinking, zizing ... then silence!
Staff came running, pattering, clomping, thudding ...
POWER CUT!
Machines stopped whirring, buzzing, clinking, zizing ... silence!
Hand pumping machines grunting and groaning
Fighting for lives, panting, rustling
My patient, dying, his heart not beating
Hand pumping machines with effort
Thudding, stomping, clinking, trying to work the machines
Trying to save people's lives
Then, click!
Lights beaming on! Machines all starting!
Lives all saved!
Silence, 'in the staff', no panting, thudding, pattering, groaning
Back to life.

Sarah Browning (Age 11)

I Think

I think he will be on a flight
I think tonight I will meet a knight
I think he will have a lot of height
I think he will bite my kite
I think his sight will be very tight
I think he will give me a terrible fright
With all our might we will have a fight
So I think I will turn on the bright light
I was right
On that very night, I did see a mighty knight.

Samantha Brooker (Age 9)

Mr Peter Kenyon

Mr Peter Kenyon was a very jolly man
Until one day he accidently broke a pan
He was so unhappy
That he ate some jelly
The jelly gurgled inside his belly
Which made him cough and splutter as though
He'd eaten a cherry
His wife didn't thing much to his actions
And she even thought about making a transaction.

Nobody knew what to do - the next day
The vicar suggested to pay
But in the end, he opted to spend
The rest of his life recovering.

Andrew Brown (Age 11)

The House

A black cat sits on the wall so high
In the misty courtyard
Behind the courtyard stands a house
A dark and dirty looking house

Up to the doors I walk and open them warily
I cautiously walk inside
There is a sooty smell in the air
The first room is completely empty
And also is the next
The next room after that
Is full with dusty furniture

I go up the stairs in the furthest room
At the top I find a party of ghosts
Laughing and having fun
I jump through the window
And land in the graveyard
I get up all splattered with mud
And run a mile from there.

Sam Blighe (Age 9)

Snow

Cotton buds floating in the air
Little fariy's dusting the ground
Snowmen on every bit of land
As the sun draws closer the snow begins to melt
The rain will soon begin to pelt

Natasha Burrows (Age 11)

I Wish

I wish I was a tiny rabbit
Hopping through the fields
I'd play all day in meadow grass
And jump through old cart wheels

I wish I was a silky dolphin
Splashing through the waves
I'd swim throughout the deep blue seas
And brave the scary caves

I wish I was a mini sparrow
Darting high and low
I'd fly through all the starry skies
And still have far to go

I wish I was a crafty cheetah
Prowling through the deep dark woods
I'd stroll around from tree to tree
And run as fast as I possibly could!

Charlotte Boden (Age 11)

Being 12

Now I am 12
I'm not quite a teen
Everything that happens
Always makes me scream
I get mad for no reason
Then charge people with treason
When the slightest things go wrong.

My old clothes don't fit
And Top Shop don't fit me
Life is so stressful when you're in between
You're too old to be a child
But too young to be a teen.

But now for the upside
Yes there is one!
I can see 12 films
And there's less restriction
On the things I can do
And the people I can see
It's at these times when I'm glad to be me!

Eleanor Bowe (Age 12)

The Falling Snow

Slowly out of his little white house,
Slowly slowly, breaks into a run
A frantic fight to plunge to the ground,
Yet lands so lightly, without a sound
Clumping clashing harder he's smashing
Hits and freezes, a little boy sneezes.
Doesn't like the season of May,
Warmer weather won't let him stay.
Soon spring flowers wave and bend
And falling snow comes to his upsetting end

Tom Batchelor (Age 11)

Rains As It Comes

It 's blue, small, tiny and sweet
Until you see his gigantic feet
Down he comes
From his little, fluffy, white home
Falling, hailing down to the ground
See him, hear him, battering down
As he hits the frosty ground
But then he stops
The last drop falls
And his enemy the sun emerges.

Josh Boughton (Age 11)

The Fox Cub Cried

The fox cub cried
Like a hungry puppy
The sound echoed around
Like thunder.

The thunder rolled in
Like a giant playing on a hill
Tossing and turning
Never stopping.

The gun was aimed
The shot was fired
Like the crack of a whip
That deathly sound.

Death knocked on the fox's door
But nobody answered
The silence is strange
But scary, but scary.

Martin Bunn (Age 11)

The Lion

The lion roared
He was the king
The other animals was bored
He never faltered about anything.
The monkeys covered their ears
The elephants turned away
Everybody carried on walking
Hoping it would be different on another day.

Keiron Butt (Age 11)

Night

I look out the window and see spits of rain,
With a background of grungy blue
It's pouring again.
The moon is damaged by smoky clouds
Street lights flooding so bright and aloud.
The air is quiet stars scatter like powder,
Midnight pussy cats prowling with power.
I look out the window and see spits of rain,
With a background of grungy blue
It's pouring again.

Nicky Brown (Age 12)

The End Of Time

My wings are the endless planes of lands never ending
My eyes, are the sun and stars in the skies which burn forever
My tongue is a sharp as a sword blade which pierces the heart
My voice is the thunder which tears the sky

My tail is a whip which lashes with the wind
I've seen the people turn to stone from the fear everlasting
I've heard their monstrous whispers telling the tale

In play I chase the shadows of night which follow into the day
In anger I breath balls of fire which penetrate anything in their way
They call me the end of time

I am the fear which scares the land
I am a never ending story
I am THE END OF TIME!

Julia Branch (Age 13)

Dreams

Dreaming is like walking on air
Dreaming is like living an extra life
Dreaming is like the most perfect place on earth
Dreaming is a place where anything can happen
Dreaming is the BEST.

Adam Blade (Age 11)

The Loss I can't Replace

You're the one I think of
Wish, dream and talk of.
You're the one who lit up my heart
My soul.
You're the one who has my dreams in you're eyes
My wishes, thoughts and hopes.
You're the one who was always there,
There to hold me tight,
There when I needed you the most.
You're the one who loved me.

Now I have lost you, lost you forever
Even though the sun still shines on
My whole world is gone.
I want you to hold me again, tight in your arms forever.
What happened to the moments we had?
What happened to the love that I used to know?
What happened to the spark between us that lit up my heart?
Your memory lives on, lives on in my heart.
You're the loss I can't ever replace.

Emma Barr (Age13)

Tomorrow

Tomorrow I'll tidy my bedroom
Tomorrow I'll hang up my coat
Tomorrow I'll do the shopping
If only you'd write me a note.

Tomorrow I'll lay the table
Tomorrow I'll cook the tea
Tomorrow I'll walk the dog
Just you wait and see.

Tomorrow I'll clean out the hamsters
Tomorrow I'll clean the bath
Tomorrow I'll clean the windows
Now don't you start to laugh.

Tomorrow I'll do my homework
Tomorrow will be too late
Tomorrow it's back to school again
I need an extended date.

Katie Billington (Age 12)

Gary Godwin

That'll be Gary Godwin
As big as Jean-Claude Van Damme
If you go and annoy him,
He'll smash you one WHAM! BAM!
Of course he is a bully
But him I'd like to be
He really, really stops my heart
'Cause he is walking up to me!

Steven Barnes (Age 12)

The Rhino

Its tusks are as sharp
As a spike

Its weight is as heavy
As a dumper truck

Its charge sounds
Like thunder

Its eyes are as red
As a flame

Its snort sounds like
A stealth bomber

Its skin is as grey
As a storm cloud

Craig Blood (Age 12)

Dreams And Nightmares!

A floating fairy in the air, bright blue eyes, golden hair
An evil spirit's daring stare, a poltergeist in a rocking chair
A sparkling rainbow over our heads
And tiny munchkins in their beds
A hell raising fire all around
With ancient bones on the ground.

They can bring you happiness!
They can bring you fright!
Which one of these will it be tonight?

Natasha Bancroft (Age 12)

The World Wind

The wind is flying though the air
Searching for victims on a cold, windy night
She is sprawling and spreading
Closer and closer through the night
Growing colder and colder.
At night when I can't sleep I can hear her
Crying and crackling as if she is upset
I can hear her creaking as if she is walking
Up the stairs, and snapping just like a ruler
She is swallowing trees that are near her.

Danielle Burrough (Age 11)

It's A Cruel World

As the fox cried
I feel the loss of its mother
The sound of a scream that's
Echoed alot
As the fox is asleep the
Echoing stops.

The fox cub cried like a
Pounding puppy
The sound still echoed like
A bowling ball.

As sharp as a knife
Sawing away
The bang of the drums
Fading away.

Silence filled the air
Silence filled everywhere.

Hollie Bradley (Age 12)

Mr Tuball

Mr Tuball is a terrible man
As he drives down the street
In his ice-cream van
Crashes into a blue car
Crashes into a red
Goes all the way back home
And straight to bed.

Samantha Bond (Age 9)

Playtime

Noisy children breaking rules
Teacher shouting and blowing whistles
Lots of boys playing football
Yoyos spinning on sticky fingers

Best friends break up
Shake hands and make up
Daniel plays football
And also climbs the drainpipe

Andrew storms around
Michael runs around
But there's a groan
As the whistles blown.

Steven Brown (Age 11)

The Lift

When I got stuck in lift at a museum in London
I was worried as we were stuck for over one hour
All I could hear was people trying to open it from the outside
And the lift motor trying to re-start
My mum, dad and sister were with me luckily
I was told not to get scared as we would be out soon
And there on the wall was a cartoon
Then the lights went out and I couldn't see a thing
All I knew was it was dark and dim
Suddenly the doors began to open and I was glad
Because in the lift I was very bad
At last we were out
And my sister began to shout.

George Buckingham (Age 12)

At The Bottom Of My Heart

I will keep at the bottom of my heart

The very first smile of a new born baby
And the first drop of the new rainfall

I will keep at the bottom of my heart

The photo of my very first dog
And the sharp blade of my bill hook
I will keep my baseball cap in my heart

I will keep at the bottom of my heart

The smell of pinewood shavings
And the smell of fresh cut grass.

Denver Butcher (Age 11)

Nature World

As swift as a bird
As delicate as a mouse
As gentle as an elephant
As small as a woodlouse

As sly as a fox
As pure as a cat
As smooth as a fish
As greedy as a rat

As poisonous as a snake
As mad as a dog
As powerful as a leopard
As skilled as a frog

Each day the circle of life
Is getting stronger
As the list keeps
Getting longer

Where will we all be
When it all ends?
When animals and humans
Are no longer friends?

Katie Brennan (Age 10)

Night time

It's night time!
Mum's turned out the light
It's night time!
And she's said goodnight
It's night time!
I can go to sleep
And I wish that I could keep
Asleep!

It's night time!
And I'm in despair
It's night time!
'Cause it's time for night time scare
It's night time!
And I wish that I could stay
Asleep!

It's morning!
And mum's come to wake me up
It's morning!
And my dream it went 'Kah-put!'
It's morning!
My wish did not come true to stay
Asleep!

Tom Bovington (Age 10)

Frost

In the dark of the night
When the snow has fallen
Frost appears as quick as a wink

He neatly spreads his razor sharp claws
And coats the ground with crumbs of unheated ice
The lake he froze first
It's freezing cold, wet and slippery

He swiftly fires round and round
Covering everything in his path
The streets and rooftops
Anything he sees

His long white cloak drags the ground
A silvery face peers over houses
Long white hair flows
And a little silver pouch with gold pattered lining

The sun does arise
And strikes on frost
Kills him dead, he disappears
Now frost is no more.

Kayleigh Breckon (Age 11)

Rhyming Couplet

He is very thoughtful
He drives me round the bend
He is very understanding
He is an honest friend
He helps me in my maths
He helps me when I'm down
He is also very caring
He is my bestest friend in town.

James Brough (Age 11)

Judas

I betrayed him
I ran from the last supper
I told the Generals to take him away
The garden of Gethsemane is where he would be
I came in walking steadily then kissed my master
They took him away
I fled to claim my silver
They tossed the bag at me
I ran until I stopped and realised how foolish I had been
I sat under a tree thinking so hard and long
I shook my head in shame
I climbed the tree taking out the rope
Then tied it to a branch
Then my neck
I felt it tightening, feeling my life edge away slowly but
Sharply
I died.

Alexander Bland (Age 10)

Under The Silence

I can hear ...
The roar of the fire, like the growl of a lion, like the eye of the storm terrorising its victims
The panic of a mother as her baby plummets down out of her arms
I can hear a plane being scattered across the runway with many people screaming at the sight of it
The suffering cries of humanity as they destruct their planet and their home
The shivers of the pilot after realising he's made an unforgivable mistake.

I can feel ...
The pleasure of being on vacation, with clouds gliding over the sun beaming down
I can feel the rage of the devil as he looks down at the good deeds being done
The faint wind of a far away tornado as people and possessions are being tossed through the air
The trembling ground as an earthquake destroys all in sight people tripping over thin air
The self-confidence when receiving a compliment when the deeds you done were easy to your standard
The warmth of the sun touching the sensitive palm of my hand
This is today who knows what will happen tomorrow.

Lenny Brocklesby-Millard (Age 10)

What Am I?

Deep sea diver
Water glider
Fish eater
Wave rider
Ice grippers
Steak flippers
Babies furry
Eyes blurry

What am I?

A Kenning.

Polly Barr (Age 10)

Thunder And Lightning

The lightning came first and moaned in our ears
Then the thunder came second and groaned so we couldn't hear
As the wind starts to twirl and curl,
The storm gets worse
Like the mysterious sounds of a magic curse
The thunder rumbles and starts to roar
The lightning clapped like it's never done before.

Katie Birks (Age 10)

It's A

Wet nose
Grippy toes
Quick mover
Good groover
Fish snacker
Rat catcher
Sits on a mat
It's a
?

Mercedes Bond (Age 10)

Listen

Silence is when you can hear things, listen ...

I can hear a butterfly
Flapping its wings, gracefully
As it passes a flower in the wind.
The butterfly's mighty wings
Shine beneath the sun.

Silence is when you can hear things, listen ...

When I hear a heart
Beating from a distance
In the warm golden sun.
Slowly the beat fades
In the soft summer wind.

Harry Brown (Age 10)

My Feline Friend

There she was in a black and white furry ball
Completely oblivious to the world around her
Fast asleep, not a care in sight, the fire crackling, golds and reds,
A scent of marshmallows lingered in the air.

Until ... catching her unawares the green and grey
Plastic cat carrier made an appearance in the hall
Not knowing whether this meant a trip to the cattery or the vets
She stared at it nervously but, with a little encouragement
From mum, stepped inside.

Unluckily for her, we stopped at the vets
Ears flat to the back of her head, hiding under the table
A screeching cry echoed through the clinic
And ... and MIAOW!
Let's to say we were not spoken to for the rest of that day.

Daniel Burr (Age 10)

Homework Excuses

I left it in my mother's car
My father left it on the bar
My dog ate my English in one go
And my maths, I'll have you know.

My sister scribbled in ink pen,
My brother left it in his den,
They stole it all out of my tray,
And on my desk a ransom note lay.

A cuckoo took it for his nest,
My hamster is wearing it is as a vest.
Aliens came and took it away,
But brought it back the very next day.

I went to Spain to visit my aunt,
I asked to do it but she said I can't.
I will not deny it anymore,
I didn't do it, I broke the law.

Gemma Barry (Age 10)

I've Got A Pet

I've got a pet
And he can fly and he swims by,
I've got a pet
He is furry, but not vicious - like a lion
And his name is Brian
I've got a pet
And he says, "Quack, quack, quack."
I've got a pet
He is so cute
He is a duck!

Jonathan Bailey (Age 8)

The Red Beetle

There lived a beetle and his face was red
He was ill so he stayed in bed

He could ring
But would not sing

He had a toy
That looked like a boy

He had a rug
That matched with his mug

He went to shut the gate
Along came his mate

He went on a boat
That could float.

Hafsah Bibi (Age 8)

Pencils

Now listen up class
We had 40 pencils this morning
Now we've only got 6
Pencils don't have legs of their own
They don't just suddenly burn
So start looking without a moan

Rummage through this classroom
You will find those yellow pencils
If not you're not going anywhere
If you don't find those pencils
That's double detention for you all!

Now listen up class
You're making a real mess
So start tidying right now
I'll watch you while you tidy
While I make a frilly dress

Have you found those yellow pencils?
I'm getting pretty tired
Those pencils cost alot of money
As well as a couple of rubbers.

Joshua Baker (Age 8)

The Breakfast Bowl

So much depends
On

The round breakfast
Bowl

Covered in soft
Cornflakes

Sitting on the
Table

Zoe Batt (Age 10)

No Known Grave

I can't face
The cards he's sent me,
My bedroom's riddled
In photographs
Of him,
Why my Dad,
Who walks out?
A Dad missing
Where is he?
Part of my heart
Gone forever
It belongs with my Dad.

Emma Bellringer (Age 10)

Dear Aunty

While you were out I popped in the house
I saw pop! our mouse trapped
In a mouse trap.

Someone broke our window
I can tell you I was frightened
I went outside to play
When I came in I saw
Your clothes burnt
All the food in the bin
Jam all over your carpet
Pippin! Your cat through the
Rubbish on the floor

I've gone home to have a break and have
My strawberry milkshake!

Maria Bibi (Age 9)

The Alien's Spacecraft

When an alien was going home
His spacecraft began to moan
It spluttered and squealed
It muttered and wheeled
But then it stopped
It fell into a black hole
It was as black as coal
The alien cried I am not going to be spied
I'm all the way down here
Then he heard someone with his own ears
It was Neil Armstrong
With all his might
What a sight
He pulled the alien out
He said "How do you do?"
"I'm fine how about you?"

Sam Bennallick (Age 8)

Darkness

D arkness is a misty cola which pours on the heavy earth.
A blurring rug shuffles along on the floor.
R ushing shadows tip toe across the creeping flat surface.
K illing light, dark weapon.
N etting cages, cover the glowing light.
E xpiring smoky shades full from the crown sky.
S urprising shelters wrap around the locked room.
S able sooty mystery's sealed envelopes spread tar around the smearing world.

Alice Ballard (Age 10)

He's Great Britain's Hero

They get up on the stands
The gun shoots and they're off
He's had a very bad start
Water splashes, splash, splash.

He's coming up behind
He goes into the lead
Bartholomew's winning
Water splashes, splash splash.

He throws his hand on the wall
He climbs out of the pool
Knowing he's won the race
Water drips, drip, drip.

He jumps onto the podium
Gold medal in his hand
The National Anthem sounds
The crowd screams out his name.

Paul Bartholomew's won
Paul Bartholomew's won
Paul Bartholomew's won
He's Great Britain's hero.

Paul Bartholomew (Age 10)

Boggis, Bunce & Bean

Boggis, Bunce and Bean
One fat, one short, one lean
These horrible crooks
Are so different in looks

Boggis likes eggs
He cracks them on pegs
And eats them without being boiled
Also he doesn't care if his taste is spoilt

Bunce likes chickens
He likes reading books - example Charles Dickens
He's very fat
Even fatter than two cats

Bean is thin
Just like a Shark's fin
Bean is very tall
Nearly tall as a hall

They are very dumb
Also they can't even hum
They never like to share
For that'll be a dare.

Tazma Bibi (Age 9)

Fighting Lightning

Snuggled in bed, covers over my head
Crash, boom, bang!
A tree cracks, a lightning flash!

Nothing to fear, there's nothing here
Boom, crack, another lightning flash!
This is getting creepy, Mummy says it's time
For sleepy!

She doesn't know how I'm feeling, just look
At the ceiling!

Dinosaurs, with wide, gaping jaws
Dragons, with deadly claws!

The thunder roars! Creaking doors
The lightning flashes! Something crashes!
It's only a vase, I'm seeing stars!

Why can't I see? What's happening to me?

I scream,
It was only a dream!

Gemma Barmby (Age 9)

The Soothing Seashore

I walked along the pebbly bay
The stones glistening like pearls
Wild white horses leaping in play
The lapping waves go round in whirls

The clear green sea sparkles at me
The seaweed quivers and shivers
Crabs scuttle and hurry past me
Scurrying in small sand rivers

Rachael Boraston (Age 10)

I Remember

I remember his floppy ears,
He jumped around his house.
His ears were fun and furry,
And his fur was soft and silky,
With little muddy paws.

I chose him at the pet shop,
I remember.
We fed him every day,
He played with our guinea-pig.
His name was Co-Co,
And he was our rabbit.

Sian Burgess (Age 9)

Along The Rocky Bay

Along the rocky bay sat a figure
A figure that was still
A figure was watching out to sea
A figure sitting 'til
Something happens ...

Along the rocky bay sat a figure
A figure that was dark
A figure as still as a tree
A figure that brings death
Then something happens ...

Along the rocky bay sat no figure
For he has gone to hell
And all that's left is seaweed
As I heard the bell strike twelve
I turned around and suddenly
Fell!

Edward Brown (Age 11)

The Chase

The beautiful creature sat elegantly upon the wall
Licking its paws gazing lazily around.
Ears pricked up as the panting was heard
Not daring to look around, he stands up, staring straight ahead.
The dog starts growling, heavy paws start pounding,
Legs start moving, howling and screeching escapes the cat.
The cat jumps from the wall and shoots across the road
Dog follows, not caring to look, pelting across the tarmac
A car horn blares
The vehicle did not stop quick enough
The dog lay on the ground
Dead.

Lucy Burgess (Age 11)

Winter

In winter the snow
Is freezing cold
Snowballs fly everywhere
Strong and bold

Your nose freezes
Like a block of ice
But when you are inside you are warm
And it feels nice

When you are out
You see glistening trees
Shining brightly in the
Light in the freeze.

Lucy Brown (Age 8)

The Magic Box

I will put in my box
The trunk of a pink elephant
A fin of a man-eating shark
The horn of the last rhino

I will put in my box
The last book I ever read
The biggest planet

I will put in my box
My favourite pencil
All of my family
Two African words

I will put in my box
The thirteenth month, a pink moon
An alien living on Earth
The Queen living on Mars

My box is made of brass, steel and foil
With snowmen smiling on the lid

I will run the Olympics and win gold
The crowd will cheer
Then I will step up and collect it.

Sam Bull (Age 9)

Maldon Town F.C.

It's sunny it's cool
It's the place to be
If you want to play football
On your balcony
It's a cool cool place
In the middle of the town
It's a football club
But you sit around,
It's the under tens
That I play for,
I've got lots of friends
That knock on my door!

Henry Brown (Age 9)

Spring

The trees are pink and white
The food tastes alright
The sky is blue
I can see you
You can hear the birds chirping
The sight of people working
You can smell the misty air
I want to be out there.

Chloe Butlin (Age 8)

New Forest Animal Fever!

The squirrel buries acorns underground
Digging up plants
He munches away on the nuts he's found

Overhead a hawk is circling
Looking for prey with his big, beady eyes
He spies a mouse and swoops down
To capture it in his claws

Down on the ground a fox is lurking
Waiting for his next victim
A beautiful creature, but quite deadly.

A rabbit hops up and down
It spots a fox and runs around
Putting its babies down their burrow
Then quickly it scrambles in away from danger

Grazing nearby, a group of ponies
Enjoy the spring sunshine
They love this time of year

Moving quietly through the trees
Is a large herd of deer
Very shy and not often seen.

Patrick Burrows (Age 9)

Monkey

I may be soft and cuddly
But I can be quite fierce
I like to eat bananas
Up high in the trees
I can swing like an athlete
Going for olympic gold
Sometimes I fall and hurt myself
But I will soon recover
And be climbing in the trees again
Before you know it
I'm asleep.

Rebecca Brown (Age 10)

Bear

The hairy bear
With big, thick fur.
It gave me quite a scare
Thought it was a he but it was a her.

The hairy bear
Fat and round.
Loads of fur,
Makes a noise like a hound.

Nathan Booth (Age 8)

The Storm

When night falls the storm comes in
Slowly, like a lion creeping to its prey
When everything is still the rain comes in
Heavily, like lead bullets coming your way
When the air is cold and black the clouds come in
Slyly, as quiet as a mouse
When everyone's asleep the wind comes in
Quickly, like a burglar through the house
When the night's as black as black the thunder comes in
Roaring, like a bear in a fight
When the night's at its best the lightning comes in
Brightly, like a lamp on a dark, still night
When the storm is at its worst the sun comes in
Happily, signalling the start of the day
When the sun comes up the storm slinks off
Angrily, creeping away.

Sam Blake (Age 10)

Hailstones

I made windows smash
I broke toys and huge buses
I spoiled barbecues and meals people ate outside
I scared children when my stones hit them
I bounce off tops of cars and houses
I badly hurt people when I hit them
I slowly stopped. the sun came out behind the clouds.

Thomas Broadhead (Age 8)

The Cat

Like a black velvet cloth draped along a sun-drowned sofa,
Ears pricked at the slightest sound.
The tickling of the chin is always pleasing,
As the roll of distant thunder rumbles from the low lying cloud.

Like a pompous lady, never quite happy with
Her appearance; always stopping to groom.
A super model who likes to be adored
And is forever showing off her new furs.

Like a creeping demon of shadows,
An old wives tale of luck.
The night sky covering its back with
Two bright stars, seeking out the slightest movement.

Clare Baker (Age 13)

I Am A Fly

I am a fly
I am stuck in a spider's web
I used to go on little adventures and explore
But I am still stuck in a spider's web.
I start to struggle to get out
But I get even more stuck
But I am still stuck in a spider's web
And I get worried about
My death but I'm still stuck
In a spider's s web
HERE COMES THE SPIDER!
I struggled again
But it is no use I am still stuck in a spider's web
As the spider gets closer I still worry about my spider's
Past, but I'm still stuck in a spider's web.
I stopped frozen
The spider let me off this time
But I'm NOT COMMIN' BACK.

Kimberley Bristow (Age 9)

My Family

My sister is a horrible thunder storm ready to break
My nan is a comfy sofa ready to be sat on
My mum is a lovely dress ready to be worn
My dad is a clever owl sitting in a tree
And my brother is a cool sports car raring to go.

Daniel Bolton (Age 10)

Families

My dad is in the front room
Watching T.V.
My dad is in the front room
Watching rugby.

My mum is in the kitchen
Making my tea
My mum is in the kitchen
Smiling at me.

My sister is upstairs
Doing her homework
My sister is upstairs
Acting like a jerk.

My brother is in his room
Playing with his toys
My brother is in his room
Making lots of noise

Jessica Brown (Age 9)

In An Hour

In an hour I can:
Go to the shops and get some food
Have my dinner and be very rude
Get really annoyed with my sister
Walk around and get a blister
Tidy my room like my mum said
Play a game in the shed
Go for a horse riding lesson
And a long swimming session
Sweep the yard with a broom
Wait in a doctor's waiting room.

Madison Bolton (Age 9)

Before School

Every morning when I'm asleep
My mum comes in and has a peep
To see if I am out of bed
Or snoring like a sleepy head
"You'll be late for school,"
She shouts at me
"So come down now and drink your tea"
I come down quick and eat my toast
Pick up the newspapers and the post
"Quickly now, you must look your best,
Hurry now it's time to get dressed"
I come downstairs, my feet are bare
And find my socks and do my hair
"Hurry up or you'll be late"
But then I stop and see the date
It's Saturday, no school today
"So can I please go out to play?"

Eleanor Bostock (Age 8)

Fire, Fire

It starts with a little spark
Orange, gold, red, lights jump out
The smoke fills the air with gas
The wood disintegrates
Coloured flames fly in the air
Flashing shiny gold, bright yellow and
Bloody red!
The fire is making a fort of fire!
The air is surrounded with death!
Smaller, smaller, it goes out leaving a
World of ash.

Simon Barnett (Age 9)

The Gods And The Mortals

Zeus's shiny thunderbolt stands shining in the sun
The mortals think the battle against the gods is just for fun
They don't think he will kill them
Or destroy all the city
They think he's being funny but he knows he's not witty
Tomorrow is the battle but the Gods will never lose
Because they are immortal and they can always snooze
So tonight they'll wipe out the mortals and the battle shall be won
Because they are never losers and they're always using bombs.

Joe Bungey (Age 8)

Corkscrew

As I wait with anticipation
I can't wait to join the fun
I somehow realise I'm not the only one
A herd of animals
A gang of kids
A couple of computer freaks
Oh great the cart's come
I jump quickly with two kids named Joe and John
From slow to fast
From up to down, around, around, around
Our cart slowed down and so'd my heart
The whole of my body stopped!

Craig Brunsdon (Age 11)

The Frog's Lament

You may think I'm slimy
Like seaweed on the beach
Or a silly, show off cartoon
Someone from a fairytale
Who princesses won't kiss.
But I have to keep my skin wet
Or else I'd surely die.
I hide from my enemies, as I have no weapons to fight
And I am scared to face them unarmed.
I can jump like a monkey
As a monkey sails through the trees
Like people on a trampoline
But my trampoline is the ground
Hopping and jumping is what I live for
What I'm made of.
My glowing green skin is like a sparkling morning meadow
That is the way I am, and is the way I'll always be.
I want respect as I have feelings too.
I want to be cared for and treated with kindness
For I am alive and I want to be loved.

Sarah Brown (Age 10)

Children

Children all over the world want the same things
Like a home, family and somewhere safe to live and play
Running, skipping, chasing, playing in the park
It doesn't matter what colour we are. We all want friends
Some children live where it's hot
Some live where it's cold
Some children don't have proper homes and
Not much food to eat
Some children live where there's war and
Are scared and frightened
Some children don't have mums or dads or
Brothers or sisters
Children of the world want the same things
A home, family and friends.

Ryan Bowles (Age 8)

Winter

Winter is cold
It is fun
When it snows
When children play
Making snowmen
Making snowballs.

Winter is cold
It is not fun
When noses run
When children shiver
Running to keep warm
Running to get indoors.

Amy Blacker (Age 6)

A Show About A Crow Who Said No, No, No, No!

One day we were doing a show about a little crow who said no, no, no
A big crow came along and said hello, hello, hello
But the little crow just said no, no, no
The river started to flow and then it started to snow
But all the little crow could say was no, no, no
Some children came along and said it's time to do the show
But the little crow just said no, no, no
The big crow came along and said hello, hello, hello
But all the little crow could say was
NO, NO, NO!

Amy Brittleton (Age 8)

Snakes

Slithering towards his prey
His eyes wide open
His scaly skin acts like a shield
Leaving a trail of slime behind him.

He camouflages in the long grass
Staring at his prey
He waits and waits until the right time
And snap! leap! his prey is gone.

Lauren Barry (Age 11)

My Brother

I walk upstairs feeling scared
And then turn on the light
I look around without a care
BOO! ARRGH! It's my brother

I look at him filled with fright
He says "Why are you so white?"
I say to him in an erie chill
"Go to sleep or I will KILL KILL KILL!"

William Bartlett (Age 10)

My Hamster

Treasure is my hamster
With whiskers long and sharp
He'll bite you if you bug him
So you better stay alert

Treasure is my hamster
That is how he'll stay
In his cage, in his ball
Having fun for the day.

Dawn Bamford (Age 11)

Tim And Rob

Have two
Football boots
Two footballs
(Well, not after
Tim kicked his
Over my next door
Neighbours's wall!)
Two tickets to Liverpool
And two best friendships.

Timothy Brooks (Age 10)

Lesson Four

Half an hour to go.
I've written the date.
What to do now,
Let's ask fate.

Look at her work.
She's done a whole page!
This essay's too hard,
For a girl of my age.

I quickly write a line.
So that I can say.
I've done some work,
In lesson four today.

One minute to go.
I stare at the clock.
I put my pen down.
Tick tock, tick tock.

The bell finally rings.
We jump up and shout.
"We're free, we're fee."
And we all run out.

Fiona Cottrill (Age 17)

Muted Winter

The vivid moon lights the world
A handful of stars are thrown into the dark sky
And brighten up the night
The hooting of owl echoes in a silence place
A leafless tree stands alone
Beneath the winter snow
A shuddering mouse shimmers in the moonlight
Snowmen stand as plump as can be
A cloak of snow paints the muted world
The never-ending artic fields with frost-bitten trees
As winter has struck.

William Barker (Age 10)

The Lion

The lion is called the king of the jungle
He stalks around herds of zebras
Always killing now and then
Probably in less than a minute he would
Already be full up
My lion has a long bushy mane
He has a small silky nose
He has a long thin tail
Which has a little orange tuft on the end
I shall protect my lion always
I LOVE MY LION!

Harriet Bailey (Age 8)

My Favourite Things

I will store on my shelf
Adventures with my action men
Drive a car
Dive down deep
Drift into space

I will store on my shelf
Happy hours watching T.V.
And all my favourite videos

I will store on my shelf
Memories of my beloved Nan
My holidays in Greece
My love for my Mum
I will store happiness.

Aaron Baldock (Age 10)

Oh Miss What Shall I Do

I told my teacher
How do you spell creature
When she told me
I raised my hand and said, "Can I have some tea."
Oh Miss I really don't know what to do.
Ok I will come for you
Well I am not helping you with your maths
Oh please miss so I know my SATS
Get your work done or you'll be with the Head
Oh please miss can I go to bed.

Abida Bibi (Age 10)

My Haiku

Secret, hide-out, place
A newt, hiding under stone
Scampering away

Gliding through water
Otters, like brown water rats,
Leave waves behind them.

The handsome peacock
Opens his splendid feathers
Of green, blue, red eyes.

Hiding in hedgerows
Rabbits, big eyes, long ears, safe -
Until ferrets come.

Florence Batten-Turner (Age 9)

Fifty Years On - Transport

What will the transport be like?
Will they be in the air or the ground?
Will they be speeding through the streets?
Will trains still have seats?
Will taxis still run or does a horse pull a sleigh
to take you through the city?
Will a car still have an engine
or run on cloud power?

Jack Bailey (Age 11)

Dolphins

D iving deep
O cean sleep
L ovely colours
P atient lovers
H iking low
I ntelligent though
N icely dodging
S ilently weeping

Stephanie Brown (Age 9)

My Friend

My enjoyable friend is not a dream
My little friend does not live in a stream
My fantastic friend does not live in the sky
My little friend is a little spy
My tiny friend is like a ball
He has a little pink nose
He is not very tall
He lives in a house
With three little children
Yes
It is my pet mouse!

Kerry Barnes (Age 10)

Night

If you go out in the night
You will be in for a fright!
Seeing bats
Creepy cats
Rustling sounds
Shadows on the grounds
Seeing rats
Hunting cats
Moon's light
What a great sight
I'm not scared no more.

Abigail Beaumont (Age 9)

Space

When there's a big rocket
Way out in space
It's no use screaming
Just in case

If you have a hole
Or run out of air
Then you're in trouble
Way out there

Moon buggies and craters
They're the best I've seen
Shooting stars and planets
Come visit my dream

Jupiter, Saturn
Mars and Venus
There goes Neil Armstrong
I hope he ain't seen us!

Huey Best (Age 11)

In The Car

In the car
We go very far

We go up a hill
I think there is something wrong with the wheel

We are going down a slope
It is like slippery soap

We are on the motorway
Hey get out of my way!

Going round the roundabout
Hey you get out

I am going in the street
I can hear a peep

I am going home
I can hear the phone.

Lina Barker (Age 8)

Storm

The autumn leaves dance wild and thrash around,
They twist and turn and rustle in the breeze.
The birds fly down and then without a sound,
They gather in their roosts, within the trees,
And on the branches, nestle, ill at ease.
The black sky creeps and settles overhead
With swirling clouds that churn on leaden seas.
The day grows drear and dark the sun has fled
And rain drums on the roof like drops of lead.

The wild wind howls and whistles down my back
And spits out icy needles made of glass,
Then from the angry sky a thunder crack
Which rolls through fields and over hills of grass.
Then lightning strikes - a bolt so bright and fast -
Illuminates the violent scene and makes
The jagged trees strange shapes and shadows cast.
And screaming wind and storm the landscape shakes,
Until the force of maddened chaos breaks.

Zoë Cochrane (Age 16)

Fire

One dark, cold, rainy night
I light my fire
His eyes are glistening peacefully
In the moonlight he eats and eats
His spirit grows
He roars his heat out
He is laughing
His jaws are massive
He's got a heart of gold
The flames dance into the night
When morning comes he will die.

Michael Bourne (Age 11)

My Secret Box

On the lid of my box
Is a humming bird of painted reeds
Writing from a different land
I will pad it in red.

I keep in my box
The first pumice stone ever to form
A perfect, twisted shell from a sunny beach
A chip of glass worn smooth by the sea.

I keep the treasures to
Remind me of sun, sea and sand
Soothe deep sadness
Protect me from evil spirits.

Alice Baillie (Age 9)

The Sky

I look up at the sky at night
What a wonderful sight I see
Those twinkling sparkling shining stars
That shine for you and me

I wonder if there's life up there
On those planets in the sky
Is it peaceful as it looks?
That twinkling sparkling sky

The moon shines bright on a starry night
It is a splendid sight to see
It makes me wish that life on Earth
Could be peaceful, calm and free.

The next time you go out at night
Take a look up at the sky
Oh what a wonderful sight you'll see
In that peaceful dark night sky.

Victoria Binnington Barrett (Age 11)

In The Park

The cold dampness of the park
Little monsters on the slide
Slow shells trying to hide
Laughter of joy, smiles of happiness

Next generation sitting on the seat
Taking advantage of the burning heat
Bag puss's purring away
Little monsters come back another day

The empty slide an empty swing
All the joy this park can bring.

Yazzy Boud (Age 11)

Oh Me, Oh My

Oh me, oh my
I see a fly
Right on the end of my nose.
I sniff and sigh
And this I cry,
"Why my nose it chose?"

It's crawling down
I start to frown
Up my nose it flew.
I feel very sneezy
And a little bit queasy
AATCHOO! AATCHOO! AATCHOO!

Anna Belsey (Age 9)

Colours

Yellow is a lot of desert in Africa
Or a field of yellow sunflowers swaying in the wind
Or long yellow hair that you can put up
Or a fluffy chick that you can stroke its fur.

Red is Millie's metal pencil tin with Winnie the Pooh on it
Or a prickly Rose that shines in the sun
Or the English postbox with lots of letters in it
Or my heart beating fast running in the hot sun.

Blue is a bright hair band that goes on people's heads
Or the bright blue sky
Or the deep sparkling sea
Or a William Harding Combined School jumper.

Aimèe Burch (Age 8)

Full Of Care

We are so full of care
When our friend falls over
We just stand and stare

One point instead of two
Is so full of care
We have no time to stand and stare

When we just stand and stare
Our life goes like a BEAR.

Jason Butt (Age 11)

My Pen Pal

I have a friend I've never seen
Never spoken to
Never even heard her voice
Because she's my pen pal.

She lives in Brazil
Is the youngest in her family
I only ever write to her
Because she's my pen pal

Wonder what she looks like?

My best ever birthday gift
Was to see her
Hear her voice
And be her pen pal.

She has brown hair
Blue eyes
A big smile
And a voice like a bell
We are best friends now
As well as pen pals.

Lucinda Bowler (Age 9)

Ocean Body

My breath like waves on a beach
My heartbeat like the flip-flip-flipping of a dolphin's tail
My blood like little fishes darting in and out of the coral reef
And my hands like crabs crouching at the ready.

My eyes like angler fish peering in the dark
My lungs like puffer fish expanding and retracting
My teeth like great white sharks jabbing at their prey
And my stomach like the blue whale digesting all its food.

My liver like a basking shark filter - feeding all its life
And last but not least
My brain like the sea itself
Forever in deep thought.

Angus Brown (Age 9)

A Dream Of The Night

The moon is glistening onto the lake
Swans drift across it
Moonlit colours shine on the swan
Just like Jesus shines on us
The swan is drifting into the night sky
The moon is reflecting onto the lake
Not a sound as the snow floats down
The snow is glistening just like stars
Sparkling in the clear night sky
Cats howl in the moonlight as if
They were singing a song of
SILENCE!

Eleanor Boyle (Age 8)

My Mum Was Sad

My mum was sad
Cause dad was gone
And I had been extremely bad

When dad came home
He was mad because
I started to moan

He sent me to bed
Without any tea
He threw away ted
And I shouted
Sorry mum and dad!

Harriet Bradford (Age 8)

Waterfall

The river flows across its bed
Calmly unaware of what's ahead
Suddenly
Crashing
Bashing
Gushing
Down
Into
Foamy
Bubbling
Water
At
The
Bottom
Of
The
Waterfall
Then softly on towards the sea

Nicholas Brown (Age 9)

Nonsense Poem

The partridge is pecking
At the roots
Of a large oak tree
The tree is full of owls
All wrapped up in towels.

Penguins are on the ice
Looking very pretty
Down came a sparrow
With a mouth full of marrow.

They all say
Bye bye
And they fly out of sight.

Louisa Broadgate (Age 10)

The Storm

A storm swept leaves
Off the trees

The storm raised the seas

The thunder was thumping
Lightning was frightening
Bumping

Wind howling - growling

Thunder was roaring
Children screaming
Grown-ups feeling sad.

Amy Bone (Age 8)

Without A Dragon

Without this creature you are lonely
Without their comfort you are sad
Without them you are scared
Without the red and orange flame they blow
You are cold.

Without a dragon you are ...
Cold as snow
Lonely as the wind
Scared as a ghost
Sleepless as a vampire
Miserable as a slug
Darker than the night.

Poppy Collins (Age 7)

Vampires

A drop of blood glistens in the moonlight
The sound of flapping in the night
Unwrap the garlic sharpen the stake
It's the dead of night, the vampires awake
Fasten the windows pull shut the locks
Tonight they'll be coming flying in flocks
Their jet-black cloaks whistling in the air
All is quiet, dark and still the land so bare
Their teeth are sharp and ready
But watch out it might be your turn already.

Charles Bole (Age 9)

Moon

Moon, a white balloon in tall sky
Moon, a round ball in high space
Moon, floats like a giant
Space ship in the galaxy
Moon, a yellow banana dangling above
Moon, a smile telling earth that it's happy
Moon, a rainbow full of all the
Colours in the world
Moon, a sphere of ice that is
Frozen in its sleep
Moon, a ball that stops glowing
In the morning mist.

Christopher Burge (Age 10)

Storm at Sea

Wind howling
Waves tossing
Seaweed soaking
Seagulls flying
People shivering
And I'm crying.

Ben Carter (7)

My Sports Poem

Sports are fun and good for you
Here are some that you can do
You can swim in a swimming pool
Or play netball with a ball
Tennis makes you run around
You kick a ball at a footie ground
In rugby you throw the ball back
You race around an athletics track
For the game golf you need a hole
But in hockey you shoot in a goal
So don't sit around, exercise is good for you
There's plenty of sports for you to do.

Donna Bowers (Age 12)

Life Poem - Pollution

I remember when I was little
Hanging out with Sophie by the stream, having fun with my boat.
In those days the stream had lots of fish.
I remember Sophie and I used to watch the herons catch the fish then hop away cautionsly like nothing had happened.
I remember the fish were free.

The plants on the ground were lively and brought beauty to the world.
The plants in the water were wavy and green.
But now, they have vanished.
The water looks miserable and the fish have died.
I remember the fish swam slowly.
Sophie and I would feed the other animals and have lots of fun.
However some of the animals became extinct.
All that is left is the flesh and bones of the fish.
The water is dirty and the fish are dying from the black oil and sludge on the rocks.

I will never forget the horrible people who did this to the animals.
We lost so many animals that we loved.
I think pollution should be banned from the water and animals.

Epiphany Constantinou (Age 10)

Snow

Snow is glittery white
As white as white can be
So white that I can't see
Snow is sparkly
White and cold
It's like a so white cloud outside
There are icicles everywhere
But I stay warm inside.

Joanna Churn (Age 7)

Cats

C hasing a mouse
A bout the house
T ortoiseshell and ginger
S leaking around.

Ryan Carter (Age 8)

Sleep

As I lay here in my bed
I think of things going round my head
Should I give my dad a fight?
Should I play out while it's light?
I don't know my head is beat
So for now I will go to sleep

Paige Convey (Age 9)

The Writer Of This Poem

The writer of this poem,
Is as noisy as a chatterbox,
As perfect as an angel,
And as sly as a fox.

As loud as a foghorn,
As playful as a kitten,
As fruitful as a blackberry,
As warm as a mitten.

As bubbly as a can of coke,
As bright as the North Star,
She has a memory like a diary,
And she's as fast as a car.

The Writer of this Poem,
May not be brilliant in every way,
She may not be the best,
But she's a good girl every day.

Charlotte Cullen (Age 11)

The Wolf

A silent stalker in the wood,
Creeping around to do no good.
His friends all surround him,
His prey right in front.
What to do next, he knows what he should.

The moon's reflection shining on the ground,
Looking at his coat without any sound.
His long furry snout snuffling at the leaves,
Trying to find food with his pack who are thieves.

His prey senses danger,
He senses its fear,
The wolf's only movement
Is a twitch of his ear.

His prey with a start,
The wolf with a sprint,
It's all over in seconds,
With only paw prints.

Emily Chester (Age 11)

The Seaside

Step on to the soft sand as soft as silk,
Step into the bright light coming from the horizon,
Feel the comforting heat against your skin,
Run down to the sea, feel and see the water whirl around your feet,
Swim in the sea and play around the waves,
Paddle back to shore and step back onto the soft sand,
Build a sand castle and make a fantasy world of your own,
Then when the sun is setting walk away from the sea and the sand,
Now you can journey home.

Caroline Coleman (Age 10)

Please Miss!

Miss, Miss don't let me stay,
I'm way too ill for school today!
My head is spinning, I'm out of breath!
I think I'm very close to death!
I've broken my leg, I'm about to be sick,
Let me go home and let me go quick!
I'm going mad, I'm about to pass out,
I've got a headache Miss, please don't shout!
For goodness sake I'm about to die!
So here I'll make my final cry.
My foot aches Miss, it really hurts,
What!?! Today's not the date for our homework!!

Madeline Campion (Age 12)

Fear

Fear is not about being scared,
It is about lack of knowledge and understanding.
For I feared mice as I knew nothing about them.
Mice in cages were fine,
They could friskily run around, squeak and gnaw on food,
But when these tiny delicate but beastly creatures were free,
Free to touch me and to scamper about my legs
Fear was present.

My mouth went dry,
Tiny beads of cold sweat,
Started trickling down my forehead.
My hands were clammy,
I wanted to get away,
But I was trapped,
They were closing in on me,
So I closed my eyes,
The world spinning before me,
I wanted to scream, but couldn't,
These mice were making me,
Drown in a world of fear.

Kylie Cross (Age 12)

Going To The Park

I'm going to the park
Quick, quick, quickety, quick
At the park I went for a swim,
Splash, splash splashety splash
Then I got an ice cream
Lick, lick, lickety lick
Then I went home.

Nicholas Chrumka (Age 6)

Unwind

Unwind in a tub
Give yourself a rub
Forget your strife
Ease the stress of life.

Oh! What heaven!
Are these from Devon?
The soothing steam
Makes you drift and dream.

Then comes the time when you want to cry
Because you have to let this dream go by
Down the plughole and into the trap
Until, once again, you run the tap.

Sarah Cole (Age 11)

Love Is A Book

Love is a book, words on a page,
Each bit is different and you never know
What is going to happen next

Love is a book, chopping and changing
Never the same, but somehow never changed
Always the same old faces.

Love is a book, contains different emotions
Sometimes boring,sometimes great,
There is no room for intrusion.

Love is a book, in its own little world
Nothing else matters, nothing is important
Doesn't care what anyone thinks.

Love is a book, but you can't see the end
It's in your hands, no-one else,

Love is a book

Vicky Cauchois (Age 16)

The Summer

The summer means a lot to me ,
The grown-ups inside sipping tea,
And all the children out to play,
We mustn't waste a single day.

While I go whizzing down the slide,
My friends go running off to hide,
I have to find them one by one,
We all think hide and seek is fun.

The grown-ups finish drinking tea,
They say they'll take us to the sea,
We jump and cheer and clap our hands,
We just can't wait to see the sands!

Six whole weeks of being free
Summer means a lot to me!

Jess Christian (Age 8)

Horror

It lies at the top of a hill
Surrounded by endless fields
No one likes it
No one wants it
It's torture
It's hell
No one dares
To set foot there
This place I can't say
You'll know it when you meet it.

James Clay (Age 13)

The Little Bird

The little bird is singing
His song rides on the wind
Like a little boat
Sailing on the sea

The little bird is flying
So elegantly he flies
Like a little fish
Swimming in the sea

The little bird hurtles through the sky
His method of transport is to fly
Elegant is the little bird
As he passes by

The little bird
A master of the sky
A graceful flyer
A beauty to behold.

David Crellin (Age 12)

A Spell To Get Rid Of My Sister

This spell is to get rid of my sister
My double, she's always in trouble.

Three smelly socks to make her faint
Then five pots of colourful paint
Two bats' wings to make her scream
Then seven scoops of mouldy ice cream
A ghost that appears in the night
To give her a fright
Then five dead rats and
Two black cats
Two thistles to give her a prickle
Five frogs' eyes and
Then eleven dead flies.

Now the spell's done
The fun has just begun
Because my sister has gone.

Anna Clark (Age 12)

Is There Or Is There Not A Monster In The Dark?

As I sat in my chair
I sat very aware
For I was scared deep down in my heart
Was there a monster in the dark?
I felt the air cold upon my face
Was it just me or was I on its case?
Nevertheless down deep inside
Because this monster's no place to hide
I don't know how this monster's found
A place to stay not under the ground
I looked everywhere, then finally I found
The monster hopping not under the ground.

Rebecca Crowley (Age 11)

Silence Is Golden

Silence is golden
Silence is golden
Silence is just a pure nothing
You can't see it and you can't hear it
But you know it's there
It's relaxing, the silence is there
Suddenly there's screaming and shouting
Disturbing the peace and quietness
Then I think to myself
Over and over again
Silence is golden
Silence is golden.

Matthew Caldwell (Age 11)

Holiday

On holiday to Nice we went
We stayed in a caravan not a tent!
There was a pool, a club and bar
I went alone it was not far.

A friend and I, we sang a song
The karaoke was all night long
The sea was near and so much fun
I've never felt such heat from the sun
And I almost lost my float
But a French boy saved it in his boat

At night we burned a candle
Whilst eating a French stick
Sometimes a horrid smell was there
It almost made us sick

We went to Antibbes land, a fun fair that was great fun
Until I shot myself with a silly gun
My lip began to bleed, and the man gave me a gift
Later when I felt better, a Bungy jump gave me a lift.

But it was all too soon over, and we had to fly back home
Who knows where I'll go next time, perhaps it will be Rome.

Claire Cole (Age 11)

Draco Terribilis

My wings are shields of great armoured knights
My eyes are bright fiery torches
My tongue is a harsh yet slithery serpent
My claws are daggers and swords
My breath wreaks havoc on the senses
My voice is both thunder and lightning
My tail is a whip of leather bound with spines
I've seen through to the bones of man and beast
I've heard the music of their last cries of fear and despair
In play I ride the storm high above
In anger I blaze and blast all things to destruction
They call me Apollyon.

Beth Churchard (Age 13)

Tramp

Sitting in a gutter with a blanket or a shawl,
Nothing to do sitting against the damp, dark wall.
The dog feels all alone, apart from his poor old master,
Wishes he could run each day a little faster.
He only feeds his dog on scraps at every meal;
All he has is a blanket coloured teal
Not a sleeping bag in sight;
Sleeps alone every night.

Susannah Cohen (Age 7)

Over Hills A Far

The land a far
Air crystal clear
Sky as blue as blue
Green stretching for miles

Birds glide in the breeze
Hedgerows break up the land
Making it look like a patchwork quilt
the stream flows at her own steady pace

See animals at rest
Seeing this sight at its best
Her beauty is magnificent
Sun glistening on blades of grass

Trees branch out in the openness
Petite hamlets scattered here and there
Their gardens full of sweet air
Surrounding these hamlets are rolling fields

For this sight is not to be missed
This countryside is full of beauty
It stands all around us.

Amanda Carrick (Age 13)

Bullying

Just because you're bigger
Just because you're stronger
Just because your arms and legs are longer
That gives you no right just because you're taller
To pick on someone weaker and smaller.

But you're not clever, you're stupid not smart
Bullies like you have got no heart
You try to act cool and think that you're funny
But all you do is pinch people's money.

You're thick, stupid, mean and cruel
There's no place for bullies in our school.

Daniel Cluskey (Age 11)

The Ideal Playground

I think the ideal school playground
Should have a quiet area with chairs
Benches and boxes of books
So that children can sit
In a shady spot and read
An area set aside cut in two.

Alex Clark (Age 7)

The River

Gliding, sliding, dividing
With a rush and a gush and a plush
As I fall
I brawl
I crawl
A splashing crashing tide
I flow in a gush, plush, splash
Bubbling, troubling and doubling
I munch through the rocks

My trip is nearly over
I have travelled far;
As long as I keep on
Gushing and plushing
And creeping over rocks
I will enter the sea;
My mother and father greet me
They welcome me to the open
Bubble and splash
I am now in the ocean.

Douglas Clifton (Age 7)

The Worm

The worm squirms
It learns
It turns
It climbs a fern tree
It has a cup of tea
It opens its house
Door with a key
Slap it falls asleep.

Ria Chapman (Age 10)

Late!

Got up this morning
Bed shook, "Go back to sleep."
"Can't," I replied. "Late."

Went to the bathroom
Shower splurted, "Wash and relax."
"Can't," I spoke. "Late."

Went to the breakfast
Drink gurgled, "Have a break."
"Can't," I said. "Late."

Put my shoes on
Shoes tapped, "Polish me."
"Can't," I replied. "Late."

Teacher shouted, "You're so late!"
Heart pounded. "I'm late!"

Andrew Campbell (Age 11)

The Door Of Feelings

Go and open the door of *joy*
Maybe there's a garden filled with song
A room full of laughter, or a fun filled disco
A room with mountains of sweets, or a chocolate river.

Go and open the door of *sadness*
Maybe a child is starving
Maybe you'll see a homeless old man
Or a world with no fun or laughter or people
Dying on the streets.

Go and open the door of *love*
Where every one gets along
Where ever you look you'll see smiles
And never crying.

Go and open the door of *hope*
Even when no one will talk to you
Even if there isn't one single smile
Even when there is no love
Hope will shine through.

At least there'll be
Feelings in there.

Katy Chilvers (Age 11)

Winter Animals

Bees sleep in their hive
Deers snuggly in their warm coats
Worms in freezing soil.

Emma Cordell (Age 6)

Why Can't We See Gas?

Why can't we see gas?
Why don't people fly?
Why are the planets so far away?
Why do stars come out at night?
Why does milk remove some stains?
How do birds fly?
How does water freeze?
Why can't solids flow like liquids?
Why can't fish walk?
Who made the earth?
Why is the earth round?
When did the Romans live?
Why do people believe in different things?
How do liquids find a level?
Why are scissors sharp?
Why do we wash our hands after playing in mud?
Why do some animals bite us?
Why can't things go near the sun?
Why do people think the moon has a light of its own?
How does air move?

Natalie Child (Age 8)

The Door

Go and open the door to your dreams
Maybe outside there's
A mystical Unicorn bounding across the green meadows,
Or a purring white Snow Leopard weaving in and out of your ankles,
A land of paradise where nothing can go wrong,
Or a star filled sky with comets floating across it.

Go and open the door of danger
Maybe a fierce Lion is devouring its prey.
Maybe a wicked witch is casting a spell,
Or a mouth is shouting "Run for your life"
Or the reflection of a reflection.

Go and open the door of distinction.
The greyest mist will shift.

Go and open the door of death.
Even if there's only
The whisper of the wind
Even if there's only
The plain walls of a prison cell,

Even if nothing is there, go and open the door.
At least there'll be a breeze.

Oliver Cannell (Age 11)

Hell And Heaven

In hell the rivers run blood red in the dark
Of the underworld, it gives a feeling of the death mark
And the strange creature called Hades.
He walks by night not by day and collects people
Who have died, he sometimes takes innocent victims into
THE WORLD OF DEATH.

In heaven the rivers run gold and silver, with
Sky as blue as blue, it gives a feeling of eternal
Happiness and the creature known as Zeus or God.
He walks by day not by night and collects the
Good people who have died and takes them into
THE WORLD OF ETERNAL HAPPINESS.

Oliver Capon (Age 10)

Spring

S unlight beaming down on the world
P oppies growing in huge fields
R abbits running through long grass
I ce creams in children's hands
N ests in the trees with baby birds cheeping
G ardens with children playing happily.

Izzy Ciechanowicz (Age 8)

The Sun

The shining sun, burning bright
Glowing out at such a height
Never ending warmth to all
Burning yellow fire ball.

Way, way up from the ground
Whirling twirling all around
Big up there but here so small
Burning yellow fire ball.

Like a football kicked too high
Like an orange to squirt your eye
Never ending warmth to all
Burning yellow fire ball.

Bringing you and me some joy
Gives you a smile like a new toy
Big up there but here so small
Burning yellow fire ball.

Will it really ever end
Burning up meteorites that we send
Never ending warmth to all
Burning yellow fire ball.

Nicola Carter (Age 10)

The Hill

Have you seen the hill?
The dark, green hill
Leaning in the mist.

Have you seen the tall hill?
The steep, bumpy hill
Standing in the frost.

Have you seen the hill?
The flower-filled hill
Waiting for the sunshine.

Have you seen the hill?
The grassy cow-grazed hill
Soaking in the sun.

Rosalie Cheung (Age 8)

Football Crazy

Balls rolling
Hands fouling
Heads heading
Goalies diving
Feet kicking
Referees booking.

Sam Church (Age 9)

Yards To Go before I Sleep

A few yards gained today
A few yards lost tomorrow

A yellow mist hanging low,
Snaking along silently,
Searching for its prey.
Holes in the ground,
A trench,
Perhaps a grave.

Ear drums bursting,
Skin pierced.
Rivulets of red,
Covering mud-soaked feet.

Darkness falls,
Beds beckon
In blood filled trenches.
A moment to pause, to reflect.
Time to rest or die,
Perhaps.

A few yards gained today
A few yards lost tomorrow.

Stefania Coronato (Age 13)

The Secret Creature

Is it a violet ant sleeping?
An orange snail crawling?
A blue spider spinning?
Let's look inside the box.

Harriet Chatfield (Age 5)

Dreamer

This is a poem about me
But if only I could see
I cannot write to save my life
But it sure will give you strife

If I win this fifty quid
I will buy a great big squid
I shall keep it in my pond
So that we both can bond

I would love to buy a car
In which would take me far
It would be very shiny
Not big, not tiny

It would have leather interior
It would be superior
My car would have to be a Beamer
But then again, I'm a dreamer.

Joshua Cole (Age 12)

A Dream

A dream is something special, that can come day or night
It tells a special story, for you to know and like.

A dream makes you feel happy, content and peaceful deep inside
It's all you ever wanted, to happen in your life.

A dream is like a wish upon a star, which you never expected to come true
It's full of great surprises, and makes the morning seem bright.

Because when the sandman comes at night and looks inside your mind
He pushes away the troubles and the good things are brought to life.

He fights against the nightmares and lets the dreams come out
He helps you have a good night's sleep, sprinkling happy thoughts around.

He loves to make you happy, he loves to make you smile
He's a dream all in himself, who helps your confidence grow inside.

Because your dreams can be inspiring, they can make your hopes soar high
Persuade you to reach for that thing you want, but never dared to go for.

A dream is something perfect, something just for you
It wants you to succeed, to be who you really want.

A dream is there to help you sleep, to assure you get enough rest
It wants you to be ready for the hard day's work ahead.

Emma Collins (Age 12)

Winter

On a chilly winter morning I opened my frozen door
An icy wind hit me in the face
I put my hat, gloves and coat on and shot outside
It was like a white piece of paper ready to be written on.

Matthew Child (Age 10)

Carcassonne Tree

Proud and erect stood the Carcassonne Tree
In the square in the castle, above you and me.
For hundreds of years it's watched history unfold
Every ring on its trunk has a tale to be told.

Each Autumn the leaves flutter down to the ground;
Red, orange, yellow, golden and brown.
And as visitors come to see Carcassonne
It's leaves from this tree that they walk on.

The late Autumn light gives a warm golden glow
To the walls of the city and streets down below.
The grey, gloomy mist comes in from the fields
The Rousillion vine-yards give the last of their yields.

The Carcassonne Tree watches the seasons go by
Its leaves tumble down above you and I.
Winter is coming, it's time to prepare
For the moment is coming when the tree will be bare.

Lauren Cantle (Age 12)

81

Game On . . . Off!

The School bell goes hip hip hooray! Jump off your chair it's time to play.
Quick grab the ball head for the field, *"Jack!"* - *"I did feel sick Miss, but now I'm healed!"*
The goal posts piled with jumpers and ties, the whistle goes, the football flies.
The championship is underway - the girls, they giggle, hold hands and play.
Discussing who they fancy now - writing lovey letters, to send somehow.
Miss arrives to brave the cold, *"Get off that field - you have been told!"*
Sir appears, coffee in hand. *"You lot move! You're all banned*
From playing football for today, give me the ball, in my room it will stay.
Jack see me at the end of school, and keep off that field, you know the rule!"
Well that's just great now what to do! The school bell sounds we form a queue.
Back into school, but do not dismay, this is only a temporary delay.
Coz when that bell goes for the end of day - we'll all meet up for . . . *THE REPLAY!*

Jack Connolly (Age 10)

From A Railway Carriage ...

I see graffiti on the coloured brick wall, grubby flats are mucky and tall.
At Kent House people get on the train, water drops on the window, passengers soaked by rain.
Office towers are so high, soaring into the bright blue sky.
Another stop, the weather is bitter, into the bin goes the disgusting litter.
At Brixton I see a statue of a man, and a real one throwing away a coke can.
Busy workmen on the track, one gets up and rubs his back.

A Eurostar races past, they'll be in France soon, it's going real fast.
Another stop, there are VDU screens, and people using ticket machines.
I see more litter on the ground, the train makes a whizzing sound.
Another station, and on the wall I see a map, as passengers get on I hear "Mind the gap."
I look out the window, Victoria at last, after a train journey furious and fast.
Out I go through the automatic door, I step onto the shiny yellow floor.

Hannah Cronin (Age 11)

Untitled

Happy birthday to you
To Joe and Sue
Wear a funny cloud hat on your head
Happy birthday to you.

Billy Catherall (Age 7)

Who Am I?

I am blond, with deep brown eyes,
Sparkling like the sun
I may be very small but very, very fun.
When you first see me, I look sweet and very light,
But when you get to know me, I'm daring and don't mind a fight!
People say I'm fun, or sometimes even cute,
I'm learning the recorder, and very soon the flute.
But the question you want to know I'm sure is this,
Who am I? The answer is not to be missed.
Well I'm not a famous popstar, or the Queen with a tiara,
If you really want my name it's sure to be Sara!

Sara Charteris-Black (Age 9)

Tigers

Tigers are rough sometimes
I couldn't fight with a tiger would you?
Give a tiger no food
Elephants are bigger than tigers
Rabbits are eaten by tigers.

Isabella Campbell (Age 6)

Computers

I keep seeing flying saucers
Whoops, no, they're my discs

I keep losing all my keys
So now I have a keyboard.

I keep forgetting to buy stamps
So now I only send E-mail.

Jack Charles (Age 9)

It Was So Noisy!

It was so noisy that
The light bulb exploded shrilly from the roof

It was so noisy that
The violent volcano erupted from the sordid ground

It was so noisy that
The windows exploded deafeningly on the active road

It was so noisy that
The school burst to bits and had to be hoovered up

It was so noisy that
All the cars crashed and burnt into an enormous fireball

It was so noisy!

Sam Collier (Age 7)

Come And Play

Come and play with me and grandpa
And how's my little dear?
Can I plant a seed grandpa?
Yes if you come in for 6 o'clock
Grandpa can we go to the park on our bikes?
You might have ants in your pants because you slipped
Grandpa can you push me on the swings?
Whee!
Grandpa can't come out to play today
Tomorrow shall we go to Kenya
And you can be Captain
Oh no!"

Robyn Connelly-Webster (Age 6)

Ashley

We have known each other since we were two
He probably likes me better than you
We met each other one weird day
And eventually began to play
We both grew up at Bonneygrove school
We went on holiday to Liverpool
We love to sit and play our Game Boys
They are just our favourite toys
He is my mate he wouldn't tell lies
He enjoys eating my mini mince pies
He comes around my house almost every day
While our parents are out earning their pay
On Saturdays we go to the cinema
Without our ma or good old pa
Ashley is a special friend
He is athletic and likes to bend.

Alex Cachia (Age 11)

Grandad

When I go out with grandad
I've done it all my life
He comforts me with warmth
I swing and sway when he
Holds my hands
With home sweet love
Then he does it twice
But today I'm weak and tired
I don't know what to do
But staying at home with grandad
Is much more fun to do.

Charlotte Cropper (Age 6)

The Wind

The wind is like a speeding child
Racing round the room
Then he trips up over a box
And howls with pain like a wolf, which is hurt
Next he destroys the room by pushing
Everything off the shelves
After he gets angry like an out of control
Rollercoaster, and breaks out
He starts shooting in and out of the rooms
Like a racing rocket.

Laurence Caulton (Age 10)

The Football Game

The whistle goes the game has started
People running up and down the pitch
Zipping and zooming
Running faster and faster
Yes I got a goal
It's half time - we're still winning

The next half starts
I start with the ball
I zip up and down
No they tackle me
Yes, we won 1 - 0.

Danny Chowns (Age 8)

The Patchwork Blanket

From the tower, up above
I see the view
I am in love
For as far as I can see
A patchwork blanket
Layed in front of me
Only the wind whistling past my face
Stirs me in this hour of grace.

Ne'er have I seen a view like this
Lit by the early morning sun
Red, yellow, green - it's bliss
It marches on to the horizon
Glorious, victorious
Until the day is done
And after that, to sleep it goes
So on to it, new seeds be sowed

I feel I must put this on paper
So others may enjoy it later.

Robert Clarke (Age 12)

Spiders

Spiders, I don't like spiders!
They creep and crawl
Up the wall
And they scare you in the shower.

Spiders, I hate spiders!
They make sticky webs everywhere
On the ceiling, or in the shed
I really wish they were dead.

Spiders, I like spiders!
They eat horrible flies
Some spiders make the greatest of pets
And you rarely take them to the vets.

Spiders, I love spiders!
They make great webs
In which they scour
And they scare everyone
In the shower!

Luke Conlan (Age 13)

My School

Ding dong goes the bell
You can hear it really well
There's a child looking at the sky
And there's a school boy running by
There's a child kicking a ball
Don't you think the playground's cool?

Elizabeth Cowell (Age 7)

Outbreak

Cranes hold the leg and stiffly the body moves
Pyres are built but no mourners come
And the coal is brought, and someone will light the fuse
TV cameras and the newspapers sound the mourning drum
Is it God's wind that spreads the germ?
That drifts so effortlessly from farm to farm
Is he telling us a message that we should learn?
Will our families come to any harm?
But we must realise that ill will befall
Upon the good and weak and old
Upon those who can barely crawl
And this tells us we must be bold
Face all danger with a heart of stone
And gently listen, but not to moan.

Lucy Cordey (Age 14)

Pollution

Somewhere in the world someone is dying.
Stuck in a hospital,
They have skin cancer,
Why do they have this disease?
It's not their fault,
It's because of you,
Us,
The population,
We could stop this happening to more people
But we don't,
We use our cars for walkable journeys,
We pump harmful gasses into the atmosphere.
We use products with harmful gasses in them,
There are holes in the ozone layer because of us.
These holes let in harmful rays,
These rays cause skin cancer.
Skin cancer kills people,
Kills you, kills us, kills the population.
Think about it.

Romana Cottee (Age 13)

Animals, Look At The Animals

A wild, whining, winter wolf
A fluffy, furry fox
A cheeky, checked chicken
A pretty, proud peacock
Animals, look at the animals.

A sticky, stick insect
A flapping, forgetful fish
A digging, dirty dog
A clever, cute cat
Animals, look at the animals.

Chantelle Coxall (Age 6)

Food

Food is great big mushy stuff
You get it on your plate
It comes in all nice shapes and sizes
All you do is eat it.

I like pizza, pasta, curry
They all taste really good
I have to say I like the best
Fish fingers, peas and spud.

I like puddings best of all
They really are fantastic
Ice cream, strawberries and jelly
Or apple strudel cake.

Your eyes pop out a mile
At this lovely sight
Your saliva glands get going
Oh, what a great delight!

I can't believe what I'm eating
It tastes absolutely gorgeous
And I just love it.

Stephanie Carpanini (Age 12)

Witch's Brew

Hubble bubble
Trubble dubble
Fire sparkle
Cauldron bubble

An old man's toes
A stinky nose
A bat's wing
A bee's sting
A dog's foot
A fire's soot
An eye of a rat
A bit of a hat

Hubble bubble
Trubble dubble
Fire sparkle
Cauldron bubble

Rosy Collop (Age 9)

WWF Style

WWF title on the line
Hell yeah, it's gonna be mine
Hardcore style is tonight
I'm gonna kick 'em left and right
Kurt Angle's olympic medals suck
Let's eat some sweets from the tuck
Stone Cold Steve Austin's Stunner
Angle the champion, what a bummer
Wrestle Mania is nearly here
Will Stone Cold be drinking beer?
Dudley's put someone through a table
It will probably be Sable
Kane and Taker
Destruct together

WWF title on the line
Hell yeah, it's gonna be mine
Hardcore style is tonight
I'm gonna kick 'em left and right!

Jake Carney (Age 11)

Old In His Youth

Alone in the cold
Never moving, perfect, motionless
His fixed expression
A story of his hopeless longings

Isolated, serene.

Despair, a reminder
Spindly fingers tear the blue
His arms raised heavenward
Ugly against the green hugging his feet.

Standing silent, asleep
Clothed only in wrinkled skin
He waits for the morning
To waken his colour

Sorrowful solemn silhouette
Hides his face
The him that once was
And will again be

With the coming of Spring
He will show his green smile.

David Cole (Age 16)

Why Are Clouds White?

Why are the clouds white?
Why do crocodiles bite?
Why is the sun yellow?
Why do people bellow?
Why do cows moo?
Why is the sky blue?
Why does it rain?
Why do people have brains?
Why do birds fly?
Why do people die?
Why do I get bored?
Why do knights have swords?
Why do people have hair?
Why is people's hair so fair?
Why do we have five senses?
Why don't we have metal fences?
Why do bees sting?
Why do bells ring?
Why do balls bounce?
Why do animals pounce?

Alison Clarke (Age 9)

Tiger, Tiger

Tiger, tiger rustling the trees
In the jungle looking for food
Tiger, tiger what a fright
Don't go in the jungle tonight
Leaves crunching
Tiger, tiger.

Tiger, tiger eating food
Tiger, tiger killing his prey
Eating deer
Ants marching
Deer running
Monkeys swinging in the jungle

Tiger, tiger rustling trees
Wait for monkeys in the trees
In the jungle
Rain coming
Tiger
Go, go hibernate
Tiger, tiger
Gone.

Sean Cohen (Age 8)

Underneath The Silence

Underneath the silence I can hear .....

The dead silence as a class takes a test
The first heart beat of new born baby
The grinding of a horse's teeth as it consumes its food
The roar of a lion a mile away
The voice of God guiding me.

Underneath the silence I can feel .....

The pain and sadness when my grandad died
The butterflies as I wait for my S.A.T.S. results
The joy and happiness as I watch a wedding
The rough surface of a rubbery tyre torn by the tarmac
The smooth book covers as I fall asleep holding them.

Underneath the silence I can see .....

The predator waiting to pounce on its prey
The chocolate slowly melting in a pan
The guns of war waiting to shoot people
The sea washing up against the sandy shore
The refugees dying in their hundreds.

Rachel Cowles (Age 10)

As Autumn Turns To Winter

Hedgehogs sleeping under the trees
Under a blanket of Autumn leaves
Squirrels rustling, bustling, scampering
Collecting conkers.
Crunchy leaves crisp and dry on the ground
I count how many conkers I have found.

As Autumn turns to Winter
I take one last look
At the leaves
And the squirrels
And hedgehogs
And head on home.

I shut the door behind me
And I go to bed.
When I wake
In the morning
It's a different world outside.
Dad has to turn on the central heating
And there's a blanket of pure white snow before me
As Autumn turns to Winter.

Naomi Crouch (Age 9)

Giraffe

Why do you laugh at my long neck?
I don't laugh at your small legs
It's good to have long necks
I can eat all the leaves on tall trees
It's good to have a long neck
I can see what's going on ahead
I have long legs
I run like a horse
Galloping across the field as I run
I run with all my friends because I am scared
I get very lonely when people forget about me
When people play with me they use my legs as bridges.
I am very good looking
I can flutter my eyelashes to get my own way.

Wayne Croucher (Age 10)

My Body

My body is a working machine
It works all day and night
It fights away bacteria
To keep me healthy and fit
My body helps keep me alive
My body can be strong
My body can be weak
But most of all
My body's a working machine
My body churns up my food
So it can leave space for more
To keep my body a working machine.

Romani Crockford (Age 10)

There Was An Old Man From Dundee

There was an old man from Dundee
Who used to eat seeds for his tea
The seeds grew inside
And he got very wide
That poor old man from Dundee.

James Crisp (Age 8)

It Was So Noisy

It was so noisy
My trousers fell quickly down!
All the drawers flew out of the tray holders.
All our lunch busted to pieces,
The sink exploded with water,
The walls tumbled into rubble.

Sam Crowley (Age 7)

The Witches Brew

A little cirrus from the sky, and a small vegetable pie
The petals of a rose and some panty hose.

Black of night, stars shining bright, moon beams falling down
Catch them before they hit the ground.

Throw in the voice of a singing bird, the stampeding of a herd
The ripples of a swan, that are never gone.

Black of night, stars shine bright, moon beams falling down
Catch them before they fall to the ground.

The olympic rings, and all sorts of things
Ahh! there's a ghost, next to the garden post.

Now cauldron will bubble, finally the trouble
Ghosts and ghoulies gather 'round, get sent back to the ground.

Black of night, stars shine bright.

Emma Carpenter (Age 9)

Why?

Why do sweets taste so nice?
Why don't hamsters eat spiced rice?
Why does rain fall from the sky?
Why do humans age and die?
Why is grass green not red?
Why is there felt on my dad's shed?
Why do trees get leaves in spring?
What does make a telephone ring?
Why does gravity not work in space?
Why was Adam first in the human race?
Why do motors run off oil?
Why does water come to boil?

William Callagher (Age 9)

Tiger, Tiger

Tiger, tiger
        Plays in the grass
        Every weekend he lets wind pass

Tiger, tiger
        Prowling around
        Watch him leap and pound

Tiger, tiger
        Is a friend
        He turns fast around a bend

Tiger, tiger
        Is the best
        He does not wear a vest!

Charlotte Cannon (Age 10)

Winter

Summer's gone, winter's here
White snowdrops appear
Ice is slippy, watch out
Icicles freezing like metal daggers

Dull sky, can't play out
White clouds, going to burst
Waking up in winter, seeing all the snow
Children on sledges swooping down the path

Trees are cold statues
Happy people, go out to play
Build a snowman, is what they want
Snowballs soft sometimes hard

Trees are skeletons on the hills
Children's cheeks are red as an apple.

Luke Chippindale (Age 10)

Spring

Leaves are changing back to green
And there's a lovely summer breeze
Bees are back and so's the sun
Spring is coming
And Winter's done.

James Croft (Age 5)

The Penguin

Penguin began
He took the movement of the waves
He took the flame of a fire
To make his flippers.

He snatched the sharpness of a dagger
He stole the colours of the rainbow
To form his beak.

He gripped the swiftness of the wind
He took the slippiness of ice
To make his swimming skills.

He grabbed the sunrays of the sun
He snatched the blackness of the night
And swiped the whiteness of the snow
To form his skin.

He captured the sombreness of a great oak
He stole the Cimmerian of moist soil
To make his eyes
And so penguin was made.

Melanie Challis (Age 10)

The Caribbean Jungle

Lions playing
Elephants trunks spraying
Snakes slivering
Not one animal shivering.

Look at the monkeys having fun
Look at the cheaters, look at them run
Watch the sun shining in its place
Look at the tiger with a grin on his face.

Look at the bird flying around
Now watch her face as she touches the ground
People cheering, cheering so loud
Animals striding about feeling proud.

The animals all fall asleep
Not one sound not a word, not a peep
Off the people go to their beds
At last everyone's asleep what sleepy heads.

Jade Cripps (Age 8)

Ice

When the frozen slippery ice
Sparkles in the moonlight
As the blizzards howl
The ice floats

Daniel Crisp (Age 9)

The Battle

As the battle begins I see extreme carnage everywhere
I see my leader Richard beheading another warrior
I see my comrades making their way towards Henry.

I hear screaming and shouting as death draws ever closer
I hear swords clashing and connecting with shields
I hear the thud of dead bodies and people swearing when they die.

I smell the leather in my helmet
I smell gone-off blood and horse droppings
I smell rusted sword metal.

I touch the dead body of my comrade getting angrier every second.
I touch the hilt of my bronze sword
I touch the dead body of the opponent I just slaughtered.

I taste nothing for my mouth is dry
I feel fear all around
I feel butterflies in my stomach.

I think that we might not win
I think that I'm going to be sick

I strike a tree and an archer falls out of it
I behead him but my time is up.

Ian Cubbon (Age 10)

Keeping Fit

Action, action! Keeping fit
Get heart pumping! Never sit!

Playing rugby I am keen
Often in the scrum I'm seen
Pounding, pounding down the pitch
Scoring points without a hitch

Action, action! Keeping fit!
Get heart pumping! Never sit!

Of soccer too I'm very fond
Being part of a team forming a bond
With fellow players trying to win
Hear the crowd cheer. We've all got a grin!

Action, action! Keeping fit!
Get heart pumping! Never sit!

For swimming I have a real skill
Break records for my club until
I'm picked with pride for my nation
I love to win, have celebration!

Action, action! Keeping fit!
Get heart pumping! Never sit!

Chris Campbell (Age 9)

Witch's Spell

Eye of newt
Toe of frog
Sting of wasp
Woof of dog

Bubble, bubble, wobble and tobble
Food come in and cauldron
Bubble!

Slime of slug
Wing of bat
Leg of spider
Blood of rat

Bubble, bubble, wobble and tobble
Food come in and cauldron
Bubble!

Tongue of snake
Nose of fox
Chin of child
Leg of ox

Bubble, bubble, wobble and tobble
Food come in and cauldron
Bubble!

Georgina Caines (Age 9)

Life

I remember when I was younger I used to play by a sparkling, clear stream with Mary ...

"Can't catch me!" she would scream
As we ran along the soggy wet banks together,
Darting in and out of the stream which felt wet and cold.
"Bet I can!" I would yell back at her.

We used to go there almost every day.
We loved to see how many wild animals we could find
In the bubbling clear stream and long green grass.
We found otters, darting gleefully in the water,
Kingfishers swimming and jumping all around us.
Once we even found a baby shrew hiding among the grass.

But then it all changed, smoke and fumes started coming
From the dirty new factory in the village,
Polluting the stream and all its wonderful plants and animals.
"It can't be, it just can't," I cried with sadness.
There were bits of broken glass scattered everywhere.
"It's not fair," wept Mary.

We found dead, cold animals almost every time we went there, so we stopped going.
I'll never forget those wonderful, glorious summer days we spent together by the stream.
I'll never forget, how could I possibly forget.

Rachel Cann (Age 10)

War

Another war has broken out
'Not again' they never seem to stop
On everyone's mind is just one thing 'doubt'
Men getting ready to go over the top
Women and children running
People crying, screaming, in so much pain
The noises in my head, 'drumming'
So many bullets coming down, like a heavy shower of rain
Hopefully it may soon be over
We may get our lives back
The men may soon be able to arrive home at Dover
And maybe the guns put away in sacks
Oh no!
I can't take this anymore.

Victoria Connolly (Age 15)

Underneath The Silence ...

Quivering leaves shaking as I walked through the forest
The evil cackle of a witch's cry, as her red hot cauldron bubbles up
Cold salty seawater brushing off the white silk sand
The wind whistling and rattling against my window pane
The crooked staircase crashing beneath my feet
A crying body of an abused child.

A soft touch of a hamster's fur as it glides beneath my fingertips
The splashing of rain on river water as it falls from the leaking sky

The soft sandy shingle licking my feet, slipping through my toes.

Lucy May Clanford (Age 11)

Dinosaurs

D inosaurs are cool
I guanodon has a spiked thumb
N othosaur is green and swims
O viraptor had a lump for a nose
S tegosaurus had plates on its back
A rchaeopteryx was the first bird dinosaur
U ltrasaurus was the biggest
R iojasaurus had a long neck and small head
S pinosaurus was a thorn lizard.

Aidan Cooper (Age 7)

Bad Spelin

I hayt spelin becos its veri difycolt
And it is borin and 2 hard butt I no
Dat it is veri inportnt and ders is ay
Problum da problum is ol werds
Don t sownd lyk how der spelt. Oldo
Iym priti bad at dem butt Iym shur
Dat Iyl improov. Mi teecha sez u have 2
Inproov den she kan mark mi werk!

Sakhawatul Chowdhury (Age 10)

My Poem

Rayleigh was the place where Fred was born
On the 1st of May just before dawn
He was small and round
And about 11 pound
And not one bit of hair, not a trace to be found
He grew up as a kid with not one friend
But there was one person who stood with him to the end
His name was Tom, he was a black cat
Not too skinny and not to fat
They were together as one
Always having fun
Playing in the sun
But one day Fred became ill
And for a long time his life stood still
The cat stood by him feeling pretty low
Then Fred said to him, "It's time for me to go."
Floated in the air and up into the sky
Higher than high and in Tom's heart he heard, "Goodbye."

Adam Clark (Age 11)

The Lions

Lions are nice
I like the fur!
They have a mane
Girls do not have a mane!

Charlotte Coles (Age 6)

Beauty

Is it in the perfection of a face?
Neither scars nor impurities spoil it.
A physical ideal presented to us
A first impression, a fantasy.

Is there beauty in a perfect friendship?
A bond to withstand the threats of time.
Time stands as still as stone
But it remains as precious as gold.

Can it be found in the eyes of a child?
The innocence of a playground rhyme.
An imagination wild and free
And honesty like an out-stretched hand.

Is it in the marvel of creation?
Carried on a stream, gently flowing.
The opening of a fresh flower
Smiling and leaning towards the sun.

Or is it the kindliness of love?
Concern for a person's well being.
A charitable deed, a selfless act
A tender embrace that dries a tear.

Tiffany Cross (Age 16)

Robin

Hunting its prey to feed its young
His leafy home hiding in the branches
Gliding through the air like an aeroplane
His light feathered wings flapping like a cat flap.

Chirping away in its high pitched voice
His teeny hazel coloured eyes shining in the sun
His maroon coloured breast
He shows it off to impress the ladies

This Christmas bird hovering high
He lands on a hedge
With a cat close by
Will he be lucky?
Or will he die?

Nicola Couston (Age 10)

Rain Cinquain

Raining
Drops on my face
Dripping from windowsills
Raindrops, glistening diamonds
Downpour.

Christine Coulter (Age 9)

I Will Mix With My Tears

I will mix with my tears,

The stories of grampa's soft voice
The smell of my nan's red rosy square blanket
And the photos of family and friends.

I will mix with my tears,

The times that were best
The times that were worst
And the times that never existed.

I will mix with my tears,

The smell of paper with hidden surprises
The secrets that nobody told
And the dreams of somebody's life.

I will mix with my tears,

The cuddles and kisses that touched me
The whiskers of my 1 year old hamster
And the cosiness of my family

And I will mix with my tears,

The happiness that came into my heart.

Madison Clare (Age 9)

This Feeling

It's so hard to discuss, too intense, I'm afraid even to whisper it into the wind, for fear it will shatter.
It's so painful it catches my throat and drops down to my chest, where it burns and smoulders.
It's so cruel to be wanting but not to be wanted, the agony is sharp like a bright shiny blade.
I can speak not a word, not a syllable about it, it can't be retracted once out it's alone.
A thought is so precious, inside you it's glowing, but once it is spoken it is marred and sullied.
If I spoke it, just once, would it come back to haunt me? Or would it grow and develop to something alive?
I can't speak, but I want to, can't touch, but I long to, can't grasp what this feeling is trying to say.
I can't ask, that's too selfish, can't beg, there's no pride, can't take with no giving, it's too hard to try.
It's a self-centred pleasure and one I will keep, just the thought can sustain me, I don't need to have ..... Him.
Him with his eyes and his words so soft spoken, him with his mind and his energy exciting.
Him with his hands his expressions exquisite, him with his foolishness, his laughter the sound.
Him with his own and no more to be wanted, him with his fear and his cowardly display.
Me with my anger, my pain and my weakness, my body, my soul, my smile and my gaze.
Me with my body, so young, so exciting, me with my spirit intriguing and hidden.
Me with my tears and my shouting and cursing, me in myself and myself is so new.
We sit separate people, one wanting, one wanted, separate in body, with one thought to share.

Gemma Charlton (Age 16)

An Olympian Lament

On my heights Immortals dwelt, as unconcerned as butterflies, and as impulsive as their flight,
My woods were the retreat of Artemis' silent scorn, as sharp as the arrows she shot.
Shy Dryads and playful Fauns cavorted in my sun-filled glades.
My slopes once trembled under Ares' anger and cowered to Zeus' rage.
Demeter's corn, like golden sunlight dawned upon my secluded steppes.
From my highest peak Hera's green-eyed gaze chastised her errant husband.

From my gently rolling foothills Orpheus' sweet music, his lament for Eurydice,
Once soared, soft and sad into the alpine air.
Aphrodite's fair feet once danced on my pastures green,
Far above Hades' black white shades that drifted down below, forever trapped and yet eternally free.

No more, no more do Pan's joyous pipes dance with Echo in my grottoes.
The tranquil lyre once echoed from my peaks,
The gentle notes once charmed cruel Cerberus to sleep, no longer ease Prometheus' torment.
Sweet flowers, Persephone gathered, omnipresent as air, their fate is shaded as hers.

Now mortal feet tread on my meadows spotless, destroying the mystery of my lofty summits,
Unknowing and uncaring of what came before, they will never understand what once was and what will be again.

Laura Churcher (Age 15)

A Twilight Dream

The midnight sun lapped down its shade
And ripples of light began to jade
The heavenly bodies of the stars, engraved a spark in the sky
Ribbons of soft whistling wind, whispered sacred secrets low and high

A shadowy glitter dusted lagoon had twining growths spurting from underneath
A wild night foxglove danced in the wind like a furnace flame from beneath

A depth of music played a chanting, hollow and lost tune
It faded hazily behind the lofty castle and headed for the snake-eyed moon.

Kelly Rose Chesters (Age 12)

Dreaming

Dreaming is like
Walking on water

Dreaming is like
Floating on air

Dreaming is like
Taking a spark from a star.

Lisa Cook (Age 12)

The Storm

People were jumping overboard,
Not wanting to suffer the wind's howling rage.
Deafening screams heard from all over the boat.
The wind has a bad criminal record (considering its age)
WHOOSH! All of sudden our boat is capsized,
All of us were frightened for our lives,
The wind was evil, a very dark sorcerer,
But there was no good sun, and by her we would have been advised.

The sea's grip round our necks was tightening,
Dragging us, pulling us, into its clutches

All the pain and suffering was far too much for us to take,
We were spluttering and coughing, crying out for help.
Another problem struck! Our lifejackets were faulty,
I had no more energy left, none to even let out a yelp.
But as we thought our lives were about to come to an end,
The wind started to die down, down, down .....
We all started cheering, so happy, so relieved.
The group swam to the capsized boat and tipped it back.
I will never forget that life threatening experience,
Just as long as it never, ever happens again .....

Natalie Copp (Age 11)

My Son

My son was made to carry his own cross
Blood ran down his innocent face
I cried and cried and shouted and shouted
But they wouldn't let him go
Veronica dabbed her cloth upon his face
And he carried on walking, walking, walking.

I wept and wept to see my son
And then a soldier let me in
I knelt down in front of him and looked up
His hands and feet were nailed to the cross
I could tell he was hurt and sad
John came and put his arm round me
Jesus said something to him and then his head hung low.

"Nooooo," I cried out loud everyone wanted him to stay
John took me away and I felt so lonely
He's my son, my son, my son.

Natalie Cook (Age 10)

Octopus

Tentacled octopus is an eight-legged jellyfish
Hunting octopus is a cheetah looking for its unaware prey
Soft octopus is a bean bag - very squidgy
Lonely octopus is a creature living in the murky, dark underwater caves
Fierce octopus is a monster lurking in the translucent water.

Daniel Chandler (Age 11)

Before School

Guiding pencil
Lead me
Lined book
Help me
Floppy rubber
Save me
Sharp scissors
Cut my way
Through the thin paper.
So may I
Escape the corrections
In this noisy classroom
As the boy
Finishes his work.
So may I
Be first to finish my task.
Living classroom
Hear me
Teasing children
Smile with me
Lead me to my work.

Ross Cameron (Age 9)

Sad

The funeral is here
Everyone is sad
I feel unhappy too and
Might be going mad

I think of heaven
And if angels fly
And I wish I could
Have said goodbye

Then Christmas comes
I feel alone
Just like a dog
Without a bone

Saphinna Cobb (Age 13)

Peace

P eople need peace and tranquillity
E arly morning dew on grass
A fter the sunset a pink glow
C alm waters rushing to the shore
E veryone should find peace in their lives.

Jade Chalmers (Age 11)

Babies

Babies can be cute, babies can be sweet
Lots of different names like Chloe, Bob, and Pete
Tiny fingers and tiny toes
Chubby cheeks and a button nose

Babies can be naughty, take good things with the bad
The drool, they scream and when they're upset they go mad
They stick pennies up their nose and eat lego bits
They throw food around the room, they get food all over their outfit

Babies stay awake all night
If they want food they won't give up without a fight
The stuff they eat - it makes me sick
They're not fussy about the food they pick

Mushy banana and mushy peas
But I bet they've never eaten mushy cheese
Babies can be cute, babies can be sweet
Lots of different names like Chloe, Bob and Pete.

Beckie Cox (Age 12)

Girlish Dreams

When I reach my early teens, I want to fulfil all my dreams
My first would be to drive a car, which would take me oh so far.

Different countries I'll see them all, through Summer, Winter, Spring and Fall
Travel the world that's what I'll do, sail the oceans deep and blue.

A sugar daddy I will find, to marry him is on my mind
A house, a boat, a jet, a pool, and children that go to boarding school.

The trouble with these plans and schemes, I know they're only girlish dreams
I guess it's time to think again, as my dream-life goes down the drain.

Good grades I'll need to get along, so study hard though right or wrong
I'll try at school and do my best, keep working hard to pass the test.

And then in time a job I'll need, to tackle the world and to succeed
Life looked so simple now it seems, so far away from those

GIRLISH DREAMS.

Ami Caton (Age 12)

A Storm At Sea

The clouds are blowing a mighty punishment to those guilty and not,
Fighting each other with winds that are twisting and sweeping.
They are black with angry bulging cheeks,
And mouths bursting open dropping a tremendously heavy spit.
The ocean's claws are slicing apart anything within reach,
Until everything dies down, except, of course for me.
I am the country's last hope and cannot rest with this on my conscience,
I must think of a way to make my name known .....
It's too late, the ocean has swallowed me.

Esther Cooke (Age 12)

Autumn

Autumn leaves tumbling fast
Upon the ever browning grass.
Brown and yellow; green and red;
Watch them twirl round my head.

The once green fields turned to gold
Ripened wheat all bagged and sold.
Bright red poppies no longer flutter
The autumn winds growl and mutter.

Calm blue seas turn to grey
Holiday makers all gone away.
Purple waves break on the shore
Summertime is here no more.

Dark grey clouds scudding fast
Light white mists swirling past
Black crows on branches bare
Tell the world Autumn is here.

Jessica Cutler (Age 13)

It Was So Noisy ...

It was so noisy that
The windows exploded

It was so noisy that
It came down in a crash!

It was so noisy that
The wall tumbled in a crumble

It was so noisy that
The T.V. was on fire in
A big bump!

It was so noisy that
The children screamed
And covered their ears!

Katy Crandon (Age 7)

Horses

Their hooves are like thunder,
They can run faster and faster,
Their colours make them proud
So that's why you see them stroll along
With boldness and proudness,
Their fur is as shiny as the sun
On a window or mirror
Can you see them shimmer?

Jamie Cowan (Age 11)

The Swan Of The Night

I come out at night
When the lake starts to relax
My white silky feathers
Sparkle when the moonlight shines on me

I don't like the sun
It is too bright
I love the moon
Because it is just right

When the sun comes up again
I go back to my nest
I sleep for the rest of the day
When the moon comes back out
So will I
I'm the swan of the night.

Lisa Cavanagh (Age 12)

Ghostly Night

The dark figures behind me
I'm feeling kind of scared
I'm really feeling lonely
It is just me only.
It is bright tonight, nobody
In sight
Only the dark figures behind me.
What will they do? What will they do?
Maybe they'll throw me in to the deep dark blue.

The air is rushing over me and the wind
Is whistling slowly.

Is this my phobia or is this my dream
I hope someone will save me before
I scream.
My brain is spinning
My head is turning.
Someone help me, someone help,
AAAAH!

Meli'sa Chambers (Age 12)

Cruelty

Cruelty is a dark sinister red
Cruelty is blazing red eyes beckoning
Cruelty is an eagle's razor sharp claws
Reaching to capture prey
The screaming of a howling gale
Whirling around in horror
Cruelty is a thousand knives stabbing at you
Flash then darkness.

Georgina Cameron (Age 11)

Autumn

Golden crunchy falling leaves,
Settling under tall grand trees.

Scary trick or treaters scuff them along,
As they sing their trick or treat song.

Browny red squirrels scurry to and fro,
Up the tree high and low.

Illuminous fireworks explode everywhere,
Go and see them if you dare.

The white Christmas season is coming soon,
Glittery decorations and cold snowmen too.

Autumn what a lovely time of year,
So let's all greet it with a cheer!

Hannah Cowan (Age 12)

The Fair!

I can't wait for the fair to come!
Neither can dad, or even mum
I'll go on every single ride
I'll play on the dodgems where the cars collide.

The roller coaster makes you sick
Even though the straps are thick
You think that you will fall to the ground
So everyone makes screaming sounds.

There is also the Ferris Wheel
Where some people laugh and squeal
Little seats to sit upon
They go higher and higher one by one.

At the fair are many treats
Many things are very sweet
I can't wait for the fair to be here
When it does, I'll sing and cheer.

Emily Coates (Age 12)

The Dark

I step into my garden
I see a shiny spooky moon
The ghostly air scares me
The great big black sky makes me shiver
Wild wolves howl
The haunted owl hoots
I run inside
I see nothing.

Alexandra Chisholm (Age 8)

Left With No Trace

The ship groaned and the people moaned,
As the waves tossed and turned smashing and crashing
Over the decks.

The ship groaned and the people moaned,
As the wind swept through every crack and crevice,
Screaming and howling like a wolf.

The ship groaned and the people moaned,
As the bow plunged through the surf,
Creating spray ten metres high.

The ship groaned and the people moaned,
As the deck split beneath them with one almighty crash.

The ship slipped beneath the waves.
The sea swelled but the people were silent.

Tom Corbet (Age 13)

My Grandfather

Do not stand at his grave and cry
He is not there, he did not die.
He is the cold wind that blows in January
He is the sprinkles of snow that fall in February
In March he's the clouds, white and grey
In April he's the showers that fall all day
He is a baby lamb, just been born in May
In June he is a bird, singing so gay
In July he is the beautiful, early morning light
In August he's a sunbeam, strong and bright
In September he's a colourful, high flying kite
In October he's a star that twinkles at night
He is a fire that burns in November
He is the cheer that returns in December
He will never be forgotten
Because he's with us all year
Don't think of him as gone
Believe that he is here.

Jemma Chambers (Age 16)

All Talk

People talking, chatting away
Life, love, family fun
And anything else which has to be done.
The jobs of today and those of tomorrow
The world's troubles and our own sorrows
So many topics of conversation
All talk no hesitation
Everyone speaking, but is there anyone to hear
The cry of the person with the silent tear?

Tanya Couzens (Age 15)

The Mistress's Reply

Dear Sir, after what you have said
I could not let you in my bed
You seem far too lustful for me
What I want is love, can't you see?
It's nice you see me in this way
But would you mind if I did say?
Although you seem to love me so
I'd prefer it, were you to go
Leave me alone, out of my life
Don't make me suffer pain and strife.
I'm going to be married soon
Next week at St Michael's, at noon
Although I loved you years before
That's over now, I've closed the door.
Please no more letters, no more notes
It's a shame for we were so close.

Simon Crowther (Age 14)

Boaster

I have a space fighter
It's the best ever
I won a galactic race
You cheat, I never!

I am a film star
I am in Foureyes
I walked along the beach
Got covered in apple pies

I am a warrior
I have a wicked sword
I am the best around
A shame I haven't an award!

Michael Campbell (Age 10)

The Sea

The sea is like a wild cat
Clawing at the beach
Stormy nights
Hissing and crashing
Against the rocks
Day returns
The sea is calm
Dolphins play amongst the waves
Seagulls swirl up with the clouds
Peace, restored with calming
Sounds of lapping waves.

Emma Carrigan (Age 11)

The Weathered Rock

I have existed for thousands of centuries, I have looked over the hills and watched my home grow.
I am now old and tired and crumbly, the lines on my face are engraved with age.
The uneven edges that disguise me isolate me from world's of comfort and warmth.
The wandering sheep that acknowledge and console me come and go like a wave on the beach.

Rain has slashed down on me; drops have raced rapidly down me,
The soil beneath my feet has been enriched, plants have grown up my sides searching for light.
Once the rain has gone the world is left feeling fresh and cleansed.

Wind has blown over me and whirled around me, challenging my right to stay where I stand, proud.
Wind has howled at me and left my ears ringing, the uncivil manner with which it whines at you,
Playing and laughing like a witch on her broomstick.

Icicles hang from me with their strong clawing fingers, snow has blanketed me and encased me in its frozen grip,
It changes my landscape beyond recognition, and leaves its mark when it goes as you try to thaw out.
It silently dares you, as it furtively escapes to imagine how unbearingly cold it will be when next winter comes.

Sun has baked me as if trying to melt me, its fiery temper flares up when I don't,
Its rays shoot down on me, heating me up like a cold-blooded lizard,
Its laser-like eyes glare down on me evilly until light fluffy clouds intervene with its path.

Night falls around me and stars wink down at me, I will remain here unmoved by the challenges I encounter.

Sara Carter (Age 15)

Stars

S tars shine so brightly in the dark night sky, look for the North Star the brightest of them all.

T he twinkling above, with not a cloud in sight, makes the sky look polka dot in pattern.

A mongst them is the moon so full and bright, it lights up the whole sky

R ed is a bright light moving across the sky, it comes from an aeroplane flying so high.

S tars in the sky so bright, there's millions of them far too many to count.
    Can you make pictures out of the stars, the Plough is one to the North Star.

Laura Cross (Age 13)

The Gun Shot

The fox cub cried like a hungry baby
The sound echoed from tree to tree.
I felt shamed!
As it was my family that caught it
The thunder roared like a roaring lion,
Hungry and depressed

The gun shot fired
It sounded like a drum smashing.
My heart stopped,
It was over!

Silence filled the air,
It sounded as if the world had ended.
All you could hear were the trees
Swaying from side to side.

George Crook (Age 12)

Death

A petrified face, writhing, shrieking, turning,
Draped in a frayed cloak of black cloth,
White spindly fingers, creeping out of the cloak.
Brown rotting teeth and revolting gums,
Chapped lips the colour of blood,
Black eyes glinting mad and vicious.
A call like fingernails scraping blackboards,
SCREEEEEAKK!
Never ending, never caring,
Mighty footsteps slapping heavily.
Stench of rotting limbs around him,
Decomposing and putrid,
Grabbing enemies fiercely,
Haunting all, the master.

Ben Charlston (Age 10)

My Cat

I once had a cat called Mischief,
He was furry and black with shiny white teeth.
He was cute and sweet,
Gorgeous and petite.
Right now to you he must sound perfect,
But he was weird, I didn't know where he'd learnt it.
And not just a bit, he acted like a two year old child,
He was really naughty, he was positively wild.
I've got to hand it to him, he did get away with a lot,
And that's something to be proud of.
Since some people's parents were pushovers, mine are not.
Even though he could be mean,
I was still sad to see him leave.
In the end my mum thought he was too wild,
So she gave him away and I was sad for a while.
I soon got over it, I think of him now and then.
My parents felt guilty, so they brought him back and I was happy again!

Lauren Crow (Age 13)

Sky Cycle

A midnight blue, a silent night
Twinkling stars, flash out of sight
Ghostly mists, a silver satin
Melting down into nothing.

A purpley pink, a vivid sunrise
The sun's like our god, strong and wise
A doorway to space, a beam of light
A shimmering power, soon to be night.

Way off in the horizon, the sun is rolling down
Still radiating light, until it's gone beyond the ground.

So as the darkness fades, the moon's a brilliant white
So as the circle's still spinning, I lay down tucked up tight.

Sarah Clayton (Age 11)

Science

For Christmas I would like to get a chemistry set

I would have such fun with a bunsen.

Mixing and stirring all sorts of different things.

I could maybe make something that would make my ears ring,

Or I could make a magic potion that could be used as a lotion,

And I could sell it and make lots of money.

Lewis Cornall (Age 10)

Clouds

Clouds,
Have no shape and have no size
Do they float along the skies?
Are they shaped in special ways?
Like models made from clay
Are our lives put to waste
With all things done poste-haste?
Is this just pointless?
Is nothing real?
Is all this pressure and all this pain
Used in utter vain?

Clouds
Have no shape and have no size
Is life shaped likewise?

Mark Collie (Age 12)

The Dragon Of Death

My wings are flames of fire,
My eyes are diamonds of all colours,
My tongue is a bolt of lightning,
My claws are sharp as knives,
My breath smells of evil,
My voice is pounds of thunder,
My tail flies as swords,
I've seen deaths of hell,
In play I scare off people,
In anger I kill of death,
They call me The Dragon Of Death

Peter Cullum (Age 13)

Summer

Leaves are green
Sky is blue
Grass is wet with the
First morning dew

Sun is shining
Clouds in the sky
Butterflies are fluttering
Birds are flying high

Brightly coloured flowers
Going to the beach
Long summer holidays
With nobody to teach.

Hannah Coombs (Age 10)

Fallen

Falling apart from heat to toe, bones crumbling,
Heart breaking, skin peeling,
Eyes burning, brain freezing.
Then there's nothing left but the ashes
And my hurting soul.

Falling apart at the seams, feelings fraying,
Eyes falling, hair greying,
Brain splitting, heart chipping.
Then there's nothing left but the pieces
And my damaged soul.

Replacing my hurting body, with different pieces,
Weak bones, cold heart,
Thick skin, scaring eyes, half a brain.
Then there's only my soul
Left to burn by the hurting ashes.

Replacing my damaged image, with different pieces,
Lost feelings, raw eyes
Dry hair, useless brain, hard heart.
Then there's only my soul
Left to fall by the damaged pieces.

Lucy Cullum (Age 16)

50 Years On

Glitz and glamour
Are some clothes
Ragged and smelly
Can be others
What are clothes?

Tracksuit bottoms
Sparkly dresses
Short skirts like
Dishcloths
What can we do?

Magnificent trousers
Short and long
Colourful jumpers
Like a song
What are clothes?

Clothes are so helpful
Clothes are so cool
Clothes can get dirty
Clothes made for you
I know what clothes are do you?

Emma Cooper (Age 11)

The Rotten Rat

I am a rat
I can't bark like a dog
I can't scratch like a cat
I can't hop like a frog

I can't swim like a whale
I can't run like a cheetah
I can't fly like a quail
I can't laugh like a hyena
All I can do is swish my tail.

Timothy Cozins (Age 8)

Moonlight Predator

Slithering round the rocks and sand
Licking it clean with his long forked tongue
Feeling for his prey

Hungry for a rat or two
The moonlight predator stalks his prey
Hungry for a mouse or two

His shining scaly body
Glistening in the twilight
Waiting for his prey

There it goes, scurrying by
Still he does not move
Eyes glinting in the moonlight

Leap, his fangs sink deep
Paralysed, frightened, unable to move
At last he gets his prey.

James Culley (Age 12)

Snow

Glistening snow drifting along
Icicles smashing in a tune like a song
White fluffy heaps shining in the sun
Soon it will melt and there will be none
Crispy ice as the snow disappears
Roof tops dripping watery tears

Victoria Crisp (Age 11)

The Bright Sun

The burning bright sun
The sea rolling gently across the beach
Catching your feet in the sand
But never to let you go

Waves roll slowly on your feet
And when you're in the sea
Plop, plop, plop, plop
In the sea

I love catching crabs
They bite my toes

I love the beach
But what I want to know is
Do you like it too?

Danielle Cragg (Age 8)

The Murderous Moon

The moon is a bright torch
Shining on a black blanket

It is a white roll
Left on a black table

The moon is a snowball
Stuck unmelted in the sky

The moon is a screwed up paper ball
Stuck to a blackboard

The moon is a huge one-eyed monster
Wearing a black cloak

The moon is a scoop of ice cream
On a black plate

The moon is a white bowl
On a black table cloth

The moon is a crystal
Gleaming on a black velvet carpet.

Jessica Cutting (Age 11)

Snow

Squelching, muddy, slippery snow
The ice is as slippery as soap
Crunching sounds like a crunchy bar
The hail is like stones plummeting down
The snow is like icing on a cake
Snow like strawberries with sugar and cream
Snow laying on the ground like sun tan cream.

Sam Crisp (Age 9)

Skateboarding

As I step on my skateboard
I feel excited
Whoosh! Down the drive I go
The kerb is just in front of me
Will I make it? Will I fall?
Bump, bump I made it
Now to avoid the bumps and holes
That appear without warning
On the twisting turning road
Around the corner - there's the ramp
The workmen have left the plank again
I stop I move back for speed ...
Here I go faster and faster
Up the ramp into the air
I'm going to make it
I'm going to get there
Bang! Down I land
I've made it! Upright I stand
That's the thrill of skateboarding
Safely completing the jump.

Jake Coulson (Age 9)

Why Do I Have To?

Why do I have to go to school?
But I like P.E in the hall.
Why do I have to get ready for school?
Anyway I don't like it at all.

Why do I have to go to school?
There's no point at all
Break time is best
Better than all the rest!

Joshua Coker (Age 8)

Special Box

In my special box I will put ...

The anticipation and excitement of a crowd before a football match,
The loud roar when your team scores a goal,
The relief and joy when your team is winning and the final whistle sounds,
The feeling of proudness when your team lifts the cup.

In my special box I will put ...

An eighth day of the week and two Christmases
The sight of daffodil bulbs breaking the earth Spring is on its way
The sound of branches crashing into the wind like a golf ball shattering a window
A tender petal smooth on my skin at the tall tip of my fingertips.

In my special box ...

Florrie Critchley (Age 11)

Midnight Robber

The streets were silent, dark and bare
And not a single soul was there
To see the robber sprint beside
The sleeping homes on which he spied.

His bloodshot eyes were streaked with red
His ears were sharp, for every tread
And every rustle he might hear
With which he'd strangely disappear.

Suddenly, he dropped like lead
Behind the wall he hid his head
His bated breath could not be heard
Above the noise which then occurred.

The blaring sirens brought him down
The screech of tyres woke the town
Police got out and searched the street
And soon secured his just defeat.

Jonathan Craig (Age 10)

In The Future

When I am older I will walk with aliens
And I will fly around in my car
I will breath under water
And fly my car to Mars
I will talk to animals
And fly across the sea
And live in a totally chocolate house
And a watch that talks to me
I will own a whale
And a seahorse if I can
And maybe a kangaroo
And a little turtle too
But I know I won't do any of these
Because miracles don't just come.

Tom Clayton (Age 8)

My Brother

My brother is small and kind,
One day he woke up
And found some jelly
He is kind and lovely,
Very horrible, but funny.
He's evil and selfish,
Tall, stupid and skinny,
Cool and very small.
You can hear butterflies in his belly,
Not nice, not very smooth,
Naughty, selfish and one big silly boy,
Not nice, bad-tempered
And uses his tools to hit his head!!

Michael Curland (Age 9)

The Big Whale

When I went away to fish
Yummy yum my favourite dish
I caught a little tiny sea snail
And a monstrous great whale!

The little tiny sea snail
Dropped gently into my pail
But, this massive elephantine whale
Only could get in his tail!

After an almighty squish
In went the tremendous beast of a fish
I put a blanket over the top
So that out again it didn't pop!

When I got home for tea
And in the lock went the key
Mum said, "take them back to the lake."
"For tea, my lad, we're having steak!"

Elizabeth Cowan (Age 11)

The Scorpion

Living in the hot desert
Burrowing in the freezing cold night
The scorpion is a dangerous beast
With pincers and a poison tipped tail.

Scuttling though the sand
Its skin sandy camouflage
Hides till the moment is right
Then attacks with a deadly sting.

The scorpion's tail is venomous
Like a stinging spear
It stings its prey, waits for them to die
Then will eat them ..... so beware!

Alexander Cooper (Age 10)

The Door

Go and open the door
Maybe there will be
A great big grey castle
Or a fat ogre
Maybe there will be
A twinkling fairy
Or a herd of green cows.

Go and open the door
There may be a black cat chasing
A little white mouse
Or a hungry wolf.

Victoria Clark (Age 8)

Bubble, Splash, Bubble

I started off as marshy land up in the Welsh Mountains
Bubble, splash, bubble
I sprinkle down the mountains starting a trickling stream

As I drift down a valley my strength builds up
Suddenly, I speed up and get thrown over the horizon I'm thundering over the brow
BUBBLE, SPLASH, BUBBLE!

As I fall down I see the rocks beneath me
I splush and gush and then I crash into the foam below me I splutter over the boulders reaching for freedom
Bubble, splash, bubble.

I start to gently slow down I tear away the bank beside me and start to meander
Pushing pebbles with me as I get wider I drop them on my bed
Bubble, splash, bubble.

As I tear away the landscape I form little cliffs and channel my way through sparkling in the sunlight
The fisherman's net slaps my surface
Bubble, splash, bubble.

I can taste the salt of the sea! I can see fish and crabs
My journey is complete now; I meet my friend at last
Bubble, splash, bubble.

Colin Coleman (Age 10)

What Am I?

As I snare
People glare
To see me jump
With a thump
Deer my dinner
But not forever
Time runs
But not as fast as me
I am .....

Rachel Chambers (Age 10)

Ten Nil

He shoots! He scores!
Ten goals to me!
And nil to the garage door!

Ceyhan Crosthwaite (Age 10)

Fish

Fishes swim
In fresh water
They move
Round and round
Parrots speak
Dogs bark
Worms slither
Mice scurry

Iqra Chaudhury (Age 8)

A Creature

Have you seen the killer of the sea?
It's a flesh eating, blood covered creature
Eating in the deep sea.

Have you seen the killer of the sea?
It's a super-speed streamlined creature
Swimming in the deep sea.

Have you seen the killer of the sea?
It's a flesh-filled, sharp toothed creature
Killing in the deep sea.

Have you seen the killer of the sea?
Lying limply in a restaurant
Being eaten by people.

Joe Claydon-Johns (Age 8)

Schools

The nets of the netball post round and small
Marked writing brick on the red brick wall
The big doors leading to the hall
And the birds with a sweet little call

Children coming out from class
On the field with green blades of grass
The goalpost a nice bright white
The leaves of the trees are very light

The stinking toilets in the corridor
And the red and white patterns on the floor
It's a long way to walk
And people play and talk.

Thomas Cowell (Age 9)

There's Something In the Bathroom

There's something in the bathroom
I don't know what it is
It's really really frightening
Its got our shopping list.

It could be behind the toilet
It could be in the sink
It could be in the water pipes
Or where the light bulb blinks.

It might be really big
Or really really small
It could be on its own
Or in another's thrall.

There's something in the bathroom
I'll go and look inside
I'll open up the door and ...
It's my father reading the law!

Benjamin Convery (Age 10)

About My Dog

When my dog was young she was very small
But now she's older she's very tall.

My dog chews bags
And she shreds up mags.

She's as useless as a caramel car
But she runs very very far.

She tries to talk
To ask for a walk.

She likes to chase a bouncy ball
But doesn't come back when I call.

She likes to get soaking wet
But she still makes a brilliant pet.

Phillip Cummings (Age 9)

Umbrellas

Umbrellas, umbrellas they keep you dry
They keep you dry from rain in the sky!
Umbrellas, umbrellas some full of holes
They're no good they'll wet your soul!
Umbrellas, umbrellas some big, some small
It doesn't really matter at all!
Umbrellas, umbrellas what colours will be
Some dots some lines different colours
Maybe!
Umbrellas, umbrellas they'll eventually break
Well that's the end of the umbrella.

Josephine Caulkett (Age 10)

Scrumptious Scotch

When I wear my crown my dogs always frown
At my shiny spooky slithery scarf
I bought a fleece from ancient Greece
And a blistering big bulky black belt
When I wear my skirt I always get hurt
Especially in my ultra handsome high heels
I bought a watch and had a scrumptious scotch
Whilst flashing my recently bought round rings.

Lauren Carter (Age 11)

Oh No!

Oh no he's done it again
Mum's flower beds will never be the same
Flopsy ate them, he's to blame.

Oh no he's done it again
Dad's shoe laces are in tatters
Flopsy chewed them, what else matters.

Oh no he's done it again
Fast asleep, curled up in his cage
Now no one's in a rage!

Emily Callaghan (Age 9)

Pollution

In years to come
Will the river still be polluted
And whales and dolphins be extinct
Or will the dolphins and whales swim around?
What will happen?
Will the sea be okay
Are the fish still being killed?
The sea might be too dirty
To swim in.
What will happen?
Will fishermen still fish
Will boats still go out
In the sea?
No one knows!

Vicky Catnach (Age 10)

There Is A ...

There is a nosy elephant inside me
That always sticks my trunk in somebody else's business.

There is a barking dog inside me
That makes my tummy bark.

There is a mad crocodile inside me
That makes me snap.

There is a chatting parrot inside me
That makes me talk.

There is a flippering fish inside me
That always leads the way.

There is a sleepy sloth inside me
That always makes me tired.

There is a crazy kangaroo inside me
That makes me hyper.

There is a roaring lion inside me
That makes me roar.

John Cronin (Age 11)

Horses

Horses galloping in the dead of night.
Magnificent body what a sight.
Cantering hooves
Like hail stones on roofs.
Sleek and shiny tail like a glittering star.
Rearing and plungering like a broken down car.

Camilla Clarke (Age 8)

The Science Poem

How do human babies develop?
What are shooting stars?
What is photosynthesis?
Why do we grow?
How many elements are there?
How does a compass work?
What is an air conductor?
What is an insulator?
Why is the sky blue?
How deep is the earth?
Why do we have leap years?
What are atoms?
What does radioactive mean?
Is gravity a force?
What does friction do?
What is electricity?

Rachael Cox (Age 8)

Storm Kicks Hard

Sea rolls
Rain beats down
Bright lightning thumps
Wind howls in black night
Big grey clouds roar
Storm kicks hard

Mercedes Cragg (Age 8)

Foot And Mouth

Foot and Mouth you scare me
Spreading throughout the country

News on
"Quiet everyone, what now?"
Spreading, spreading further.

Foot and Mouth you scare me
Spreading throughout the country

Worsening situation
"Quiet everyone, burning carcasses!"
Spreading, spreading further.

Foot and Mouth you scare me
Spreading throughout the country

My desperate Dad
Will it reach our farm?
Spreading spreading further.

Foot and Mouth you scare me
Spreading throughout the country.

Isabel Collings (Age 11)

Lightning

I illuminated the sky one day.
I shot a tree with direct aim.
I made a house fall down
In five seconds flat!
I killed a person with a powerful shot,
A shot as hard as steel.
I went to the top of Mount Everest
And destroyed the ice.
I stopped and found the badness in me
And started to fade away.

Richard Cowley (Age 8)

Me!

I may not be slim and sporty,
I may not be cool and trendy,
But I like me 'cos I'm me!

I may not be rolling in money,
I may not be good at rhyming,
But I like me 'cos I'm me!

I may not be girly and clean,
I may not have long hair,
But I like me 'cos I'm me!

Jessica Cross (Age 10)

My Cousin

"Do you want to play a gun game?"
"No thanks"
"Do you want sweets from the shop?"
"No thanks"
"You need a haircut do you want one?"
"No thanks"
"Why not listen to Eminem?"
"No thanks"
"Want to play rugby at the rec?"
"No thanks"
"Why not call Brett, or go to his house?"
"No thanks"
"Want to race with our remote control cars?"
"No thanks"
"But what about watching T.V?"
"No thanks"
"WELL WHAT DO YOU WANT TO DO?!!"
"No thanks."

James Clayton (Age 10)

The Animals

The monkey swings from vine to vine
Oh, how I wish that monkey was mine

The elephant with his mighty tusk
His trunk is swinging from dawn to dusk

The tiger with his flashing stripes
Is enough to make a bird shout yikes!

When I see the neck on the giraffe
It always seems to make me laugh

The lioness with her body so fair
Prowling around with her short golden hair

From hog to dog, from zoo to zoo
You always seem to find the animal for you!

Olivia Cripps (Age 9)

Fantasy

Through the secret door I can see, a crumbling and the ghost of Henry VIII
Through the secret door I can see a U.F.O. in Romford, poisoning the people
Through the secret door I can see, Harry, Ron, and Hermionie
Through the secret door I can see Man. U, at the bottom of the Premiership
Through the secret door I can see my future as a poet, and of course I can see me.

Jack Cole (Age 11)

My Sister

My sister is a black storm growing day by day
She is more annoying than an itch in your mouth
She is as bad as pins and needles
She is as horrible as sloppy spinach
She is like a lump of hair blocking the plug hole
She is like a spider waiting for the kill
My sister is a black storm growing day by day.

Ellis Collins (Age 9)

The Feathered Poodle Bird

It wears a red and white scarf with a green hat
But definitely not very fat
Bright blue boots with purple socks right up to his shins
Eats plum pie and boiled potatoes in their skins
Its favourite drink is coca cola and prune juice fresh from the fruit
He's no big brute either
His hooked long beak pulling at his feathers cleaning them
His eyes gleaming like a gem
In his high pitched voice he says, "It's poodle bird time."
His voice is like, a wind chime.

Dorian Cottle (Age 9)

Keep Going

Come on Jesus you can do it
You can't give up now
You can make it to the top of the hill
Where the worst is yet to come

No matter about the weight of the cross
Or people laughing at the crown
I believe in you, I do
To make it to the top

Soon you'll be in paradise
With me, that's right I'm God
But first you have to go through
The pain of nail through skin

You've told me to forgive them
Those people killing you
And though it's hard to do so
I'll do it if you please

Here you are now sitting by me
You made it into heaven
And now down there on earth
Your mother has your body.

Nicola Conway (Age 10)

Water Poem

As the water goes down the stream
Not having a clue where its been
Hoping that it won't fall
Trying to be brave and waves stand tall

Water comes form the sky
If we did not have water then we would die
Water can be snow
When the ice-cold winds do blow

If it's rain, ice or snow
The river can so gracefully flow
Into lakes, the oceans or the seas
It will do just as it pleases.

Michael Clayton (Age 9)

Pushing Boulders Down

Bubble, bubble goes the water
Trickle, trickle from the source
Splash, splash goes the tiny stream
Crunching and munching the earth away
Lifting pebbles and boulders
And crushing them
Down the waterfall
And pushing boulders down
Curling, twisting and rounding
Through the meanders;
The river slows down
And drops its load
It gets eaten up by the sea.

Matthew Charlton (Age 8)

Today I'm A ...

Today I'm a bear
I sit in my chair

Today I'm a rabbit
To eat lettuce is a habit

Today I'm a mole
I love digging holes

Today I'm a cat
I live in a hat

Today I'm a mouse
And I live in a house

Today I'm a bird
And I love lemon curd

That is the end of my animal world.

Amy Clarke (Age 9)

Elephants

Somewhere in Africa far far away there will be an elephant
Resting, standing, sleeping, underneath a special tree.
This elephant will be dreaming about eating luscious green leaves
And finding a cool calm water-hole to splash about in.

Walking stomping stamping about an elephant will be doing
Watching her young, scared of nothing.
She's found a water-hole that is what she's been wishing for.

I like elephants
I like their great big flapping ears
And their grey long trunks.

Elizabeth Cole (Age11)

The Battle Of Bosworth

I see bloody heads rolling around helplessly
I want to see the battle end and no-one be killed
I smell freshly burned ashes mixed with fresh red blood.
I feel as small as a beetle.
I hear the army's blood chiling war songs.
I trudge through cold mud in my bare feet.
I think Richard is mad for risking so many lives.

Sophy Cooke (Age 9)

Fear

Burning inside
Torturing the heart
Throat dry
Brain aching
Try not to let it out
But it fights to escape
The only thing to do is to
Hide

Cassy Childs (Age 11)

Please Miss Sydenham

Please Miss Sydenham, this boy Alex Way
Keeps kicking me under the table, Miss, what shall I say?

Tell him to get lost, dear, tell him to go away
Tell him just to go, my friend, I don't know what to say

Please Miss Sydenham, this boy Alex Way
Keeps pinching my legs, Miss, what shall I say?

Tell him you'll do it back, love, shout it out loud
Say what you want, girl and just make me proud.

Please Miss Sydenham, this boy Alex Way
Keeps shouting out the answers, what shall I say?

Tell your friends his answers, love, say them before he does
Put your fingers in your ears, you little wimp and stop annoying us!

Steven Clark (Age 8)

Water - A River

A shimmering blue is the river with mud and grass around
It flows so calmly onwards, from the mountains going down.

On and on goes the river, getting wider as it goes
Always getting faster, faster as it flows.

Things are in the water, crisp golden leaves
Jamming up its pathway, but the river breaking free.

Down and down it goes, getting nearer to the sea
The salty seaweed mixing with fresh water, could it be?

Now we've come down to the sea
The waves lapping gently, gently on our feet.

Children playing loudly, happily in the sand,
Everybody's joyful, as the waves break on the land.

Elise Clements (Age 9)

Chimpanzee

You think of me as a weirdo
But I'm not
All I want is to be funny
I say I'm hilarious
But you think I'm not
I climb to tree to tree
I play games with my family
I run along the floor
To get to my food
You make fun of me
Because the way I look
My cheeky face
A happy smile
From my funny mouth
I have big ears
And a hairy chest
When I hit my tum
It hurts
Trying to act like a gorilla
I'M A CHIMPANZEE!

Michael Coomes (Age 10)

Why?

Why is the world round?
How do people stay alive?
Yes, I have troubles with the world, do you?
Why do people treat animals so badly?
How do animals survive cruel people?
You treat them well.....don't you?
Why are people treated cruelly if they are black?
How come people's skin colour is different anyway?
You could do something to stop this forever, couldn't you?

Nicola Coker Gordon (Age 9)

Fluffy - My Rabbit

My bunny lies under the hot orange sun,
Then she leaps up and skids around the corner of her run.
She sits all curled up in a small furry ball,
Then she rubs herself on the warm brown wall
Washing her face with her little pink paws.
Her ears flop as she crouches right down
She is the BEST bunny in the whole of our town.
Her soft brown fur touches my hand,
Like the feel of some soft golden brown sand.

Vanessa Coker (Age 11)

Today At Felixstowe

Children in warm clothes shivering
As the rain beats down strongly
Hard icy hailstones attack unwanted visitors
Monstrous cranes tower over cuboid containers
Like giraffes eating their food
Motionless rides sitting silently waiting
For summer visitors to arrive
Ancient driftwood carelessly thrown
On the unfriendly beach
Frightened birds wrestling the wind to
Keep away from the mighty waves in the sea.

Benjamin Cracknell (Age 10)

A Spell To Make Titania Agree With Me

Black cat tails
With loads of snails
Some fairy dust
With metal rust
Titania's hair
And an ear from a bear
Four tulip petals
Two stinging nettles
The witch's cackle
Sounded like a baby's rattle
Mix it altogether
Let the spell last forever!

Cherie Chapman (Age 12)

Woodlouse

An armoured knight
Marching along in a black cloak
Fighting for its life rather than its country.

In the moonless night it's hidden
But in the light
It has to scuttle into chinks, cracks and crevices.

A miniature armadillo eating leaves
Instead of ants.

It lives in the woodland
Scooting into bushes and trees.

Ready to roll
Into a blackened berry at any time
To be protected from the human world.

Emily Cheek (Age 10)

Beautiful River

Twinkling like the scattering stars
Shimmering, glimmering
Glistening, listening
To the tale you have to tell.

Tranquil as the morning bird
Rushing with the silent breeze
Singing to the mountain side
Content and peaceful
Rushing down the waterfall.

Loving every bit
Rippling, sighing
Flowing to the estuary
Gliding in happiness.

Josie Carter (Age 8)

Katie

My sister has just started school
Stephanie thinks she's clever
My best friend thinks she's really cool
Tina and me play together
Polly and Jay think they rule,

Now Katie's moved away
Mrs Taylor thinks I'm slower
Now Katie's moved away!

Robyn Caufield (Age 9)

Storm

The wind sounds like
A giant insect buzzing and
A steam engine, with smoke like paper.

On a windy day I imagine myself on
A giant hamster wheel,
A balloon being deflated.

The wind makes children lively.

The wind is like an angry god,
A thick swamp blizzard,
A brilliant blasting storm,
A mini rollercoaster for the snow.

The wind plays tricks like
Making shapes with trees. It bites you!

John Chapman (Age 8)

My Wilderness Poem

There is a mouse in me
Small and petit
Always looking
For something to eat

There is a parrot in me
Squawking and talking to everybody
Always having something to say
To all my friends and family

There is a cat in me
Bright eyed and bushy tail
Glowing like torches all night long
Cat by name and cat by nature

There is a dog in me
Always sitting on Terry's knee
Always having someone to see
Listening to people regularly.

Stacey Catt (Age 11)

Animals, Animals, Animals

Animals, animals, animals
A furry fox
An enormous elephant.

Animals, animals, animals
A curly cat
A fat fish
A wiggly worm

Animals, animals, animals.

Liam Cossey (Age 7)

I Will Store At The Back Of My Memory

I will store at the back of my memory,

The smell of an Indian meal cooking
The sound of a choir singing
The sight of West Ham winning the F.A. Cup.

I will store at the back of my memory,

A glass of water from a geyser in the desert
A jar of jam over two hundred years old
A bottle of milk which never goes out of date.

I will store at the back of my memory,

A pool of lava taken from an active volcano
A box full of my grandad's model aeroplanes
A universe which has six planets full with little green men.

I will store at the back of my memory,

A candle which hasn't blown out for centuries
A watch exactly the same as James Bonds'
A pop group who play classical instruments.

I have filled my memory with peculiar things
My memories will never be forgotten.

John Cackett (Age 11)

My Silly Cat

I have a really silly cat, it goes everywhere
On my desk and on my chair
On top of my piano and on the ledge
It goes in the middle even in the edge
It hides in the cupboard with my frocks
And even throws all my socks.
Even though it's a silly cat
It always listens when I tell it to sit on my lap.

Faryal Choudary (Age 10)

The Door

I open the door and see the world at war
The eruption of a volcano causing disaster
Hurricanes demolishing towns and cities.

I open the door and see trees being cut down for paper
People fighting
Children living and sleeping on the streets.

I open the door and see more hospitals being built
Children on the streets having homes to live in
Fox hunting and bull fighting being banned
I shut the door with all the beautiful things in my mind.

Ben Chandler (Age 11)

Nicholas Dean

Nicholas is his name
Rugby is his game
He is just the best
No one calls him lazy
He runs and runs around the pitch
Like a good old stick.

In rugby he never goes off
He never gives up
Even if he is on the floor crying
He runs after people with the ball and takes them down.

Nicholas and I have been friends right from the start
Nicholas is the friend to have
He always makes you laugh
He uses funny words
That is what I like about him
He will be my friend from the start to the very end
That is what you call a good old friend.

Adam Chantler (Age 11)

Washing

What is all this washing about
Every day, week in, week out?
From getting up till going to bed
I'm tired of hearing the same things said,
Whether I'm dirty or whether I'm not.
Whether the water is cold or hot
Whether I like or whether I don't
Whether I will or won't
"Have you washed your hands and face?"
I seem to live in the washing place
Before a meal is ever begun
And after a meal is done
It's time to put on the waterspout.

Please what is all this washing about?

Charlotte Carter (Age 9)

Kingfisher

K ingfishers are the best
I n the classroom we work hard
N aughty children don't exist in our class
G ood children don't get red cards
F riends spend most of their time chatting
I ngenious we are
S pend most of our time working
H ard workers get special badges
E veryone is great in some ways
R ough children are extinct in our class

Hannah Coveney (Age 9)

My Four Seasons Poem

The flowers come out of their house to play
The sky has been freshly painted
A bright green rug the soil puts on
And the trees grow their hair

    Like a fire the sun burns
    Back from holiday the birds come
    Like a candlestick the ice cream melts
    And the hose is a slithering snake

The trees have a hair cut again
And the grass gets a golden hat
Their nice green coats the bushes take off
And on the road the leaves race.

    Trees pull on their white hat and scarf
    In a shining white blanket the grass sleeps
    A hard silver rug spreads over the lake
    As the south the sun's warmth flies.

Hannah Carter (Age 9)

Life As A Golden Eagle

I stand up tall all bold and proud
Like the king of the Highlands in which I am
My golden feathers spread out far
As I glide straight through the whistling wind.
My beak as sharp as a Samauri's sword
As I snap and trap my helpless prey.
Down goes the slimy food as
My stomach rumbles with satisfaction
Why does the valley fear me?
I think as I flap my huge wings under
The setting sun. Why?

Michael Cross (Age 10)

Christmas Is .....

A time to be jolly
Hung on the ceiling is the holly
Children sleep peacefully in their bed
While visions of Santa Claus dance in their head

Down the chimney Santa Claus comes
To deliver the presents to everyone
To all the children here comes the fun
So whoosh up the chimney before rising sun.

Jade Corby (Age 8)

My Favourite Birthday

My favourite birthday was when I was six,
In the house round balloons and streamers were fixed.
Family and friends arrived holding large boxes.
And friends from my class who were known as The Foxes.

Soon the party and music was into full swing
Everyone ate the food, nothing left, not a thing.
We sang on my old karaoke machine,
Though my shy sister Tamsin, wasn't too keen.

Soon small party bags were quickly shared out,
Full of sweets and surprises and received with a shout.
Later cars sped down the driveway, ruining Mum's flowers,
Which she planted in May, taking several hours.

Holly Crouch (Age 11)

Science Week

S cience is everywhere
C onstruction and design
I nformation is mine
E veryone uses science
N ew ideas, new appliance
C lever solutions get us on our way
E very single day.

W ithout it we'd be stuck
E dward wouldn't have a truck
E laine couldn't cook
K evin wouldn't read a book.

James Cornall (Age 10)

Senses

Tasting is a kind of sense
Eating things we like
Smelling is another sense
To smell the homemade bread
Seeing is an important sense
To see the birds fly round
Hearing is an ear sense
To hear the bees buzz
Touching is a brilliant sense
To touch my fluffy teddies.

These are all my 5 senses
That I have in life
People also have these senses
In their lives too.

Helen Coupe (Age 9)

The Door

Go and open the door
Maybe there's a flock of vultures
Circling their prey
Maybe there's an apple tree or the sun rising.

Go and open the door
Maybe there's a chicken laying eggs
Or a snake slithering
Across the dusty desert.

Go and open the door
Maybe there's a T-Rex
Or a frog jumping into a pond
Or Santa with Rudolph.

Go and open the door
Maybe there's a
Bit of peace and quiet for once.

Charlie Clark (Age 9)

At Sea

The wind whipped against the sails
And rushed in and out beneath the boat

The seagulls squawked
And soared up high

The bubbling waves climbed and slipped
Up and down the craggy rocks

In the distance
The dolphins splashed and leaped

The seaside smell
Whiffed through the air

The horizon stretched across the sky
As the boats gently cruised through the waves.

Laura Cawley (Age 10)

Swimming

Swimming is fun, swimming is not bad
I go every day because I like it there
I try to force my grandad to let me stay
But it never works.
He comes and lifts me out
So then I have to go home.

Eleanor Chetwynd-Hay (Age 8)

Magic Of The Morning

While the morning is still early,
And dew still on the grass,
The mythical creatures venture out to greet the morning sun.
But the earliest riser of them all drinks from the brook,
He pricks his ears and lifts his golden hoof.
He turns around and paws the ground and swiftly runs away,
If you want to know where he goes, come with me today.
He canters past the fairies' lair much to their surprise,
I look at him, he looks at me with his amazingly blue eyes.
He jumps over streams,
He goes to a land where unicorns are free and dragons are supreme.
He slashes through ivy with his golden horn.
He keeps himself to himself, he's seldom seen by men.
I've asked mum if I can camp out tonight just to see him again.

Kate Chandler (Age 9)

Three O'clock Friday

Three o'clock Friday my auntie's at last
Time to forget the weeks passed.

On Monday break they stole my tennis ball
And threw it over the wall.

On Tuesday morning I came in late
But they were waiting at the gate.

On Wednesday afternoon in games
They made fun of me and called me names.

Yesterday, they laughed after the test
Because mine was the lowest in the whole test.

Today, they trampled my books on the floor
And I got sent to the Principle because I swore.

Three o'clock Friday I can't believe it, I'm free
Then I go back to my auntie's for tea.

Martin Chetwood (Age 10)

The Sea

The sea climbs cliffs so high
It runs up beaches and reaches for the sky
When night comes, it seems so calm
But when a storm hits, it can cause alarm
The creatures swim to hide, so scared
As it wakes, there is more danger.
It rocks back and forth, like a rocking horse.
It beats on the rocks like a big base drum
And strokes the sand
Until night hits and all is calm.

Tanya Card (Age 11)

Playtime

I play basket ball with my friend
We like to play tig tig
We like to play cricket
We like to play bench ball
We like to play tennis
The best of all we like to play FOOTBALL.

Iqrab Chaudhury (Age 8)

Teachers

T eachers can be terrifying
E ach day they can change
A s my opinion, I like them
C oz they like me
H uman teachers don't have sense
E ach time, I see one, I can tell
R eally, because of their pretty faces
S o teachers are my best mates.

Elizabeth Chan (Age 11)

Ghosts!

They float around at night
They will give you a scary fright
Their chains rattle as they fly around in the darkness
They make funny noises like shrieks
Their invisible bodies haunt old mansions
So if you're in bed beware of the ghosts.

Daniel Callow (Age 8)

The Great White Shark

I swim merrily
In the big blue sea
I bring fear to all who see

I live in the sea
With all my friends
We feed from the fish

We don't mean to bring fear
We only want to play, we are friendly

I glide like an eagle
I am as fast as a blink of an eye
I have to go play now
Goodbye!

Marcel Corriette (Age 11)

St. Valentines Day

De only good ting bout St. valentines day
Is getting a girlfriend and your own way
February's here January garn
Happy days here lonely days garn
Me mum say "Boy you're on your own no more."
Keep loving on from nine till four
From nine till four I keep it cool
But in the evening real love rules!!!

Tom Capel (Age 9)

Head Teacher

Our Head Teacher is the best
She never thinks we're a pest
She's very kind
And she has a great mind
She works so hard she needs a rest.

Emily Cusens (Age 9)

Untitled

There once was a man called Richard
Who landed in a great big ditchard
He found some jam and some bars of wham
And then his death was pictured.

Loella Chlebowski (Age 11)

School

When I wake up in the morning
And find that my sister's been snoring
The last thing I want is to go to school

We've got a really hard test
And got to try our best
Other people are getting it right
I just might

Can't wait till playtime to have some fun
Plus lunch yum yum!

In Art today someone thumped me
And spilled the paint
I got told off
And caught a nasty cough

But now it's got to start again tomorrow
But I don't care because I've got a day off
Hurray!

Alice Collinson (Age 8)

Hi-Tech

Have you seen my hi-tech thingermewotsit?
>*Your what?*

My hi-tech thingermewotsit?
>*You mean your hi-tech spinitaroundalot?*

No! My hi-tech thingermewotsit.
>*You want the hi-tech spinitaroundalot*
>*On top of the hi-tech thingermewotsit*
>*In the hi-tech wotdoyoumacallit.*

Yes!
>*Sorry. I don't know where it is.*

Paul Chessman (Age 11)

Lanzarote Market

Apples, bananas and juicy pears
Coconuts with prickly hairs
Tangerines and mango fruits
Leaf green limes with big roots
Oranges, bread fruit, juicy plums
Lots of people with hungry tums
Clementines, grapes and lovely melon
Fish, meat and a yellow lemon
Sea, sand and a beautiful sun
Sorry I've got to run.

Louisa Cirillo (Age 9)

School

The clean and lovely football pitch,
Even though it's got a very muddy ditch,
The coloured green and white grass,
On Thursday we have a brilliant football class.
Pick up a book little or big have some fun,
But then it comes to the very sad part you're done,
Give it a try.
When you're walking by you always have fun in the library.
At playtime I play the fool,
The others play cool,
Nathan is mad,
And Joe is bad.

Ben Carless (Age 9)

Fang Fun

Creaking stairs as if a mouse was
Squeaking
A little spider on its web peeking
The moonlight shining
As we saw the spider climbing
We saw the curtains swinging
Something was pinging
The clock was ringing

We were going
We heard a loud bang
And saw a man with fangs
That was just a vampire
"A vampire."
Ahhhhhh!

Joshua Cottle-Barker (Age 10)

A Snowy Day

It is dawn
I am in my garden
I watch as the wintry snowflakes
Fall pure on my icy hands
Snow all around me
On the ground
On roofs
I see people shovelling the crisp snow
Off their drives
Horses run along with arctic hooves
On the solid earth
It is dawn
I watch as the wintry snowflakes
Fall pure on my icy hands.

Neesa Marie Curzons (Age 10)

Midnight Sky

The sky at midnight is black and blue
With the silver moon shining on you

Sometimes it rains from a grey cloud
It makes the midnight sky feel proud

The midnight sky is a lovely sight
With the shining stars living bright

Let the midnight sky live on and on
Let it stay forever strong.

Poppy Cracknell (Age 10)

Cottage Of Grief

By the road, a silver leaf,
Flutters around the Cottage Of Grief.
From near the door, there came a roar
Which echoed through the walls.
In front of the old front door place, there appeared a face,
That was all too dark to remember.
When nipping into the house he stepped on a mouse,
And went skidding into the wall.
The police force came, what a shame,
It had been the same as last year's robbery.
By the road, a desperate thief,
Stands beside the Cottage Of Grief.

Richard Carter (Age 9)

The Otter

I was walking along the boggy bank
Then I saw it - the otter
Its running hair was clinging to its flank
Its matted fur holding tight to its head.

It was diving gracefully, speeding to the river bed
Then it changed direction, speeding to me instead
I watched it play like this til it sunk like lead
Then, almost like, "Come with me," it had said
Its eyes, alive eyes, fierce eyes, moon bright
Even in the darkest, deepest night eyes flashed.
I could feel the wildness at its height.

Elizabeth Carpenter (Age 9)

The Snow

The snow tickles down your neck
It is ice cold, and
A whitey colour

It comes down
In little shapes
Like stars in the sky
Only falling down

They're beautiful snowflakes and icy
But very, very, very cold
They fall like a dazzling bird
Floating in the air.

Niamh Chamberlin (Age 8)

The Memories

The greyish mist hangs
Just like the memories
Oh the memories
How they have torn me inside
The years have passed
But the memories
Lie like in all young boys' minds
Untouched.
But the face has aged
For years of mourning
Have blurred my eyes
Just like the memories
And the memories live forever.

Caroline Carter (Age 10)

A Golden Eagle

Gliding slowly a dark shadow creeping
Quietly waiting for its frightened prey
Eyes looking this way and that searching
For any sign of movement in the spray
Of rain falling hard on the muddy ground
Talons stretching and closing claws ready
Ears listening for a muffled sound
Feathers ruffling as he turns round slowly
As he looks he sees and dives speeding down
Watching the hare race across the flat plain
Landing and taking off like a small clown
With a small brown prize which is his to claim
Flying over to his nest for sleeping
Gliding slowly a dark shadow creeping.

Georgia Cleasby (Age 11)

The Snow

The snow runs down
Your back.
White cotton balls
Wetting you.
It's soft and woolly,
They are like star shapes.

Icy cold shapes.
Pull on your wellies
To go and play.

Elizabeth Credland (Age 8)

Monkeys

M onkeys are known for their tails
O ther things they are known for is climbing and eating bananas
N o other animal is like them except my brother
K een on heights
E verybody likes them
Y oung kids are called them along with devils
S ome monkeys do funny things.

Jamie Cristofani (Age 10)

The Witch's Kitchen

In the witch's kitchen a horrible smell drifts the air,
There were rat brains that stunk the lair.
Little sounds came from the witch's kitchen
And one of them was the hissing snake.
No one dares to enter the witch's kitchen
Because who knows what's in there.
So all day and all night the witch is waiting for someone to come
For it will be her last ingredient for her magic spell.

Ryan Cock (Age 9)

Millennium Dome

The Millennium Dome
Is big and white
It really is a peculiar sight
It's not to everybody's liking
With its huge poles all long and spiking

I am the Dome
The Millennium Dome
The beautiful white Millennium dome
The Dome is there every day
For you to say, "That's my way."

Katie Coates (Age 9)

A Walk Along The Beach

Walk along the beach
What do you see
Pearl waves
Stormy
Surf lashing high against the sandy shore

Swimming under the sea
What do you see
Sea caves
Dark and soundless
Sea beasts huge and scary.

Luke Curran (Age 11)

Anger

I'm angry
Everything I do makes me angry
Even talking. Its like I've been cast a spell
It's like something malignant happening every day
I don't know why I'm angry
Only to me
Why only to me?

Jessica Cobb (Age 11)

My Baby Sister Makes So Much Noise

My baby sister is a pest
I can't even do a test
She has a big belly
And is very smelly
Chloe knows how to use a pencil
But doesn't even know how to use a stencil
I'm beginning to like her now
I take her in the bath
With her baby giraffe.

Jade Collins (Age 9)

Silky

Silky's come back from her walk
Dripping wet muddy water in a puddle on the floor
Minutes of drying later
She sits in her basket
She feels the warm fire burning bright
She slowly rises to her feet
And pads gently towards the heat of the fire
She collapses gently in front of the flames
Her silky black coat shining by the firelight.

Elisha Connolly (Age 9)

Dead Night

Death surrounds us
Suffocated by loneliness
So many lives lost
Taken by mother nature
Sorrowful cries of devastated children
A mother's red eyes
Search the deadly water
For her lost upset child.

Faye Cook (Age 10)

A Trip To Tescos

"How may I help you today, Miss?"
"Just a packet of crisps please"
"We have a special offer - buy one apple, get one free"
"No thank you, just a packet of crisps please"
"How about carrots or garden peas?"
"No, nothing but ONE packet of crisps please"
"Can I satisfy you with some black chocolate?"
"You may satisfy me with a packet of crisps please!"
"Do you want any chocolate chipped cookies?"
"How many more times? Just a packet of crisps please!
"OK, what kind? Plain, frizzy and what flavour-"
"CRISPS, a packet of plain crisps. How hard is it?"
"Not that hard, Miss"
"Then get them! Do you hear me?"
"Yes mam! Why didn't you say? We're having a buy one get one free today."

Anthea Chilton (Age 10)

Colours

Black, white
Red, yellow
Blue, green
Cream, grey
They are
All colours.

Blue, red
Gold, silver
Orange, pink
Yellow, mauve
I love colours.

Geoffrey Collins (Age 6)

Clowns

Clowns have bright red noses
Big shoes and squirting noses
They have dark orange hair
And always fall down the stairs!

Clowns have crosses for eyes
And always throw apple pies
They walk on tight ropes and never look down
But all you need to know is I am that funny CLOWN!

Becky Cox (Age 10)

The Milkshake

The straw to my milkshake sticks to my tongue
With a suck and a slurp it goes right to my tum
It's cold and thick and very pink
It really is my favourite drink
Drink in sips, freeze my teeth
Goes down my body to my feet
I'm half way down, it's getting thinner
Hope there's room for my dinner
Swish, swash, it's nearly gone
The cold is tingling in my palm
The end is near, it's very true
I enjoyed the milkshake, hope you did too!

Daniel Coopey (Age 8)

Animal Poems

Cunning cobra
Scary mouth
Slither along
Go south!

Vicious vulture
Soft wings
Pointy beak
Always sings!

Beastly bear
Really furry
Teeth sharp
Eyes blurry!

Cheerful cats
Loves food
Big eyes
Very rude!

Charlotte Cobb (Age 8)

Mixed Up

I bought a wart hog
I thought it was a dog
And I bought a jar
I thought it was a car
I bought a tin
To make me thin
I thought if I would yawn
It would be dawn
And I tried to grow a horn
But as it turned out I was just born
As I grew older
I tried to stand on my shoulder
And it ended up with making a folder
I tried to behave
But I had to shave
I had to fake
For goodness sake
I washed the dirt
And scrubbed the skirt.

Kieron Coles (Age 9)

Spring

The sun's ashine
The wind's ablow
The lambs are born
In the meadow

The flowers bloom
Babies are born
Squirrels, horses,
Stags and fawns

The meadows are
A rich, rich green
Where rabbits hide
Not to be seen

Winter's gone
No rain or snow
Instead there's sun
And a breeze that blows.

Rebecca Cullen (Age 8)

Suzie The Bunny Rabbit

The floppy furry bunny has fur like a panda
Her ears are soft and long as a long slice of cheese.

Her nose twitches like mad
Suzie has big floppy feet that stomp around the garden all day.

The tail is like a squashy cotton ball
Her eyes are sparkly as lights shining onto a pool.

Melissa Cuddy (Age 11)

Football

Playing football in the blinding light
I passed to Mike, he passed it back
I took a shot and scored
I ran up the pitch waving my arms
Listening to that wonderful sound of clapping and cheering
I looked at the ref
He blew the whistle
I knew we had won.

Thomas Cooke (Age 10)

My Cute Pet

My cute pet is furry and it's really purry
My cute pet is black and white sometimes it gets into a fight
My cute pet is very fat but I love her, that's my
CAT!

Lydia Cowburn (Age 9)

The Bullet

The bullet
Slips through the air,
It's slim body swirling and curling,
Turning and churning.

At the speed of light
It leaves the gun
Held by a German,
A man of 'Hitler.'

Still it shoots
On and on
Men lunge out of the way
Just in time.

Eventually it hits something
To make it stop dead:
The flesh of an innocent man
Is punctured harshly.
The
    Bullet
        Kills.

Rosie Clarke (Age 10)

Dolphin

The dolphin swims swiftly
Gliding to the ocean floor,
Searching, searching for his family,
As he wanders through the dangerous shipwreck,
Hear his frantic cry.
But he is trapped.
That cry was his last one.

Rebecca Collett (Age 9)

Pets

Cats
    Dogs
        Hamsters
            Rabbits
                Horses
Are all kinds of pets
        Pets, what's the point of them?
    They make such a mess
        (Dropping droppings everywhere)

Verity Clark (Age 9)

Mud

Mud in your earholes
Mud in your fingernails
Mud between your toes
Mud up your nose
Mud in your pyjamas
Mud on your bananas
Mud in your bed at night
Mud everywhere.

Sarah Craske (Age 9)

My Brother

"Do you want to play with the cars or go outside?"
"No".
"Play in the garage or clean some stones?"
"No".
"Play with the guns or call for Jackie?"
"No".
"Taekwondo or soldiers, which will it be?"
"No".
"Do you want to read then?"
"No".
"I'll give you a game of noughts and crosses"
"No".
"Want to play pirates then?"
"No".
"WELL WHAT DO YOU WANT TO DO?
"Play some football"

Christopher Doonan (Age 10)

Weather

All the different types of weather
Like thunder, lightning, storms, all types of weather
The thunder strikes and lightning dashes all types of weather
The weather snow freezes the air, all types of weather.

Weather! Weather, all types of weather
Weather in the U.K. weather in the U.S.A.
Weather! Weather all types of weather.

Benjamin Cottrell (Age 8)

Rain

The rain is splashing in the puddles,
Racing down the window panes,
Glowing on the fresh newly washed bushes.
Diamonds trapped in spider webs.
Raindrops flying through the sky like birds,
Bouncing in and out of the puddles
Colourful umbrellas light the grey wetness.
Sparkling like stars in the sky.

Jordan Dormer (Age 7)

My Mental Mate

Some people think you're cute and kind and big, soft and gentle

My friend I know you're really nuts and very flippin' mental.

As you rise out of your bed your hair sticks to your head

There's dribble on the pillow and you feel nearly dead.

Joe Connaughton (Age 10)

Fish

Big fish, small fish, tall fish, short fish,
How many more fish do you need?
There's fat fish, thin fish, skin fish even
Slim fish, swim fish and twin fish
But the odd one out is the win fish
Because he goes to bed with me.

Henry Dean (Age 7)

The Witch's Kitchen

The witch's kitchen stinks like a skunk
A cauldron bubbles and boils in the huge black pot
Toad's brains are motionless on the grey black chopping board
The black cat purrs on a squishy cushion
Rats creep round the disgusting objects
Slugs make trails of slime like paths and roads
Spiders' hairy legs scuttle along the kitchen floor.

Joe Cruse (Age 9)

What Happened To Sid

There once was a kid called Sid
Who hit himself with a lid
He's got a great lump
Where he got a great thump
And that's what happened to Sid.

Michael Dowling (Age 10)

The Jungle

The jungle is a wild zoo with no entrance fees
Crocodiles are logs in the water waiting for lunch
Orang-utans are humans that swing on vines better than Spiderman.
The bees are dots moving through the skies
The piranhas are rats with big teeth and huge appetites
A cheetah is a Ferrari at top speed hunting prey
The jungle is a city with the animals as the inhabitants
The monkey are people sharing their lunch
The jungle is a big garden that has been neglected.

Mark Collinson (Age 10)

Recipe For Spring

Take five blades of green grass
And three bunches of roses
Add two clouds and
Five cups full of colourful butterflies
Stir in some pink blossom and one green bud
Sprinkle some bright green leaves
And six bunches of raindrops
Decorate with a meadow and
Five fluffy lambs
And you have made Spring!

George Daniel (Age 7)

It Was So Noisy

It was so noisy
I couldn't hear the dog barking loudly
It was so noisy
I couldn't hear the television blasting out
It was so noisy
I couldn't hear the workmen's buzzing drill
It was so noisy
I couldn't hear the ice-cream van's music
It was so noisy
I couldn't hear my baby niece playing happily

It was so noisy!!

Michaela Dowling (Age 7)

The Ideal Playground

I think the ideal school playground
Should have somewhere to keep the sun out of your eyes,
Because sun hurts your eyes.
We could have a hammock if we want a rest
Or we can have skittles to play
Because they are fun to play with
And we could have a slope for toy cars

Isabelle Dean (Age 6)

The Fox Hunt

I heard the hooves,
I heard the barks
I ran like mad.
I came to a big holly bush,
I jumped for it.
Would I live or die?
I landed with a thud,
I ran on.
I came to my burrow,
I thought I was safe,
I was wrong.
A few minutes later
I heard a bark,
I knew then,
I was not safe.
A dog sniffed the outside of the burrow,
It barked.
Then they all started barking.
A man looked in and saw me.
The next thing I knew a gun was pointing at me,
The last thing I heard was a bang.
This was the end.

Anna Drysder (Age 10)

Winter Days and Nights

In the winter, snow covers the green,
It gets so dark you can't be seen,
The sky turns grey; the nights get cold,
Winter, I wish could be put on hold.

Rain and snow is all that fall,
Children cry and scream and bawl,
Because of weather in the winter,
So cold, so dark, so rainy and bitter.

After a while there comes a day, when,
The horrible winter shall go away,
Leaving all his cares behind,
Children have summer in
Their mind

Patrice Dolor (Age 10)

Corey

There was a man called Corey,
Who had a girlfriend called Tori,
They were wedded one day,
But she passed away
And that's the end of the story!

Peter Davies (Age 10)

Untitled

Boredom

Boredom is grey,
It smells like a dull, smoky night,
Boredom tastes dark and rotten,
It sounds like a deserted village,
It feels like all your energy is sucked away,
Boredom lives in a lonely heart.

Happiness

Happiness is bright pink,
It smells of ice cream,
It tastes of chocolate,
It sounds like a busy shopping centre,
It feels like you're really excited,
Happiness lives in your favourite place.

Crabbiness

Crabbiness is a dark shade of brown,
It smells of anger bubbling up,
Crabbiness tastes like old apple cores,
It sounds like yelling,
It feels like a burning forest of hatred,
Crabbiness lives in an angry spirit.

Juliet Denny (Age 9)

Underneath The Silence

Underneath the silence I can hear

The faint cries of an infected infant,
Screams of pain as the boy sits upright,
His mother crying by the boy's side,
The doctor saying all is not well,
The beeps of the heart machine as it monitors him,
The mother praying.

Underneath the silence I can feel

His mother's soft silky hand stroking him,
The dreadful disease attaching to his lungs,
The boy losing the battle to live,
The anguish of the mother
As she watches the boy's life slipping away,
A weak heart beating against some fragile ribs,
The despair of the mother as she watches her son die.

Luke Donovan (Age 10)

Dragon Heart

He waits for his prey
His pounding eyes watch it closely
His piercing, jagged, sharpened teeth
Shining in the sun
His whipping tail curls up slowly

He waits for his prey
His enormous wings shut tightly
His flaming fire blazing
His red and yellow colours
Shoot out!

He waits for his prey
His sharp fangs glint in the sun
His eyes eager to strike
He flickers his eyes
Then shoots and grabs his prey
And lays down chewing flesh
And blood . . . .

Tom Dyball (Age 11)

Bumble Bee

B uzzing round looking for honey
U p and down the garden flowers
M aking every visit worth while
B ecause Autumn's nearly here
L eaves are turning gold yellow and red.
E venings passing by.

B efore you know it winter's here
E very flower will disappear
E very bee will be hibernating

Rebecca Dymond (Age 11)

Untitled

A fast runner,
A fawn colour,
A lake drinker,
A field eater,
A good jumper,
A deep sleeper,
A spotted creature,
A den maker.

Marike Denyer (Age 8)

The Moon

It is dark at night,
And the stars shine brightly.
Wolves are howling at night,
And hunt in the moonlight.
People are sleeping in their beds,
Pillows under their heads.
There is a clock,
It strikes midnight.

Thomas Davies (Age 8)

Sir Winter Icicles

He arose from his bed as gracefully as a snowflake
Turning soil into snow he made a sleeping potion, with silver icicles.
The rabbits, mice and moles watched him like a Hawk.
As he threw his shining silver potion,
The animals ran off into the mist to their snug little homes.
That was his first job done, now to another.
He knew there was something to do but he could not think what.
He thought and he thought "Ahh Frost and Cold"
His duty was nearly finished, his day was nearly done.
So he danced off to the lab to find the forsaken potion book.
As he put a blue potion in a bottle and clicked his fingers
His job was done.

Harriet Davey (Age 10)

Where's Everybody

At the farm dips
Outside the gates
In the barn
Cows mooing for food
In the farm house
Farmers watching the news and crying
On the road, closed sign
Cars stop to look at them
In the parlour
Cows being milked
And don't know about the danger
I hate the foot and mouth crisis

Ottalie Day (Age 9)

Gruesome Teachers

They're called the gruesome teachers
They come from outer space,
They'll fry your brains with English
And, with Maths the human race

They resemble normal Earthlings
But that's just a mask you see,
And when you have something they want
You see how they can be.

Their eyes, black like a raging wind
Their teeth made of thick ivory
They shine like 'thousand death stars
And their insides run like flowing sea

Recharge their brains in staff room
Where they talk of how to eat
Cherry cakes, digestive bakes
And little children's feet.

Be careful if you see them
You might not even dare,
To peep down in the basement
Look in front, I see one there!

Tétévi Davi (Age 11)

The Husky Tiger

The husky tiger
Chases its prey to eat it
And rips its heart out.

The husky tiger
Takes a swim and catches fish
For his lunch and tea.

The husky tiger
Climbs a tree to have a nap
And to lie in shade.

The husky tiger
Is very hot and sweaty
And very tired.

Adam Deacon (Age 10)

My First Day At School

All the people stared at me
When I got introduced
I went bright red
I was so nervous I didn't say a word
At break I met a friend called Ben
He was kind and friendly
We played at home and at school
My first day at school

Jack Dunn (Age 8)

Ten Silly Snakes

Ten silly snakes trying to get some eggs,
One crossed a magic spell and grew some legs,

Nine silly snakes wasting their breath,
One of them has got a choice; life or death,

Eight silly snakes started to sing,
One got hungry so he went to Burger King,

Seven silly snakes spoiling my rhyme,
They're not doing anything, but wasting time,

Six silly snakes making you laugh,
Hang on a minute, one's taking a bath!

Five silly snakes going very slow,
One said, 'The kettles on, I'm going to have to go'.

Four silly snakes think they're in a race,
They all want to win, but can they stand the pace,

Three silly snakes slithering through the grass,
Out jumps a fat cat, will it let them pass?

Two silly snakes doing all they can,
Oh look, the sun's come out and one wants a tan,

One silly snake wanting to survive,
If he goes near those eggs, will he stay alive?

Richard Duffy (Age 9)

The Train Crash

Then a crashing sound fills the air
Like a gunshot on a silent night
Darkness. Glass and bodies fly through the air
Some people injured
Some people dead
With glass through their head
Jammed people cry for help
No-one hears them in the struggle to get out
What will happen to these people?
Will they survive or will they die?

Hannah Daley (Age 9)

The Imaginary Cupboard

A cupboard is a giant book
The doors are the cover
Open them and it will lead you to an imaginary world,
It is a world of adventure and surprises
The only boundary is your own imagination
It's the words of a story coming to life.

Christopher Stuart Dean (Age 9)

Ape

Ape began
For how it eats
It stole it from a dusty pig
But yet from a rodent

Its eyes
Are snatched from the aged hands of time
And caught from the leaves of an autumn breeze

It's intelligence
Was taken from the hands of the almighty God
And pilfered from the humans

Its movement
Was taken from the skill of water
And the swiftness of the breeze

Its colour from the blackness of night
And the glimmer of the oyster

Chris Dillon (Age 11)

Mark's Night Light

The stars are fire flies caught in a net
Full moons are skinless Baby Bells for us to bite,
Fading, flying torches in the night.
The planets are balls playing snooker.

Mark Dodson (Age 10)

Spring

Spring is when all the lambs are born
And running about in the fields
Spring is when eggs are laid in nests
That hatch and grow into birds

Spring is when daffodils and snowdrops grow
And blossom appears on the trees
Spring is when the weather turns warmer
And when we can venture outdoors

Spring is when Easter eggs are in the shops
All ready for us to eat
Spring is when Summer is on its way
Holidays, picnics and trips are planned

Spring is when lots of things happen
A time for us to enjoy
Spring is when lots of things change
Including us girls and boys

Rebecca Davies (Age 8)

My Pets

I have three cats, one called Molly,
Who loves to play with holly,
She's the mum of my other two kittens,
Whose white paws look like mittens,
Biscuit was the first to be born,
She likes to play on the lawn,
Fudge is a boy,
And likes to play with toys.
They're just my cats!!!

I have two hamsters, Velvet is the first,
Who looks like she's going to burst!!
Frisky is the last,
She can run very fast.

I have one dog and Rio is her name,
And she's tame.

My last pet is a goldfish who's name is Gold,
Who is quite old.

Jessica Draper (Age 10)

My World

My world is a friendly, caring world,
My world has no World War 1 or World War 2,
My world is a peaceful world,
My world all people agree,
My world everyone is friends,
My world you live your life in harmony

In my world

Jordan Dean (Age 10)

Santa Claus

People kissing under mistletoe,
Santa comes in and says Ho Ho Ho.

Reindeers eating carrots and milk
While you're snuggled up in a quilt.

Looking for presents all day long,
Open the door and the singers have gone.

Santa gets stuck in the chimney
And all the children are laughing with glee.

Soon the star on the tree will glow,
Hopefully outside it will snow.

Open the door with a key,
And you'll see a lovely Christmas tree

Dominic Dalley (Age 9)

Colours

Yellow is the hot sandy beach,
or a field of lemon coloured tulips,
or the fur of an angry, roaring Lion,
or a yellow ripe banana sitting in the fruit bowl.

Red is the English flag,
or the red sunshine at the end of the day,
or the red Liverpool kit that Emile Heskey wears,
or the red hot fire burning in the wood.

Gold is the gleaming new Liverpool away strip,
or a glittering diamond ring,
or the most amount of money I have seen,
or the eagles of the jungle on my bedroom wall.

Patrick Davitt (Age 8)

Teachers

T errifying when you see them the first time.
E vil when they give you homework
A nnoying when there are
C hatter boxes
H orrible when they give you detention
E ager to get on with their work
R evolting habits they have
S hout a lots they are.

Stephen Dolan (Age 10)

Wonderful

Hold my mum and I hold my dad
Don't understand why they get so mad
Lost my girl on a lonely street,
She slapped me so hard I fell off my feet.

I lie in bed at night,
When nothing's gone right,
I hear them shout I hear them lie,
They say things that make me want to cry.

Close my eyes when I get too sad,
I think thoughts that I know are bad,
I wish I could count to ten,
Everything would be wonderful again.

I live my life in a lonely way,
I watch TV all the day,
I sometimes wonder where and when,
Everything would be wonderful again.

Nick Davis (Age 12)

Making A Decision

Everybody has been in that position,
When you have to make a decision,
It's the hardest thing trying to choose,
Because you don't know what you could lose,
Have you ever tried choosing clothes,
My brother always goes into a doze,
It's even harder choosing how to have your hair,
You need to make sure the boys don't stare,
It's always difficult choosing lunch,
Next time I think I'll just have brunch,
If you're bored it's always hard choosing what to do,
I end up trying on my mum's best shoe,
But the hardest decision my mum has said,
Is when she thinks I should go to bed,
Well the hardest decision I've ever chosen,
Is what I should write in this poem.

Hannah Donald (Age 9)

My Tiger

I have a furry tiger sitting on my bed
He is so cute and cuddly he just
Likes me standing on my head
He has a name called Sulton
He's my favourite sitting on my bed.
He says his bed is his favourite, that's what he said
So he's my lovely tiger playing near the sea
All he does is look and stare at me.

Louise Deigan (Age 12)

My Best Friend

My best friend never criticised,
She never would condemn.
My best friend was always there,
She's a friend I'd recommend.
A tender hug when I was down,
A long run could be fun.
My best friend grew old and weak,
A walk was all she'd manage.
My best friend has left me now,
My heart, the only damage.
I miss my friend, I always will.
I wipe my eyes, to dry my tears,
But deep inside I cry.
You've left a space deep in my heart,
A space I can never fill.
Your big, brown eyes, your wagging tail,
Forever will be still
God bless my dog, my friend and pal,
Why did you have to die?

Jenine Davey (Age 11)

The War Game

The smell, the stench, the sight,
Men not coming back from the fight.
The rotting of feet,
And the rats aren't so sweet,
There's lice crawling, biting you all over.

The gas, the guns, the bombs,
Then there's the sound of our songs.
As you look over the top,
You see your mates drop
And left just to rot on the field.

Some men think war's a game,
My opinion's not the same.

But if war is a game, who's the winner?

Kathryn Davis (Age 14)

Internet

It holds the world at your finger tips,
Information is bootleg! Illegal!
Its mind is like a crisp.
It can alter, reform into www.wild electronic monster.com.
But it can kill the truth.

It can help to broadcast favourites to the world,
The technical way of communication!
To contact the world back
Messages in the 21st century.

Niall Dalton-Banks (Age 11)

The Midnight Fox

The fox cub cried,
Like a lonely puppy,
The sound echoed through the valley,
It made me feel as weak as a new born foal.

The sound of the thunder
Like a clash of a drum,
Hallowed through the tall dark trees,
It was as loud as a giant's stomp.

The gun shot,
It sounded like the end of the fox,
It was the worst sound I ever heard,
I felt guilty like no-one could ever know.

Then after the gun shot.
Silence filled the air,
As if no-one comes around,
Bang . . . . . Silence.

Charlotte Davies (Age 12)

Friends

Friends are always there for you
when you're feeling down,
Friends are always there to make
sure you never frown,
Friends are they to understand your
problems however they may sound,
Friends are always there to keep my
feet upon the ground.

Friends are the people who care the most,
Friends should never boast,
Friends should never think they're better
than the rest or think they're the best,
Friends are those who call me D,
Friends are the best thing in life
without them where would we be.

Danielle Deakin (Age 11)

The Little Rabbit

There once was a little rabbit,
Who was eating a bright orange carrot,
He ate it up quick,
With his two front teeth,
And that was the end of the carrot.
He liked it so much,
He ate many more,
And looked in the mirror,
And found he was orange.

Rosie Dawson (Age 8)

Please Mr Davidson

Please Mr Davidson, this boy Alex Way,
Keeps kicking my leg sir, what shall I say?

Go sit on the loo, take his work with you.

Please Mr Davidson, this boy Alex Way,
Keeps pinching my ruler sir, what shall I say?

Say don't do that Alex Way,
Don't think but do say.

Please Mr Davidson, this boy Alex Way,
Keeps taking my work sir, what shall I say?

Tell him not to let me see,
Do what you think but don't ask me.

Adam Douglas (Age 8)

The Wobbling Rainbow

Why do stinging nettles sting?
Why do alarm clocks ring?
Why do the stars glitter?
Why do we have Winter?
Why do we have night and day?
Why do we have today?
Why do we have hair?
Why is some people's hair fair?
Why does the wind blow?
Why does the sea flow?
Why do we have land?
Why do we have yellow sand?
Why do we have pencil lead?
Why do we go to bed?
Why do we have paints?
Why do we have saints?
Why do we have dads?
Why are we sometimes sad?
Why does the world go round?
Why do we walk on ground?

Annabel Dos Santos (Age 10)

Excuses, Excuses

Excuses, excuses,
I'm full of excuses,
I always have an alibi,
So I don't get told off by Mrs Cefai,

Excuses, excuses,
I'm full of excuses,

You don't really have a headache,
You're just a big fat fake,
If you keep on lying, I'll call in your mum,
And I'm sure she'll make you do your sums,

Excuses, excuses,
I'm full of excuses,

Excuses, excuses, my teacher says she knows them all,
She doesn't know this one; I lost it at the Mall,
Excuses, excuses,
I'm full of excuses.

Martin Dalgado (Age 11)

The Forest

It is a dark black night in the forest.
A wolf is howling in the moonlight.
A squirrel is cleaning his tail and looking for nuts buried in the leaves.
An owl was woken by the noise of a mouse scuttering in the leaves.
He turns his head around to watch the Vermin vanish from sight,
Into the undergrowth.

Stephanie Davies (Age 8)

Space Man

I am a space man in the sky
Looking down from ever so high
I am up in my space ship
On your radar I'm just a blip
I am going to live in space
On the moon will be my base

David Davis (Age 9)

The Boy Called Tim

There was once a boy called Tim
He kicked a girl called Kim,
He got chucked out of the gym,
And broke a limb,
And that was the end of him.

Jacob Dore (Age 9)

Friends

Friends are the best
Better than the rest,
Why?
They help you through the tough times
And the happy times,
They even help you in the sad times.

How?
When you're sad they cheer you up
When you're happy they make you laugh
If you are stuck they will help you
Friends are the best.

If your friend is loyal
He will never let you down
If your friend is honest
Your face will never frown.

My friend is always there
To help me whenever, anywhere,
His name is Billy
He is my best friend!

Ben Davis (Age 11)

The Future

In the future,
Will we have space holidays
Or maybe hand held computers?

Will there be hover cars
So we can hover each day?
Could there be robots that help around the house?

Will we have TV in our cars
To keep us all happy?
Will all this happen?

Toby Dagger (Age 8)

The Crow

The crow flew down on the ground
The crow flew down on the ground
And was joined by a postman.
The crow flew down on the ground
And was joined by a postman who gave him a letter
The crow flew down on the ground
And was joined by a postman
Who gave him a letter and the crow picked it up.
The crow flew down on the ground
And was joined by a postman who gave him a letter
And the crow picked it up and flew away

Kayleigh Davies (Age 8)

What Is A Cloud?

A cloud is a soft, white bed
Equipped with covers and pillows
Floating across the clear blue sky
A bath of foaming bubbles
Tipping cold water on to
The unsuspecting people on the bustling earth
A face silhouette in the sun lit sky
A soft, fluffy cat playing with a big ball of wool
A giant boat, sailing across the misty sky

Rebecca Louise Dring (Age 10)

The Witches Kitchen

Shrivelled, scruffy, stiff rats, lay silently in the corner,
Dead frogs stuffed under boxes,
Foxes lay on the floor with their eyeballs popping out,
Spider legs stuck in dead peoples eye sockets,
Bats echoing mice squeaking, dogs barking in cages,
Cut off heads on top of eyeballs,
Horses clopping in a beautiful deserted place,
Snakes hissing under spider webs,
Dogs barking while spiders are spinning,
Spiders webs covering dead animals on the rusty well.

Jamie Dingle (Age 8)

Disaster At The Zoo

The monkey banged his head,
The zebra broke his leg.

The panda received a black eye,
The giraffe got splat with a pie.

The lion lost his roar,
The tiger hurt his paw.

The elephant hurt his trunk,
The kangaroo cannot jump.

The snake shredded his skin,
The bear broke his shin.

The keeper went to sort it out,
And was eaten by a trout.

Lana Dutson (Age 10)

It Was So Noisy That . . .

It was so noisy that
The door slammed
The children put their fingers in their ears

It was so noisy that
The windows smashed
The children shouted

It was so noisy that
The shelves dropped on the table

It was so noisy that
The children screamed until the roof crashed

It was so noisy that
The floor tumbled

Natasha Darby (Age 8)

What Is It?

People scream people run,
There is not time to have some fun.
The sky turns black, booms appear
The Mayor says "evacuate here".
Soldiers come fiery sparks fly
Many good men will die.
Here come some fierce planes.
Check points on pretty country lanes.
People get captured and taken to camps
Then get locked in dingy cells with no lamps.
The enemy is finally driven back,
Ammunition is a great lack.
People fall down, dead on the ground
Others are deafened by the sound.
But one sad day, the officer shouts,
"We surrender" without any doubts.

Oliver Dawson (Age 8)

Mr. X

The spiky hair
The jet black eyes
The malicious mouth that tells naught but lies
The ears that hear the pin drops ping
The brain that knows most everything
The feet as big as giants toes
The face that holds that crooked nose
This is X, are you like him?
Only you know

Scott Dobbie (Age 10)

A Beeswax Candle

A short cylinder,
narrowing as it spirals from bottom to top
like a nose-cone of a rocket.

A dark yellow
like mustard powder -
smelling weakly sweet like pollen;
but fatty to smell and touch
like margarine from Mummy's freezer.

A bumpy surface
with hexagon patterns -
it feels rough
like driving over a ploughed field;
becoming sticky and greasy
in my warm hand.

I light the wick -
it burns slowly;
melting with a beehive smell,
lighting up my homework.

Marc Durodie (Age 8)

It Was So Noisy

It was so noisy that the windows expelled
With a gigantic crash!

It was so noisy that the floor rattled madly
And made a bang!

It was so noisy that the tables overturned
With a gigantic crash!

It was so noisy that the notepaper
On the wall toppled!

It was so nosy that the wall
Tumbled down!

Hannah Darby (Age 8)

Christmas

C is for Carols drifting across the night
H is for hugs from my family just right
R is for robins with their chests bright red
I is for ice under my sled
S is for Santa falling down the chimney
T is for trees all sparkling and twinkly
M is for mince pies, dessert on Christmas Day
A is for acting our pantomime play
S is for snow - a snowman -hurray

Alison Day (Age 10)

Jumbling Up Words

I like chips and pizza
I like pizza and chips
Pizza and chips I like
Chips and pizza I like
Like Pizza and chips I
Like chips and pizza I
I pizza and chips like
I chips and pizza like
Like I pizza and chips
Like I chips and pizza
Pizza chips and I like
Pizza chips and like I
Pizza chips I like and
Pizza chips I and like
Pizza chips like I and
Pizza chips like and I
Chips pizza and I like
Chips pizza and like I
Chips pizza I like and
Chips pizza I and like
Chips pizza like I and
Chips pizza like and I

Jamie Dimond and Ben Courtney (Age 10)

Predator

Lurking in the deepest, darkest shadows,
So patient . . . So quiet is the panther
Adapted to kill
Focused on the task at hand,
The only sound being made . . . .
An eerie groan of hunger from her stomach.

How tall and proud she is
Atop the food chain,
The perfect killing machine,
Fast, agile and above all viscous.
Keeping perfectly static,
Waiting for the perfect prey.

Pointed to razor sharp teeth,
Only used for one thing.
Eyes at the front for keener eyesight.
With claws, so unforgiving.
Instinctive, at one with nature,
Prepared for murder.

Nothing to fear, except of course . . .
       You!

Lewis Dyson (Age 12)

A Star

When I take my morning stroll,
Down my garden nice and slow.
I hear a voice cry out to me,
Just have a guess at who I see?
But only just my rabbit Hans,
Loved quite dearly by my great nan.
There he is so cute and sweet,
I'll give him one of his special treats.
A few days later, but where could he be?
But right in front of my window,
Looking straight down on me.

Sarah Dabrowski (Age 11)

Absence

Where are you?
I no longer know.
The pain curls around me
And leaks through my tears
Like the waves that crash on the sand
As a storm poised, ready to break.

The lightning struck tree
Riven like my heart broken in two
And yet in the distance somewhere there is hope.

Jenny Douglas (Age 13)

For Every Single Day

You were always there for me,
In every single way,
For every single moment,
For every single day.

I'll never forget the jokes that we shared
And never forget the amount that you cared,
Because you were that stone, that rock for us all
And if we had a problem we only had to call.

You were always there for me
Through the laughter and the pain,
And life without you both
Will never be the same.

But now that your spirits
Are as free as the birds,
My love can not be expressed
By simply using words.

But you will always be in my thoughts
In every single way,
For ever single moment,
For every single day.

Gemma Dyer (Age 14)

The Fire!

The fire blazes in the dim, cold room,
All is silent, except for the crackling of flames,
The entire room is brightly lit,
By the warm colours of the dancing flames,
Leaving its burning glow behind,
The fire rises as the coal is burnt,
The heat warms my body,
From the bitter cold outside,
I feel the warmth of the glowing fire,
As I drift off to sleep.

Stephanie Dunleavey (Age 13)

Yellow

Yellow is the sun,
And symbolises fun,
Yellow is money,
And sweet tasting honey,
Yellow is bright,
And gives out light,
Yellow is hay in a manger,
Yellow is a coward in danger,
Yellow is the beach,
And dirty looking teeth,
Yellow is gold,
And the colour I love.

Ravi Dhanak (Age 12)

Underneath The Silence

Underneath the silence I can hear . . .

The impatient seagulls vigorously flapping,
Joyful laughter filling the air.
The pestering sea rocking swiftly,
The sand, a sheet of golden silk.
The sun gazing as time goes by,
The pebbles clacking beneath the shifting tide.

Underneath the silence I can feel . . .

The serene ocean glistening in the sunlight,
The calming touch of an infant hand, walking side by side.
Sand like quick silver beneath my toes,
Salty air prickling my skin.
The coarseness under my feet of the ocean battered rocks,
A desire to fall asleep under the setting afternoon sun.

Gabriella Davies (Age 10)

Spring

When all the buds begin to sprout,
The farmer starts to shout, shout, shout.
"There's a lamb over there being born,
Look it's nearly dawn.
The daffodils sparkle in the sun,
Now the day has just begun.
All the rabbits hop about,
The farmer starts to shout, shout, shout.
"There's a calf being born in the born.!

The little chicks begin to hatch,
Oh look ones got a little brown patch.
The farmer feeds the mother hen,
Then begins to shout, shout, shout again.
"A foal is being born in the stable,"
The day is drawing to an end,
But spring is here and is my friend.

Hannah Dawson (Age 8)

It's Mothers Day!

You stay in bed without delay,
I'll go and get you a big bouquet.
I'm happy to tuck you up in your cover,
So all I can say is you're the best mother.
Thankyou for all you do for me,
Put your feet up, I'll make some tea.

Gary Dick (Age 10)

The Moon

The moon is a giant's apple, a tasty little treat.
A football that has been kicked too high, is floating at his feet,
A basketball that's been thrown too high, is all you ever see,
You can compare him with nothing in the day.
The moon is a banana, that's ready to be eaten,
The moon is a light bulb, that lights up the night sky.

Sean Drake-Brockman (Age 11)

Worst Birthday.

I know birthdays are supposed to be fun, but think of the times when they can go wrong!
Everything's planned and everyone comes, even the troublemakers invited along.
You couldn't wait! Suddenly people push through the door,
Don't hesitate all they say is 'Hello' and no more.

In comes a group not even polite, run through the door and then start a fight.
Mum's china has broken, trophies smashed on the floor!
Dad's cigars smoked trouble-makers soon bore.

Into the dining room grab all the food
Someone yells, 'BOOM!' mum disappears in a mood.

Jelly's thrown in your face, someone lets out a scream
STOP! IT'S A DISGRACE!

Looks at all, who are seen. GET OUT OF MY HOUSE!
DON'T BOTHER TO MOAN! YOU'VE SPOILT MY PARTY
AND MY HOME! they run to the door
And I start to cry, there's food on the floor,
Mum returns, wipes my eye. 'Don't worry darling, it'll soon be all right,
We'll clean this mess up before it is night!'

Christina Davis (Age 11)

When I Am A Grandma . . .

When I am a grandma I shall wear bright green,
With purple gloves which do not match,
And a blue hat that does not suit me.

When I am a pensioner I will not use the bus,
I will drive a limousine with a wide screen tv,
And spend my pension on brandy.

When I am an old woman I will drink and gamble,
I will drop litter in other people's gardens,
And learn to swear and spit.

When I am a grandma I will eat as much as I want,
And wear fish-net tights and three inch shoes,
So my grandchildren don't call me boring.

I will enjoy being old and a grandma . . . I think,
But maybe I should start to practice,
So my friends are not shocked when I wear bright green.

Elinor Douglas (Age 13)

Rose

Down at the bottom of my garden,
A rose stands tall.
It's royal red colour stand out,
Against a green background,
With petals made from silk,
It portrays great splendour.
And with its protective stem,
No intruder can pass.
It's not tall as a sunflower,
Nor small as a daisy.
But no matter what it's splendour,
A rose will always be,
Queen of the flowers.

Anne-Marie Donnelly (Age 12)

Jayne

Knowing you'll be there, come what may
Comforts my mind and comforts my soul
Someone to witness the achieved goal
You help guide and advise me on my way
My leading light, like a sun ray
On the stage of my life, you play a leading role
You help me to my feet whenever I fall
In my heart forever is where you will stay
I can tell you anything and you always speak true
You ask for nothing but all I have you receive
Thankyou, thankyou a hundred times through
No-one could want a better friend than you
You're always there and you never deceive
Love, joy, happiness, shared by two.

Beth Danaher (Age 14)

A Visit To The Dentist

It's that time again
Oh, what a pain
Off to see that man with the drill
What a thrill

Along the corridor breathing in the medicated air.
Open the door,
"Hello make yourself comfy in my chair"

He pokes and prods and finds decay
"You need a filling right away"
Injection, drilling
Then the filling

Thank goodness it's done
I get up and run
At least I don't have to come back for a while
That really makes me smile.

Christina Dack (Age 13)

Pocket Money

"Put it in a bank account" says mum
"Buy a book with it" says dad
"Buy me sweeties with it" says little sis
"Put it in my motorbike fund" says big bro
"Hide it under the bed" says granny
"Put it towards your pension" says grandpa
"Blow it all on clothes" says best friend
"Hand it over" says bully
"KEEP IT" says I!!

Joanna Davey (Age 13)

What Are You Like?

Have you ever noticed how sisters
Compare greatly to roses, daisies and
WEEDS!!

Have you ever noticed how brothers
Compare greatly to puppies, kittens and
SKUNKS!!

Have you ever noticed how parents
Compare greatly to chocolate, ice cream and
BRUSSEL SPROUTS!!

What are you like?
Sunshine, fluffy snow or
STORMS!

I Wonder . . . . .

Hannah Doherty (Age 11)

The Mistress's Reply

Had we had this world and time
Your love for me would not be mine.
The idea of us being together
Could never be forever and ever.
You say you would love me every day
But I don't want you so go away.

Your tone of voice is one I don't like
Stop trying to bully me don't be tight.
Your chances with me are fading fast
The love you have for me can never last.
All your interested in is a bit of a ride
Go somewhere else for your bit on the side.

You may think I'm being a bit rude
But I think you're just plainly crude.
I don't like you in any way
So don't come back another day.
I'm afraid to your proposals I must refuse
I'm not waiting for the conversion of the Jews.

Oliver Daniels (Age 14)

My Science Poem

Why does the moon need the sun to shine?
Why do bees sting?
How do rainbows appear?
How long does it take for the earth to turn round once?
Where on a map is the north pole?
Where is mars?
Are stars really pieces of rock?
Are aliens real?
Do you think aliens will come down to earth?
Do you think the earth will be destroyed?

Bandi Dikki (Age 9)

Thoughts Of Spring

The birds are singing in the trees,
With pretty, green spring-time leaves,
There is a flurry in the street,
With pigeons feeding at my feet.

The daffodils creeping from the ground,
Settling safely on the land,
Their lush green stalks stand out in a crowd,
"You're ever so pretty," I say aloud.

The sunshine peeping from the clouds,
Its beams shine down on many towns,
New born creatures dance around,
A new world is made from the snowy ground.

Eleanor Dayton (Age 10)

Images Of The Mind

The time I feel sad I really feel bad
It gets me really really mad
When I see animals feel bad.
It feels like I'm all alone with shivers and quivers,
It definitely makes me in a dither.

Feeling sad is so bad
Feeling glad I get so mad
I give a big sigh when I'm about to cry
When I fiddle I love to giggle

When I look up out the window
I see the cars driving fierce
And the ground staring up at me.
When I look up to the sky
The sun is setting gently
With the birds still cheeping sweetly

Feeling sad is so bad
Feeling glad I get so mad
I give a sigh when about to cry
When I fiddle, I love to giggle

I can feel glad, mad, happy and bad
But all these things makes my life complete.

Laura Dawson (Age 13)

My Little Kitten

My little cat
Cute and sweet
Shy lies on the mat
And eats and sleeps
She is brown and white
With furry stripes
She goes out at night
I love my furry cat!!!

Matthew Duncan (Age 9)

The Balloon And The Band

As the sun set in the sky
A balloon floated, it was so high,
A band played a tune,
To this balloon,
As the balloon on the wind, floated nigh.

At that moment, the band did stop,
And with that, the balloon did pop,
A gasp went round,
At that very sound,
And pieces floated down, on the bandstand top.

Alex Deam (Age 11)

Escaping Ape

Dear Mr. Charlie Barly,
I have heard you are a master,
At catching animals,
It's never a disaster,
When you are on the job.

Well my animal's escaped,
Out of all the animals it could be,
It had to be an ape,
It got out through its cage.

It fled right from the zoo,
As something had upset him,
It was a giant poo,
I suppose it did smell bad.

I'm trying to look for it,
But it just runs away,
I may just have a fit,
I have some thrilling news.

I'm ready for the choke,
But you have been fooled for this was just a joke!

From Con Jon.

Tom Dauncey (Age 11)

Beware Of The Tiger

All tigers are extremely fierce,
With a long low roar,
They catch their prey with very sharp teeth.
Beware of their pointed claws,
Beware of their four strong legs.

Sam Davies (Age 11)

My Witches Song

Eye of a mouse, blood of a bat,
Leg of a spider, tail of a rat,
Tongue of a snake, slime of a slug,
Roar of a Lion, Leg of a pug,
Beak of a crow, In they go,
Mix and throw, bubble, bubble,
Thunder crash, turn a slug into mash!

Nose of a fox, shell of a snail,
Eye of a horse, blubber of whale,
Wing of a chicken, chin of a child,
Skin of a snake, lion from the wild,
Wing of bee, that's the end
Of my spell whoopie!
Bubble, bubble, thunder crash,
Turn a slug into mash!

Lauren Davis (Age 8)

A Day At School

First we line up at the door,
Then we walk on the cloakroom floor.

We line up quietly in a straight line,
Our teacher says "Go in please, one at a time."

We walk down the corridor very neat,
But all you can hear is stomping feet.

We go into assembly and sit right down,
On his face Mr Young has a frown.

We come out and get ready for maths,
"Can you go to your groups?" your teacher asks.

Today we have had times tables,
Then in English we had to read some fables.

It is finally time for our short break,
We play chase, and that is great.

Back to English that is boring,
Everyone in class is nearly snoring.

After lunch we have P.E,
Someone falls over and hurts their knee.

Then we go home to watch T.V,
Before you know it it's time for tea.

Katie Dickson (Age 10)

My Dog Alfie

Alfie my dog has a huge soft coat,
He has eyes like fire balls.

His ears are like old pieces of leather,
His nose is an old squash ball.

Alfies whiskers are thin pieces of wire,
His tongue is as long as a wet juicy flannel.

Alfie my dog has teeth like daggers,
His tail is like an enormously fat sausage.

He has beautifully soft padded feet.

Charlotte Dynes (Age 10)

The School

School, school, school you can smell school
Look at school hear school, school, school
School you can go in school, work in school
Come out of school, school, school, school.

Jonathan Dean (Age 8)

Air Raid

Engines buzzed like angry wasps,
Puncturing the sky's mute tranquillity.
Dark sky hid darker intentions,
Moulded in the shape of planes.
Incendiary bombs fell like knives,
Slicing up the sky.
Fires burned through musty streets
Illuminating faces of pain and anguish.
Guns pounded the sky like rabid dogs,
Mauling their mechanical prey.
Shouts of warning flew through the air,
Adding to the panic.
Buildings shook as bombs made earth crumble
And rocks shatter.
Clouds of smoke rose, toxicating the air;
And poisoning water.
Mothers and children wept as their houses were destroyed,
And their loved ones shot down.
Sirens droned on and on,
Piercing the darkening gloom.

James Dickinson (Age 10)

Cats

Running,
Jumping,
Walking around
Mainly laying on the ground
Looking,
Creeping,
Diving on birds
Sorry but I've run out of words.

Emma-Jayne Ditchfield (Age 8)

Moonlight

Moonlight's dancing on the plains
Moonlight's dancing on the wave
It jumps it swings it twirls and leaps
It dances while the world's asleep

It dances on the trees and grass,
It dances on the wind and clouds,
It's feet is as light as the air it's on,
As it dances to it's moonlight song.

The stars marvel, the planets adore,
They want the moonlight to dance some more,
And so the moonlight encores.

But the moonlight gets tired,
It's song is drowned out,
The sun came out and the birds soar,
And soon the moonlight is no more.

Sachini Dharmaratne (Age 12)

On The Cross He Died

They called for him, Barabbus,
I called for my son,
But Barabbus won.
They put a wooden beam on him,
His own cross he had to carry,
Judas hung himself, but I bet he would be sorry.
They put nails in his hands and feet,
At the hill Golgotha,
And in the crowd there was no laughter.
We went to see him,
And I cried and cried,
In the morning Jesus died.
The soldiers took him down from the cross,
In the pouring rain I hugged Jesus.
What has Jesus done to deserve this?
The miracle person, the Messiah.

Sarah-Jane Dorme (Age 9)

Love

What is love, is it the sound of the wind
Whistling down an alley,
Or is it the diamonds
Shining so brightly in the night sky,
Or is it the sweet music of a cricket in a meadow
Full of sweet smells and a carpet of colours
Spread on the meadow's floor
Or is it snow drifting down gently
Like a gentle cat purring softly,
Or is it all of these in one heart
And beats as one!

Lucy Driver (Age 11)

Wish, Wish, Wish

I wish I had a big palace
I wish my name wasn't Alice
I wish I could draw
I wish my nails didn't look like claws

I wish I had a ginger cat
I wish I had a woolly hat
I wish I had a dog called Jack
I wish I didn't have a lump on my back

I wish I was slim
I wish I was like Jim
I wish I had long hair
I wish I had a cuddly bear

I wish I had a donkey
I wish my teeth weren't wonkey
I wish I had a garden
I wish people would say pardon.

Lindsey Davis (Age 9)

School

School is a part of life
You may go through some strife

Teachers nagging in your ear
"It's for the best, my Dear"
That's, all you ever hear

You have to work your socks off
And must go, even if you have a horrid cough

You wonder what it's all for
Like the teachers say,
"It will open a door"

So you bite your tongue and try your best
Hoping you'll shine above the rest,

That sums up life,
It's one big test!

Wayne Davies (Age 13)

The Scarlet Man

The scarlet man, darkens and fades,
It changes colour, orange black glades,
When it falls,
The blazing sun calls,
It spins the man around,
Until it is found,
They dance together,
They change the weather,
The scarlet man, darkens and fades.

Kate Dauwalder (Age 11)

Eyes

Green, blue, brown and grey
See things every day
If you had no eyes
You would not see
The telly, computer
Or even me!

You must remember to protect your eyes
Or otherwise you might turn blind

Now you are going to use your eyes
To read these words with a sigh
They may be short
But they're meaningful
This is the end
Shut your eyes
Adios, Goodbye!

Martin Dathan (Age 12)

The Murder?

A teenage girl of the age of thirteen,
Was very happy or so it seemed
Her parents were kind and loved her so much
But she had no close sibling as such

When working at school she was very bright
And this plunged her into a sorry plight
And then one evening she phoned her friend
Telling her that her life will end.

Later that night, her friend phoned back
I think she just wanted a friendly chat
She was then told that her mate had been killed
She then felt her spine get thoroughly chilled

The poor soul had been thrown into the road
And far into the country was she towed
Sixteen years later her body was buried
But the murderer can still not be carried
To prison where he belongs.

Eleanor Davies (Age 12)

My Perfect World

A lot of fresh air
Everything is fair

A lot of trees
No stinging bees

The nice hot sun
Everything is fun

Not a lot of flies
No-one dies

Charlie Donnachie (Age 9)

Water

Water sparkles in your eye,
So blue and clear like the sky.
It falls from the clouds like hundreds and thousands,
Tastes of nothing.
Smells of flowers.
So pure and clean,
A glittering stream,
It's the ingredients of a waterfall.
Makes bubbles and tears,
More beautiful than it appears.
It's a baby blue,
A tinted turquoise,
Doesn't come in any shape or a particular size.

Kayleigh Deacon (Age 14)

Hibernation

I am so big and cuddly,
But I also get very muddy.
For when my fur coat grows,
I have to go and hibernate.

My colour can be camouflaged,
But people think I'm fierce and large.
I have to go and get some food,
And go and hibernate.

I have a problem, it's really bad,
People think it's cool, but I think it's sad.
I am going down and down,
My eyes are closing for hibernation.

Rachael Dowding (Age 11)

Ocean Sunset

The soft, silky sea laps peacefully.
Gentle yellows, reds and pinks
Spill out out from the sinking sun
Temporarily staining the tranquil wavelets.
A slight breeze spreads ripples
Across the surface.
Whispering messages...
Whispering songs...
Whispering.
A white shadow bobs calmly on the turquoise water.
It is the moon,
Relaxing in the sky
Watching the wavelets on the shingle.
Lapping, tapping.
Lapping in a beautiful dance.

Elizabeth Daw (Age 10)

Life In The Future

In the future will life be like it is now?
Will we still have to do our jobs or will robots do them for us?
Will we still go on holiday to Greece or Spain or will we go on space holidays?
Will there be more entertainment in our cars, Playstation, T.V?
Handheld computers for every child.

Flying car in the sky.

Who knows what life will be like in the future?

Jessica Dobson (Age 8)

What Are You?

Your leather does stink,
But you're not pink,
You fly in the sky,
You land in the mud,
So I kick you out with a thud,
You land in the goal,
You have no soul,
Your liked by all,
You're a football.

Grant Dobson (Age 10)

Imogen

Imogen is one year old,
Imogen is small but bold.
Imogen has lots of curls,
Imogen's head is full of whirls.
Imogen's a special girl,
Imogen's worth more than a pearl.
Imogen's a small, white dove,
Imogen's heart is full of love.

Laura Dewey (Age 11)

Wizardy

We named our turtle after a pokemon, Squirtle.
Which always fights with a scolding shape-shifting sheep.
The lost dwarfish lizard belonged to a wicked wizard.
Who hunts and eats doomed dissolving doves.
Williams wonderful horse set up a racing course.
Then raced a weird doleful domestic dog.
My cowardly cow made a dog howl.
While eating a dish of fidelity fish.

Andrew Donald (Age 11)

Windy Days

Wind howling and knocking on windows,
Whipping leaves down the road.
Clattering dustbins, rolling down the path,
Raging through the sky,
Showing off it's powerful strength,
Tangling up shirts on the washing line,
Blowing sleeves round and round,
Slicing through the air like a knife,
Making clothes somersault and dance,
Slowly, the wind dies.

Harry Dodd (Age 8)

Oh Burnley

Oh Burnley oh Burnley
When are we going to beat the league
It could be the cup
Or even the shield

But who cares?
No one cares!
Everyone cares!

If we hit rock bottom
We will just have to sit on our bottoms
To see the lads play so bad
Is like to hear your mother blag

But who cares?
No one cares!
Everyone cares!

Because they're the Burnley!!

Samantha Duerden (Age 14)

Lazy Cats

The male lion is lazy,
He sits in the sun,
While his wife goes hunting.
And when he gets his food,
The female lion stars grunting.

When he has finished,
He goes back to sleep.
And he is not looking,
She starts eating his tea.

Rosie Davey (Age 10)

Scared Of Night

It's going to get me,
When I'm asleep.
It's dark and it's shadowy,
I'm scared of the night.

The twilight is eerie,
It's blue and it's grey,
It tastes of dust,
And smells like night.

Now the light is turned on,
The shadows a thing of the past.
The curtains are drawn,
And my mind is at rest at last.

Katharine Davies (Age 10)

Dramatis Personae

I look across the room to see the
Door open, you shuffle in
No fleeting glance today, no eye contact
No chance of a smile
I say "Hello" or some
Useless word - the language
Does not exist to explain exactly how I feel.
Rather I look and hope and
Suffer under my uncaring facade.
And then you turn
Your smile, missed for a weekend
The arc I can see with closed eyes
And then your eyes, that say to the world
All that your mouth is too shy to
Even as they make me ache inside they are
Comfort to me as I rest that night
Content to know that you too are
Resting under the same sky.

Aaron Davies (Age 16)

The Love Poem

Tulips are red
Bluebells are blue
I think you're cute
The sun is bright just like you
Grass can be green
And I think you should be seen
Purple and yellow can always be matched
Just like you and me
Even though blue and green should never be seen
I say you and me should always be seen
And I will always love you

Katie Dunne (Age 9)

The Noisy Crew

There was a man with the flu,
Who had a large noisy crew.
He shouted so much,
In healthy dutch,
And that was the end of his crew.

They swam and swam to the shore,
Until they couldn't swim anymore.
He started to shout,
Then his voice ran out,
And they didn't have to listen much more.

Shannon Dudley (Age 9)

Global Warning

Because of man there's global warming,
And even now the earth's end is dawning.
Killing creatures big and small,
And also trees that are very tall.
Now the world is ruined because of us,
And elephants will lose their tusks.
As the gases start to rise,
The earth will shrink too a smaller size.
And as technology gets too good,
Places on earth will start to flood.
Just as professors think today,
The world will start to worsen that way.
The earth will crumble under out feet,
And our technology will be complete.
And when the earth is no more,
We will lose what we adore.
This is a warning of the future,
Take note of this and help the earth cure.

William Dearnaley (Age 13)

Colours

Clouds are blue,
Pigs are green,
The sun is pink,
Trees are cream.

Beach is red,
Sheep are violet,
Sky is brown,
Birds are lilac.

Grass is gold,
Horses are jade,
Glass is ruby,
Strawberries are beige.

Peaches are blue,
Flowers are tango,
Roads are purple,
Rain is indigo.

China Drewitt (Age 10)

Pants

Red pants
Blue pants
Poverty pants
Spotty pants
Chequered pants
Large pants
Small pants
Fussy pants
Rancourous pants
Senseless pants
Vindictive pants
Wet pants
Quixotic pants
Polymer pants

Ryan Davies (Age 13)

The Place

Imagine a place
Feel the warmness
Hear the green grass shimmer in the wind
One more step and you are there
Drift in the garden while the geese go by
Sleep in the comfy bed that lays by your side
Look out of the window and gaze up into the heavens
See your own cut grass down blow in the wind
Sleep tight little baby you hear your mum say
Now sleep tight me what a day I've had.

Tamsin Davis (Age 8)

The Birdwatchers Attic

Telescopes tower over you in the birdwatchers attic.

Jackdaws spy on you from above,
Mice squeak from below in the birdwatchers attic.

Cameras and contraptions view as good as eagles,
No cages, the birds fly into the trees in the birdwatchers attic.

Sometimes the birdwatcher stares for hours,
Just staring at the exotic birds in the birdwatchers attic.

Joe Dingle (Age 8)

Chocolate

In all shapes and forms it comes
In all different colours too
You can even get it in buns
With white mice and chocolate shoe
We all love to eat it
No matter what the price
It doesn't help us get at
Buy hey! its so nice
It helps me when I'm sad
And also when I'd down
When I break up with a lad
It helps me not to frown
In times of stress and worry
Always look to a a McChocolate Flurry

Elizabeth Drain (Age 15)

Whispering Wasps

There were
10 whispering wasps and 1 got stuck in a bin and then there were 9
9 whispering wasps and 1 got stung then there were 8
8 whispering wasps and 1 stung me then there were 7
7 whispering wasps and 1 got swallowed then there were 6
6 whispering wasps and 1 started to drown then there were 5
5 whispering wasps and 1 got stuck in paint then there were 4
4 whispering wasps and 1 got left out then there were 3
3 whispering wasps and 1 slipped away then there were 2
2 whispering wasps and 1 blew away then there was 1
1 whispering wasp and it flew away and then there were *NONE*.

Michelle Dubois (Age 10)

The Door Of Night

Go and open the door of night.
Maybe outside there's
The sinister silhouette of a bat gliding across the moon,
Or a young black cat darting from shadow to shadow,
Or tawny owls hooting spookily in the quiet night.

Go and open the door of night.
Maybe outside there's
A pinprick of light from a car's rare journey down a country lane,
Or a skulk of foxes rummaging through dustbins,
Or the first howl of a baby wolf.

Chris Douglass (Age 11)

Those People

The people in those worthless countries,
Without no food or life.
These people have no property
No spoons, no fork, no knife.

If you see these people living all alone,
With only scraps of animals
Whom they will devour to the bone.
If you were one of those people
No parents no life
Think about those people
With no fork, no spoon, no knife.

Christopher Drury (Age 12)

My Bunny

My bunny,
Is funny,
He jumps like a kangaroo,
He twitches his nose and twinkles his toes,
He jumps like a kangaroo.

Kirsten Etheridge (Age 8)

Mayday

The sudden beam swirled,
And the small children danced in the limbo
Laughing in the blue may.
The ribbons flew around her hair,
As she sang with coloured tones.
She sat down and listened to the birds,
Until the sun left her sitting all alone.
She was cut and slashed with shards of grass.
The twilight stranded,
In the corner of the sky,
Making way for the cackling moon.

Hannah Desmond (Age 15)

The Terrible Car Wash

When I was three I went in a car wash,
Just a plain boring car wash.
But back then I saw it as a monster,
A huge, fierce, blood thirsty monster.

It opened its almighty jaw with a groan,
And sprayed its deadly venom.
I screamed like a parrot with a bomb on its head,
I think I got the world record!

Then, everything went pitch black,
All there was to see, was darkness.
Silent darkness.
I was terrified.

When the light appeared,
I thought the fright was over.
But I was wrong,
A volcano erupted from the monster.
We drove out of the car wash,
To my amazement, we were still in one piece.

Thomas Eaton (age 9)

The Iron Man

BASHING! CLASHING! buildings falling down,
Squashing, smashing trees near town.
Squeezing squashing car, lorry, van,
Crash, bang! The Iron Man ran.
Noise all around,
Squelch, squelch walking in the mud.
Squeak, squeak rusting in the food,
Noise all around,
Noise all around,
Noise all around.

Callum Davis (Age 8)

Dreamless Enchantment

What do you see when you look up to the skies?
A dream floating on the wings of faith?
Or a hopeless shattered emptiness?
Do you see the hands of God reaching out for your soul?
Another life force given or stolen?

What was the start of all this?
When did the cogs of time begin to turn?
Are we the ones so lost in the flow of time,
That it is impossible to tell now?
Even though we hurt others we still hurt ourselves
I can hear the echoes of my childlike laughter behind me.

So now I look up to the skies for a clearer day
Can I be living under a preconcepted dreamless enchantment
I do hope so.

Helen Dickson (Age 16)

The Wobbling Rainbow

Why is the sun shining bright?
Why are elastic bands so tight?
Why are brass instruments so loud?
Why are footballers always fouled?
Why are houses made of brick?
Why does glue always stick?
Why do flowers always bloom?
Why do vehicles send out fume?
Why do we have hair on our heads?
Why do we have to sleep in our beds?
Why is the sun still in the sky?
I think I know how to bake a pie!

Helen Etheridge (Age 10)

Loneliness

Loneliness is as black as the velvet-sky
Loneliness tastes like stale bread
Loneliness is a single railway ticket blowing
Across an empty railway platform
Loneliness smells like a single unpicked flower
In a field full of grass
It looks like a black and grey room
It sounds like someone weeping in a darkened room
Loneliness feels like a dull empty day with nothing to do.

Kayleigh Deol (Age 12)

The Train

In and out of darkness
Through the meadows green
Zooming through my past time waiting to be seen.
On and on still faster, past the silver stations,
Waiting to be cleaned, past the gleaming golden stream,
Going faster, faster zipping back in time.
Galloping through the darkness, to face the day ahead.
In and out of darkness through the meadows green
Zooming through my present time, through the golden clouds
On and on still faster, to face the day again

Jonathan Davies (Age 12)

Radical Rebel

I found my cap while doing a rap,
In my shameful, shabby T-shirt.
I borrowed a fleece from rich Denise,
And suffered terrifying, tiger tattoo.
My combats are the colour of furry wombats,
For posing on my striking, streaked skateboard.
I wear my sporty trainers when I take my inhalers,
While dangling my spectacular, super shades.

Nicholas Ellaby (Age 11)

Dogs Are...

Dogs are
Ankle fighters,
Food biters,
Cat chasers,
Pull the laces,
Catch the ball,
Jump over the wall,
Dig a hole,
Meet a mole,
That's what I think of dogs!

Rosanna Elliott (Age 6)

Rain

The rain gleams as it falls, making diamond webs.
The spider, surprised to see the rain in the web.
Flower faces twisting to catch the rain.
The pavement shining with colour.
Rain playing drums as the rain splashes into puddles.
Sparkling and gleaming it falls.
The rain gently falls onto my face with a soft touch.
Tiny ripples in the puddles.
The drops fall to the ground.
The umbrellas light up the grey day.

Zara Dyer (Age 7)

Dragons

I am a dragon, raw, raw, raw
My teeth are sharper than my claw,
I am mean and cruel
Any man who fights me,
Is a fool,
I shoot through the sky
Going ever so high,
I go out night and day
For I know the way,
Home.

Sophie Elliott (Age 8)

Lunch Time

Eating my sandwich,
Saying spanish language.
Taking a bite,
Takes all night.
Swapping food,
With a dood.
Now it's playtime,
DING-ALING-ALING!
Oh, oh work time.

Michael du Boulay (Age 8)

The Ducks Talk

You may think of me as a pathetic thing
That waddles and swims,
I don't mind that but when you put me in a sailor suit,
That hurts.
You could appreciate me,
Give me some bread and admire my shimmering golden beak
That's what I want.
Did you like the taste of my cousin
Wrapped in a Chinese pancake,
I can't change what I am so I'll always be
A Duck

Ross Dimmock (Age 11)

It Was Very Noisy...

It was so noisy,
I couldn't hear the telephone ringing on the wall.

It was so noisy,
I couldn't hear the T.V on downstairs.

It was so noisy,
I couldn't hear my Grandad snoring in the chair.

It was so noisy,
I couldn't hear the traffic roaring by.

It was so noisy,
I couldn't hear the people talking down the road.

I was *so* noisy!!

Tré Eustace (Age 7)

October Road

From the middle of the road he could see Oak Street
Where this road, willow, intercepted the other.
The looming sycamores and flailing foliage
Masked and distracted from the call of his mother.

Whose kitchen backed onto the lush side - lawn,
Of the house in which they together stayed.
The trees' huge leaves would cover the garden where
That game which they played and the songs they have sung.

This aching legs soothed by the rest
Of sitting cross legged at the intersection of Willow and Oak
He was only tempted back into the house,
With a motion toward the pool, in which he used to soak.

Andrew Dickson (Age 16)

Food

I love food,
Especially Italian dishes,
From pizza,
To pasta,
Even lasagna.

I adore desserts,
Pancakes,
Fruit cakes,
Sweet cakes,
Hot cakes,
Cream cakes
I love them all cakes

Christiaan de Lange (Age 13)

Little Blue Fairy

Little blue fairy cast a spell,
Something to protect us, like a magic wall,
It would keep all people safe and well,
Maybe stop illnesses, save lives and all.
Make it powerful to stop the war,
And strong enough to right the law.

Little blue fairy make some magic,
Something to save us from the cruel,
It would save our futures from being tragic,
We would have a ruler whose worthy to rule,
He will save us from the dark side,
His name is Jesus, no need to hide.

Little blue fairy chant a rhyme,
To save us from this wicked place,
Make sure that we have enough time,
To solve this nasty case.
If we die let us go to God,
And be thankful to walk on earth where Jesus trod.

Lereesa Easterbrook (Age 9)

A Witches Spell

Double, trouble, boil and bubble;

Witches nail and a brain of a dog;
Humans spine and guts of a hog;
Babies snot, alligator's liver;
Then toss in a boy who quivers.
T-Rex's urine, a widow's heart;
A cuckoo's egg and a little girl's fart.
The Devil's soul sent up from hell;
Widow's skin, let this work well!
Double, trouble, boil and bubble,
Ha! Ha! Ha!

Casey Enkel (Age 10)

The Pig

As happy as can be
And as fat as a sumo wrestler
As pink as a hippo
As far as I can see

He stares at the open sky
As he bathes in some mud
And stands still like a statue
Wishing he could fly

As the farmer gives him food
He gets his snout ready
And then enjoys his snack
After that he's always in a good mood!

He wishes that he could be a dog
Herding the sheep
Or maybe on elephant
Knocking down trees
It might be quiet as a log!

Tim Edwards (Age 10)

My Dad And I

My dad and I like to go fishing
My dad and I like watching the stars
My dad and I could go to MARS
My dad and I are the best of friends forever.

Stephanie Louise Emery (Age 10)

The Police Dog

He looks real tough and mean and scary
He's big and black and a little bit hairy
His name is Bruno which sounds pretty mean
At night his eyes are the only things seen

He catches the criminals and gets them locked up
You wouldn't think it, but he is still a pup
He's very playful but aggressive as well
The criminals would say he's a dog from hell

He's got his own van and kennel too
He likes dog food and a bit of shoe
He likes to run around and play with the ball
Although he's bitten a few bottoms in all

He chases the birds and runs at the rabbits
Like all dogs he's got some funny habits
He jumps up at you and reaches your shoulder
It feels like he is the weight of a boulder

He larks and shouts at passers by
And looks them menacingly in the eye
My mum's so scared she stays inside
Whenever he's around everyone hides

James Evans (Age 13)

The Imaginary Mum

The imaginary mum's hair is quite weird
It's straight, shiny and blonde on one side
And curly bouncy and brown on the other
Which looks very strange.

Her face has a combination of colours
Which blend together like a rainbow,
The colourful colours are, red, blue,
Green, purple, orange, turquoise and ochre
Her lips are a sweet and shiny gold
She has beautiful illustrations on her colourful face.

She has a smooth nose as smooth as velvet
There is purple on the right side,
Orange on the left side and blue down the bridge of her nose.
The texture on her ear is just like silk.

Her eyes are a sky blue and when she looks at you
They look like puppy's eyes
When the puppy has just opened its eyes.

My question is would you like an imaginary mum like this?

Yasmin Essalmi (Age 9)

I Should Like . . . .

I should like to touch the people on the other side of the mirror
I should like to smell the smoke of a frustrated mind
I should like to hear the cryl of an unborn baby
I should like to take home the glow of a radiant sun
I should like to understand the fear of a man in a lion's den

Josh Edwards (Age 11)

The Fish

The fish is like a melody
With beautiful chromatic scales
And you can easily tune-a-fish
And entertain squids and whales

The fish is like an aeroplane
That glides through sky-blue seas
Where miraculous athletes do stunning stunts
And ride on water skis.

The fish is like a metaphor
Rainbow fish don't fall from the rainbow
And when was the last time you saw
An angel fish with a halo?

Tropical fish are magnificent
The best fish I've seen yet
Well - I suppose you'd understand
If you had koi-carp as pets!!

Gemma Elsey (Age 12)

Acrostic Poems

A crostic poems are too hard,
C os' they are awe-inspiring!
R eally they should be barred,
O bviously I feel like snoring,
S o I'd rather wear a leotard,
T antalisingly boring!
I think I'm going to change the subject,
C an't cos' otherwise I might be in for it.

P leased, I cannot be....
O n poetry roaming around, *FREE!*
E nthusiasm? Never heard of it,
M eanwhile we kill poetry bit by bit!
S oon acrostic poetry should be gone....

HOPEFULLY!

Thomas James Edgar (Age 11)

Dragon

My Wings are sheets of lightning
My eyes are hot coals burning like fire
My tongue is sharp and pointed
My claws are spears
My breath is a bolt of fire
My voice is deep thunder
My tail lashes
I've seen many lands
I've heard screams of fear
In play I set things on fire
In anger I tear people apart
They call me the feared one

Sarah-Louise Eley (Age 13)

Monster Storm

Bodies submerged in blood red water
victims of the monstrous thing
Crabs and fish devour the leftovers,
Though there was not much left
The lightning struck, the boat left blazing
The thunder applauding
BOOM! BOOM! BOOM!

The screams of drowning people
The panic aboard the smouldering ship
The ferociousness of the storm
Bellowing out loud into the sky

The monster calms down, the killing ends
The survivors left hanging on the edge
The clouds have gone, the sun out of hiding
Warm fingers bringing back life
That is the surging spectacular STORM!!!

Rebecca Eddy (Age 12)

Bengal Tiger

They glare at you
Those greedy stripes of the jungle
And they don't think or care
All the time they prowl,
Bright and wide they growl
With their horrific face.
In their eyes are antelope, gazelle and buffalo.

At daylight they come out ready for the kill
Once they have gorged themselves
They sag back home to their den.

I do not like tigers
I feel fear when I hear them
Watching me as I go through the jungle.

I'm glad I'm not an antelope, gazelle or buffalo.

Aimee Evans (Age 10)

Harvest Poem

Ears of wheat no longer stand,
Have withered, collapsed and given way,
To a fractured land that is parched and scorched.
Replaced by only grains of dust,
Children's bellies are full for now,
But how long can the food sustain?
An ailing people so full of pride,
Take our help but would they truly like,
Not our pity nor money too,
But to be self sufficient and equal too.

Lisa-Jane Elkins-Jarret (Age 10)

Two Countries Two Homes

Two countries are attached to me in my life
Both, after time have become precious in my eyes
On a cool Spring day in one of these I was born
From which at nine I would be borne,
Made to leave my one and true home,
Not knowing when again in the fields would I roam
This sudden change changed my life forever,
I'd never see the small homely village again ever
So off we flew to a new country, new life,
As I watched I had tears in my eyes.

When I saw our new home my heart skipped a beat
The roof was thatched and where I would sleep!
Fields spread before me, sheep looked back at me
Oh how many things there were to see!
Morning has dawned the birds are singing,
Their music and the wind in my ears ringing.
I soon learnt to love this home so dear,
And turn aside every worry and fear,
But nothing would be as dear to me as my true home
One day I will return I won't give up hope.

Nora Egressy (Age 12)

The Journey Of The Plougher

Long, long ago there lived a plougher, whose bread was stale and water was sour,
His name was Denos Pinopous, and he had an opportunity to choose.

It was between a deadly journey through a far off country, or not to.
Some terrible creatures lay in store for this plougher, young and poor.

So off he set on his trip, despite receiving a sackful of lip.
He'd hardly gone far, when a man jumped out, made of tar.

He fought him off with his trusty plough, with yells of "Eee" and Oooh" and "Ow".
And as he approached the town of Beebo, out of the bushes jumped a sheep named Leefo.

This sheep wasn't sheepish and he wasn't a fool, but Denos finished him off with a blow from a stool.
The Plougher was sleepy and stayed the night, then when he walked on he was caught in fight.

It was an evil satyr who challenged him so, but he could not defeat Denos, oh no!
The young man was injured, but not too badly, when suddenly a dragon appeared, sadly.

This dragon was a chief and owned a fortune and was from a place called Wartune.
But Denos was strong, though it took him some time to defeat the creature last in line.

He took all of the dragon's things, including his fabulous rings,
And then to celebrate he stayed up very, very late.

Christopher Edwards (Age 9)

Noise

It is now night time and the moon is spinning round and round,
I wonder why the moon does not make any sort of sound?
The stars are shining bright as ever, no noises to be heard,
All you hear is the cawing of a little bird.
I am at school but here I can hear noises all around.
I have done my work and now it is time to go home, where there is not a sound.
It is now night time and the moon is spinning round and round,
I wonder why the moon does not make any sort of sound.

Katie Eccles (Age 10)

Tiger

Tigers creeping through the trees,
Very quiet unlike the bees.
Quietly hunting for its prey,
Hoping it's better than yesterday.
Only scared of other beasts,
Afterwards lots and lots of feasts.
Jumping on its prey
Eating it on its holiday.

Tiger creeping through the trees,
Very quiet unlike the bees.
Now this creature
Has many features,
Like its claws
And tearing jaws,
With nerves of steel
Watch out because this thing's real

Stephen Eyre (Age 10)

The Feeling Of Autumn

As I walked out my front door a bunch of fresh, crunchy leaves
Blew all over my body.
As I walk down the hill I am knee deep in leaves
I wind my way down the hill
It's like a swimming pool except you don't get wet
As I reach the forest it was hailing with leaves
As I look around me I see scarlet and brown acorns
Every one I see I pick up
The feeling of Autumn floods me with happiness and also leaves
I see squirrels scampering around
Collecting all the acorns that I haven't found first
I went to pick up another acorn
But I prick my finger on a hedgehog "Ouch" I said
I decide to go home
I can't go very fast because of leaves
When I get home
I take one last look at Autumn for the day and close the door.

Devon Elliott (Age 10)

The Raging Waters

The big, bulging waters take over land,
Washing over innocent plants and sand;
With claws clinging to ghastly creatures,
Creating distant images, fearless features.

And still the fiery waters rise,
Just as if on the throw of a dice
Soaking fields lie beside the meanders
Bringing to the world more wanderers.

Homes washed out, woods flooded
The wondrous land and controlled rivers are vivid.
All the land in sight becomes a giant lake,
Who knows what more can it take.

On and on runs the Raging River
Being now a giant, wilder, bigger.
Down the cliff in a waterfall,
In a dying lake, spreads before all,

Reaching its final goal.

Kinga Egressy (Age 12)

Dancing

We're trying to move to music,
But doesn't seem to work,
Belinda's trying to help us,
Going through some steps.

Now we're at the drinks bar,
Asking for a drink,
Now it's back to work again,
Time passes in a blink.

Sammi-Marie Earnshaw (Age 8)

Listen

Listen. What can you hear?
A boy eating crisps.
Listen. What can you hear?
The sea splashing against the shore.
Listen. What can you hear?
A girl peddling her bike.
Listen. What can you hear?
A cat washing itself.
Listen. What can you hear?
The boats sailing rapidly on the sea.
Listen. What can you hear?
A clock ticking one, two, three...
Listen. What can you hear?
The end of this poem.
Going, going...gone.

Mica-Lee Etere (Age 10)

Moonriver

As the waves rolled
Moonriver watched
The planets saw
A sight beyond imagination

Moonriver sat there
Eyes peering like a hawk
The stars looked down and saw
A sight beyond imagination

Then a splash in the water
Moonriver's head turned
She saw a fin in the water
A sight beyond imagination

As the waves rolled
And the stars and the planets looked down
Moonriver had seen
A sight beyond imagination

Alice Edwards (Age 10)

The Desert

Desert, Desert
Hot sandy desert
Sand storms blowing
The wind shivering and shimmering
High sand dunes to climb
Side winder snakes slithering across the sand
Scorpions scuttling around on the sandy horizon
Desert rats running around wildly
Desert, Desert

Ashley Earll (Age 11)

Colour

As black as the night,
As blue as the sky,
As green as the trees,
As I pass by.

As orange as the goldfish,
As yellow as the sun,
As red as the jumper,
Which was made by my mum.

As gold as the lamp,
As silver as the moon,
As pink as the pigs,
I'll see you soon!

Charlotte Edwards (Age 8)

A Flamingo

A tall pink flamingo standing in a river,
Looking for fresh shrimp,
All the flock are with him all standing on one leg,
"Look out," said a flamingo,
For behind the eating flamingoes was a big green crocodile,
Ready to take a bite!

Snap went the crocodile,
Flap went the flamingos,
But before the crocodile could take a bite,
The flamingoes had gone!
Flying through the jungle,
"Here's a tasty spot," said one,
They landed in a different river,
"We don't know why that crocodile wanted our shrimp," they said.

Georgia Ehrmann (Age 8)

Winter

Winter is here, it is cold and dark all the time
We wear woolly warm clothes to keep the cold away
The wind is howling at night keeping everyone up
We wake up and all around is white fluffy snow
The lake has turned to ice, slippery ice.

Taylor Every (Age 10)

Jesus' Point Of View

My life had been fine up until now
When they shouted for Barabbas a murderer
He is released and I am to be crucified
They strap my hands with rope to the wood
Like a cotton thread being sewn to a piece of material
My crown of thorns on my head like knives
I am forced to carry a piece of my cross
I am like a slave

My friend Nicodemus says goodbye to me
He says it in a way only I understand
Veronica puts a cloth to my face to heal my cuts
I cannot walk with my cross but I am forced to
I arrive painfully at Golgatha
I am thrown to the ground
Then stripped of my red cloak and crown of thorns
They nail my hands and feet to the cross
I am pulled up between two thieves
One insults me and the other protects me
I say forgive them Father for they know not what they have done
The sky goes dark as I hang my head and die

Nicholas Elliott (Age 10)

If You Want To See An Ogre

If you want to see an ogre
You must go down to the castle of danger

I know an ogre who's living down there
She's very bad mannered and so rude

Yes, if you want to see an ogre
You must go down to the castle of danger

Go down to that castle and say
"Giant woman, giant woman
"Giant Woooman"

And up she'll get but do not stay
Run away!!

Siobhan Ennew (Age 8)

The Night

I don't like the night,
It gives me a fright,
There's a man in my room
With a great metal broom,
He tries to hit my head
But luckily it hit the bed instead,
My mum doesn't think it's true
But I said one day it will happen to you!
So I went back to my room
And grabbed the metal broom,
And hit him in the eye
And I wished he had to die

Natasha Elvidge (Age 9)

Sing A Song Of Children

Running up and down.
Hear the trees rustling
And giggles all around.

See the boys play football,
Smell the smell of chips,
Girls playing handstands,
Little boys playing with their ships.

People playing races,
Boys starting fights,
Girls try to stop them,
So boys pull down their tights.

Sing a song of children,
Running up and down.
Hear the trees rustling
And giggles all around.

Danielle Etherington (Age 10)

Creation

Dolphin began -

It caught the motion of a ball on the surface of the water,
It captured the flapping of the leaves,
And gave her power to swim.

For her skin -
She grabbed the royal blue from the sky,
She grasped the feel of a tongue.

To make her senses -
It took the constant bubbling of the running brook,
And it stole the roundness of a tube.

Then deep down in the dark, cold sea -
She stole oil drops with dazzling pearls,
She caught ghost white snowdrops,
And created her eyes.

And so -
She made her power to swim,
Her skin,
Her senses
And created her eyes

Then the dolphin was born.

Lauren Eames (Age 11)

Mum And Dad Going Mad

When my dad went mad
I was very sad.
When my mum went psycho
I was very very hypo

(This did not really happen)

George Elliott (Age 10)

The Mantis

The Mantis is very sleek,
It's deadly to a fly;
It's cleverness is at its peak,
Every fly it sees will die.

The Mantis is not very nice,
He can kill a fly,
Every time he uses a dice
A fly will DIE!

Thomas Eastaugh (Age 8)

The Country Road

I saw a fox running through a bush
He stopped to get some air.
What shall I do said the fox
Along came a hunter with a shot gun
Bang, die said the hunter
The fox got away

Ashley Earl (Age 10)

The Telephone Call

Hello! Is there anyone up there? I'm fed up of life, which is thoroughly unfair.
I wonder if you could tell me, please, whether destruction and poverty will ever cease?
Oh, it's only the answerphone. Alright then, I'll wait for the tone.
Here's my message loud and clear, hope you'll get it, hope you'll hear.

Could I enquire as to why I exist? Was I just a dropout from your Heavenly List?
If so, could you tell me the reason for this exception - What did I do wrong?
How did this happen? Is it nice up there with no worries or concerns,
Watching eternal episodes of our world as it turns?
Do you ever confer with that guy down below?
Do you ever wallow in depression or sorrow?
Have you actually seen the suffering down here? It seems to be getting worse, year after year.
Did we offend you at some point in our lives?
Are we doomed to damnation when the Final Hour arrives?
Are you going to blow us up when you've had enough?
Get rid of the problem when the going gets tough?
I know you may be looking at us askance
But . . . is there a possibility of perhaps a second chance?

Well, tea break's over, I'd better go. When you've heard my message, do let me know.
My warmest regards, and thanks for everything,
When you've thought of the answers, just give me a ring.

Jean Eu (Age 16)

Secret Of The Sisters

I have a sister called Zoe,
She's a pretty normal girl,
But when her friends come round,
She's an alien to me.

She's only mean to me.

To boys she changes too,
A sweetheart with pigtails,
She smiles all the time,
With puppy dog eyes.

She's only mean to me.

To mum and dad she's a perfect kid,
Who does all the washing up,
The cleaning too,
She also cleans her room.

She's only mean to me

To me she's an awful kid,
Who kicks and screams,
Why?
It's the way things go

She's only mean to me.

Kirsty Elwell (Age 12)

The Door

Go and open the door
You might see a tiger
Or a big fat bear
You could see the future.

Go and open the door
You will see
Big tall mountains
And a giant.

Go and open the door
You will see a big balloon
Floating in the air
A big, tall cupboard
That reaches to the sky.

Go and open the door
You might see a prince
And princess by their palace
Proud and tall.

Rukaya Ellison (Age 9)

Family

De brother in de bedroom,
He tidying up,
De brother in de bedroom,
He throw de cup

De mother in de front room,
She looking at me,
De mother in de front room,
She drinking her tea

De dad in de kitchen,
He cooking our tea,
De dad in de kitchen,
He drop his key

De cat in de basket,
She looking at me,
De cat in de basket,
She eating her tea

De hamster in de cage,
He fell right down,
De hamster in de cage,
He gave me a frown.

Perry Forrest (Age 8)

Ruined

Silhouetted corpses on a battlefield of flame and muggy fumes;
Once were docile creatures, toffee-nosed, velour-skinned and rubber-nosed,
Farmer watches, bleary-eyed, as bolts pummel holes in his cattle and his once bulging cheque book;
Cold winds whip the embers of a heartless funeral pyre
Twisting tortured tentacles of city-grey fumes snake their way through every life.

Jenny Edmunds (Age 11)

Autumn Colours

Golden crunching falling leaves,
Children playing under trees,
Through the crispy carpet the children wade,
The colours of Autumn brightly displayed.

Red is for shining juicy apples,
And for bright rounded berries,
Gold is for harvest corn,
And for gleaming varnished acorns,
Brown is for crinkled, crunchy leaves,
And for dark polished conkers see them gleam,
Orange is for tiny oval hips like coloured raindrops falling.

The colours of Autumn are warm and bright,
Making the darkest trees look light!

Rebecca Ekers (Age 12)

It Was So Noisy...

It was so noisy,
That I couldn't hear my music playing in my bedroom.
It was so noisy,
That I couldn't hear my dog barking in the garden.
It was so noisy,
That I couldn't hear my mum shouting dinner.
It was so noisy,
That I couldn't hear the helicopter landing in the east.
It was so noisy,
That I couldn't hear the crowd shouting goal!
IT WAS SO NOISY!!

Michael Eley (Age 8)

The Monster

It hides under my bed
It hides in the closet
It hides in the tree house
It's the Monster
The big, scary, naughty, Monster

Its teeth are sharp,
Its claws are evil,
Eyes are red, body purple,
Legs blue, arms are green head black
It's the Monster
The big, scary, naughty, Monster

It eats 1,000 cows a week
It eats children for desert
It's the monster
The big, scary, naughty, Monster

James Escott (Age 9)

Mist

Mist
Calm swirling
Mist
Lighter than air
Hanging there
Calm swirling
Mist

Mist
Deadly
Mist
Misleading innocent people
Into its trap
Deadly
Mist

Jane Ebdon (Age 11)

Pollution

Which one to buy?
So many to choose
Yellow, red, blue, green, orange
Every colour under the sun.
I have now made my choice
A whole nine hours later
Dark blue and costing
Eight thousand pounds
It runs on leaded petrol
Then I had a hint
That it would make more pollution
To our highly polluted world
So I sold it and bought instead
Well, can't you guess? A bike.

Alex Etheridge (Age 9)

Dream

My dream was to become a dancer,
I started at five doing ballet, tap and jazz,
Then from there on to a stage school.

Then the day I'd been waiting for all my life,
I became a pupil of the Royal Ballet School.
Being moved up to upper school was a big achievement to me.

Then in 1987 a man named Sir Kenneth MacMillan spotted me.
This meant the ultimate challenge I was the happiest lady alive,
Performing on television and travelling around the world.
Being able to have good ballet tuition,
I have enjoyed every moment of my career
And being able to receive several awards

Lucinda Eccleston (Age 13)

Captured In Time

As I watched the river winding her way,
As slow as a baby opening his eyes for the first time,
And the willow tree sleeping peacefully by,
The image was captured in my head,
All other scares for the moment dead.
A rabbit scurried across the long grasses,
It's nose twitching, ears pricked, her nervous eyes
Glinted from the morning dew, like fresh raindrops
After a heated drought.
A single bird sang a song, the only noise to break the quiet.
A breath of wind kissed the swan awake,
Like a flower opening towards the sun,
And she glided forward in her own sweet time,
For time was captured in this wondrous land
He could not break free from its depths
Not even man could disturb the peace.
The sun, alone, shone weakly in the sky,
Trying not to break the moment.
God looked down upon that morning
And was pleased with the way things were.

Laura Easton (Age 13)

Nonsense Poem

If I were to lay in bed all day,
My dad would go mad and say,
Get up young vet unless you want to get very wet.
I would retort in the middle of a snort,
No way I'd say and then eat my hay,
You dare you cheeky bear, I'll shave your hair.
Go on then you smelly hen but then,
When he got his razor out, I had to get my lazer out,
He put his razor back and I did the same with my lazer
A truce said Bruce no way, said Mum and hit him up the bum.
"Ow" he said after hitting his head
I got out of bed when my mother said the dog is dead

David Ewington (Age 11)

Falling Leaves

As the bitter wind blows
Past the trees
The leaves hang helplessly
To their branches
When they get too tired
And they can go no more
Twirling, whirling, fluttering,
They fall to the ground
Dying in quiet corners.

Lisa Edens (Age 9)

My Cat

I used to have a cat,
Who was rather fat.
So we took him to the vets
With lots of other pets.
When he sat down,
He gave a big frown.
When we got home,
He answered the phone.
It was . . . . Grandma!!

Tom Elliott (Age 11)

This Bunny

This bunny is funny
He jumps like a kangaroo,
If you stand on his back
He will jump down the track
Just like a kangaroo.

This bunny is funny
He jumps like a kangaroo,
You catch him in a net,
Just like a kangaroo.

Glen Etheridge (Age 11)

Football Players

Andy Andy
Ran for goal
Ran up the pitch
And scored a goal
What a goal! What a goal!
Then he scored another goal.

Teddy Teddy
Crossed the ball
Andy ran on
To head the ball home
Then the other team scored a goal.

Ole Ole
Came on for Teddy
Then Ryan kicked the ball
Ole ran on to score a goal.

Craig Edwards (Age 11)

Sport

Football,
A game of two halves.
Tennis,
A game of sets.
Golf,
A game of pars.
Cricket,
A game of wickets.
Basketball,
A game of points.
Rugby,
A game of tries.
Boxing,
A game of knockouts.
American Football,
A game of touch-downs.
All of these sports are popular,
What do you like best?

Thomas Fay (Age 11)

Sam Froment

Rugby liker
Big speaker
Good hiker

Makes friends
Good mum
Likes playing
Hates rum
Cabbage hater
Fanta fan
Brother good
Friend Dan

Sam Froment (Age 8)

The Metaphoric Dragon

My wings are a perfect example of swimmers flippers.
My eyes are firing flames on a raging bonfire.
My tongue is a sizzling, stinging snakes defence.
My claws are astonishingly sharp, in fact, as sharp as shattered glass.
My breath smells of rotten vegetables that have been in the fridge too long.
My voice is a mans voice shouting into a loudspeaker placed in front of your ear.
My tail is a long fluffy branch swinging from side to side with happiness.
I've seen very little because I am blind.
I've heard very little because I am deaf.
In play I am evil and cunning.
In anger I am joyful and full of happiness.
They call me anything because I cannot hear them!

Tony Fernandez (Age 12)

Holding The Baby

She's so tiny, pretty and clean, mind you, she does smell.

I feel, well, excited and special, a bit nervous holding the baby,
They said they're taking a photo of me holding the baby,
They told me not to drop her,
I stood up, holding the baby.

She's very heavy, I fall back onto the bed
But I'm still holding the baby.

She wakes up..........................OUCH!
She's *pulling* my hair!

Mum says all babies pull hair,
I say that's it,
I'm *not* holding the baby.

Katie Fitzpatrick (Age 7)

The Teachers

The teachers have so many cups of tea,
One has a knobbly knee.
The one next door prefers coffee,
And she is not even as sweet as rotten toffee

The one last year was so young,
She had a very unhappy lung.
She smoked all day,
And said no play.

The head teacher that we have,
Does not clean the smelly old lav.
He got the cleaner to do it,
She said no way, and gave him a hit.

Sinead Flannery (Age 11)

War In The Palestine

The young man feels horror.
He looks at the gun.
He wears only a T-shirt.
No uniform or gun.
He is scared.
And looks at the gun.
He throws a stone.
The gun looks at him.

Richard Frost (Age 15)

Kenning

A fish-eater
A wavy-mover
A person-killer
A fluent-swimmer
A fish-scarer
A food-chaser
A mean-predator
What am I?
I'm a snake!

George Fox (Age 9)

My Love

My love, my love
You will always be my love
My first, my last, forever
My love, my love
Our everlasting love
Shines bright in our hearts
My love, my love
You are my angel,
My spirit and my soul.

Katy Fieldhouse (Age 12)

School Is Great

When I wake up I just can't wait
Till I go to school I'm never late.
Maths I could do without
But I love giving the calculators out.

Science is good but I
Don't like the writing.
But blowing up the bottles
Destroys the lighting.

Netball is fun
But I like to get the netballs and the netball net.
English is alright
But I'd rather it was night.

Art is excellent as you can tell
But I love at the end of the day to ring our school bell.
So school is great but it's getting late
Best of all is going home to see my mate.

Charlotte Froud (Age 9)

The Door

Open the door it could be,
The pathway to your destiny,
The stairway to heaven,
The boat to hell,
Or playing football at the Dell.

Open the door you might see,
A smiling face filled with glee,
A rollercoaster spinning round and round,
Or a BMX flying over a mound.

Open the door you could hear,
A crying screech filled with fear,
The swish of the sea as if being painted,
Or the sound of a sportsman that's dedicated.

Open the door you could have,
The whole world in your hands,
You could see the world like a shining diamond.

Declan Finney (Age 11)

Greetings From The Costa del Azahar

Spanish seas, my nose is running
Free on the sand.
White crested waves dabbing at the nostrils.
Too weak to go to the supermercado,
Two weeks of this nightmare to go.

Throbbing head.
I want to smell the paella.
Land of flamenco, tapas, and my enfermedad
Told me "The sea air'll do you good",
And the drizzle blurs my sea-view window.

Eye-lids won't stay open much longer,
The shutters of these Valencian apartamentos.
I'll have another glass,
Vino Médico,
My wine of the prescription.

Sunday night's escape from hell,
Wrap up warm in the red arena,
Temperatures plummet at night.
So my coughs and splutters don't feel out of place,
Behind my scarf in the artificial daylight.

Chris Fear (Age 16)

The Bee Sting

Why do bees sting?
Why do elastic bands ping?
How do monkeys climb?
How do robbers cause a crime?
Why does wood float?
Why do we ride on a boat?
How do we eat fruit?
How do we wear a suit?
Why does food come on a tray?
Why do we have to pay?
How do lions roar?
How do we count to four?
Why do we make things out of wood?
Why are boys good?
Why are girls fussy?
Why are cats called pussies?

Matthew Fysh (Age 8)

My Mum

My mum she is the best,
She always tells me to wear a vest,
My mum she is so tidy,
Well she is the best, if my mum was a toy,
She wouldn't be in the shops,
Because she is too advanced,
I love my mum she is the best,
And we will be together forever.

Andrew Ferns (Age 8)

The Pictures In My Mind's Eye

Paths etched on the map of memory.
They have been well worn since then,
As my mind recalls the picture.
The setting sun shines brilliantly,
Over the dark shadowy hill.
The camera's shutter opened so briefly,
You could hardly tell.
Captured in both worlds;
The world of mind and that of body,
Intertwined and separate.
The dusty earth beneath my feet,
Looks like golden sand in the light,
But soon is dark, as the day turns to night.
Stars pale at first quickly become bright.
So many more than in the choked London.
They are beautiful.
I stand amazed at the intricacies of God's creation.
So many pictures that I will never understand.

Matthew Finn (Age 15)

My Dreams

My dreams are filled with unanswered questions
Unrecognised faces
Haunted by shadows and sounds

My dreams chill me
Fate waiting in the distance
But the fog clouds my view

Images tear through my head
Destroying reality
Clawing at my sanity

The darkness vanishes
The images fading
A dark figure...

Waits

Rebecca Fuller (Age 14)

Word Chant

Visitors, castle, old, man,
Working, company, driving, van,
Factory, making, food, plate,
Meat, fish, cod, bait,
Fishing, sport, tennis, ball,
Hit, animal, snail, crawl,
Baby, cry, die, sad,
Murder, burglar, robber, bad,
Weather, rain, water, sea,
Liquid, coke, drinking, tea,
Coffee, beans, import, man,
Working, company, driving, van.

Simon Frais (Age 13)

In The Sky...

In the sky flying so high,
Is an elegant bird.

Swooping amongst the cliffs,
Where he goes is a myth.

On a journey long and far,
Where many little worlds travel apart.

Not startled or flustered does he get,
There is nothing in the way to trouble him yet.

But worst is to come when the wind beats,
He is luckily flying in a fleet.

Others join into his world,
Where there is no woes and is not controlled.

How gallantly they rise,
To a scared prey of his demise.

All this to get along in his world,
Yet none is effected the bird in the sky.

John Frayne (Age 13)

The Snow Child

He wanders about late at night,
All alone without fright
His clothes glisten silver also a speak of white
Then he tries to make snow all his might
It's freezing cold yet he still wanders about late at night
Before he goes he whispers
"My name is Jack Frost, goodnight!"

Sophie Frost (Age 10)

Sacrifice

Is this really the Son of God?
Shall he die should we nod?

He shall die upon a cross
On a hill of grass and moss

How sad I was to see him die
In a bleak tomb he shall lie

He rose again on Easter Day
Hallelujah we all did say!

Forty days later he rose to heaven
To stand beside his true Father

He suffered for all
Us Christians to call.

Alice Foster (Age 10)

A Kenning

A prey-catcher
A black-striper

A lazy sleeper
A long-strider

A meat-eater
A family-sneeker

A proud-walker
A fierceful-hunter

What am I?
A Tiger!

Eloise Ferrari (Age 9)

Footy

The hardest game we've had to play,
A draw until half time,
A win never sure when we play away,
I wouldn't bet a dime.

A muddy pitch makes it hard work.
The players are all worn out
You can't see the number on my shirt.
But winnings what it's all about.

The match is finally over.
90 minutes done.
Twice scoring in the extra time,
And now the game is won.

Trooping to the changing room,
We are cheering all the way.
The cup final can't come too soon,
Any doubt is blown away.

There's one other more important,
That comes back to my mum,
I love to play my football,
But cleaning the kits not fun.

Simon Fitch (Age 12)

Spring

S pring is a season.
P lants begin to grow
R ather than no leaves.
I t's traditional to have a spring clean
N o untidy houses.
G oats and other animals are born.

Ned Foster (Age 8)

A Forest

The howling of the wolf,
The squeaking of the mouse,
The crying of the eagle,
The swishing of the wind.

The dropping of the leaves,
The thumping of the monkey,
The buzzing of the bees,
The tweeting of the bird.

The crunching of the twigs,
The sparkle of the stars,
The hissing of the snake,
The cracking of the twigs.

The chopping of the Lumberjack,
The roaring of the bear,
The cracking of the fire,
The creaking of the tree.

Joe Flint (Age 10)

I'll Follow You

I'll follow you
deep in the jungle
over ropes and trees
where the Rhinos charge to you.

I'll follow you
over animals
round bushes
where the Tigers catch their prey.

I'll follow you
up trees
past Lions
and down holes from which no-one can escape.

I'll follow you
anywhere you go
past attacking monkeys
I'm not lying, you know.

Alexander French (Age 9)

Cats Eyes

Have you ever seen cats eyes in the dark?
Do you know what actual colour they are?
Are they blue, green or brown?
Or are they like the headlights on a car?
Their eyes reflect light just like a star at night,
Even though their eyes are strange,
They are a funny sight.

Aisha Farmilo (Age 12)

The Storm!

Rushing, rowdy, rain,
In the storms booming build.
Dense arms ripping up the earth,
As it glides it's feet across the blue ocean.

The enormous domineer shakes his hips,
Yet tearing up more land.
Wind whistling throughout many ears,
Tossing the cryptic sea to and frow.

The crash of lightning trembling in the sky,
The repulsive bully screams to warn.
Trees are parted from the earth,
As the storm roars like a lion.

The storm whistles more words,
To warn many around, again and again.
Trying to balance as its form vibrates,
But can't keep still, knocking over yet another building.

Matthew Francis (Age12)

Daisy

My pet dog Daisy is very lazy
She sits around all day
But sometimes she goes really crazy
Falls over and gets grazes.

She barks in the night when she has a fright
She then wakes the baby
Who cries and screams like crazy
She's like a cow big and fat
Only moves when she's hungry.

She gets frustrated by many things
Flies, wasps and bees.
She growls at people walking by
Who hear her bark then run and cry.
That's my dog Daisy who is ever so lazy.

Jodie Field (Age 13)

Tanka: Hang Glider

Gracefully gliding
Clear blue water beneath him
Inhale scenery

Bird wings floating through the air
Falling free, high down the sky

Neal Freeman (Age 11)

Love

You pulled me from the gutter,
You washed away the dirt,
So, why, I ask you now,
Have I ended up hurt?

You opened up thoughts and emotions,
The ones I kept tightly closed.
At the time it felt like the 'real thing',
In retrospect I feel exposed.

And you knew what you were doing,
And look what you've finally done.

You've captured my heart and entire mind,
It's like a twisted dream,
You've drained away any ounce of love,
And you've just come away clean.

You know I'll always be tied down to you,
Because I have nothing left to offer,
I feel weak, stamped on, broken in two,
"It was all a game I played with her."

I will never be able to truly forget,
Because I am soaked in your love.

Imogen Fry (Age 16)

The Reason Why

Here is a poem about, how I got voted out,
Of the Christian group, I'm forced to look for a new troop.

Some people go to church, just to try and search,
I try and get in, but I have too much sin.
They may not agree, but for me it's to be,
I wish they would see, that I am me.

Why, they ask, but they don't know my past,
People look at me, just to see,
The way I really am, but they don't know how deep my feelings go.

If they only knew, why I act like I do,
Maybe they would understand, I wish they could,

I may not believe, but I wish they could see,
It really doesn't bother me, I wish I could be,

What they want to see, but deep down it's just not me.

They say they're true mates, but really it's all fake,
Just for their own sake, why can't they make their own mistakes.

Maybe one day in the future they will see, a whole new me!

Davina Francis (Age 15)

War Time Poem

Red blood gushing out from wounded men,
Gun noises raging with fright,
Children getting evacuated with horrified faces,
Everyone running around the place when the bombs go
BANG!
BANG!
BANG!

Verity Fuller (Age 9)

April Showers

Streams of rain run down my window,
Tipping, tapping on the sill,
I see birds shelter in their nests,
Whilst frogs leap into the rippling puddles,
I watch some children having fun splashing about in pools of water,
I hear their boots squelching in the soggy, brown mud,
And their cheerful spurts of laughter ringing in my ears.
The sky is filled with black and grey clouds,
Squeezing out their litres of water,
Blinding is the sun as it peeps out of a dull, grey cloud,
Silence as the rain comes to a halt.

Jamie Fisher (Age 10)

Friends

I've got lots of friends,
But my special friend is Meg.

Me and my friend,
We'll never end,
Me and my friend,
Always depend on each other.

I've got lots of friends,
But my special friend is Meg.

Me and my friend,
We'll never end,
Me and my friend,
Always depend on each other.

We're the best of friends!!!

Eleanor Field (Age 10)

Green Wellies

So much depends upon
Old green Dirty Wellies
Splish Splash in puddles
Living on a farm

Lara Fincken (Age 9)

There Once Was...

There was once a man from Dover,
Who had a big dog called Rover,
He lived in a shed,
His wife was called Fred,
And he couldn't stop falling over.

Jack Fitzgerald (Age 10)

As I lay In My Bed

As I lay in my bed,
Pleasant thoughts in my head.
With flailing arms and legs,
All scorching and stuffy.
I try to feel for something cool,
But instead caress something fluffy.
Suddenly I remember the wall,
It calls to me with outstretched
Arms like a loving mother.
As I scramble and squirm I fall.
My eyes open and I wait for them to adjust.
I crawl back into my berth.
My eyelid flickers and then just shuts,
Like a chamber door or a just stabbed corpse.
As I lay in my bed.

Nicola Fraus (Age 12)

The Midnight Fox Poem

The fox cubs cries floated through the window,
They were like a lost puppies cry,
They seemed to pierce the air like a knife,
It made me feel very distraught.

The thunder crashed in the sky,
Like a giant stamping his feet and stomping around,
It was as dark as a cave,
And as loud as a pair of cymbals.

The gunshot filled the air with an echoing bang,
It was as sharp as a dagger,
It was as fast as a bullet,
And as sudden as a cracking whip.

After the gunshot silence filled the air,
All you could hear was the wind,
And the trees swaying in the breeze.

Adam Fitzer (Age 11)

Children United

The world could be a better place,
But the adults now don't care.
They enjoy the war, they enjoy fighting,
Nothing now is fair.

The children are the future,
We're the ones who are tame,
But when we are the adults,
Will that still be the same?

Melissa Flight (Age 10)

I Watched...

One late afternoon,
A little boat was sailing
Under the light, gentle air.
The water was rippling
The sand was soft...

I watched this yacht,
As it rowed gracefully
To the hailing sunset
I could smell the clean air;
I watched as the sea
Turned the rocks into marble
And I loved that cam, tender, subtle breeze!

Joel Faulkner (Age 13)

The Dog

Sometimes I'm just a blur,
Because I'm fast at running just like lightning,
With a look that's frightening.

I bark a bald men,
Although I'm mans best friend,
My fur is long and silky,
Black and white's my colour.

When you're kind to me I lick your face,
When I'm hungry feed me dog food or biscuits,
Not too much because I will get tummy ache.
In the night I stay awake,
While in the day I slumber,
In my dog basket I will sleep,
Or on your settee will do,
But don't let your Dad find out,
Or I will be put out.

Please look after me because I do love you.

Gemma Fisher (Age 10)

Josh

Josh is someone that I know
With wacky ideas always on the go
He comes to school in a taxi that's red
With a driver that looks like he hasn't been to bed
Josh is my friend
Do you have a friend like Josh?

Drew Frisby (Age 9)

Before Christmas 2001

Sparkling lights,
Sparkle on me,
Spectacular christmas tree,
Astonish me,
Huge presents,
Excite me,
Empty toy box,
FILL UP!
Freezing snow,
Don't freeze me,
Gigantic toy shops,
Empty yourself,
Flaming fire,
Warm me up,
Loving Santa,
Please will you bring me all the presents I would like,
So then I will be happy,
Like I was last year.
Make me excited christmas 2001!
Thankyou.

Emma-Leigh Flahaut (Age 9)

Underneath The Silence

Underneath the silence I can hear...
The soft bubbles rising from divers in the dark depths of the deep water.
Crying, screaming of those who have lost there loved ones in an earthquake.
Parent's voices shouting, arguing repeatedly over and over.
The endless joy as the explorers reach their destiny.
Fearsome waves lashing wildly against the jagged rocks.
The devastating gun shot of a serial killer as he claims another life.

Underneath the silence I can feel...
The pain, loneliness of newly orphaned children.
The raw anger of a raging farmer as the last of his sheep are slaughtered.
The desperation of a mother as she searches through the clouds of dying.
The sadness of the mourners round the open grave.
The humiliation of the belittled student.
The raging heart of a running fox.

Sarah Frewer (Age 10)

Spring Time

S pring is the time when daffodils grow out of the ground.
P ounding fowls jump up and down.
R abbits run through the hole.
I n the garden we see a mole.
N ice sun shining in the sky.
G ardens get filled with millions of flies.

T he spring flowers grow all around.
I n a house somebody found lots of ants in a mound.
M y dog saw a very black cat.
E veryone likes spring they sit in the garden on a mat.

Jordan Ferry (Age 7)

The Cat That Scratched

The cat looked tough and very, very mean,
He looked quite chubby,
Even though he was clean.
Clever he was but clumsy too,
Anywhere he went he tried to cook.
Then one day he started to itch,
Then he looked and looked,
He had the nits!
Anywhere he went he itched, itched, itched,
Run everybody I've got nits!
He went to the vets, owners screamed,
Dogs huddled together like a Rugby team!
Cats yowled, children shouted,
The vets said "lets cure him, no doubt about it!"

Claudia Fuller (Age 7)

Description Of A Baby

It yells and grumbles,
It screams and mumbles,
It cries and slurps,
It bellows and burps,
It doesn't sound like any other,
It sounds just like my baby brother.

Michelle Filmer (Age 10)

Birds

Birds fly,
Birds peck for food,
Birds steel food,
When they are at the sea side.
Birds make nests,
Birds lay eggs.

Kayleigh Foster (Age 6)

Untitled

I like Juicy apples.
I like hairy pears.
I like juicy bananas.
I like red tomatoes.
I like green grapes.
I like fat chips.
I like sweet peas.
I like raw carrots.
But I don't like strong onions.

Lewis Farquharson (Age 6)

Run For It!

Quick, the monster is coming,
Boom, Boom, Boom,

Here he comes!
Look at that shadow!
It's a giant rat!
No, a giant mouse!
Eee, eee, eee,

See I told you it.....
Boom, Boom, Boom,
Run for it!

Again we ran,
Down the street,
The monster's right behind us,
So run for IT!

Paul Fellows (Age 8)

155

Alien Attack!!!

Aliens come in all shapes and sizes, and lots of them have won prizes,
Some are as wobbly as mum's jelly, some are hard and have a big belly,
They have so many different eyes, some are as big as cherry pies.

Some can even breath fire, some are as thin as a piece of wire,
Some eat eyeballs for their tea, some prefer a human knee,
Some even eat slobbery tongues, or maybe some raw lungs.

Their spaceships are really strange, their planets are well out of human range,
Some are big some are small, some are short some are tall,
Some are clumsy in different ways, some are in the latest craze.

Some have even flown to the moon, on a supersonic spoon,
Some catch comets with one hand, some make ringed planets with rubber bands,
If you meet an alien you won't know what to do, some might zzaap!! you in two.

They're in their spaceships and coming to you, watch out they might eat you,
They're in our galaxy, they're going to get everything but hopefully not me,
So earth be ready here they come, they come from everywhere even the sun!!!

Matthew Fairbairn (Age 9)

Winter

The world frosty white, the world icy cold,
The snowflakes falling, the sky like the
Moon's falling down to earth, down to earth.
So I snuggle up in my warm, warm bed,
In my warm, warm house.
And outside I leave the freezing, freezing cold.
In the morning wrap up warm,
I'm going outside to build snowmen and throw snowballs,
I shake snowy trees so all the snow falls on my head,
I feel all cold and shivery,
Now, I go inside by the warm, warm fire,
And go to bed in my warm, warm house.

Katie Fenlon (Age 8)

Koala

I live in the forests and climb gum trees,
I'm a cuddly bear, I'm one of my own species.
I'm bigger than a female, medium in size,
I have a smooth nose and pearls for eyes,
I'll walk really slow,
I'll rub against your skin,
I'll love you to bits,
Did I mention I live in Australia?

So come visit me you'll have a really good time,
But you better not make a gum out of me.

Luke Flacks (Age 11)

Snow

I brought children out to play,
With their big woolly hats and scarves on.
I hid gardens, trees and flowers beneath my white.
I turned the roads slippery and made the cars and people skid.
I made the ground soft and cold.
I stopped adults going to work and children going to school
I forced animals to stand and stare.
I felt something...I started to turn to slush.
I made the children go inside.
My body turned to cold water.
I wet the streets and the roads in cold grey water.

Abigail Fox (Age 8)

My Best Friend

My best friend is the best,
She would beat all the rest,
She runs and leaps and jumps up high,
We will never say goodbye,
We love each other and go for walks,
We don't swap clothes,
We don't have talks,
But I tell her all my secrets,
And she listens well,
She's a very special kind of girl,
I don't know if you've guessed my rhyme,
But she's none other than a canine!

Eliza Finch (Age 9)

Colours

Orange is a juicy satsuma sitting in the fruit bowl,
Or the sun setting in the sky,
Or a tasty pointed carrot.
Or a halloween pumpkin glowing at midnight.

Blue is the swirling sea,
Or the dolphins splashing in the sea.
Or the blue sky with the white clouds.
Or ice on the fridge.

Red is the sun setting in the sky,
Or blood on the floor.
Or a poppy of war.
Or your heart beating,
Or a rose.

Silver is the moon shining through the window,
Or the stars sparkling the sky.
Or the rain falling to the ground.
Or the ice in the winter.

Danielle Fernandez (Age 8)

My Ginger Cat

My ginger long clawed cat,
With tiger stripes sits on your knee
With its claws moving
And its big green eyes staring
Straight up at you
When you don't know it might,
Start blaring at you
Those gigantic whiskers twitch when,
You don't know that tail wriggles
And waggles now and again
When you see it down the road watch its tail.

Simone Fletcher (Age 10)

Claude Monet

C laude Monet came from France.
L onvingly painted for us to see.
A ll his life he created beautiful paintings.
U sually of places where he lived.
D edicating his life to the beautiful sights.
E ugéne Boudin made sure he did.

O ver the countries he did travel
S ketching and painting his art.
C reating his own worlds of memories.
A round the towns and villages.
R oven Cathedral, he painted and water-lilies

M any thousands collect copies of his work.
O nly a few have the real thing.
N ew or old it doesn't matter.
E veryone loves the art, that he painted.
T ill his eyesight started to shatter.

David Flahaut (Age 13)

Deep In Space

Deep in space,
The shining gold star rushed past me,
Beautiful red rocket window,
My beautiful rocket is red with some others.
I fly through space like a jumbo jet,
Flying through the bright blue sky.
Look there's the moon it might be cheese,
But it's definitely mouldy cheese.
There's the sun!
Oh dear, we're too close,
We're going to burn up!
We're going to be frazzled like a sausage,
Oh dear, we just did!

Neil Furness (Age 7)

In The Future

In the future people will race about in rocket-ships,
Inhabit other planets,
Ones not even thought about the astronomers of today.

In the future we'll do business with aliens who've got skin that's blue and green,
Making things that have never before been seen.

In the future we'll have holidays a million miles from earth,
Take a space cruise right around Mars and Jupiter,
In space-ships ten miles long.

In the future we could cook a roast and it would take two minutes,
On the television we could watch what we want when we wanted to,
While robots did our homework,.

In the future...

Alex Feuchtwanger (Age 9)

My Sense Poem

Listening to the birds squeak out their song,
Listening to the wind go past me.
Listening to the rustle of a page.

Touching the silky sun,
Touching a poult of a prickly gun.
Touching a bubble then pop!

Looking at the silky sun that was up high,
Looking at the colour of the leaves.

Smelling the lavenders on a branch,
Smelling the soap that is on me.
Smelling the fresh air of the world.

Tasting my mum's lovely dinner,
Tasting fresh apples, CRUNCH!
Tasting the galaxy chocolate.

James Finch (Age 7)

My Animals Poem

Rabbits are silent,
Wasps are violent
Cats are sweet
Lions eat meat
Hamsters always run around
And parrots hardly ever touch the ground
Ferrets are smelly
And spiders go in your welly!

Nikki Fell (Age 9)

Untitled

A rude oinker,
A mucky paddler,
A brown spotter,
A four legged walker,
A muddy roller,
A water drinker,
What am I.........

Daniel Frost (Age 7)

The Sun

Warm and cooking hot
Scolding and bright
Sun warm sun.

Sizzling and golden
Gold and boiling
Sun warm sun.

Catherine Flaxman (Age 7)

My Hamster Climbing

M ischievously she starts climbing
Y earning for the top

H er claws trying to keep hold
A scending up the soft material she slips
M anaging to cling on for a moment she repositions herself
S topping only to re-adjust her grip
T eetering threatening to fall
E very muscle tries to keep her on
R egaining balance she carries on

C linging to the long curtains oblivious of the height
L ike a climber progressing up a mountain
I nquisitive about what is at the top
M aking progress climbing onwards
B raving every part of the journey
I nvesting strength for the top
N ow she is at her destination
G uess how she gets down. (She falls.)

Jim Furness (Age 10)

The Dog Who Lives In A Bog

There once was a dog
In the middle of a bog
It was a scared pup
In case the bog munched it up
It tried to get away
But it's still there today.

Stephanie Flanders (Age 10)

If I Had Wings

If I had wings
I would touch
The corner of the world and scratch the atmosphere.

If I had wings
I would taste
The water coming down from the raindrops.

If I had wings
I would listen to
The tornado roar as it sucked me up.

If I had wings
I would gaze
At the sky ripping its clouds apart.

If I had wings
I would dream of
Eating the candy floss from the blue.

Joe Forsyth (Age 9)

Spring

Spring brings winter's end.
As daffodils begin to show.
Lambs about to be born.
Grass begins to grow.

Awoken by a birds song.
Leaves appearing on the trees.
Days becoming longer.
Pollen being collected by the bees.

Emma Foster (Age 8)

Snow Poem

Snow is soft
Snow is chunky
Snow is skiddy
Because I skid
On the Ice.

Jason Fenn (Age 6)

Snow

I love you beautiful snow,
And you make the sun sparkle,
But if you get in the sun,
I'm afraid it's time to go.

Chloe Gibbons (Age 7)

The Girls

There were some little girls
Their eyes shone like pearls
They went out one day and played on the swing
As they were on the swing they wore their diamond ring
They were butterflies all around the place
The girls laughed gracefully
Because the butterflies had a little race.
One died,
Because it lied,
And everyone cried.
That's the end of the little girls.

Katie Fry (Age 8)

Favourite Place - Under My Bed Covers!

No-one can come in because it's private.
No-one can come in because it's secret.
Under my bedcovers, I'm so dozy,
Under my bedcovers, I'm so cozy.
No room for seating,
But it has heating.
Little bears next to me,
Fallen asleep next to me...next to me... next to me.
Goodnight!
Sleep tight!

Sally Fletcher (Age 10)

The Colour Blue

The pale colour of a deep blue ocean shimmering in the sunlight,
Crystal raindrops, puddles, a glass of cold water.
The colour of a summer sky with a sunbeam exploring the expanding blue blanket.
A bluebell is dispersing its seeds.
A dolphin swimming on an expedition.

Michaela Francis (Age 11)

In the Park

Empty swings surround me,
I listen only to the drifting clouds.
Coldness of the slide fills me,
I wish she was here again.

Charlotte Ford (Age 10)

Farmer Chant

Sister animals, brother animals, mother animals, father animals,

Oh wool givers, Oh milk givers, Oh meat givers,
What have you in store for a poor farmer today?

From my barn I throw food for the animals to eat.

Sister animals, brother animals, mother animals, father animals,

Oh wool givers, Oh milk givers, Oh meat givers,
What have you in store for a poor farmer today?

Jenny Fletcher (Age 8)

Untitled

5 1/2 oz flying through the air,
As hard as a nut,
As red as a holly berry,
Made of cork,
Score 6 or 4 or many more:
It's a cricket ball.

Theo Flack (Age 8)

Autumn

Leaves are going brown
And some are falling to the ground
Squirrels gathering nuts for winter
The nights are getting longer
The days getting shorter

People wrapping up warmer
To shelter from the colder weather
And in autumn trees are going bare
Howls through the night
Owls hooting through the night
While I sleep so snug and tight.

Melody Greenwood (Age 7)

My Brother

My brother is cute,
Sometimes he pulls my hair,
His hair is cute too.

Lucy Green (Age 7)

My Fish

My fish was in a pot,
My dad was cleaning him out,
My fish jumped out of the pot,
And my dad gave a shout!

Lauren Grimston (Age 5)

Summer Flowers

I live near some flowers,
All they like is april showers.

Sometimes bugs see them,
Some buds upon my stem.

They also like some sun,
They all have lots of fun!

All together,
Just forever.

Growing for the clouds,
But they are very loud.

Chat, chat, chat they never stop,
They carry on going like a spinning top.

They sometimes grow in herds,
But I always see some birds.

Just forever,
All together,
In the sun.

Hayley Graham (Age 7)

Lion

Knock, knock who lives here?
A terrifying Lion.

His eyes are massive.
They glow in the night.
His jaws are strong.
They eat people.
His sharp teeth can cut.

Knock, knock who lives here?
A very sleepy head.

He can run and pounce on his food in the day.

Jack Gilgunn (Age 6)

The Storm

The ship was swaying up and down
Rolling through the storm
All the things were wrecked and torn
And all the clothes were washed and worn
I hope the wind will stop the storm.

Lisa Gooday (Age 12)

Snow

Slippery, sloppery snow
Squelching, muddy slippery snow
Lovely squelching snow
Soft cold snow
Ice as slippery as soap
Snow falling like an avalanche.

Game over!

Simon Foster (Age 10)

My School

V ery good things happen in my school.
E verybody must be kind,
R eady to help is the golden rule.
N o one is quite like me at my school.
O ur teachers like to help us,
N umbers and puzzles we like to do,

I n fact we always do a few.
N aughty children we have too many,
F antastic teachers too.
A nd amazing activities we all do
N obody gets left out
T HE SCHOOL IS COOL!!

Hannah Gradwell (Age 7)

The Mighty King

When I lay in my room
Staring at the stars
I divide the sky
Into many different parts

The North, the South
The great lion's mouth
The East, the West
The duckling's nest

The moon now comes
Gleaming brightly by the stars
The sun is next
But what about all the rest

The rest is kept a secret unknown
Though the only one thing that you will always know
The sky shining bright is a wonderful thing
And rules just like a Mighty King!

Grace Gardner (Age 12)

Untitled

An Old English Sheep Dog is sliding on the slidy snow.
Beside him lay a tree,
With glitter tumbling off of it onto the dusty squelching ground,
As he ran inside,
The floor was as white as white can be.

Ellen Frost (Age 10)

Spring

Spring has come from the south of the world,
Bringing with it all the colourful things,
Tulips, sunshine, lambs and chicks and bubbling brooks,
We have been waiting so long,
So give it a great big cheer,
For all the world to hear

Eleanor Gould (Age 7)

The Crow That Sat On The Evergreen Hedge

I look out of my bedroom window and see a crow
Sat on the evergreen hedge in the garden.
I watch the crow for ages with his dark cunning eyes and his dark black feathers
That shine in the moonlight and glow against the silver stars.
He just sits there and gazes into our kitchen window,
Watching our every move, waiting for his long, lost love.
Sometimes he flies over to our bird bath and looks at his reflection in the water.
And sometimes he will have a drink and you see his
Long slender beak ever so slightly touching the cool fresh water.
And when night comes near he just flies away,
And I can see his shadow against the moon.

Katie Greenwood (Age 12)

Abandoned Track

A lonely track lies in the mists
Of stormy clouds clenched like fists
Remains of ancient railway tracks
Flaking paints, rusty cracks

Puddles are scattered along the lane
Water gurgling in the drain
Woven willows blow in the breeze
Churning streams carrying leaves

The track, it's become just gloomy bogs
Heavy sleepers, rotten logs
Nettles wrap the sodden banks
Like unevenly lain wooden planks

Rain is pouring from the sky
Horrendous rain clouds travel by
From the sunset to the dawn
It lies there abandoned till the morn.

Miriam Gooch (Age 10)

War

They are sad,
Her son has gone to war.
His father has gone to fight.
Will he come back?

Cassie Gray (Age 14)

What Is Blue?

Blue is a dolphin jumping in the sea.
Blue is a plant called a Bluebell can you see.
Blue is a colour nice and bright.
Blue is the sky very high.
Blue is a school sweatshirt.
Blue is an iceberg all blue and cold.
Blue is a firework sparkling.

Naomi Gent (Age 7)

The Companion

I'll always remember my good old friend,
He was my pride and joy,
He was taken almost everywhere,
Without doubt, my favourite toy.

When I needed a cuddle, or just some advice,
To my dear friend I would go,
For Mum and Dad were very busy,
And he would never say no.

When it came to the luxurious holidays,
He too had a seat on the plane,
All the journey we were chatting,
Whilst people looked round as though we were insane!

But by the end of my childhood,
He was nothing but threadbare,
Although he provided many memories,
And gave much tender, loving care.

So I'll always remember that good, old friend,
Wherever I was, he was there,
Following my every footsteps,
That was my bear!

Kelly Gosford (Age 11)

The Battle

The day after King Harold was dead,
An eyeball fell out from his head.
And while that happened the army fled.

Niall Gray (Age 6)

The Hamster's Escape

When I escape from my huge cage,
All the grown-ups are filled with rage.

I chew the wires from the phones,
And pretend I am Indiana Jones.

I swing around on a giant cable,
I skid around on the kitchen table.

I eat tasty apple and drink fresh water,
I bite the fingers of my owner's daughter.

They pick me up in the air,
I really think it's not fair!

They shove me back inside my cage,
Now I'm the one who's filled with rage!

James Green (Age 9)

Pain

There are so many things that could hurt you inside,
internal wounds that never bled,
that hurt so much you broke down and cried,
and a thousand tears you'd shed.

Flames that touched you but never burnt,
the pain when you'd committed a crime,
when you'd spilt the blood of the innocent,
and their clock of life forgot the time.

When you got scared, your heart missed a beat,
when someone says a nasty word.
The feeling of a secret that you know you can't keep,
but you shouldn't know it, you overheard.

The pain when a memory is slipping away,
when a special bond is broken.
The pain when a deceased loved one, you pray,
and you'd forgotten the special words they'd spoken.

The pain of a selfish whisper in your ear,
when no-one ever answers your prayers,
remember, everyone cries with fear,
it's a pain that everyone shares.

Natasha Goldup (Age 12)

Summer

Summer is the best season,
Usually it is so hot,
Mornings are longer in summer,
Melting Ice Creams.
Eating Ice Creams is really fun,
Really hot in summer.

Charlotte Gregory (Age 7)

Before I Go To School

As I wake up from my sleep
I know it's time to get up
By the sound of my alarm clock going beep, beep, beep
I get up and do my hair
And get my uniform off my chair
My breakfast is orange with toast and marmalade
It is scrumptious and lovely
Then I get dressed and do my teeth
And put my socks upon my feet
I call my brother and we get in the car
Mum drives us to school
I play with friends until the bell rings
Then go into class and do lots of things.

Stephanie Gawler (Age 9)

The Passion Of Purple

Purple is an orchid
Blossoming in the spring
And pansies, and hyacinths
Pretty as an amethyst ring

Purple is the Queen's robe
Made from gracious silk
And represents a cat's curiosity
As it slowly sips its milk

It reminds you of a Himalayan mist
Perhaps a poison drink
For someone you hate
That should make you think

Purple is a lovely lotus
A dark summer night
Some delightful blueberries
Or maybe a violet white

Purple is a beautiful mauve
A stormy indigo
A coat made from Russian velvet
A theme for an exquisite show.

Satpreet Grewal (Age 13)

My Favourite Thing

My favourite place to sit must be,
My bed, not the tidiest place, I agree.
But it is calm, as calm as can be.
In my bed quiet, just for me.

Sarah Gulliver (Age 9)

Sunburn

On a winter's morning,
It starts to snow
It falls thick and fast,
No plants still grow.
To be outside in day,
I dream of it so.
I need to leave,
I want to go.
I hate the indoors,
It leaves me low.
The snow melts,
Water starts to flow.
Oh, to go to a fair,
To watch a show.
You're all too ignorant
To really know.
It is the sun,
That hurts me so.

William Gurton (Age 14)

The Lion

He is king of the jungle
When he walks and growls you hear a rumble
No man would ever go near him or run past
Because the lion runs too fast

He fights for his domain
And has a fantastic feature called his mane
He has razor sharp sight
And you don't want to get on the wrong side of his bite

He has sharp claws
And huge great big paws
The lion is very proud
And when he roars he is very loud.

He has golden fur
And unlike a cat he does not purr
You don't want to get on the wrong side of him
Or you could be chopped up and in a bin

Nicholas Gardner (Age 12)

The Woodland Of Tranquility

The woodland, now like a garment, wears
The beauty of the sunset, golden and fair.
Trees and branches, are like tall, strong, bodies
Standing still in the night.
The once twittering birds now rest their heads,
Other animals are now in an enchanted sleep.
As the night clouds come overhead,
Darkness re-appears again.

Grace Gibbons (Age 9)

Patience

Some people probably think my Grandma is either deaf or daft,
And in a way, I quite understand . . . .
She repeats herself over and over again,
"Would I like another biscuit" for the twentieth time,
"How was school today", when it's the summer holidays!
She is 80 years old.
A lovely lady - full of love and kindness.
With a wicked sense of mischief!
Apparently, she has alzheimer's disease,
A memory problem.
She can tell me in vivid details
All about the war and her days in the A.T.S.
But as for what she has had for dinner,
Or where she has been that day,
She hasn't got a clue!!
Sometimes, I get annoyed . . . .
But I remind myself, it's not her fault.
For I feel sure, that one thing she will never forget,
Is how much she loves me.
After all, she tells me many times - every day!!

Laura Gray (Age 12)

The World Is An Eggtimer!

The world is an eggtimer green turns to black
As the pollution makes its echo attack

We drive our cars and pollute the air
To the trees I don't think this is very fair

I dream of a world with blossomed buds and trees standing tall
A place with no pollution at all

I fear this dream will never come true
As people don't care and have nothing better to do

The eggtimer nearly over the world nearly black
Pollution hasn't won the battle only the attack.

Hannah Grimes (Age 10)

The Heart Rage

It had my year, my month, my life,
My hours, my minutes, my controller.
It was my dream-Now it's in fire
But it rolled away.
She had the key to my heart,
The lamp of fire stopped raging like a dart.
Make the soil keep the spirit strong.
All the things that happened stay strong in my heart.
It had my light, my power.

Adam Gladden (Age 9)

Mother's Day

Soon it will be Mother's Day,
The day we celebrate our mums,
The day I say "I love you mum",
The day they have breakfast in bed.

Soon it will be Mother's Day
The day we celebrate our mums,
The day I say "Thanks for everything mum",
The day of love and care.

Soon it will be Mother's Day,
The day we celebrate out mums,
The day I say "You're great mum",
The day of kisses and cuddles.

Soon it will be Mother's Day,
The day we celebrate our mums,
The day I say "You're the best mum ever",
The day that dad does all the chores.

But all of this shouldn't just be done on Mother's Day,
It should be done every other day of the year too,
The cooking, the cleaning, the having fun,
I'm glad my mum is my mum.

Chelsey-Marie Gellett (Age 11)

Mice

I think mice are rather nice
Their tails are long,
Their faces small,
They haven't any chins at all.
Their ears are pink,
Their teeth are white,
They run about the house at night.
They nibble things
They shouldn't touch
And no-one seems to like them much
But I think mice are nice.

Sophie Griffiths (Age 8)

Animal

Man's best friend
Runs like the wind
Up and down the hill
With one word
She could go
Left or right
She was a fine border collie bitch
Before she died
It was a sad day when she died
I got another dog but it wasn't the same
So now I go without.

Paul Groves (Age 11)

The Wolf

As the shadow of the Gods,
Glides over deserted grounds,
The tiny rodents shuffle,
To the weird and eerie sounds.

The sounds enough to make you tumble
This howling, weeping call
For the wolf, the king of the coldes plains,
Scares all in his terrifying rule.

As proud as a rewarded soldier,
And as fierce as a lightning bolt,
The pack is a military squad
Led by the Chief Adult

His fur is smoky and almost worn,
His nose is black and damp
His ears are a devils pointing horns
And fangs, those of a vamp!

As the shadow of the Gods,
Glides over deserted grounds.
The pack of wolves made rodents shuffle,
With weird and eerie sounds.

John Goddard (Age 12)

Snow Leopard

It captured its sleek fur from ink blots
Splashed on white silk
It kidnapped the showered cacophony for its roar

It stole oiled springs for its legs
As it darted through the dewy grass
Its sinewy body was taken from a snake
Which was hiding in moistured mud

It hi-jacked the gracefulness of a dancer
As it padded on the pebbled ground
It seized the chameleons form of camouflage
As it eclipsed itself in the condensated grass

Its fangs were grabbed by icicles
Which were as deadly as gulping down poison
It stole falcons swift movement
For its bolt lightning

It snatched piercing bullets
For its moonless midnight eyes
It took shiny sharp toenails
For its claws

So that was it, the Snow Leopard, was ready.

Sam Grant (Age 10)

My Toast

I like buttery toast, crunchy toast,
Buttery I like it best hot and toasty
Yummy, delicious lovely it is
It is crunchy I can eat it, munch
I like it, it is nice
It is so nice it's so nice it's delicious
Nice, nice, nice it is crunchy
It's good food toast, nice.

Tayyab Ghazanfar (Age 8)

Bats

Bats have shiny leather wings
Bats do many clever things
Bats doze upside down by day
Bats come out at night to play
Bats cavort in soaring cliques
Sounding ultrasonic waves
Acrobatic in the sky
Bats catch every bug they spy

Spike Godding (Age 11)

My Teacher Is A Wicked Witch

My teacher is a wicked with
She always tells us off
All the time she shouts
That's just about what she does

She walks into class with a big cheesy smile
Her smile stays there for a while
She has blonde brown hair
And she wears red lipstick

She talks and talks
And never gives up
And no-one ever listens
At the end we all get bored
And then no-one listens

She sits at her desk
And never says a word
All the children are quiet as mice
And never speak a word
That's why we love it in her class
Because she is a wicked witch

Laura Gaskell (Age 12)

Dreaming

Dreaming is like
Taking a bright sparkle
From a shining star
Dreaming is like swimming
In sharp, coarse rocks
Dreaming is like gliding
Calmly on breezy air.

Dreaming is like
Taking chunks of cheese
From the mysterious moon
Dreaming is like
Walking on flowing water.

Corrina Gillies (Age 12)

Eminem

I listen to eminem all day and all night
When my little brother turns it off
I get into a fight
So I hide all my tapes and all my CD's
And when my brother finds them
It really annoys me
So I lock them up and hide them away
But he doesn't know where they are
And he starts to cry

Stephen Gibbs-Barlow (Age 12)

Love Lost

A whirlpool of regrets, flood into her head,
Of all the things she should have said,
When her chance came, she let it go
There are so many things that he should know
And all the time that he was there,
She didn't tell, she didn't dare,
Cross the line, to the other side,
To say how she felt, deep inside.

And now all the time they've been apart,
Still time doesn't hide her broken heart.
Months will pass, as will years,
But that won't cure her countless tears,
That she shed for him over the love she lost,
Because of that line, she did not cross.
And even though he didn't know,
The love she had, but then let go.

It still feels like a stab in the heart
Because now, they are still far apart.
There were so many things she could have said,
But now, as before, they still lie in her head.

Laura Graham-Clare (Age 15)

Santa Claus

While the children are out to play
Santa Claus is on his sleigh

While the children are asleep
Santa Claus has come to creep

While the children are awake
Santa Claus not a sound he makes

Elinor Gaskin (Age 9)

England's Hopes

E very tournament comes and goes,
N ever before have we waited so long.
G lory has been missing since 1966!
L ots have tried and lots have failed,
A t last the right man, has come to be hailed
N ow, again, expectations are high
D estiny sir, is in your hands.
S ven Goran Eriksson is his name.

H e has promised the goods, but can he deliver?
O nly time will tell!
P eople hope and people pray, that,
E ngland will again, some day,
S tand at the top, where they belong!

Michael Godden (Age 15)

Shooting Star

On a winter's night,
I looked into the sky,
And shining down on me
Was a big bright shooting star,
It was burning bright in the middle of the night,
I wished and wished for it to die
And tumble down beneath the sky,
I might see you burning bright,
Hopefully some other night,
I'll see you shooting very fast,
Past the moon and home at last,
Please come back and fall to me,
So I can see you glistening free,
Like a shooting star across the midnight sky
I'm gonna fly high,
Just to be with you tonight

When I wake up in the night
Will you be my guided light,
So . . . please tell me where you are
And everything will be alright
Like a shooting star across the midnight sky!

Katie Griffin (Age 15)

Imagine

Imagine a field without scarlet roses,
Imagine a sky without snowy clouds,
Imagine a pond without sapphire water,
Imagine a book without any print,

Imagine

Imagine a pen without runny ink,
Imagine a tree without crusty leaves,
Imagine a plate without any food,
Imagine a mouth without gleaming teeth,

Imagine

Lucy Goodwin (Age 9)

Money - A Phenomenon

I've seen people come and go
But it's stayed and battled on its own.
I've seen people cry and weep
It's always stayed on its feet.
There's talk about it changing names
It's making people shout and wane.

But if you keep it
And hold it tight
Never let it out of your sight
It'll serve you well
For years to come
Money - what a phenomenon

Paul Gregory (Age 15)

The Tears From My Heart

I met a boy with big blue yes and thick brown hair
He was beauty I was beast,
Was it love at first well for me!

My heart is crying, the tears are falling
Night after night it weeps for his love
I saw him again with my best friend
I sat beside her, he smiled
Was it love? more like unrequited

My heart is crying, the tears are falling
Night after night it weeps for his love

My friend said it was just friendship
Would it be like romeo and Juliet
More like Samson and Delilah

My heart is crying, the tears are falling
Night after night it weeps for his love

Amelia Griggs (Age 13)

Food

Coming home feeling hungry
Maybe a fry-up or a hamburger,
Possibly moussaka would be great
Perhaps a salad
Washed down with a glass of pineapple juice
For pudding a banana split
With cream running through the gaps
Loads of ice-cream melting, melting
Into a sticky mess.
YUMM!!
For breakfast maybe scrambled egg,
Or just a boiled egg, with soldiers,
Perhaps a bacon buttie
Anyway back to school

David Goodyear (Age 11)

Love

The candles were lit
He was coming at seven
The gorgeous man who I love
Was coming straight to my door!
Through the gate and past my tree
I knew he only had eyes for me.
As I talked to him on the phone
As he whispered sweet nothings in my ear
I knew he felt no fear.
The doorbell rang and I checked my face
My heart started to race
As I slowly turned the handle . . .

Katie Gerrish (Age 15)

The Mouse Butcher

I'm sitting on the wall watching the birds
Something moves down below
It's a mouse in the herbs
I jump down and pounce
That's the end of the mouse
That's why they call me
"The Mouse Butcher"

I lie in wait for another mouse to appear
But not one comes in sight
I wait a little longer but now it's not so light
So I go off to hunt somewhere else
I catch a rat and devour it myself
That's why they call me
"The Mouse Butcher"

I go inside to have a nap I curl up on the floor
I dream of mice and all things nice
Then I wake up and go to the door
I'm the best hunter in town and most places around
That's why they call me
"The Mouse Butcher"

Laura Guerin (Age 13)

Mars

What would it be like on Mars?
Looking round at loads of stars,
Not the singing type,
Or Gladiators lean and mean,
Nor Paddington or Mr. Bean.
The shiny sort,
Up in space,
Lights that twinkle in your face.

Yes what would it be like on mars,
Looking round at loads of stars?
Playing Footie in that red dust,
Scoring a goal, but only just.
The footprints and skid marks will really last,
To be made a feature of the past.

Ailsa Godden (Age 11)

Spider

Sitting in the corner listening to you scream,
I'm only a long-legged spider.
You hit me and squish me but I don't know why,
So I run away hoping not to die.
Why are you scared of me?
All I want is a nice warm home
With a nice warm fire.

Tom Guilfoy (Age 11)

Flippy The Fish

I have a friend,
No ordinary friend
A fish,
A special fish,
His name is Flippy,
Very cute!

Every day I or my family feed him
With his two brothers
Tashy and Ginger,
He has an old helmet
And a small bridge,
That they play around in

In every way he is
Special to me,
He is my long living fish.
There are many ways in which
I could describe him,
He is healthy, round and fat
With ginger and white patches,
He is Flippy the fish.

Elliott Grant (Age 11)

For Miss Monks

Teacher, teacher you're the best,
Better than all the rest.
You put me back in my place.
When I'm in an awful state.
Spellings and the rest,
Are not my best.
Teacher, teacher you're the best,
Better than all the rest.

Jasmin Grimshaw (Age 9)

A Sad Winter

Icy icicles light up the lane
I'm so cold it's not a game!

Is it frost or is it ice?
I'm not sure but it isn't nice!

My feet are frozen
Was I chosen?

As I weep on a road that's steep
I take a look as the tears roll down my cheek
"I am not the chosen one
It's not funny it isn't fun."

I simply hate it when I'm this sad
People tell me it can't be bad
If another person says that to me
I will fall down as I weep.

Paul Guille (Age 11)

Midnight Black

The sleek, black body
Moving silently in the night.
The howling wind comes around,
And the body goes stiff and tight.

Down comes the rain,
Glimmering then splattering,
Drop, drop, drop on the window pane
Slap, slap, slap on his silky mane.

The hair gets wet and heavy,
He felt the cold air bite.
He shivers and quivers,
But keeps moving on into the night.

The sky darkens still.
What's that bright light?
What lies on the road side?
The black cat's body as dead as the night . . . .

Antony Glass (Age 13)

What Am I?

The thing erupting like bombs crashing
The red hot steam comes pouring out
People running keep on bashing
Hear lots of big loud booms
Everybody running out of their burning rooms
All the mountain any minute is going to explode.

Jonathan Guthrie (Age 8)

Home From School

Home from school, no homework to do,
The only peace and quiet is locked in the loo!

Brother whining about his scraped knees,
Telling mum he can't eat all his peas!

I sit there and snigger as hell is let loose,
Get smacked round the head for being no use!

Mum shouts and screams, the chicken is burnt,
Dad sits and stares as if he is hurt!

Bedtime is nigh, the household is dead,
I think we should all climb into bed!

In this household I cannot cope.
I have no hope!

Sarah Green (Age 12)

What Do You Like To Eat?

What do you like to eat?
Baked potatoes, boiled feet.

What do you like to eat?
Flies and banana flavoured meat.

What do you like to eat?
Some apple spaghetti, with stinky Pete.

What do you like to eat?
Boiled worms and Shreaded Wheat.

What do you like to eat?
Creepy spiders, yummy sweets.

What do you like to eat?
Burnt cranberries, frogs under heat.

What do you like to eat?
Squashed pizza, yucky meat.

Emma Game (Age 10)

Summer

In summer it's lovely and warm
Then I can go and listen to the birds,
Summer is WONDERFUL!!!
Because it's HOT!!!

Georgia Goode (Age 8)

Late For School

Your mum wakes you up,
Then you find you're late,
Have to drink out of a baby's cup,
But it's a long time to wait.

Your mum wakes you up,
For your food,
You hate getting up,
In a bad mood.

Your brother wakes you up,
To brush your teeth,
Then eat your breakfast up,
I hope it's not beef.

The school bus beeps,
For me to come,
While I'm asleep,
Then I have to come.

Daniel Green (Age 9)

Christmas Poem

Tinsel twirling round a tree,
Tinsel curling around me.

Reindeer pulling the sleigh,
While children go out to play.

Santa starts to shout with glee,
I wonder what we're having for tea?

Bows on the presents,
For tea we're having pheasant.

Lots and lots to see,
While I sit on Santa's knee.

Santa's shouting Ho!, Ho!, Ho,
Mums saying No!, No!, No!

Connie Griffin (Age 9)

The Jungle

I am walking through the Jungle,
I meet a big furry animal a bit like a human,
Who likes to eat yellow moons.
Now I can see lots of zig zag roars,
I'm walking through the mist,
What's that . . . It's a huge fluffy teddy,
I'm moving through the trees,
I can see a hissing rope.
I'm coming out of the Jungle now,
I can see a huge yellow ball in the sky.

Emma Gedge (Age 10)

Tyneham - The Ghost Village

As I sit and look to sea
From a village where life used to be
I close my eyes and see the ghosts
Of people walking by.

I wonder how it was for them
As life was so much harder then
The daily toil from dawn till dusk
Where time now stands still.

The church stands tall the graves are quiet
The houses are in ruins
The history of much better times
Are only in their memories

War time came, the land was taken
No more fishing in the coves
How sad to know that village life
Will never return to Tyneham

Victoria Gladden (Age 10)

Forest Adventure - Frightful or Delightful?

As we walked through the dense forest,
The trees waved their arms vigorously, scratching us in the face.
Oozing mud clawed at our wellingtons,
Hauling us into the slime.

The cold charged at us, stealing our warmth.
Something it could never understand.
As we approached the water
The wind gave its last moan and died.

The vast currents dragged us along,
Burbling and grumbling as they did so.
Suddenly, a bright light shone upon us.
It was the sun! He made us feel content.

For hours we endured the river.
Then damp crept upon us, invading the corners of our wellingtons,
We saw a mysterious tunnel. Should we enter it?
Fear confused our minds.

After the 'Forest Adventure' we rushed into the 'drying room'
And met with heat, who rubbed its hands and stamped its feet.
Our next activity is - the 'Team Exercise'.
I wonder if there will be anymore surprises?

Bethany Godfrey (Age 11)

Cat

The luminous green eyes make you shiver,
Fur so black it can barely be seen
Fangs as white as pearls and bigger than a Wolfs
Sneakier and cheekier than a monkey.
Balance is better than a squirrel's,
In one bite there's as much venom as two bites of a snake.

Jamie Gillett (Age 11)

A Visit To B & Q

"Can I have a green tape measure please?"
"Have two, maybe even blue"
"No just one please"
"How about pink that'll make you wink"
"No just green please"
"What about five to measure a bee hive"
"No just one please"
"Maybe you want black to hide in the shadows"
"No just GREEN PLEASE!"
"How about six to go with the mix"
"No, just ONE PLEASE!"
"What about seven to send up to heaven"
"NO, DO I MAKE MYSELF CLEAR
JUST ONE GREEN TAPE MEASURE!!"
"Oh sorry dear you could have made yourself a bit more clear."

Douglas Gill (Age 9)

At School

School is fun,
You get to jump and run,
The people are nice,
Because they don't like mice.

I like school,
Because you can play in the hall,
And run,
And have fun.

School is cool,
Because it's got a swimming pool,
You get to play outside,
And get to run and hide.

I like school,
Because the people here are cool,
I like to eat my lunch
And give it a crunch.

Chloe Gaskin (Age 9)

Mr. Magpie

There is a magpie up in the tree
Guarding his nest of silver and gold
You should see its fur it's black as coal
It takes silver broaches and shiny gold rings
It also has lots of other lovely things
When the magpie tries to sing
It's quite the opposite to a ring
When the magpie goes squawk! squawk! squawk!
It's only him trying to talk!

Moss Goodwin (Age 9)

Silently

Silently, Silently
Over the trees, the moon passes by
On an invisible breeze.

Gracefully, gracefully
You walk to me,
I can see in your eyes great idolatry.

Calmly, calmly
Drifting above, the moon shines on me
Like a fluttering dove.

Quietly, quietly,
People asleep after long, nightly wonderings,
Finally we'll meet.

Peacefully, peacefully,
Now you are free, even though you're miles away,
You're still with me.

Sangeeta Grantham (Age 8)

Memories
(In Memory of my Dad)

I hoped for you

For you are wonderful,
You are good and friendly,
For you are colourful,
At everything.

You help me,
To understand you.
I wish to be,
With you.

When I die,
Hug me,
And then I'll cry.
For you will be with me.

Charlotte Godfrey (Age 12)

Nothing's Like It Seems

I'm good but I'm bad
I'm happy but I'm sad
I'm here, but I'm gone
I'm right but I'm wrong

I'm fast but I'm slow
I said yes, I said no
I'm confident, but shy
I said hi, I said bye

This story has no moral
This story has no end
This story only moans
Nothing's like it seems

Jeanie Gumble (Age 14)

Cats

Cats are very marvellous things
They also jump at
The slightest RING!

Cats are rats
Living in a carefree world
Eating bats
Makes them purr!

Cats tails
Are long, knobbly things
They wave and wave them
around
Then give a PING!

Their feet prance around
Beware if they're naughty
They'll be thrown in the pound!

Laura Griffin (Age 11)

The Winter Queen

Winter awakes gracefully and peacefully in her glistening bed.
Rubbing her gleaming eyes she slips her feet into her transparent icicle slippers.
Brushing her diamond covered hair she shakes snowflakes to the cotton-wool-like ground.
Gliding on the ice, she then opens the door to the outside world waiting for her to come.
Leaping, she takes off from the ground as pearls descend from her.
She lands and breaks the icicles off a frozen tree to make a wind chime.
With this she puts the animals to sleep.
Tired and hungry her job is done.
She sweeps to her castle, glides up the banister into her silver couch and goes to her slumber.

Rebecca Greenhalgh (Age 10)

Fake Dreams

It couldn't be true, really it couldn't
My worst enemy, he's king of the school
It's all my fault, I let him win
You see, on Thursday it was all up to me
To show him I'm better than him,
That Raymond Briggs he's such a bully

We'll get back Thursday, the big punch up,
Me and him on the BIG playground
I thought I would win, I really did
But he squirted me like a fly
I was knocked out, they were all saying
        END OF DREAM
"Wake up, wake up, it's time for school
Oh, hi you were in my dream it was fake.

Douglas Gibson (Age 10)

The Games I Play

I play rugby
Tackles and all
I play rugby
With people tall

I play football
With people fit
I play football
Learning bit by bit

I play cricket
Oh what a run
I play cricket
Oh what fun

I play tennis
In the warm sun
I play tennis
That's my games all done!

Joshua Golding (Age 9)

Football

Look at that,
What a save,
Look he let in that,
Save this,
Save that,
He must be good at that.

He looks at him with his false eye,
Look at that shot,
But how about that,
They come home,
With their trombones,
What an exciting match.

Tom Goodwin (Age 7)

Doggie Poem

Dirty dog
Very muddy
So soft
Really cuddly
Soft tail
Slimey nose
Long tongue
Smells a rose
Likes washing
Hates food
Quite strong
Really rude
Brown eyes
Likes digging
Black, white
Enjoys picking

Lauren Gregory (Age 9)

Winter

Frosty shimmering spider webs
Glisten under the just risen sun.

Trees covered in chalk white snow
Makes them look like icy giants.

Spotless snow lay
In the untouched fields

A tiny robin perches itself
Grandly on a fence post.

Freezing, round snowballs
Fly through the winter sky

The world disappears
As a blanket of snow silently falls.

Snow sleeps on everything.

Jessica Gilbert (Age 10)

Late

Got up this morning
Bed shook "Go back to sleep."
"Can't" I said "Late."

Went to the bathroom
Shower spurted "Wash and relax"
"Can't" I replied "Late."

Went down to breakfast
Cereal crunched "Have a snack"
"Can't" I whispered "Late."

Off to school
Car squirmed "Give me petrol"
"Can't " I shouted "Really late."

Matt Green (Age 11)

Untitled

A
Trickle of
A raindrop
Is a joyful spirit.

A splash of a puddle
Reminds me of my friends tears.
A drop of a tear
Is very salty but I don't mind.

These three are a secret to me.
So nobody tell them to anyone
PLEASE.

Emily Garrigues (Age 8)

Why?

Sitting in the window looking at the red sky,
I see a bird go past the sun and I wished I could fly.

The autumn leaves and golden leaves,
Are so plane which make me freeze.

The clouds are souring away free,
Wished it could have seen me.

The cool air is everywhere,
Near, far, there everywhere.

The sun is high,
The chimney smokes are wooshing across the sky,
Sitting in the window thinking why,
Why is it I can't fly right to the sky?

Zubaida Gul (Age 10)

Balloons

Balloons in flight
Rising up high
Often on a summer night
They fly high
Higher than a kite.

The colours are just right
I look ahead
And something beautiful is in my sight
Some day I'd like to be there
Some day I might.

To my delight
I see with my eyes
The burner burns bright
Flames are alive as they rise
In the sun set light.

Sophie Gornall (Age 10)

The Night

Slowly and steadily the night swallows day,
Through the neighbourhood he creeps,
Like a mouse he doesn't make a sound,
He moves towards children's houses,
To check they are asleep.

His face jet black, from the shadows,
His eyes burn bright, just like a flame,
The clothes he wears are torn and worn,
His mouth small and has black lips.

the darkness falls upon us all,
No matter where you are, he'll catch you,
Once again he fades away,
But he'll return the next day.

Neil Garside (Age 11)

Angel

Here I stand before you,
Brown, colour of the mountains,
Wrapped so deliciously,
Within my own joy and misery,
Feathers of my wings,
Paralysed by the distance of my mind,
Frozen by the potential of me.

Jack Gould (Age 10)

Snow

Its flakes tumble down like water dripping
It's as soft as a cat
Children having fun and playing in it
It's as white as paper
Snow scrapers clear the snow

Thomas Gradidge (Age 8)

The Boy I Love!

The boy I love
His short brown hair
His big brown eyes
His soft red lips
So kissable
So kissable!

The boy I love
His shiny black shoes
His dark blue jeans
His long black coat
So touchable
So touchable!

The boy I love
His funny jokes
His scary stories
His melodic singing
So loveable
So loveable!

Holli Gatley (Age 12)

The Clock

On a clock the hands go round,
With just a little sound.

Tick-tock Tick-tock
Is the noise of a clock,
When the hands on a clock go round.

Lisa Glanville (Age 11)

A Recipe For Mud Pie

My recipe for mud pie,
Will definitely catch your eye,
First of all you get a bowl,
It really doesn't have to be whole,
Then comes the mud, slop,
Drop a mouldy spud in, plop,
Put some wiggly worms in, clop,
Make sure it's all nice and firm,
This will make the worms squirm,
Drop some crusted beetles in,
Make sure they aren't too little,
Stir it up nice and fine,
Add a drop of home-made wine,
Now you are ready to dine,
Wait a moment not so quick,
You really don't want to be sick,
Now your recipe is finished!

Chloe Goss (Age 10)

Colours

Yellow is a gleaming sandy beach,
Or a field of yellow sunflowers.
Or the bright, bright gleaming sun.
Or a yellow fluffy chick just hatched.
Red is a fire burning down a long, long corridor.
Or a warm jumper keeping me cosy.
Or a really scary devil I run away from
Orange is an orange sitting in the fridge.
Or orange juice waiting to be drunk.
Or a fish swimming in a pool
Or a thick jumper which keeps me warm in the winter.

Nathan Guy (Age 9)

The Elephants

Standing there in the grass so innocent and natural
Why do we destroy that scene, WHY?
We place you on our shelves and wear you on our necks
As the other elephants run you get left behind and drop to the floor.
As you hit the ground a cloud of dust appears, it's like a dream.
You know you want to awaken but you can't
Then there is no more!
Men cheer as if it's an achievement
Taking away all the beauty in your face
Leaving you there dead but without your beauty
You are no more and soon there will be no more of your kind.

Amy Gibbs (Age 13)

It's A . . . .

Sardine eater
Mouse beater
Wet nose
Licking toes
Sits on knees
Carrying fleas
Sleeps on the mat
It's a . . . . . ?

Victoria Greenaway (Age 9)

My Pet Cat

My pet cat, his name is Pat
He sits there all day on the mat
He brought a mouse into the house
I screamed in fright, I thought it might bite
I switched on the light to see a horrible sight.

Carly Gunn (Age 13)

Monkeys

I think that . . .
Monkeys are funky
Some monkeys are hunky
Big monkeys are grumpy
Fat monkeys are lumpy

So . . .

Monkeys are tall
Some monkeys are small
Big monkeys are fat
And some monkeys are hairy as mats!

James Grange (Age 12)

Down At The Seaside

Hip hip hooray
We're going to the seaside today
With our bucket and spade sitting in the sun
Well still we're having great fun
We go into the arcades to play on the games
We always look at the lights but they look like the same
Candyfloss and ice cream we like it alot
We keep on eating it but we can't stop
At the end of the day we feel like we want to stay
We've had so much fun today
Playing in the sand and splashing in the sea
We've had such a great day today, just you and me!

Kirsty Gifford (Age 13)

The Magic Garden

In the magic garden the perfect place is the magic pixie soaring through the air.
Bringing happiness to all the girls and boys
She lives in the willow in the garden where every day is a happy day.
Listen to the wind as it sings its song, whips through the trees it swirls and swishes around.
Listen to the waterfall as he sings his song gleaming in the sun trickling and gleaming to the ground.
Listen to the trees swaying around in the breeze swishing swaying.
Listen to the magic garden as it sings its song.

Jason Giddins (Age 11)

School

Starting school is a wonderful day
Teachers smiling as parents drive away
Brand new books and school bags too
All tables and chairs clean and shiny looking brand new
But not in this school
This one is quite different
Ghosts and zombies and a vampire in the distance
The stairs are made of dead students' bones
I'm really scared now
Someone take me home
I want to run and scream and shout
Someone, anyone please let me out.
What is happening
Where am I going?
Out of the gate
Onto the road.
Where am I?
I'm awake.

Erika Gulbrandson (Age 11)

My Week

On Monday I feel joy
On Tuesday I am sad
On Wednesday I go mad
On Thursday I have hope
On Friday I'm in luv
On Saturday I will forgive
On Sunday at last I'm Happy.

Hannah Gilbert (Age 12)

Death!!

Death is a funny thing!
People die for no good reason
Is it because they are past there sell by date!
Death is a funny thing!
Why do the people you love the most have to die?
Is it because mother earth is sly.
Death is a very funny thing!!!

Liam Greenwood (Age 13)

Rainforest

Angry tigers roaring are thunder clashes
A monkey's cry is a person screaming
Beautiful birds singing are rainbows speaking
Hissing snakes wriggling on the ground like overgrown worms
Rebel rain hitting the ground hard
Howling wind blowing the trees out of the way
The overlord of the jungle fighting off prowlers
Spheroid stout spiders sneakily creeping around
Perfect panthers thinking they are paramount.

Kayleigh Green (Age 11)

My Island

Let me tell you about my island,
It has lush, green tropical plants
With sweet juice berries covering them
The sky is a light pink with a hint of blue
The stream which runs through the middle of my island
Is full of refreshing water which glitters in the sunlight.
Next to the stream is grass which glistens with dew.
In the day the sun comes out and shines brightly,
At night the bone, white moon comes out instead of the sun
So you can see my island is wonderful
Please come and visit anytime,
All you need to bring with you is your imagination.

Natasha Gibbins (Age 13)

The Swallow

The swallow swept gracefully across the cloudy skies
Weaving in amongst the trees·away from prying eyes
Swooping and swerving with lots of dips
In amongst the rosehips
Its streamlined shape amongst the trees
As quiet as a whispering breeze
The swallow is flying south now, down the River Nile
Where it will be staying for a little while.

Lorraine Gunn (Age 12)

Love

Love is a pepsi, cool and refreshing
Love is a twix, crunchy, chewy, creamy
Love is a hedgehog, sharp on one side but soft on the other
Love is a whirlwind, short tempered but with a calm centre
Love is a zig-zag, it goes up and down

Jamie Gibson (Age 12)

Imagine

He is BIG and SHINY
He always knows what to do,
Purple and gold the strands of his hair,
BIG and tough as strong as a bear,
Blue, black and white the colour of his many spots,
He has teeth of gold, pink, purple and blue!
His tail is white, green and purple,
He is from the kingdom of Beemyland,
But he prefers here,
He loves apples and bananas,
Actually any kind of fruit,
He is named managookaloop
My imaginary friend

Daniel Good (Age 12)

The One

The wings are miles of flame filled pastures
My eyes sparkle like jewels under the stars
My tongue is a fiery cobbled street leading to nowhere
My claws are as strong and sharp as diamonds
My breath smells of erupting volcanoes
My voice is the roar of a thousand lions
My tail slashes and tears like an axe through wood
I've seen man progress through the ages of time
I've heard the secrets of mankind
In play I am a friend as well as a foe
In anger I turn to a rage of destruction
They call me, the one, the bearer of fear.

Tom Gowler (Age 13)

Teenagers

I feel like the needle in the hay stack,
I feel lost,
What price do we have to pay to find happiness?
How much will it cost?
Adults today think 'kids have it easy',
They think we're full of lies,
We are always told they know best,
Because they're older and more wise.
We try to achieve the highest grades to keep parents proud,
And keep up with the latest trends to fit into the right crowd.
I know we can drive parents up the wall,
With our answering back and constant phone calls,
But adults please understand,
We do not mean to moan,
Give us a few years to grow,
And get out of this twilight zone.

Bethany Grainger (Age 15)

A Bowl Of Stew

Once a man ate some stew
And was sick in the loo
Then along came a dog
And turned into a log
And then the log started to moo!

Kieran Griffiths (Age 9)

Where's The Dog?

A woman was walking her sausage dog.
A woman was walking her sausage dog with her daughter.
A woman was walking her sausage dog
With her daughter her daughter was hungry.
A woman was walking her sausage dog with her daughter
Her daughter was hungry and ate the poor sausage dog.
A woman was walking her sausage dog with her daughter
Her daughter was hungry and ate the poor sausage dog.
The mother is searching for the lost dog.

Hayley Gorman (Age 9)

My Best Friend

When I had my friend I felt she was the best,
I really liked it,
It was a cat called Tigger,
Every time I went out,
I always called it,
People looked at me, it was nice,
We always played out together
She always jumped around.

When I took it on holiday
Everyone thought I was funny.
I always took it wherever I went
Best of all she was with me,
All of the time!

Emma Gould (Age 11)

Stars!!

Twinkling and blinking as stars go by,
Hover throughout the dark night sky.

They shine so brightly from the Earth,
As a huge ball of gas burns from its birth.

Shimmering over the wonders of space,
While they twinkle, they gain their pace.

Blowing up in a great flash of light,
Explodes, explodes, night after night.

Callum Green (Age 10)

School Feelings

Soft chair under your bum,
Feel rumble in your tum.
Soft wood, Chris' coat hood,
In assembly fish I caught her,
Trickle of water, other people talking.

Tom Gawthorpe (Age 9)

The Sounds Of The Village Shop

I can hear birds singing
The birds go tweet tweet
I can hear dogs barking
The dogs go woof woof
I can hear people talking
The people go yap yap yap

I can hear the wind blowing
The wind goes swish swish
I can hear cars going
The cars go brum brum
I can hear footsteps

Michael Gawthorpe (Age 9)

A Tiger

Deep in the grass
Hunting down deer
Is a stripey cat
In its eyes you can see fear

Deep in the grass
Hungry as a dog
Thinking of food
While looking at a hog

Sneaking slithering around the prey
Waiting to pounce some time today

Deep in the grass
The meal is served
A tasty deer
For a hungry tiger

Katie Grundy (Age 9)

I Dream Peacefully

I switch off the lights and dream,
I see lights as bright as the sun,
I hear angels singing as soft as a robin,
Trees as tall as sky scrapers,
Children shouting as loud as drums,
I wake in the morning

Arnold Gangaidzo (Age 9)

The Killer

It makes no sound the candle
As the darkness falls behind it.
It seems to dance forever,
The shallow pool upon it is a drip, drip, drip
Of its fair white blood
The glowing orange is a halo round his spinning head,
It soon turns to a thick white cloud of smoke
The candle, the candle, the candle.

Tom Gardner (Age 10)

I'm A. . . .

I'm a
Quick one
White one
Deadly one
Silent one
Deep sea diver
Wild one
Arrrrr
What Am I

Gregory Goodridge (Age 10)

Deers

D eers are cute
E ating grass
E very day I look for them
R eindeers are my favourite
S oft, shy deers.

David Groves (Age 9)

My Favourite Thing

My favourite place for sitting
Is by a fire, so snug
It keeps me warm and cosy
Like a beetle in a rug.

My favourite place for looking
Is out through the window pane,
All the cars go rushing by,
Like carriages on a train.

David Gallimore (Age 10)

A Kitten

He's nothing much but fur,
And two round eyes of blue
With a giant purr,
All lovely and new.

He's small and very, very sweet,
He sleeps all day and night
He really loves the heat
He's scared of heights.

Molly Gibbs (Age 9)

The Waterfall

Water rushing, water gushing,
Onto the stones below.
Into the deep, clear water,
Where it will flow and flow.

Down the valley and through a village,
And into a river at last.
Where it meanders along to the sea,
Running slow then fast.

Meryl Green (Age 10)

I Should Be On The Cross

My gang told the people to cheer for me even though,
I should be on the cross.
Jesus helped people and cared for them but I killed and hurt,
I should be on the cross.
I couldn't believe it when Pontius Pilot announced Jesus was going to be crucified and not me,
I should be on the cross.
They've been looking for me for years and now they're releasing me!
I should be on the cross.
Jesus did nothing wrong,
I should be on the cross.
Oh well, at least I'm free.

Luke Grimshaw (Age 10)

177

Car Park

Birds go cheep cheep
Dogs go woof woof
The wind goes shhhh
In the sky fly fly they go and come by
Birds go cheep cheep
Dogs go woof woof
The wind goes shhhh
Dogs run dogs woof and they are very funny
Birds go cheep cheep

Dogs go woof woof
The wind goes shhhh
The wind's there the wind's not,
Nobody knows if it's here or not
Birds go cheep
Dogs go woof woof
The wind goes shhhh

Hannah Gennard (Age 9)

Imagine

Imagine a bat
As big as a cat
Imagine a seal
As small as an eel
Imagine a shark
As big as an ark
And a bee as big as a tree

Imagine a frog
As long as a log
Imagine a mouse
As tall as a house
Imagine a snail
As big as a whale
And a flea the same height as me!

Stephanie Giles (Age 10)

Spring

Spring is in the air
The daffodils are about
Lambs are playing in the fields
Blossom is on the trees

Spring is in the air
Easter is nearly here
Chicks are chirping in their nests
Baby bunnies learn to hop

Spring is in the air
The sun comes out to shine
There are April showers
Everything starts to grow

Rhys Gibbon (Age 8)

Darkness

Darkness, the silent witness of the night,
Casting shadows over the moonlit sky,
Encircling the land, absorbing the light,
Matching with unsleeping, unblinking eyes.
Darkness, concealing mystical secrets,
Hiding the truth people do not wish known,
Lighting the stars with the pain it reflects,
Shelt'ring the answer hardly ever shown.
Darkness, the cover for night-time creatures,
Helping the predators, hiding the prey.
Enhancing mysterious, dim features,
Stealing colour seen only in the day.
Darkness, its mood changing from hour to hour,
Ne'er lets you forget its mighty power.

Alice Hill (Age 16)

Crocodile

Slowly and stealthily the croc creeps,
Deceiving the buffalo,
The devil of the deep.

Sly and fast, he jumps,
The buffalo run,
Bit the razor blades win.

Blood is dripping from his fangs,
The vampire of the lake,
The god of death.

Predator not Prey.

Ben Gale (Age 11)

Poppy The Pussy Is Purrfect

Poppy the pussy is purrfect
She curls up and purrs all day
It's all in her own special way.
Whenever I'm feeling lonely
She's the one and only
To make me feel ok!
She thinks she's a ferocious tiger
But all she's brought home is a dead spider.
She'd like to catch a rat
But really she's a scaredy cat
But to me that makes her perrfect.

Charlie Griffiths (Age 8)

Cyprus Friend

Victoria is a lovely girl
We had our happy times
And I used to see her every day
But now I never do for she's gone away
But still we have our happy times
Whether we are in Cyprus or England
It is my birthday very soon
I wish she could come along
We send emails, letters, pictures and presents
I talk about my outings
She talks about her new dog
And how she's settling in.

Annabel Grace (Age 8)

The Deep Sea Beast

A whale is a deep sea giant singing at night
A whale's song is an echo chiming in the distance
A whale is a monster, ripping and tearing
A whale is a dancer, skimming the sea
A whale is a swimmer, speeding through the water's depths
A whale is a guardian, protecting the ocean
A whale is a submarine rising for a breath.

Jessica Hurst (Age 12)

I'd Rather

I'd rather write out a book,
I'd rather sing a soppy song
I'd rather get thrown a dirty look,
I'd rather go down a water flume
I'd rather get an electric shock,
I'd rather swallow a balloon
I'd rather take a dip in the lock,
I'd rather swallow dynamite

Than go to school,
Now that's a fright!

Nicholas Gill (Age 9)

A Dog

It barks loudly
Dark green eyes blink in the moon light.
Light gnashy teeth crunch together like breaking eggs.
Dark running black nose like yolk out of an egg.
Light fur like fluffy balls of snow.
A waggly tail like a wiping paint brush.
Hard black paws like stiff card.
Sharp claws like a sharp sharp knife.
It's friendly and fluffy but after a while
It goes to bed and has a nice dream.

Jack Gradidge (Age 8)

Flowers

Flowers make sweet lovely Autumn smells all year round
Smell all the flowers in the park everywhere even over there

Flowers have different colours the best is the daffodils
I like the daffodils best because of they're bright yellow petals

Flowers flow like a field of pure gold in the sunlight
Flowers smell like the most expensive perfume in the world.

David Groves (Age 8)

Dogs

All curled like a croissant on a plate,
Lies a dog asleep on the floor.
He's in a deep slumber,
His dreams in his head,
He's snoring and twitching his paw.

He's up like a flash,
He's ready to go,
Woken by the movement of the door
He sees his lead and takes his chance,
To get out in the world and explore.

Dogs are very cute and lovely,
Just one problem,
They can't resist a gnaw,
Sometimes it's painful,
When he bites my finger sore.

Sam Greaves (Age 11)

Beans

Beans on your shirt
Beans on your head
Beans on your trousers
Beans in your bed

Beans in the class
Beans in the books
Beans on the sheets
Beans on the beach

Beans on the flowers
Beans on the bees
Beans on the grass

Beans, Beans, Beans and Beans

Tom Grundy (Age 10)

Animals!

I am an animal that lives in the cold.
People kill me for my big fur coat,
Then they leave me to mould.

Please don't kill me!
Are you warm in my fur coat?
You've left me to lay in my flesh and bones.

I run as fast as I can,
I slip and you get me.
Are you happy for what you have done?

Why do you want my coat?
It is supposed to be mine!
If you wear mine,
Please can I wear yours?

Lydia Hiscock (Age 10)

179

Fox Hunt

My sharp ears pricked up as the hunting horn trumpeted through the mist
I started to run through the long grass, wet with dew.

The horses hooves thundered, following the pace of the dogs
The dogs
The massive, wiery-haired black dogs, slobber dripping from their fangs
The fangs
That have
Killed
Many foxes, and would
Kill
Me if they got the chance.

The men's horses sweat badly as they aimed their weapons at my behind.

I have to go on
Even if my lungs explode
Even if my muscles turn to statues
Even if my feet fall off, numb with running over uneven ground
Even if I die
I plunged into the darkness of the stream
I wasn't dumb
I knew they'd lose my scent if I stayed there, but .....

Alison Hill & Natasha Willis (Age 11)

Snow

I made the children play in my white wool,
I made roads mushy and slushy,
I made the world white,
I made everybody cold,
I made people wear hats, gloves, coats and scarfs,
My flakes fell like a million leaves.

Joshua Hancock (Age 8)

My Nan And Grandad

My Nan and Grandad live in a house,
And in the garage they keep a mouse.
My Grandad's very mad,
My Nan's not sad.
Their house is big and fat,
They used to have a cat.
So if you go there, you'll see it first thing,
And if you have good ears, my Grandad might just sing.
They are both very good fun,
My Grandad weighs a ton.
They always give me sweets,
And lots of nice treats.
They have a room for me to play,
It gets messier through the day.
They tidy it for when I stay,
Then again when I'm away.
It's very clear and plain to see,
That they are very good to me.

Sarah Handy (Age 8)

Niall And Tom

We both like football
We both like chips
But I don't like some of
Tom's silly tricks.

We don't believe in Santa
We giggle in the hall
We share a can of Fanta
And we don't care at all.

We like to watch a video
Flubber is our best
I think the film Flubber
Is better than all the rest.

We meet at school
We meet at home
We play about a lot
We will be friends forever
Whether the teachers like it or not!

Niall Higgins (Age 9)

Babies

I want my bottle
I need my nappy changed
I want daddy
I want my hair brushed
Mum I feel sick!
I hate this cot
Can I have dinner?
Whahh!
Whahh!

Ashleigh Haynes (Age 7)

Water Poem

Winter water hard as iron
Or just as vicious as a lion
The frosty days upon the moors
With white horses galloping into shores.

The beast has slept throughout the summer
Without as much as a single shudder
The beast is woken in the winter
An icicle as sharp as a splinter

Oasis in the desert plain
Give only pleasure and not pain
In the summer full of glee
A pool's a pleasant place to be

The humungus ocean old and wise
(Swimmers don't think about its size).
It's just wonderfully deep and blue.
I love it, what about you?

Conrad Harrison (Age 10)

Have You Seen My Ferrari?

Have you seen my Ferrari?
My well-driven Ferrari
In your pit lane.

Have you seen my Ferrari?
My shiny gravel-skidder
At the start line.

Have you seen my Ferrari?
My light, speedy metal-bodied car
Over the hill.

Have you seen my Ferrari?
My one-seater hill-driven car
On the gravel.

Have you seen my Ferrari?
My four-wheeled, big-engined car
Round the chicane.

Have you seen my Ferrari?
My bright coloured rubber-tyred car
Being tugged by a truck.

There's my well-driven Ferrari
Dangling on top of me
Whoopee I can race again. CRASH!

Tristan Hawkings (Age 9)

My Question Poem

Why does milk clean an ink stain?
Why do stars sparkle?
Why doesn't the moon have a light of its own?
Why does chocolate melt?

How do birds fly?
What's the point in gravity?
Why do we have cold and hot weather?
How do our insides work?

Can ostriches fly if they try to?
Why aren't sweets good for you?
Why is the earth round?
Why does detergent clean clothing?

Why does hot water set a stain?
Why does the wind blow?
Why does an elephant grow?
Why is water wet?

What does protein do for you?
What temperature does water freeze at?
Why is the sea salty?
Why are there different kinds of rock?

Emily Hinks (Age 8)

The First Time

The first time I looked at the sun,
It was a big orange ball.
The first time I stepped on the ground,
I took a big fall.
The first time I swam in the water,
I felt like a dolphin.
The first time I ate some food,
I felt very alive.
The first time I closed my eyes,
I went into a dream.

The first time I had a friend,
I played with him all day.
The first time I picked up a toy,
I cuddled it all night.
The first time I had a brother,
I jumped around his cot.
The first time I spoke to someone,
I spoke to my mum.
The first time I went to the park,
I swung on a swing.

James Hickling (Age 9)

Best Friends

My friend is a good friend
He is always there for me
But sometimes we fall out
When I am in a mood you see
Yes I get in a mood
And shout and stamp about
And then my best friend
He just grumbles
Instead of giving me a clout
I go weeeee! Can you see
I want to go swimming in the pool
And I take him with me.

Jake Higham (Age 8)

The Stray Little Kitten

The stray little kitten
            Was a tabby little kitten
The stray little kitten
            Was a dirty little kitten
The stray little kitten
            Was a black little kitten
The stay little kitten
            Was a fluffy little kitten
But best of all
            The stray little kitten
Wasn't a stray little kitten anymore
            It was a loved little kitten
The loved little kitten was mine!

Becky Hickling (Age 9)

Snow Poem

Light drifting snow flakes
Landing peacefully on the ground.
As I amble across the green
I don't hear a sound.
The trees are painted white
With a glinting touch of glitter.
It's snowing a bit harder now
Pitter, patter, pitter.
The snow is slippery
Like someone squashing soap,
OH! NO!
The snow is stopping now
Let's hope it's not, let's hope.
Oh no it has.
My snowman has gone . . .
I'm never going to enjoy the day that the sun shone.

Charlotte Harman (Age 9)

Old Trees

Old trees whistling in the darkness
Old trees are lonely
Old trees are bare
Oh trees where are your leaves?

Sarah Hicks (Age 6)

A Story About My Pets

This is the story about my cat
She wears two boots and she wears a hat.

This is the story about my dog
His nose sticks up so he looks like a hog.

This is the story about my hamster
Who took his holiday in a camper.

This is the story about my rabbit
And picking his nose is a nasty habit.

This is the story about my fish
Who would really look nice on a dish.

This is the story about my guinea pig
Who looks very really, really big.

This is the story about my parrot
Who looks rather funny chewing a carrot.

This is the story about my spider
Who is a very good bicycle rider.

This is the story about my horse
Who likes her hay all dipped in sauce.

Now that my story has come to an end
I'm glad'cos they're all driving me'round the bend.

Philippa Holden (Age 11)

Fairies

Fairies are invisible beings,
Who appear in younglings dreams,
With golden dust to shrink you small,
To give you the power to fly and fall,
Once flying with the fairies bright,
Far and beyond into the night,
You reach that strange, unfamiliar place,
With different creatures of different race.
The mushroom houses big or small,
With WELCOME mats outside their doors,
Intricate seamstresses working for all,
With gossamer dresses for the fairy ball,
Outfits made of silk and dewdrops fair,
With spider web gowns, and petals in their hair,
To be presented to the fairy King and Queen,
Bowing and curtsying, all must be seen,
Dancing and singing will go on throughout,
Until it is time to up and fly about,
For an exit, only fit for royalty,
We must be returned to our own mortality.

Kirsty Henderson (Age 14)

Tiger

I live in the jungle,
I live out of sight,
You're my prey or maybe a little taster,
My eyes are like fire in the dark,
My teeth are like knives just ready to hunt,
I have padded paws just ready to leap,
You never know just one day we will meet.

Lauren Hilsden (Age 10)

I Wish . . . .

I wish I was a slow sloath,
I'd lounge around all day,
Or I could be a greedy hawk,
And take the sky away.

I wish I was a cute furry rabbit,
I'd eat all the yellow clover,
But might I be an otter?
And turn over and over and over!

I wish I was a hungry fox,
But I'd have to eat Brer Rabbit!
Or I could be a colourful fish,
But I'd have to eat pink maggot!

I wish I was a jaw snapping shark,
I'd drink all the water in all the sea,
Actually, none of these would suit my life,
I'd rather just be me!

Lucy Hayes (Age 11)

182

The Pied Piper's Revenge

No-one knew there lived baby rats,
Hiding under beds and old smelly mats.
They then sneaked out to the unexplored cave,
To see the piper and food he gave.

He gave them apples, carrots and peas,
And leaves and conkers off the trees.
Day by day they grew and grew,
Bigger and bigger than me and you.
They went different colours pink and blue,
Then out of the caves into the town they flew.

Around the corners into the cracks,
Pushing people over, breaking their backs.
Finally they got to the mayor,
Nibbling his skin and splitting his hair.
Then the mayor had to give up,
When they chewed his precious pup,
The Pied Piper's money the mayor gave,
The piper says goodbye and gives a wave.

Caroline Helm (Age 11)

Recipe For Spring!

Take five fluffy little lambs
And three small fat clouds.
Add a massive meadow full of bright green grass.
Sprinkle in a big coloured rainbow.
Decorate with three splashing little streams,
And you have made Spring!

Guy Hipwell (Age 7)

The Charge Of The Carp Fish

Strike-quickly, strike-quickly
Got to catch this carp today
Among the hundreds of cod it swam
Although one cod grabbed my rod
I still fished for death

Catch this carp I would say
Anyone might pay
Sitting on the soggy mud
There it is, I know that's just
The fish that snapped my bait

Thinking of playing a harp
Well would you look at that
I've caught a carp.

Ben Holman (Age 11)

The Monster Tree

Down in the garden
There's a monster tree
It likes to eat kids
But it doesn't eat me!
It ate my sister
My mum went mad
I said ha, ha, ha,
But then I was sad.
Mum sent me to bed
Without any tea
I looked out the window
A sad sight to see . . .
With a mighty crash
Dad chopped down the tree.
Out came my sister
Mum jumped for glee.
I'm glad she's happy
But there's no more monster tree
I suppose we'll play together now
Just my sister and me!!

Brett Hayter (Age 7)

My Dog

I've got a dog
He's called Luke
He chases cats every day
He sits on the floor
And gives you his paw
I think he can stay
We take it for a walk
And stay on the path
If it could talk
It would ask for a bath.

Ryon Hoyt (Age 13)

Monkey Swinging

Monkey swinging
Monkey swinging
Children littering
People watching
Making faces
Calling names
Monkey swinging
Monkey swinging

Monkey swinging
Monkey swinging
Singing a happy tune
Want a friend
No foes
Want a family
Wish to have freedom
Monkey swinging
Monkey swinging

Laura Hinckley (Age 9)

Ponies

I have a friend who has a white pony,
Sometimes about feed she is rather moany,
She gallops and canters up and down,
To other people she must look like a clown!

I have a friend who has a white pony,
Without other ponies she gets quite lonely,
When I'm riding she bucks and rears,
And when I get off I'm almost in tears!

I have a friend who has a white pony,
With no grass in the field she's very boney,
Now she's in a very big stable,
I'll have to add that to my table!

Emma Holroyd (Age 10)

Behind This Door

Behind this door
Lies a crew in dismay
Stands a sturdy ship crushing
In the ice
Waits a nervous captain on the
Verge of madness
Cries of prayer and hope
Echoing down the crevices
Gleams the sparkling snow
From the sunlight.

Graeme Hill (Age 13)

The Real War

I am standing in horrid mud being deafened by gunshots, it's terrifying,
I am finally getting away from it all, I can go home and rest thank God

The men are so tired that they don't know where they're walking
And some of them don't know where their shoes are.

Gas shells are going off behind them and they don't even notice
"Oh my God there's poisonous gas all around us, run!"

We struggle to put on our gas masks
One soldier is too slow he cries out in agony as the gas leaks into his lungs.

The gas is very thick it looks like pea soup. I can't see a thing. Oh God!
The man who inhaled gas is coughing and choking. He is dying.

Would you want to walk in front of a wagon carrying a dying man? That 's what I had to do.
He was screaming and was going blue in the face as his brain was starved of oxygen.

The man is now choking on his blood and mucus. He is very rapidly dying
Would you like to see it? It makes me want to throw up.

After what I've experienced I don't think it is glorious to die like this for your country.
It's disgusting and very upsetting.

Naomi Hastings (Age 14)

Trouble In The Playground

I was in the playground minding my own business.
When they came, Tom, Billy, Jack and the rest.
Pushing shoving kicking for no reason.
Boasting that they were the best.
It was the new girls very first day.
She saw them hurting me and I began to cry.
She took one big breath and came along
And ran and kicked them in the thigh!
The bully boys never came to the front any more.
Me and Emma had great times together.
The bully boys never came to bully us any more.
And nobody never broke our friendship, not ever.

Lucy Hutchinson (Age 8)

Happy Yellow

Yellow, yellow, yellow
Yellow is a warm and happy colour
Yellow tastes like a sharp lemon
Which makes your eyes water
Yellow sounds like a bird chirping
Flying early in the morning
Yellow feels warm and gentle
Smooth and calming
Yellow is happy and beautiful
Yellow looks like the sun
Beaming brightly
Yellow, yellow, yellow.

Rachel Harris (Age 12)

Pants To Poverty

Pants to poverty they say,
Pants to poverty,
Red nose day is here to stay
So, pants to poverty.

Children suffer everywhere
No water, food or clothes,
Charity from those who care
From those who wear the nose.

Red nose dogs, and red nose deer,
Red nose people too,
Helping those who live in fear
Of hunger, drought and flu.

A little money goes quite a way
Some tender loving care,
What you have for red nose day,
Please give for all to share.

Pants to poverty they say,
Is heard in every bar,
These words that mean so much today,
For children near and far.

Alan Hooker (Age 11)

Mangoes

Give me a mango.
The perfume was heavenly,
Thick and sugary.
Its sleek skin shone like the sun
Under the light of a candle and the stars.
Smooth and soft under my hand,
The tang on the tongue
As wild as the music swinging me on,
Exotic like him.
Mangoes,
Shaped like a tear,
Seemed to watch us and smile a blessing.
Give me a mango
And I will remember.

Katy Hope (Age 13)

School

The ring of the bell, as school starts
The scraping of chairs, as everyone is seated
The turning of pages, as they look through their books
The screeching of chalk, as work is put up
The scribbling of pens, as they write away
The whisper of pupils, as messages go around
The shuffling of shoes, as everyone stands up
The ring of the bell, as school ends.

Aimee Heathcote (Age 11)

Black And White Or Colour

"I see it in the deep
But it's too steep;
It will never happen
If I don't imagine.

The sky is like a stream
Held sweetly in my dream."
"But it's all not true;
What's happened to you?"

"In the sky are little birds
They say no words."
"But they flutter slowly down
And lie motionless on the ground."

"Can you see the little children play
In the fields far away?"
"No! I can see some children sad
And other children mad.

You don't understand,
Take my hand;
It's not all black and white you see,
It's in colour like me."

Natalie Hamill (Age 12)

Storm

Lost at sea,
All alone,
Is anyone out there,
I don't know,
Bits of wreckage floating by,
I'm starting to wonder if I will survive,
In the distance sharks I see,
I can't help but wonder whether I will be their tea.

Luke Harvey (Age 11)

Family Poem

Families are a part of life
Even if we don't see them
Sometimes your mum has a new husband
And sometimes he has a new wife
You may have a brother or sister
Larger or smaller than you
Some may have lived for longer
Some may be rather new
You may have nans and grandads
They're great as well
But you don't know what they'll be like
You just can't tell
It might not be that plain to see
But families are special to you and to me
Families are a part of life.

Rebecca Halls (Age 11)

185

Nightmare!

Late that night outside I saw,
A strange looking figure at the door,
Dressed in black from head to toe,
Male or female I do not know,
Without knocking they walked away,
Who it was I could not say.

Late that night I had a dream,
When I woke up I had to scream,
It was that figure dressed in black,
I don't know who it was but they were back,
Again without knocking they walked away,
Who it was I could not say.

Early morning when I was calm,
I sat up and waited for the alarm,
Then looking out of my window clear,
A bright white figure did appear,
And said to me, "Do not be scared
That dark black figure was your nightmare,
But now you've overcome your fear,
That dark black figure will not appear."

Emily Haslam (Age 12)

The Christmas Star

Christmas star, shining bright,
Christmas star, where's Jesus?
Christmas star which way?
Left, right, left right?
You are getting closer and closer.

Michael Hadjipourou (Age 6)

Books Wonderful Books!

When the book was open it began to sing
The words so loud and clear
It was singing its usual song
"Once upon a time."

Its arms embraced me and asked me to read on
The book flapped its arms in joy
It laughed as I tickled it
It asked to be my friend

The words danced over the page
To the rhythm of my reading
The similies danced with the metaphors
And the adverbs danced with the adjectives

The pictures came alive and started talking
They took me into their world
And let me join in the fun
Some games, some tragedies, but all magical

Books, wonderful BOOKS!

Luke Harris (Age 11)

I Was Alone

I was alone in the darkened forest,
I was alone in the misty night,
I was alone when the rain started pouring
Down on me from the clouds above.

I was alone when I saw a shadow,
I was alone when it crept in close,
I was alone when it saw me sat there,
I was alone when the shadow stopped.

I was alone when it started to scare me,
I was alone when I started to run,
I was alone when it caught up on me,
I was alone when it overtook.

I was alone when it went away again,
I was alone when it started to fly,
I was alone when I realised suddenly
That the shadow really was a bird.

David Hopkins (Age 12)

Eggs

Mummies lay eggs
And the babies hatch
Out of the eggs.
Then the babies fly
Up to the sky
Very high.

Eleanor Hewish (Age 4)

Will The Trophy Be Mine?

Come on team
It's nearly full time.
Just 5 minutes left
And the trophy is mine.
Just kick it out
You're doing just fine.
With 4 minutes left
And the trophy is mine.
Oh no, he's on the run
It's their number nine.
With 3 minutes left
And the trophy will be mine.
They have scored
We were doing just fine.
With just 2 minutes left
And the trophy will hopefully be mine.
We have scored a penalty
It is now full time.
How lucky am I
Because the trophy is mine.

Jason Hughes (Age 13)

The Devil

I am hell and I live in darkness.
I am the nightmare you pray you will never have.
I am the thing under your bed, the unusual sound outside.
I am why you are scared of the dark,
I am the terror that surrounds your world!
I take souls to make me powerful,
I can make your life a living hell
I always watch you, nothing can stop me,
I'm hotter than fire, colder than ice.
I have handcuffed lightning and thrown thunder in jail!
I don't have power, I am power, the ultimate power!
You think God can protect you? Forget it!
He is just a grain of rice compared to me!
I make the impossible, possible!
I watch and laugh at the tough people of your world,
I'm looking forward to seeing them terrified when they meet me!
YES! YOU KNOW WHO I AM!
I'M THE
DEVIL!

Jamie Houston (Age 13)

Dragon Poem

Fiery brute with a long scaly tail
Red, green and yellow, male or female
Scanning the land for gold
Never growing old.
Scaly armour protecting the fiery heart within
Beware or their charms will draw you in.

But some are quiet, some hold secrets unknown
That humans will never own.

So be careful all slayers of which one you choose
For in the end, you will always lose!

Emma Hazlett (Age 11)

The Cauldron And Bubble Restaurant

Here we serve strange recipes
Menus needed necessary!
Immortals hungry, serve them quick
Once they smell this food their appetite will stick!

Hurry up the serving
Usually there's often a burning
In the restaurant, there is smoke
Whilst we are still dishing out our special worm coke!

We put the fire out
Then for a while we hang about
After closing there is nothing to do
So we whip out our recipes and make a stew!

Cloey Horton (Age 12)

Evening Till Morning

Like the colour of a star filled sky,
Dark blue mixed with black,
The evening birds rushing by,
The speckles of an owl's back.

Trees turn to sharp, black claws,
The slither of a silent grass snake,
Branches move like creaking doors,
And the rippleless, dark lake.

Petals protecting their inward flower,
Grass blades dancing in the wind,
Hawks sweeping with such amazing power,
Up in the clouds, and through the wind.

Orange specks break through the black,
Morning sun awakes,
A pile of leaves which result to a stack,
The evening's power breaks.

Catherine Hornby (Age 14)

We Went

Through the bushes and the trees
We went, we went
Through the jungles and the seas
We went, we went

Past the school and the flag poles
We went, we went
Past the paddock and the horse foals
We went, we went

We went ...

Emily Holmes (Age 12)

The World

Some people treat the world with respect
They walk around with banners saying
Save Our Planet and things like that
They are the good people

Then you have some people
Who wreck the world
They destroy things like the rainforest
And pollute the sea with oil

And then there's people like you and me
Who write poems about the world
Or talk about it to our friends
But we never do anything about it.

Daniel Hardy (Age 13)

Things I Could Do

The things I could do if I could be bothered
A model, a singer, a star
There's millions of things that I could do
But I don't want to travel that far.

The things I could do if I could be bothered
A scientist who can make rockets
There's thousands of things that I could do
It would be easier just to sell lockets.

The things I could do if I could be bothered
Travel really far into space
There's hundreds of things that I could do
I think I'll just stay at my base.

I don't really think that I could be bothered
I'm really useless in every way
There's not a lot that I can do
I'd rather stay at home any day.

Rebecca Hall (Age 13)

What I Love

I love the smell of a
Forest scent.
I hate the smell of
The scent of autumn though.

I love the wind blowing.
I hate strong wind blowing.

Michael Hale (Age 7)

Spitting Cobra

The spitting cobra raised its
Diamond shaped head to see
Its prey more clearly
Knowing if it moved too fast
The baby buffalo would see him.

Its long curling twisting tail
Flashed brightly in the sun
Its golden-brown scales
Shone and glinted moving
Well in the gold sand.

Then arching once again
His back and looking
Towards the buffalo
Making sure he didn't see him
Then he rushed forward
Dislocating his jaws and
Engulfing the buffalo whole.

Peter Hynes (Age 13)

Earth, Moon And Stars.....

Earth's like a ball, massive and round
Lots of pollution, noise and sound
Countries all shapes, some large, some small
All dotted round a massive-like pool
Glide in the sky or float in the sea
The oceans are endless come swim with me

The moon shines out in a sky so dark
On a cloudy night not even a mark
No life up there or so we think
When no one watches aliens wink
The shuttle is launched to go and see
No life just craters, no you, no me

The stars shine out in a moonlit sky
On a cold winter's night people walk by
They shoot through the sky on a crisp frosty night
In array of colours yellow and white
I claimed my star and it was mine
From now till I die my star is divine.

Leanne Hill (Age 12)

The Mistress' Reply

To you sir here is my reply.
I must admit I would rather die
I would not sleep with you not ever
Although I haven't had better
I'd like to keep my dignity
Including my virginity
You say that the insects shall try
So can you please then tell me why
My beauty shall no more be found
When I am dead and in the ground?

Wesley Healey (Age 14)

The Wreck Of The Zanzibar

Great aunt Laura died today.
She left me her diary,
I went up stairs to read it.
This was how it goes;
There were lost of storms on Bryer.
The wreck of the Zanzibar was the worst.
My brother Billy was on the ship.

My dad was hurt
So I rowed to save them.
We rescued all of the Sailors.
It was good to see my brother.
When we were on shore,
Cows corn, rice and wheat came out of the water.

Emma Louise Harragan (Age 12)

Napoleon Vs Wellington

Napoleon round, short and fat as can be
Had a most terrible temper and he
Had a rival, arch enemy Wellington you see
A quick witted and elegant adversary
There followed a battle which none could foresee

The land that they prowled was a great treasure trove
For its high vantage points that were precious to both
Avoiding the formidable, dank undergrowth
Wellington growled a most terrifying oath
That would see Napoleon end up as meatloaf

They came face to face in a green open glade
Supported by troops, some of which laid
In the grassy arena of death where they had been slain
Thankfully neither leader with their lives had paid
But many a battle scar had been made.

On hearing the moans Mrs Smee jumped to her toes
And sped from the house without all her clothes;
She picked up her cat, which lay by the rose
How could you Wellington? Nobody knows
Look what you've done to Napoleon's nose!

Nathan Hand (Age 12)

Love Is ...

Love is the colour of fluorescent pink
Love is the look of my boyfriend
Love is the taste of heart shaped chocolates
Love is the sound of kisses
Love is the smell of red roses
Love is the feel of my heart beating.

Hazel Hill (Age 7)

The Beach

The warm sun's rays beating down on everything below.
Adults relaxing on the beach and chatting to each other.
The tingling sensation of your feet sinking
Into the golden, warm, silky sand, laden with
Fragile shells of different shapes, sizes and colours.
Striped deckchairs and umbrellas litter the beach.
There are children building sandcastles
And splashing in the warm water, 'SPLASH.'
If you look up you can see the sky as
Pure blue and clear as a sapphire, no clouds in sight.
The exotic animals that live and breed in the deep depths of the ocean
The gigantic, frothy, white waves lapping against the rocky shores
The beach is like a box of treasures!!!

Rachel Hindley (Age 12)

Memories Of An Old Man

A twisted, gnarled figure
Crouching in a doorway
A doorway on a street full of grime and disease
His lips are hard and cracked
And his hair is thin and greasy
He's so old he looks dead among the shadows
His head is full of misery and loneliness
Dreaming of his young girl lost in the breeze
His eyes twinkle like crystals in the fog
As he recalls the times with his long lost love
On the night they parted
Her cheeks were streaked with sunbeams
Though the day had long since passed
Her movements were like silk, delicate and smooth
Her perfume was like rich velvet, soft and beautiful
Her shiny black hair streamed out behind her
And slashed across his face
He blinked for a second and then she was gone
He's lost everything trying to find her
Now he is old he knows she won't come back.

Lucy Hancock (Age 11)

The Snake
(In Sand)

A snake in sand smells as if it was gold
But, it's not
It's cold blooded in every way
Its bite is a kiss of death
A tail of warning means business
Then it attacks!
You would probably die in seconds or even minutes
So let this be a warning not to annoy a snake
In sand!

Luke Holmes (Age 12)

The Weather

Frosty, foggy, icy rusty
Cold, wet, thunder and lightning
Boom! Bang!
Raining, hailing, snowing

Windy, trees blowing
Tornadoes, hurricanes, typhoons
Swoosh! Swish!
Earthquakes, sleet.

Blue skies, shining sun
Gentle, soft wind, birds chirping
Tweet! Tweet!
Everything is still.

Matthew Harris (Age 12)

I've Never Had A Friend

I was the one who was always alone,
I was the one who sat in the corner,
Or on the bench at break,
I'VE NEVER HAD A FRIEND.

After school I never went out,
I just stayed in hearing the children scream and shout,
I don't even know what friendship means,
I'VE NEVER HAD A FRIEND.

I never cried, I never moaned,
I just waited till I got home,
Because remember life goes on,
I'VE NEVER HAD A FRIEND.

I sometimes think it is not fair,
Because other children can go somewhere,
I never knew what fear was like,
I'VE NEVER HAD A FRIEND.

Mark Harding (Age 13)

Black Canvas

A black canvas pricked with twinkling stars
Or like a child with deep hurtful scars
Trees blow under the canvas, they wave in the breeze
A child is punched and falls onto his knees
The grass is damp and shiny from the dew
The child is weeping, this is nothing new
The moon is up full of shining light
It shines on the child who is out cold like the night
The canvas penetrates into the eye
Of a child on the grass, asleep under the sky.

Elizabeth Holden (Age 12)

Teenage Girls' Lurve Guide Poem

If a boy comes up to you and asks your name and number
Stay calm, don't freak out, and oh, say your real name
But if he is an awful boy
Give him the wrong number it will bring you much joy
If he asks you what you are doing tonight
Remember this, say "Sorry I'm washing my hair tonight."
And if he is a grotty boy with dirty fingernails and greasy hair
The thought of soap and water should give him a fright
Then he will not ask you to go out another night
But if he makes your heart beat a million times more
Your knees wobble, hands shake and you faint on the floor
Then by all means take my advice
Give him your number and don't think twice.

Giselle Hyam (Age 12)

Nocturnal

At night I rise from my comfy, snug den
In the light of the stars and only then

The moon shall guide me on my way
And tell me when to flee from the lustre of the day

As the sun sets to rest its head
This is when I, creep from my bed

I shuffle along the woodland ground
Snuffling for food, to see what treats can be found

If the scent of hibernation is just around the bend
I prepare for my tranquil nap, from autumn, to winter's end

A badger I am, grey, black and white
Coming to life in the dead of the night.

Jennifer Hardy (Age 12)

Homeless

I look on the street
There's people at my feet
They sleep in a gutter
They don't even mutter
They can't afford bread and butter
As I walk along the street
Seeing people at my feet

Jesse Hurrisett (Age 11)

The Mysterious Sky

The Sky is a huge blue blanket
Covering the world

The Clouds are fluffy white sheep
Floating in the sky

The Stars are little stickers
Stuck on a black piece of paper

The Sun is a big yellow beach ball
Thrown high into the sky

The Moon is a white hamster ball
Rolling on a blue carpet

The Planets are big scoops of ice cream
Lying on a black plate

The Sky is a huge blue monster
With lots of twinkling eyes.

Victoria Hewett (Age 11)

It Was So Noisy

It was so noisy that
The doors rattled madly and made a giant bang!

It was so noisy that
The windows exploded with a big crash!

It was so noisy that
The tables tipped over with a big giant bang!

It was so noisy that
All the displays fell off the walls!

It was so noisy that
The walls crashed down!

It was so noisy!

Cassie Holland (Age 8)

Octopus

He is big,
He is purple.
He lives in a big cave.
He has eight legs
Made of tights
And newspaper.
He has big eyes
But no mouth ...
He eats black things.
He is *different.*

Sean Hamilton (Age 5)

My Haiku

The Nudi is pink
It wibbles, wobbles all night
It wiggles away

The Orangutan
It sits in old trees eating
And enjoys climbing

A pretty Panda
Enjoys eating bamboo sticks
They are endangered

The Queens are pretty
Lady cats have good manners
They hide in their dens.

Lise Honeyman (Age 9)

School

School is a dungeon holding children captive
School is a demon you can't get away from
School is a torture chamber with children inside
School is the devil burning with rage
School is a hell mouth waiting to open
School is your enemy waiting to attack
The School at night is a ghost town that's abandoned
The School during the day is a zoo with charging animals.

Simon Hodder (Age 12)

Boy Called Leighton

There once was a boy called Leighton
Who lived in a town called Clayton
His mate went to Devon
His mum named him Kevin
And changed his name to Satan.

Thomas Benjamin Hodgkins (Age 9)

Without You

I couldn't imagine life without you, things just wouldn't be the same
My world would crumble and there would be no more happiness left.

My sun would die down and my rain appear
I thought everything would change and never be the same again.

And as you walked out of my life, I realised what would happen
I would be left all alone, all alone in tears.

How could you walk out like that and leave me all alone?
I never knew what to do, I was just lost, lost without you.

Times never changed and still I think
What you could have done for me but you didn't stop to listen.

You took everything important out of my life, how selfish was that
Why couldn't you just stop and think about how I would feel?

But oh no, you just walked out and left me all alone, with everything dying away.
If you would have stopped for a minute and thought, none of this would have happened to me,
And I would be in such a state, living ...
Living without you.

Hannah Harrison (Age 14)

Life In A Rubbish Bin

The dark dank smell
A vision of hell
The clang of the lid
As more rubbish is rid.

The smell of cabbage, all mouldy and green
Oozes through my toes, a sight best unseen
A bin with no corners nothing to hold
Except from sides covered with rotting green mould.

The flies are my friends, I talk to the rats
Sometimes I'm visited by scabby old cats
The occasional slug likes to slime its way round
And the maggots are tasty, but chewy I've found.

So why am I here and what have I done
To live forever with the sight of no sun
They think I'm mad, I'm considered a fool
But let's be honest, it's better than school!

Daryl Holcombe (Age 12)

Waves

Waves flow about the sea
They wet the sand near me
Waves are fun, they sparkle in the sun
If you play in the waves
You'll see.

Francesca Hobson (Age 8)

Land At Night

The thunder clapped, the lightning flashed
The sea was rough, the sky was blue
The ship was sinking was sinking quickly
Along with all the crew.

The captain, the officer
And the crew on board
Shouted to the passengers
"Pray to the lord."

"We're sinking, we're sinking"
They shouted and screamed
"Launch the lifeboats"
They are under the main beam.

"Land ahoy" shouted the cabin boy
Now row with all your might."
It is a wonderful sight!
To see an Island at midnight.

When the sun rose in the east
There was a huge sigh of relief
All the people aboard the 'moray'
Had survived to tell their story.

Katie Herbert (Age 13)

Hurcott Lake

The wind in the trees catch the dead leaves
Sweeping them across the lake's water
Eventually they can go no further
In they fall causing the ripples to spread
The water mirrors the jumping fish
As it leaps out of the lake

On land a fisherman stands
Wistfully watching the fish at play
The heron readies himself for flight
As he flaps his wings and takes a fish
The man can only wish he could do the same

The sun reflects on the man's hairless head
And on the water around him
Fish come up to laugh and jeer
Watch out
The heron comes in for the catch
Lands and enjoys his prize.

Sonya Hardy (Age 13)

Play Time

I play netball with my friends
Olivia got a shot
Oh no Jess fell over and
Bumped her head
Tears.

Danielle Hopley (Age 9)

The Merry-Go-Round

Round and round the galloping horses
Red and white, brown and blue
Golden poles twisting and turning
My mum waves as I set off

Faster and faster round I go
Galloping horses begin to take off
Glistening stars, I'm approaching
As I fly past a star twinkles

Eventually we land on some snow
Meet a big man in a bright red suit
He calls for his reindeer, with a large red nose
To my amazement, we're at the North Pole

The merry-go-round starts turning
I jump onto a white horse's back
In a flash we all whizz down
To our home back on the ground

Slower and slower we are turning round
The man stops the merry-go-round
I run to my mum and give her a hug
Back at home, I dream of my flight.

Sally Hoolin (Age 9)

Enormous Elephants

Nine enormous elephants sitting with their mate
One met a girl and then there were eight

Eight enormous elephants travelling to Devon
One got sick and then there were seven

Seven enormous elephants sitting in a fix
One cried himself to sleep then there were six

Six enormous elephants standing by a hive
One was stung and then there were five

Five enormous elephants learning the law
One fainted then there were four

Four enormous elephants getting chased by a bee
One ran away and then there were three

Three enormous elephants sitting on the loo
One didn't hang around and then there were two

Two enormous elephants setting up a con
One chickened out and then there was one

One enormous elephant eating a cream bun
He choked on a raisin and then there was

NONE!

Abigail Howse (Age 9)

Snow Poem

Crispy leaves frosted in the snow
Screams of laughter as a sleigh speeds down a hill
Frosty ice as the day gets darker
Ponds have a glaze of sparkly ice

Camilla Hobbs (Age 11)

Party

Floor vibrating
Noise level high
Scoffing down food
Acting crazy
Steaming down the stairs

Now I'm tired
All worn out
Not too excited
I'm all in the dark
There's still a bit of life
In this party, fading more and more
Can't tell left from right
All I know now I'm fast asleep.

Joshua Humphreys (Age 11)

My Baby Sister Makes So Much Noise

My baby sister makes so much noise
When ever I go in her room she slaps me
If I play with her stuff like toys
She pushes me away and slaps me

I wish she could be in mum's tummy
If I could, I would get the baby in trouble
Then I could have my mum back
I would get the baby from over the road to make a couple
With my sister

If I was rich I would pay someone to foster her
I really want my mum
When I have my dinner I get splattered with food
I wish I was still in my mum's tum

When I go to have a bath, mum puts the baby in with me
If I had the choice I would keep the cot but not the baby
I need my mum back
Well if I want my mummy and daddy
I suppose I'll have to keep the BABY.

Christopher Howe (Age 8)

Playground

I went to play out with my friend.
My friend skipped with me and we play funny games.
We play funny jokes and up and down in the playground.
Then it was time to go my house with my friend and my sister.
The teacher looked at my friend and my big sister and
My brother and my family went too,
And my mum was very happy with me.

Zobia Hussain (Age 9)

The Bubble And Squeak Jelly Monster

Not last night but the night before
I heard a rustle and a rumble from my bedroom door
I opened it up and there I saw
A Bubble and Squeak jelly monster
Stand before my floor

I struggled and screamed
But nobody came
For a scary moment
I thought he spoke my name
I opened my mouth to let out a scream
But then I awoke
...... It was only a dream!

Pia Holliday (Age 9)

Dreams

She twists and she turns
She pants and she sweats
He's getting closer

The blanket is dripping with her anticipation
Will she wake up
Or will this be her fate?

Wake up! Wake Up! Wake Up!
Why can't she wake up?
Ahhh Ahhhh!

He's here
She can taste his smell
She can see the crumbs on his lips.

His red eyes glint
Why can't she see his whole face?
Help! Her mind thunders.

A reflected light shines into her eyes
Oh my God, he's got a knife!
Zooommmm.

She's back in her bed again, gasping for air
Once again exhausted from a shattering dream.

Gemma Hughes (Age 14)

War

She is crying
She has lost her husband
She is shouting
She is throwing her arms about in despair
She is thinking about her children
When is it going to stop?
WAR!

Susanna Hampshire (Age 15)

The Computer

It always locks up
It always blows up
It always stops working properly
It always crashes in a game

I like to play on paint
I like to draw and play
I like to search the internet
I like to play lots of games

It will always be fun
It will always be my friend
It will always be my favourite
It will always be there for me.

Ryan Hussey (Age 9)

Deep Water

Quiet, peaceful, morning blue misty air,
Satin, frosty pebbles
That I creep toward.

The weary Winter's here;'
Soothing the landscape, but
Awakening the creatures
To a chilling white frost.

Seaweed entangles
My every movement and thought
I own the coast;
Everyone of my crests; a powerful force.

Enveloped in an icy foam
The silent sleeping shells and starfish wash up onto the bay.
I will not be Winter's victim
For I am the sea, and only answer
To the call of the sun; my duty is Summer's command.

As the cruel truths of Winter are turned aside,
Scintillating sun shines down on the sands
Summer dawns, breaking smile to face and sparkle to shore.

My crashing tides reflect in the mirror of strength.

Samantha Hutchings (Age 15)

When My Sister Sings!

Fa la la that's my sister trying to sing
Don't worry there's no point trying to bring
Some earmuffs to keep the sound out
'Cause all she'll do is knock you out
She really doesn't mean it
I promise you she doesn't
She says she sounds like an opera singer
But it's more like a pig squealing for its dinner!

Caroline Howes (Age 9)

There Lies A Place

There lies a place, far north amidst the sea
Numerous dwarf-like isles encircle the rugged land;
Like birds floating in the sky, the inhabitants are free
To roam the golden shores, over the silky, soft sand
The clear blue ocean shimmers in the gleaming sunlight
Though the temperamental waves frequently rise above the shore
To collide violently with the rocks at such a height;
Returning always to tranquillity once more
The silence can be heard lingering in the atmosphere
Occasionally interrupted by the sweet song of a dove;
Lucky are those who have had even a glimpse of here
To experience once is to eternally love.
There lies a place, far north amidst the sea
As well as forever deep in the heart of me.

Amy Hinks (Age 15)

Hamster

Hamster crawls slowly
Try and catch it, it moves quickly
Flexible to fit through small gaps
Dark green penetrating eyes

Teeth like axes
Greedy little pet
Pouches as big as balloons

Big cage with wood flakes
Tunnels to explore
It's a jungle in there

As I watch
It hurries to stuff his pouch
With food and goodies
To eat for lunch

Noisy during the night
Fun during the day
It's a small fluffy critter.

Jamie Hunt (Age 10)

Alpe d'Huez

The blanket of mist hangs below the pure
White world of snow,
Silence is broken by the soundless
Purring of engines activating the lifts.
The gentle falling of snow settles on
The sloped roofs,
The bitter coldness from the north brings
An icy breath.
The bright orange snow cannons specify
The pistes.
The first skier climbs on a lift,
The day has begun.

James Hooper (Age 11)

The Darker Side Of Love

In many ways a hot water bottle is like love
It's cute fluffy cover will make you fluttery like a dove.

Only after a while when you get inside the cover
Its cold rubbery personality you will discover.

Oh sure, it's warmth will comfort that pain in your side
But soon it will give you the cold shoulder, you'll just want to hide.

When you wake up one night and it's cold in your bed
The love has all gone and IT's there instead.

So this is a warning as soon you will see
How it's apparent warmth and affection isn't all it seems to be.

Louise Hastings (Age 15)

You

I never really realised all you are to me
And how great a friend you really are and all I need to be

Whenever I need support you lend a friendly ear
Never judgmental of my feelings or critical of my fears

You help me through the bad times and celebrate the good
You never ask too much from me sometimes I wish you would

In the past our friendship has overcome a lot
Even on those many days when it seemed we always fought

I couldn't live without you and I wouldn't want to try
To think one day I'll have to, makes me want to cry

I cannot find the words to say how much I really care
So I want to thank you one more time for always being there!

Jenny Harding (Age 16)

My Pet

My pet is quiet and still
Always trying to get up a very steep hill

He's soft and cuddly
Warm and happy

Can you guess what he is
He's a hamster of course he is.

Rebecca Hussey (Age 8)

My Pet Dragon

My pet dragon is green and blue
And likes his tummy tickled
He likes to eat all different things
And loves his onions pickled.

He is only about two years old
And acts like a tiny baby
If he is smart enough
I could take him to school, maybe.

I keep him in the garden shed
With a bale of hay and straw
He likes to have a cuddle
And likes kisses even more.

I love my green and blue dragon
Although he can be a pain in the neck.
He never breathes flames of fire
Or the shed would be a wreck!

Zoe Hundley (Age 11)

Peter And The Wolf

Dear Mum
I went into the meadow and opened the gate,
I saw a strange fellow, it was my mate;
It was a bird up high in the trees,
And then along came some bees.
Peter saw a cat with greedy eyes,
It was trying to catch some flies;
The cat wanted the bird to play,
But then the bird flew away.
Along came a wolf with an empty tummy,
It thought the duck was very yummy;
He caught the duck and ate it,
And then the wolf was very fit.
Peter got a lasso and caught its tail,
And then stuck it on the rail;
The hunters came and shot the guns,
And out of the guns came strange buns.
They stopped shooting and put it down,
Then someone went down to town;
They took the wolf to the zoo,
And then the animal went "Moo!"

Shoaib Hussain (Age 10)

Autumn

Damp misty mornings,
Spider's webs like silver thread with trapped
Precious diamonds inside,
A carpet of colourful leaves on the wet ground,
Bright leaves dancing in the playful wind,
They madly make up a crazy dance,
As we walk there is a crunching
Sound under our feet,
Trees gently casting off leaves,
They are floating lazily,
It is the end of summer,
Soon the trees will be bare.

Lauren House (Age 9)

The Two Seasons

The best season is Spring
Because new life begins
With long grass waving in the wind
And buzzin' bees after the flowers
Ants go marching one by one
With people happy nearly everyone

The least favourite is Autumn
Because leaves go around and around
And fall on the ground
Flowers droop and die
And hardly no birds fly
Hedgehogs hibernate
And I do hate Autumn.

Sarah Holmes (Age 8)

Tests

Before a test everyone's nervous
All wondering how they will do
Is it going to be easy
Or shall I just copy you?

The gym is waiting, waiting to snatch you
Within its walls so freezing cold
With its basketball net
Going to cheat, ready to peep at my answers, so bold.

Once the dreaded test begins
Teachers start prowling round
You reach those horrible tricky questions
Not hearing any type of sound.

Tests are a nightmare
Wake me up from this bad dream
Tests are horrible
Or so they seem.

Relieved from having all that pressure
Wanting a break after this tiring day
Chattering loudly with delighted grins, because ...
It's all over! - until next May!

Sarah Hook (Age 10)

I Like The Sunshine

I like the sunshine
I like the rain
I like the wind and snow
Any kind of weather it's okay with me
Yo ho ho ho ho

Kerem Hussein (Age 8)

Love

Out there where the skies are blue
All I want is to be with you
We will share all our love
On a sandy beach, with pure white waves

I will love you forever
For eternity and a day
We will soar on the back of an eagle
And share our secrets and laugh and play

Out there where the grass is green
We will talk and not be seen
The world is our oyster
And forever it shall be

We will be in a room withe pearly white doves
They will flap around our heads
And we will feel their fleecy soft feathers
I will love you forever, and forever love shall remain.

Shelly Haggas (Age 13)

Dolphin

My name is Lauren Melissa
You might think it's funny
That I would buy a dolphin
If I had loads of money
I could ask my teacher
If I could use our pool
Not for a long time but
Let my dolphin live at school
At home we would be digging
A pool makes lots of mess
My mum would get fed up
And wish the dirt was less
After a few days
I would have my dolphin pool
The dolphin can go home with me
And no longer live at school.

Lauren Melissa Holt (Age 9)

Firefly

Its tail flickers gently in the shadows of the night,
It hovers around effortlessly when in flight,
It's amazing how it manages to shine so bright,
Glittering through the sky with its radiant light,
As it flickers gently in the shadows of the night.

Stephanie Hovey (Age 11)

Fight

The fight for territory has started, dominant male lions are fighting everywhere,
The lionesses stand back not wanting to get hurt.
Soon the group will know who will get the plains, the east one, with the gazelles all over it.
A puddle of blood collects on the ground, a lion must be bleeding.

The pain is getting worse and worse
The blood is gushing out of the wound, the pain, the pain.

Memories are coming back, I think it's the pain. He remembers when he first saw light,
The taste of blood and flesh was new to him, now it was an everyday thing.

The pain is getting worse and worse
The blood is gushing out of the wound, the pain, the pain.

Memories are coming back, I think it's the pain.
The first catch, the run, the run, the feeling of eating something that he had caught.

The pain is getting worse and worse
The blood is gushing out of the wound, the pain, the pain.

Memories are coming back, I think it's the pain. When seeing his best friend in pain,
But when seeing the cubs he felt better, seeing them grow up was the best thing.

The pain is getting worse and worse
The blood is gushing out of the wound, the pain, the pain.

The last breath, the last blink, the last move, now the deed is done,
Battle lost and won, he had lost, he was dead.

Alyshia Harrington-Clark (Age 10)

My Crucifiction

I walk on, the crown of thorns scratching to my head.
The cross pushing on my back.
The mob crying and shouting and screaming to let me go.
I fall down, I can see nails and hammers,
I scream for help, I shout for freedom.
The blood dripping down on the ground.
My scars on my body stinging.
I scream in pain.
They hang me up,
The guards letting my family through.
They stare at me,
They weep, weep, weep.
I am getting weaker by the second.
They take my mother away.
The clouds are closing and the sky is grey,
Then I drop my head.

Jack Hatcher (Age 9)

Snow Is

Snow is a white puff of smoke
Snow is pearls drifting from the sky
Snow is crunched up tissue
Snow is glitter sprinkling from the sky
Snow is a sheet of white blankets.

Joe Heywood (Age 9)

An Eight Legged Traveller

The spider succeeded under the door
Just missed being splatted by mum on the floor
He tore across the living room like grease lightning
When my sister came down he gave her a frightening
He didn't stick around to see what she'd do
Instead he crept to my bathroom and fell down the loo
Then to the landing our traveller searched on
But to my room he trotted, be careful little one!
Up the wall and down the cord and
Over my book of the silver sword
You don't have a weapon, you don't bite or
Sting, unfortunately for you, you don't have wings
Take heed my dear traveller going over the bed
Because if I wake up you'll surely be dead
All of a sudden I heard our cat hiss
Then I woke up and tried to hit but missed
Just when you thought you'd escaped under the mat
I jumped out of bed and stood on you, splat!

Charlotte Howson (Age 11)

It Was So Noisy

I was so noisy that
I couldn't hear my sister shouting.
It was so noisy
That I couldn't hear the pump on the fish tank.
It was so noisy that
I couldn't hear myself.
It was so noisy!

Thomas Harding (Age 7)

Sorry!

Why do all the teachers hate me? I can't see what I've done wrong!
I'm only chatting to my friends or singing my favourite song.

But I have to say sorry!

Why do all these teacher hate me? When I was aged three or four
I had a fight with my best friend and was forced to clean the floor!

And I had to say sorry!

Why do all these teachers hate me? Aged 12 I was kicked out of French
Because I scratced my name with a compass into the side of the teacher's bench.

Sorry!

Why do all the teachers hate me? My GCSEs all went wrong!
Instead of writing the answers I wrote the lyrics to a song.

But to whom do I say sorry?

Why do all the teachers hate me? A levels are nearly upon me.
It's too late to say sorry now, so I'll have to admit, I was wrong!

Paul Hayler (Age 16)

A Riddle

He is always there to greet me
When I open the front door
Tall and straight and never late
He stands upon the floor

He has a kind, round face
And must be at least 6 feet tall
I can hear his heart beating
As I walk into the hall

His hands move across his face
As the day gives way to night
His wooden limbs are old and stiff
Yet he really is quite bright

I love my dear, old grandfather
I have known him all my days
I couldn't bear to part with him
And his time-keeping ways.

Serene Husseini (Age 12)

Springtime

I like Spring
Because of the flowers
Some grow tall
Just like towers
If I was a flower
I would be
A daffodil
And stand very still

Nathan Heels (Age 7)

It

The thing is tall
And very round
Its feet are small
All three bound
One eye is big
One is flat
One is square
And one is fat
It has no hair
Tied in a green bow
It has no fingers
Although ...
It's thumbs are pink
With no nails
Its hair is sleek
On all four tails
He's now sitting
In the back row
And what it is
You'll never know!

Caitlin Hopes (Age 12)

My Island

Let me tell you about my island
The sun shines down all the day
As you go up a path it guides the way
Huge waterfalls rush over the rocks
Seagulls fly over in great big flocks
You can lie in the sand and watch the fish
Whilst sipping coconut milk from a dish
You can fall asleep at night to sounds of birds
To find fault with my island is truly absurd
Now surely really can you see
Why you wish that you were me.

Stacey Hawke (Age 12)

Seasons

Spring is when the leaves come out
Lambs and cows are all about

Summer is my favourite time
Sucking a ice-pop the flavour's lime

Autumn is the best one of all
When the pretty leaves fall

Winter's the time when the winds blow
And on the ground lies lots of snow.

Donna Henderson (Age 13)

Football

Football is cool
It's so great
You could never play it
While you are eating cake
David Beckham is the best
He is better than the rest
Schmeichel is so very cool
He is the best at saving the ball
Another player is Andy Cole
He misses the goal and hits the pole

Ashley House (Age 9)

It's A ...

Bell ringer
People singer
Burial garden
With Vicar pardon
A holy room
With sadness and gloom
It's a ... ?

Matthew Hoff (Age 10)

The Love Of My Life

Her body is as smooth as a cheetah's skin
She is, also very, very thin
Her front is as smooth as a baby's bum
But she pulls me around, just like my mum

She steers me in the right directions
But sometimes I have to make some corrections
Her grip on me is truly great
When I'm with her I have a high heart rate

We run around in the night sky
But to each other, we cannot lie
Her eyes twinkle like a star
It's the one
The only
It's my dad's car!

John Harkup (Age 12)

What Is It?

He eats meat
He runs like a car
He is related to a lion?
He has brown spots on his back
So who is he?

Jamie Howden (Age 10)

Love

Love is a wave going high, low, up, down and all around

Love is an empty box of chocolates, from a broken heart

Love is a cloud, soft and fluffy but with threatening rain

Love is a tree, growing but dying as it gets through the year

Love is the world lasting forever.

Shaun Howard (Age 11)

The Magical Planets

The planets are footballs floating in the sky
The planets are marbles on a black table
The planets are pieces of fruit bobbing on the water
The planets are eyes watching you all night
The planets are basketballs roaming the night sky
The planets are snooker balls rolling across a black table
The planets are papier mache balloons flying through the air
The planets are ball bearings rolling along a black sheet of paper
The planets are Christmas baubles hanging from a black tree.

Scott Hellings (Age 12)

Witches' Spell

Little maggots wiggly whirl
Maybe we can make this spell
White shark's tooth
And a black horse's hoof

Turn the cauldron turn, turn, turn
Destroy the castle make it burn!

Hippos tongue in sewage slurp
Round the cauldron the witches lurp
To and thro, up and down
The witches have to go to town

Turn the cauldron, turn, turn, turn
Destroy the castle make it burn!

The witches scan the bowl all day
The smell will travel far away
Add a touch of human spit
And some boots with a football kit

Turn the cauldron, turn, turn turn
Destroy the castle make it
BURN!

Charlotte Hows (Age 8)

The Tiger

The tiger has keen claws
To kill his prey on the moors
Then he goes back home for tea
To eat a lovely chimpanzee

After tea he goes to sleep
Dreaming of some lovely meat
Then he awakes to a roar
But then he finds it was a snore.

Dominic Hall (Age 10)

Baby Turtle

Bursting out of his nest
Attending his journey to the sea
Blinded by grit
Yolky, sticky shell

Tracks of a hundred
Up the mountains of sand
Rolling into giant-sized footprints
Taking tiny steps
Leaving small dots
Ending at the water's edge.

Natalie Harris (Age 10)

Haggis!

Along come the haggis'
They'll nibble your toes
Along come the haggis'
They'll bite you on the nose
Along come the haggis'
You'll find them here and there
Along come the haggis'
They'll nick your underwear.

The people were fed up
They tore their hair
The people were fed up
Buying underwear.

They asked the nutty professor
To make them a gun
To blast the haggis' to kingdom come.

Down came the haggis'
With a shimmering cry
But one cheeky haggis did not die
Soon the day of the haggis will dawn
So dig a hole and hide under the lawn.

George Harley (Age 10)

My Motorbike

Smelly, shiny, noisy
Exciting, good fun
The oil in my motorbike smells
The shiny silver bike shines in the sun
Riding my motorbike is really fun
My motorbike is shiny and red
I think about it when I am in bed.

Stephen Harris (Age 11)

The Friendly Giant

There is a giant living in our village
He loves to roam the forest
He is always there to help
And some how makes us smile

He always keeps the bad away
And keeps us nice and safe
He has a friend yes me
Yes it's always been me

He wears a cloak, he wears a hat
And his huge big boots
They are so big I could, pop
In and go to bed.

Kristina Harpur (Age 10)

Underneath The Silence I Can Hear .....

Underneath the silence I can hear .....

A feather whipping the air on the witch's magical command,
Summer flowers slowly growing in a green garden,
A tulip revealing its beautiful petals at last,
Curled, shrivelled leaves flickering from an old gnarled oak in autumn,
White puffy clouds floating across a perfect sky,
Grass cutting blowing across peaceful meadows.

Underneath the silence I can feel .....

The soft warm quilt as I lay down to sleep drifting into a land of dreams,
My heart thumping after running a tiring race,
Goose-bumps on my arm as someone drags their nails along the blackboard,
Sadness weighing down my shoulders at the devastating funeral,
My head buzzing with thoughts at the excitement of the party,
Coldness in my stomach as I am so hungry, nearly starving.

Chelsea Haughton (Age 10)

The Witch's Kitchen

The cauldron bubbling rapidly
Stinking of cooking socks
She sat down her owl-hooting yellow tea
The cat smelling of boiled bogey
The witch sat, her owl-hooting yellow tea in her hands
Staring at the jar of whistling brains
And the bin full of tattered old broken broom sticks.

Jake Harper (Age 9)

So Many Choices!

There was a rich man from Kent
Who didn't know what to give up for lent
His wife said cakes
His brother said lakes
So he ended up putting his house up for rent!

Andrew Herd (Age 11)

It Was So Noisy

It was so noisy that
I couldn't hear the cleaner buzzing really nosily.
I was so noisy that
I couldn't hear the train going past with his hooting horn.
I was so noisy that
I couldn't hear my brother screaming loudly.
It was so noisy that
I couldn't hear the ice cream man playing his lovely music.
It was so noisy that
I couldn't hear the washing machine blazing really loudly.

Alanna Hawker (Age 8)

Cat

Cat, cat all alone
Cat, cat no home
Cat, cat want a home
Cat, cat needs milk
Cat, cat very hungry, sad
Cat, cat fall over
Cat, cat cry forever
Cat, cat happy again
Cat, cat in the garden
Cat, cat playing with grass
Cat, cat eat grass
Yuk! Yuk!
Cat, cat be sick.

Katie Haralambous (Age 8)

The Dark

A horrid spooky graveyard
Ghostly spirits
Cold rock tombs
Stones
and
the Dead

Alexander Hassett (Age 9)

Animals

De dog by de bowl
Eatin some food
De dog by de bowl
He's in a bad mood

De rabbit in de garden
Runnin around
De rabbit in de garden
Den he heard a sound

De mouse in de hole
Is eatin cheese
De mouse in de hole
It must be very pleased

De bear in de woods
Huntin for fish
De bear in de woods
It will be delish

De penguin in de water
Waitin for something to eat
De penguin in de water
You're surely in for a treat.

Sophie Hayes (Age 8)

Flame Of Life

My flame of life is to be no more
For now I cease to be
Can you feel the wind, see the sun
From every breeze of the wind
And every ray of the sun
That's where I'll be
When it's time for your flame of life
To be no more ... that's when you'll see again
Until that day, take comfort from me
Feel the wind, feel the sun
That's where I'll be
As the breeze blows, my arms are about you
As I stoop to kiss you the sun will glow
As your flame of life burns on
My love continues to grow
Apart in life we may be
Together in spirit we are
But only until the flame of life
Ceases to be ...

Ann Horton (Age 16)

Walking Through The Jungle

I was walking through the jungle the other day
When I saw a huge gorilla coming my way
"Hey" said the gorilla, "Have you lost your way?"
I stood and trembled.
I was walking through the jungle the other day
When I saw an angry tiger coming my way
"Hey" said the tiger, "Would you like to stay for dinner?
As long as you don't get any thinner."
I was walking though the jungle the other day
When I bumped into my friend Jay
Who showed me the way.

James Hook (Age 9)

The Millennium Dome

Like a breakfast bowl turned upside down
Vampire teeth which haven't been brushed
With blood stains at the point
Glued to the top

Twelve metal cylinders
Dotted around the outside
Each humming its own tune
With nobody listening

In the night it's lit up
With fallen stars on the ground
Clatter! Clatter!
The last person's footsteps fading away
Shutdown
SILENCE!

James Hosegood (Age 11)

What A Gift

The car sat upon the windowsill
And unfortunately it sits there still;
Its azure paint job dulled by time
The victim of a forgotten crime.
Not used, the velour of its seats unseen
The bodywork now far from clean
(The owner of this car, you're thinking, surely must
Be mad to leave it unused) whilst it just sat there gathering dust
A scale replica of the Chevy Corvette ('52)
An electric shade of sparkling blue,
Bought by an over-caring, portly aunt
Out of touch with her niece so she can't
Understand why Lil' Lucy found her gift a bore
"But it goes vroom, vroom." (Lucy wanted something more)
It's not a Barbie, its only flaw
What a gift for a girl to ignore.

George Hoare (Age 16)

My Pet

I asked my mum "Could I have a dog?"
She just said, "When you're nine."
I only had to wait four years time
The years went by in time
I asked my mum, "Could I have a dog?"
"If you want we'll go to the shop."

We went to the shop to get my dog
We came home with my dog that day
We had a very good play
My dog ran off, almost got shot
She came back home very worried
Thinking she would never stay alive.

Annabel Hurford (Age 9)

A Gorilla's Feelings

I move like a human
A fierce manlike creature
But humans are my enemy
They hunted down my family
Wife, child, dad and mum
My only family are my adopted mum and dad.

I am a lonely creature
A beast to some of you
But if I bump into one more human
The first I kill is you!

I eat green leaves
And monkey's fleas
The first I eat is
YOU!

Benjamin Houlbrook (Age 11)

Mixed Brews

There was once a horrible witch
Who lived in a deep dark ditch
When she stirred a fast spoon
With many little baboons

For her food she made ugly things
With spiders and frogs together with some pins
The cauldron used was black and fat
Many rats appeared from the holes and sat

In a corner she had a dirty mat
For her scary cat
Her cat caught some rats
And enjoyed her meal on the mat
And became very fat.

Sobia Hussain (Age 10)

The Key To My Heart

She's my year, my life
She's my day, my wife
She's my fire, my water
She's my heavens, my food
She's my soul mate, my earth
She's my love, my week
She's my good, my bad
She's my earth, my lady
She's my key to my heart.

Jess Hall (Age 10)

Late

Got up this morning
Bed trembled, "Get back in"
"Can't," I said, "Late."

Went to the bathroom
Shower gurgled, "Have a spray"
"Can't." I said, "Late!"

Went to the kitchen
Kettle whistled, "Have another"
"Can't" I said, "Late!"

Went to the front room
TV blipped, "Watch me"
"Can't," I said, "Late!"

Went to the hall
Shoes tapped, "Polish me"
"Can't," I said, "Late!"

Went outside
Car choked, "Fill me"
"Can't," I said, "Late!!!"

Robert Hawkins (Age 10)

Journeys

I walk through the valley
Explore the abyss
I'm on top of the mountain
I roam the fields of emerald green grass

I am the strider
I hear the ocean, call of the dove
I see the heavens over the ocean
I shall go to the heavens

A new age is coming
I shall leave for a new life
I'll be eternally glad
Over the sea to the heavens I shall go.

Max Hebditch (Age 10)

Reading

R eading is fun and cool
E ndings are the best
A nd so are the middles
D eadly parts of the story are fantastic
I gnoring the beginning
N othing like TV
G eorge is the best at reading.

George Hamson (Age 9)

Tea Time Across The Ocean

Flying in the air
Without any underwear
Wind on my back
I hope I'm on the right track
Across the ocean blue
Ships a sailing through
Waves climbing high
The sun is in the sky and so am I
Here I come to my summer home
A swallow all alone
Landing in the tree
Just in time for tea.

Mark Helm (Age 11)

Tea

I'm going to tea with grandma
I wonder what she will cook
Tuna pasta or fish and chips
From her new recipe book

I'm going to tea with grandad
I wonder what we will have
Strawberry tart, strawberry ice cream
And a cold refreshing drink.

Megan Harcombe (Age 6)

Sea Shell

My sea shell
Buried in the sand
Not a thing to see
Along the glossy strand

In comes the sea
To wash the sand away
And it all happened
A day in May

I pick up my find
Put it to my ear
Listen very carefully
what do I hear?

That is all from now
On this sandy strand
My sea shell is now gone
To a foreign land.

Alistair Holmes (Age 9)

The New Year

Stuck inside,
While outside the harsh wind beats everything on its path,
In the distance storm clouds gather
And rain pelts down on the bare fields.
There are no signs of life,
Everything is asleep now for the winter.

But the ray of hope for a new year lies ahead,
The world waking up from its dark slumber.
Trees and plants coming alive to see the new beginning,
Animals creep out of their cosy dreams.
Everything wakes up to start again
In this new year of light and hope.

Sarah Johnson (Age 15)

What A Busy Night!

I went down stairs
And fell through the roof
I went in the bath
And flushed the toilet
I got out my pencil
And changed the ink
I put on my shoes
Then my socks
I was watching TV
Then I turned it on
Then Caterpillar hopped me to the zoo
Finally I went to bed
And had some breakfast
What a busy night!

Adem Holness (Age 11)

Fish

Water glider
Super swimmer
Going deeper
Sparkly scale
Shimmering tail
Cunning catcher
Bubble maker
Shark dodger
Water flipper
Ocean hurdler
Thin fins.

Sarah Hampson (Age 12)

Sad Turtle

Okay I'm slow 'n' lazy...
Not so quick.
But believe me...
I'm gloomy and sick.
Nobody really cares...
Don't have any friends
I can't keep up with
All the cool trends.
I wanna get killed
Get away from this place...
There's no point in living
As I am full of disgrace...
Why am I hated...
It's not fair, why me.
I need big help,
I'll never, ever be in glee.

Dilwor Hussain (Age 10)

The Sun

The sun is high
In the sky
The sun is shining on my face
It's fun to have a race

Sharaz Hussain (Age 9)

A Man From Bengal

There was man from Bengal
Who went to a fancy dress ball
He thought he could risk it
And go as a biscuit
But the dog ate him up in the hall.

Sheraz Hussain (Age 10)

The Clock

Tick tock tick tock
What is the time?
When it's 12 o'clock
It's eating time

When the clock strikes 12
Come on get eating

Eat eat, yum yum, tasty
Food for me

When the clock strikes s3
It's painting time
We paint the clock, we paint
It yellow and you know what
The clock makes a noise.

Something popped out of it.

Mohsin Hussain (Age 8)

The Tree

Crispy golden leaves falling down the tree
Golden old leaves falling down the trees
Huge lovely giant trees standing any where
Brown dirty leaves falling down on the muddy ponds
Lovely birds' nests on the lovely new tree branches
Giant thunder, lightning hitting the old branches
Bananas and apples on the new trees lots
Of monkeys jumping on the trees and eating all the fruits
Crunchy golden leaves giving me a lovely chase while the wind is blowing
Spiky sharp trees like a shark's teeth
Giant spiky, crunchy leaves blowing everywhere
It's magical and turns in to a big pond
Woodpeckers banging their beaks on the trees
Little trees grow in to the giant trees
Growing lots of fruits and everybody picking them
Squirrels jumping around the base of an old tree
Twigs standing on the new and old trees
IT'S A TREE!!!

Asjad Hussain (Age 10)

The Ghost House

The Ghosts are in the house
There is a creaking in the floor
I shiver with fear
White sheets cover the furniture swaying in the wind from the broken windows
I get goose bumps
I feel really frightened
The hairs on the back of my neck stand on end
Cobwebs stick to my hair and clothes
I run to the door my heart is pounding
Run down the street screaming.

Stephanie Howard (Age 13)

Untitled

I looked up at the stars and I saw the Great Bear
I looked out at the sea and everything was free
I looked out at the land and all the animals there
I looked at my house and saw the smoke coming from the chimney
And I knew it was time to go home.

Rebecca Harper (Age 8)

Weather Watcher

What is lightning?
God taking a photograph.

What is fog?
The breath of God in the winter.

What is thunder?
A thousand motorbikes starting up their engines.

What is snow?
A slushy ice cream spreading across the earth's surface.

Adam Holborow (Age 11)

Weather

What is snow?
God laying down
With a plain white blanket over him.

What is rain?
Water spitting down
From the clouds.

What is light?
A blaring beam
Of yellow from heaven.

What is frost?
God's earth
Covered in diamonds.

What is thunder?
Banging hammers
On the ground.

Ryan Hosier (Age 10)

I

I am in a vase
I am near food
I get soaked every day
And I can't help it

I am on top of a roof
But I don't know how I get soaked
I am with soil
I smell very nice
People come and smell me

My house is on top of a table
I can see rooms and things
I can't go out anywhere
I don't like it here.

Ifzah Hussain (Age 10)

Peter And The Wolf

One day I saw Peter
Sitting on the heater

He saw a duck
Who was writing a book
Along came grandfather with his stick
And he started to be sick

The wolf was Peter's friend
And that was the end.

Rizaul Hussain (Age 10)

It Was So Noisy

It was so noisy I couldn't hear
The school bell ringing.

It was so noisy I couldn't hear
My sister scream the loudest scream my sister has ever done.

It was so noisy I couldn't hear
The baby crying.

It was so noisy I couldn't hear
My dad hammering a hole in the wall.

It was so noisy I couldn't hear
The motorbike whizz past.

It was so noisy.

Jonathan Hughes (Age 8)

A Farmer And His Animals Chant

Sister animals
Brother animals
Mother animals
Father animals
Oh egg givers
Oh milk givers
Oh friend givers
What have you in store
For a poor farmer today?
Oh animals I feed you, I look after you all year round.
I hope you give me lots of eggs and milk and wool
Sister animals
Brother animals
Mother animals
Father animals ...

Emma Humm (Age 8)

My Amazing Creature

My amazing creature has .....

A head the size of a gorilla's
Ears the size of rabbit's
A nose the size of a hedgehog's
As many legs as a centipede
A body the size of a dragon
The ability to fly
Run as fast as a cheetah
Jump as far and high as a kangaroo.

My creature can do all these things and has them too.
I love my creature and he loves me too!

Jason Harvey (Age 11)

My Darkness

My song goes dark
My light hides away
I let my troubles out again
The world stops to tell me, it's over now
I go away, depressed
But I still shout out loud
Please stop it
Ban all life to be on the planet
My life still goes on.

With no one to talk to
But myself
I'm all alone now.

Jessica Holley (Age10)

The Gardener's Friend!

Moles, they don't care
Digging in gardens
Everywhere! .
Twitching whiskers
Quivering noses
Making tunnels in the roses!
Little gentlemen in velvet waistcoats
Grabbing worms by their throats.
Giant paws like spades
For digging they are made
Everywhere that they go
Lovely, crumbly soil that they throw,
They really are the Gardener's friends - NOT!

Sarah Hunt (Age 11)

Snow

Snow is a shiny spark floating in the air
It dances in the moonlight
It's like twinkley flakes falling on the grass
It's like sequins in the sky

Joanne Harvey (Age 9)

Poem For The Verbally Confused

Got down, enthusiastically read my bed
Swam quickly through my cereal
Chucked school out of the window
Hungrily ate my literacy lesson
Danced with break time doing a waltz
Nibbled my numerals
Laughed at my lunch
Crazily drove the car home
Sat heavily on my dinner
Murdered my sleep.

Catherine Havers (Age 10)

Sunshine

What I hate about sunshine is
It's too hot and makes me sweat.
What I like about sunshine is
My mum lets me have an ice lolly.
What I hate about sunshine is
I get big red marks on my arms and legs
And I have to put the fan on.
What I like about sunshine is
How it shines on the leaves of trees
I like that because it's peaceful.

Simone Heath (Age 7)

Springtime

Spring means a lot to me
New flowers growing I love to see
Leaves on the trees turning green
Lots of things I haven't seen
Birds flying on high and singing flocks them all in the sky
Picking up straw and winging their way, to make nests on high.

Claire Hedges (Age 8)

Spring Is Here

Spring is here, so give a cheer
One beautiful day as we went out to play
Skipping, dancing and jumping around in the playground
There are people in a boat whistling singing and wearing a coat
As the day gets colder and turns into night
Out of my window there is a beautiful sight.

Alice Henney (Age 8)

School Senses

S chool, school, school doors slamming, cooks
C ooking, school, school, school, people speaking
H orrible school. But our school is nice
O ld, old, old school. Working is fun, fun, fun
O ffice people working for their jobs, jobs, jobs
L ittle, little, little school but our school is big

What is your school like?

S chool, school, school
E arly at school, I really like school
N aughty children in the school, but there's
S ensible children in the school. I love being
E arly at school because it is the best
S chool, school, school.

Rochelle Harman (Age 8)

My Goldfish

Sparkly fish in the bowl
Swimming about
Round and round
Waiting for his dinner
Sprinkle the food in
Gulping it down
Swimming about
Round and round
Waiting for his dinner.

Samantha Hampton (Age 9)

The Eagle And I

The eagle up there hovering high
Above the busy shops
While I'm down here trying to buy
A bunch of lollipops.

Harriette Hartle-Ryan (Age 8)

Leaves

In the cold frosty autumn nights
Silently, the leaves are spinning to the ground
They lie sad and lonely
Children scatter them far and wide
They crunch them carelessly
The broken leaves cry out
"Stop them, stop them, leave us to sleep!"

Simon Higgins (Age 10)

The Headmaster's Poem

"Our father who art in heaven,
Bruce! look at the front,
Thy kingdom come,
Oy! your work must be done,
On earth as it is in heaven,
Tie your laces,
And forgive us our trespasses,
Joe don't kick Justin,
Lead us not into temptation,
Don't turn on the waterworks!
For thine is the kingdom,
I don't want to go to school,
For ever and ever,
Amen."

Jonathan Hall (Age 11)

The Flood

It started slowly, gradually
Dripping off the leaves
The rain had begun with
Ever increasing speed and volume

The river below swirling silently
Its meandering course commencing
The rain becoming a downpour
Sliding down the riverbanks

The wind gusting along through
The green of the trees
The rain being sprayed over
Homes of animals and birds

The water now rising from
Days of travelling upwards
The rain still continuing its
Damp course through houses

The destruction of homes from
All who live there
The water's receding as rain
Comes to an abrupt halt.

Matthew Hazleton (Age 10)

The Rain

The rain stamps down
Pattering on the roofs
Sparkling in the sunlight
Splashing in the stream
The grass shining wet.

Kerry Heron (Age 8)

21st Century

Harry Potter and Play Station 2
Robotic pets they're all brand new!
No more skipping or cat's cradle
Just inventing machines to lay the table.

Lots of cool computer games
Even some with funny names!
The Millennium Dome came and went
Though some enjoyed the big white tent.

The London Eye creeps round and round
High to the sky then low to the ground
Nearly everything has been upgraded
But there's just one thing that hasn't made it!

For it is homework
Yes it's true!
There's still a load of homework
For me and you!

Sophie Harris (Age 9)

Africa's People In Need

Why are Africa's people in need,
When crops don't grow from the seed,
The rain on earth does not pour,
Rivers dry like a scab on a sore,
Drought dries out the land,
Turning grass into baked sand.

In another country seeds grow good,
All around fields, forests and wood,
The rain it pours to feed the earth,
A new born baby has just been given birth,
Another country covered in snow,
And freezing winds blow and blow,
And the seeds do not grow,
Under the freezing rivers flow,
Flooded land from the pouring rain,
Crops been washed away again,
The weather changes everyday,
Gases rise and cause decay,
So the sun it burns us and the land,
So lets sort it hand in hand.

Sam Harris (Age 9)

The Future!

What will become of our world
Maybe we might be living on Mars
Could we stay alive until we are 200
Will we come in contact with aliens
Will our aeroplanes be going the speed of light
Will our cars hover
Fish, what will become of them
Will there be thousands of Fort Knoxs'
But, what will become of us?

Samuel Harwin (Age 10)

In The Distance

Galloping slowly across the moor
Pausing freely from time to time
Listening gently for signs of wake
During the night time hours

A clatter of hooves
Swishing of a tail
Signals the arrival of a lone stallion
With his head held high

Dawn is breaking
So he comes inside
Thinking gleefully
Of his roam of the countryside.

Nadine Heinz (Age 10)

Counting Rhyme

10 brand new angels going up to heaven
One fell back to earth and there were 9

9 devils fishing in a little boat
One was pushed in and there were 8

8 young schoolboys on their way to school
One was kidnapped and then there were 7

7 trapeze artists learning something new
One failed to grab the bar and there were 6

6 fishes swimming, swimming all day long
One was eaten up and then there were 5

5 books on a shelf waiting to be read
One was taken away and there were 4

4 children working with their friends
One child went to the loo and then there were 3

3 pen writing on a piece of paper
One ran out of ink and then there were 2

2 pencils drawing with their owners
One pencil snapped and then there was 1

1 silly rhyme going on and on
Suddenly it ended and then there was none.

Charlotte Hare (Age 9)

Freedom

As I walked through the grass
A butterfly came to me
As I swam through the sea
A gleaming fish came to me
And they all said how good it was
To be free!

Tristan Hammant (Age 10)

My Cockatiel

Crazy Billie the bird has cheeks
The colour of a sun setting sky.

His beak is as grey
As a dull, dark cloud.

He wakes me up every morning with a cherp
The sound of a blocked up whistle.

He rattles his cage as if he tries to escape
And then charges round like a bull being chased.

He buries his head in his food
Then lifts it up like a horse bucking.

He spreads his wings at night and
You wouldn't know he's there.

Russell Handy (Age 10)

Please Mrs Ramsden

Please Mrs Ramsden
This girl Amy Bower
Keeps following me Miss
What shall I do?
Run away to sea
Go and hide in the toilet
Do whatever you like
But don't ask me!

Please Mrs Ramsden
This girl Alice Walley
Keeps pinching my ruler Miss
What shall I do?
Hide it up your vest
Put it in the bin
Do whatever you like my lamb
But don't ask me!

Rebecca Heathcote (Age 8)

Bullying

Bullying is a horrible thing
Punching, kicking and spitting.
Some bullies do it for fun,
Others do it to be popular.
Phrases like shut your piehole,
Spill the beans or else
And you big baby, that's to be precise.
I know people who have been bullied
For nearly their entire life,
Hate it they might.
Some people stick up for themselves
Realising how stupid they are.
Bullies are usually large so
They can bully the weak and small.
Nastiness is their motto
But they have a weakness
And that is the person firing back.

Freddy Hartley (Age 11)

Sam The Snake

I am a snake, my name is Sam
I have teeth like a vampire
Rats, mice hmmmmm
I'm deaf, not slimy and
I attack very very quick and I'm scaly.

Black and red the pattern on my back
Rattle rattle goes my tail
Poisonous as a black widow
Follow me, by my trail.

Nicky Hardaker (Age 9)

Winter And Summer

W inter time is here
I n a cold blanket of snow
N obody is outside
T onight is cold and silent
E very night is the same
R ound up the hot water bottles

A ll day winter is dying
N o more cold days
D ay by day comes summer

S ummer is now here
U nderneath trees is the best place for shade
M um is watching
M y brother playing
E very day is warm and bright
R ound up all the drinks with ice.

Chloe Hart (Age 10)

My Killer Whale

My killer whale is black and white
If you meet him he'll give you a fright

My killer whale loves the sea
So it's easy to catch his tea

My killer whale loves to eat fish
So I always serve them on a dish

My killer whale is the best
He sometimes gets bored so what do you suggest

I suggest you play with him more.

Abigail Hart (Age 10)

Wondering Weather

What is frost?
          A crystal necklace.
What is sun?
          A flying ball on fire.
What is rain?
          Tears from the spirits of dead.
What is wind?
          Gods anger blowing on the earth.
What is lightning?
          A strike of golden fork.
What is a rainbow?
          Joseph's multicoloured dream coat.

Victoria Haywood (Age 11)

What Is The Weather?

What is sunshine?
A golden sunflower held up in the sky
What is snow?
A layer of clouds falling from the sky
What is wind?
God yawning when he's just woke up
What is frost?
The lacy veil of snow white's dress.
What is rain?
A bottle of water that's just been split.
What is thunder?
War time in the sky.

Beverley Harris (Age 11)

Homework

I think homework is smelly
I'd rather go for a walk
In my welly
S!
I think literacy is really boring
Oh no! It's raining! It's pouring!
I think numeracy is BRILL!
Brrr I'm getting a chill.
I think spelling is quite tricky
Man! This mud is sticky!
Sometimes HOMEWORK gets me in a muddle
I'm going to jump right in this puddle.

Edward Harris (Age 9)

The Sea

In the depths of the sea the tides
Go homeward bound
The mermaiden who's the Queen of the sea
One of sea beasts
The bay sprays sand as the seaweed appears
Where the sea - covers see the salt.

James Heyes (Age 9)

In My Head

In my head I have a dream
To be in the Secret Service.

In my head I can see myself
Saving the world from destruction.

The things I will do will stop war and
Weapons being used by little children.

In my head I will do this, but not now -
When I'm 21!

Chris Hall (Age 10)

School

Class 1
Lots of fun

Class 2
Everything's new

Class 3
We're planting a tree

Class 4
There's knocking at our door

Joshua Harvey (Age 8)

Slugs

Slugs slither
Slugs are slime
Slugs are small
But not very tall
They don't go fast
They go very slow
They creep and they crawl
You'd be surprised where they go.

Alex Hardy (Age 8)

Colours

C is for colours of the rainbow
O is for orange a nice bright colour
L is for light and bright colours
O is for original colours
U is for ugly dull colours
R is for red my favourite colour
S is for silver the colour of the moon

Rebecca Hare (Age 8)

The Desert

The crisp sand that looks like broken minute glass particles.
The sidewinder snake that slithers over shattered sand.
Blinding sandstorms which sting your eyes.
You can see shivering, shimmering sand in the distance.
Extremes of temperature going from boiling to freezing.
Dehydrated and extreme thirst.
The sand as hot as the surface of the sun.
Intense heat makes you want to collapse as your energy is drained.
You feel hot, dry and sticky.
Mountains which look like semi circular waves.

Simon Harding (Age 11)

Sun Sun!

Sun sun!
Why do you come out/
Why are you so bright?
How come you go in at night?
Do you talk to the moon?
Why are you so hot?
Why do you let the rain and wind take over you?
Why don't you stay in England?

Megan Harper (Age 9)

Pigs And Elephants

Pigs and elephants.
I am giving out these letters not to invite you
To a meeting I held last Tuesday.
I have not invited you here today to tell you
About something I now nothing about.
As the meeting is about to start
I'm going home!

Richard Hennessy (Age 10)

The Ocean

Slowly as it breathes
Gentle ripples dance upon the surface
Casting ever-widening rings;
As the sun forms a golden pathway
Along the glistening ocean
Sea life locked away from the world
Nestle safely under water.

Lauren Heffer (Age 10)

Writing

When I have been asked write
I cannot think quite straight
All the letters tumble
Everywhere over the page

And ...

When I have been asked to do sums
My head is filled with confusion
All the numbers flying around
Inside my aching head.

Sarah Hetherington (Age 10)

Slithering

Slithering and wriggling guess what it is.
It runs very fast, it is quite big.
It makes a loud sound.
It is an animal.
It's lovely and soft.

Can you guess what it is.
May be it's a girl or maybe it's a boy.
My nanna has one, it is very lively
It has droopy ears, it likes to chase cats
Yet can you guess what it is, it's a
DOG.

Bryony Hearn (Age 8)

The Creation Of Questions

What is sunshine?
      A leak in the golden ball of God.
What is a hurricane?
      A twist of breath to a furious suction.
What is warmth?
      A quilt of joy, across your heart.
How do you part the sky?
      By tampering with the soft white blankets.
How do you end the world?
      By blocking the leak in the ball.

Charlotte Hacker (Age 11)

Snow

I always find myself in winter.
I cover the roads and paths
With a layer of white cotton.
I see people shiver because of me.
My flakes float down like leaves in Autumn.
I make children build snowmen out of me.
I freeze everything ...
Then my worst enemy shines through the
clouds.
She melts me into a thousand puddles.

Connie Hartley (Age 8)

Cats

Loud purrer
Deep sleeper
Mouse killer
Dog killer
Milk drinker
High pouncer
Quick pouncer
Fast runner
Very gentle
Good meower

Thomas Harrison (Age 10)

The Arms Of A Cloud

The arms of a cloud reach out screaming with terror.
They've been sucked in never knowing whether or not they'll get out alive.
Their screams are the lightning that electrocutes the trees.
Their shouts are the thunder that comes with the chilling breeze.
The arms of the clouds hang on to the bars of hell.
The bars are so strong that not even satan himself could break them.
The rain is their cries of help when they shout "Let me out, let me out."
No longer have they got any respect for one and other.
The mist is the good souls that gave up long ago.
For now all is quiet all is still, until one day the arms of the clouds may reach out to get you ...

Jade Hill (Age 11)

Sebastian

S mashed the downstairs window
E nded the baby's life
B roke all the valuables
A te all the food
S tole all the money
T ried to escape
I n the end got caught
A sked to be set free
N ever, said the police

Greg Hilton (Age 11)

A New Day

Morning mist fills the air
With a stare of golden sun,
Farmers wake with a shake
And amble to feed the animals.

The brilliant sun burns down at noon
The animals graze peacefully,
Soon the flowers give bloom
And the rabbits play merrily around them.

As the light fades the darkness appears
And sparkling stars as bright as new spears,
Whispering, whispering sounds all around,
Clouds start to appear
To begin another new day!

Rachel Hewitt (Age 9)

Animals

The slow slithery slimy snails
The floppy flippy flappy fish
The curious clever cats
The enormous elegant elephants
The dippy dodgy dogs
The running rascal rabbits
The silly scary spiders
The brave bold bears.

Georgie Hinton (Age 9)

My Friend

My friend is as black as the midnight sky
She's a real friend I cannot deny
She is my dog and I love her so
I would dearly hate to see her go

She says 'hello' with one tiny lick
She says 'don't ignore me' with one little nip
Her face is long and full of joy
She loves it when we play with her toys

When she goes out for a run
She jumps around, she has so much fun
When she comes back, her tail in the air
I know I could not find a better dog <u>anywhere</u>!

Georgia Hewlett (Age 11)

Marvellous Monkey

Marvellous monkey,
Banana crazy,
Colour brown,
Very lazy.

Long arms,
Likes swinging,
Loves yellow,
Always singing.

Three t-shirts,
In trees,
Quite thin,
Buzzing bees.

Jessica Hemming (Age 8)

The Toyshop

In the toyshop,
There is a very fierce lion,
That roars a lot.

In the toyshop,
There is a very helpful bear.

In the toyshop,
There is an ostrich,
That tries to fly.

In the toyshop,
There is a rainbow unicorn,
That is quite a mischief.

Sarah Hirst (Age 5)

Stable

Swirling azure Jesus
Copper bronze stable
Murky dimness created Jesus to cry
Fluttering birds make faint chant
Tiny strokes appear to make out this dinky grey stable
Aquamarine, green grass smears as the painting dries
The glistening star leads to the snoozing baby
The tears from Jesus trickle into Mary
Sparkling red pastel runs over the copper bronze
Sparkling yellow hay.

Claire Hills (Age 11)

Christmas Star

Christmas star when is it Christmas
Christmas star gold and silver
Christmas star twinkling bright
Christmas star twinkling in the night

Christmas star shining brightly in the night
Christmas star nice and high
Christmas star up high with the moon
Christmas star letting us see.

Megan Hutchins (Age 6)

Springtime

I like baby animals
Because they look sweet.
When I have a race with them
I look and they are beat.

I like my garden when it is Spring
Because I can smell the flowers.
I think they smell nice
After all of them have had a shower.

When it is sunny I like it
So does my rabbit.
Every time I see what it is doing
But every time I see it, it is always chewing chewing.

Emma Hawkins (Age 5)

Sharks

Sharks are fast, clever and cunning.
I start to shiver as it stares at me,
Glares at me, it thinks I'm its prey.
I start swimming
I think I'm winning
But what's that NO!

Gliding through the dark and dingy waters of the south,
It's got a gigantic mouth
As it comes to the surface it ROARS!
It leaps up to grab a bird,
It swallows it in one whole gulp.
I wouldn't want to be in those jaws.
Would you?

Michael Hall (Age 9)

It Was So Noisy

It was so noisy that
I couldn't hear my mum screaming loud.

It was so noisy that
I couldn't hear a budgerigar crashing through a window.

It was so noisy that
I couldn't hear Miss rattling the little board.

It was so noisy that
I couldn't hear the police sirens whirring and whizzing past.

It was so noisy that
I couldn't hear the Welsh rugby players singing proudly the National Anthem.

James Harris (Age 7)

Best Friends

Best friends are very special very hard to find
But no best friends are as special as mine
They are always very kind to you all always
And always help you out and always
Have lots of fun and laugh a lot too
They always try to make you happy when you are sad
And all your troubles don't seem so bad.

Declan Hunt (Age 7)

Demons

Demons have a never ending rage,
It's like a fire that never stops burning,
Demons only see burning colours like red and orange,
Their rage builds and builds,
They have an urge to torture and destroy,
Demons never feel happiness or love,
Only anger and hate,
To them a valley of mountains would look like a rocky hell,
Beautiful fields full of lush grass would look dead and brown,
Demons have murderous minds,
They like to suck the blood of rabbits,
And chop off the heads of squirrels,
They like to spear sheep with arrows of fire,
So watch out,
You never know when there could be one behind you.....

Michael Joyce (Age 12)

Winter Poem

The blustery snow is like a wind blowing you on the ice.
"Stop! Stop!" I would say, "Go to Alaska far far away.
They'd say "Oh how lovely this is to be wrapped up nice and warm.
Take me to the coldest place to have some rice in a bowl."
"Lunch time," mum said, "Say goodbye."
"Goodbye friends, stop staring at me I'm having my lunch."

Matthew Hobson (Age 7)

A Kitten

A kitten is a miaowing fur ball,
It is a soft fluffy fur ball rolling into walls.
It is a ball of fun.
A kitten is a bed, all warm and cosy,
Keeping children safe in their dreams
Until they wake in the morning.
A kitten is a fluffy teddy bear,
Which children cuddle at night,
Also thinking about it in the day.

Lucy Elizabeth Harrison (Age 10)

I'll Follow You

I'll follow you
To the changing rooms
Where the showers
Spray puddles
I'll follow you
To the water slides
Where the water
Makes it slippery
I'll follow you
Under water
Where you can't
Stay for long
I'll follow you
To reception
Where it smells funny
I'll follow you
Where you swim
To the shallow
To the deep
I'll follow you.

Rachel Horner (Age 7)

Lullaby

Go to sleep, little baby
Close your sleepy eyes
I'll wake you in the morning
When the sun begins to rise.

When you're sleeping softly
When you're tucked in warm and tight
You will sleep so soundly baby
Until the morning light.

Reece Harbon (Age 10)

Bonfire Night

Fireworks beaming
Gleaming, screaming
Rockets flying, squealing

It's bonfire night
Everyone's laughing, having fun,
The smell of smoke reminds us of Guy Fawkes burning.
Children are holding sparklers which shine, sparkle, and glisten in the moonlight,
Red, blue, purple, green.
BANG
Go the rockets, down cascade the colours pink, yellow, orange and gold,
The bonfire is getting smaller,
People are starting to leave.

Happy Bonfire Night everybody!!!

Hayley Ismay (Age 10)

The Boy Was Sleeping

The boy was sleeping all night.
The boy was sleeping all night 'till midnight.
The boy was sleeping all night 'till midnight and 1 o'clock
The boy had a bad dream and couldn't sleep.

Liban Ibrahim (Age 9)

A Kenning Poem

A white hopper
A quick runner
A cute fluffy thing
A round tailed animal
A fluffy pet
A carrot muncher
A roly poly ball
What am I? .....

Sam Howell (Age7)

Rainbow

Rainbow colours,
Floating in the blue sky, high up.
Red, orange, yellow, green, blue, indigo and violet.
High in the sky, sitting with fluffy clouds.
Will never be found
Never will be seen
Rainbow colours.

Rainbow colours,
Brightly shining,
High in the sky,
Where clouds float by.

Rainbow colours,
Bright in the sky,
The clouds twinkle, shining,
With their lovely silver lining.

Emily Ingram (Age 10)

Night Time Fun!

She wakes up at night
She's not all that tame
She's my pet hamster
And nibbles her name.

Her fur is all soft
Fluffy and white
Her teeth are real sharp
And boy can she bite!

She hangs on the bars
And plays in her wheel
She drinks her water
And eats her meal

And in the morning when I wake up
And creep downstairs to have a peep
Where is nibble - has she escaped?
No She's all curled up fast asleep.

Catherine Irlam (Age 8)

Acrostic For Millennium Party

Marvelous fireworks zooming through the air,
Indescribable excitement,
Lights flashing all around,
Laughter echoes round the house,
Excited children staying up late,
Nearly there, ten seconds to go,
Impatient folk waiting for midnight
Unbelievably loud music,
Mighty bangs heard from miles around.

Peaceful blob lamp, blobbing away,
Amazing costumes add some looks,
Roaring rockets, shooting into space
Tasty food, being devoured,
Year ends, count down begins!

William Ingram (Age 9)

Colours

Blue is a whale in a sea,
or rain in the sky,
or school uniform,
or a dolphin in a swimming pool.

Red is blood in your skin,
or ink in a pen,
or red t-shirt,
or a flame or berries.

Silver is the moon up in the sky at night time,
or silver earings in your ear,
or a coin
or silver ink in a gel pen.

Yellow is the sun out in summer time,
or a yellow star,
or a sharpener,
or like a pencil case.

Green is like grass on a hill,
or green grapes,
or a book,
or like green paper.

Rabia Imtiaz (Age 9)

The Window

W e always look out of the window
I always see the sunny sky
N ever see the rain drop by but sometimes
D own the drainpipes I see the rain go
O h no! I need to go to bed but,
W e always look out of the window!

Billie Jury (Age 7)

Cars

Cars go far away.
The cars crash
Into
Bars
And
Old Grandpas.

Cars go fast.
Cars
Pollute
The air
And their fumes
Stick in your hair

Cars make me excited
And want to go fast
In my own
Lamborghini.

Mark Innes (Age 12)

My School

I like school
It's cool
Lots of friends
Friendship never ends

Year 1
Lots of fun
Year 2
Classroom new
Year 3
That's me
Year 4
Eager to learn more
Year 5
I'm alive
Year 6
How time ticks

Nicole Ilott (Age 8)

My Aspiration

As I close my eyes,
I can visualise,
All the things I want to be,
All the things I want to achieve.
I can picture myself flying,
I can see myself crying,
I want to reach my maximum ability,
I want to be the best I can be.
I want to become,
The greatest sportsman,
I want people to know,
How much I love sport so.
I want people to say,
That I am brilliant when I play.
So all but today,
I leave, and I'll say,
I will never stop,
Until I reach the top.
And I will never rest,
Until I can be at my very best.

Leyla Ibrahim (Age 14)

I Saw A Giant On The Cinema

I went to the cinema
I got some popcorn
Pop! pop!
I saw the dawn then
I saw the plant
When it was time to go home
It was time for bed
Then I saw the
GIANT!

Jordan Illiingworth (Age 8)

Pictures From My Mind

When I shut my eyes at night
I then appear in a magical land.
Waterfalls running and children running around.
Then I wake up and realise it's just a dream.

Then I shut my eyes again
But I don't appear in my magical land.
I am some place different.
In a dark, dark gloomy forest.
Trees branches reaching over me like claws.

I try to escape, I keep on running
But it seems like I am getting nowhere.
The forest acting as my enemy instead of my friend.
I realise I am in a nightmare
I come to a door and open it.
Then I wake up
I thought to myself it was just a . . . dream.

Rae Ives (Age 12)

My Worst Nightmare

I'm standing at the end of the pier watching the sun set fade.
I hear footsteps, who is it?
I start to wonder.
As this spooky feeling starts inside,
A ringing started to fill my head.
I turned around and was looking eye to eye with two dark men.
As the orange swirled around the ringing started to get worse.
I fell to the floor holding my head.
Screaming so loud my throat hurt.
All of a sudden the ringing stopped.
I slowly got up.

Natalie Inns (Age 12)

My Dog

My dog is as brown as a bar of chocolate.
My dog has teeth as sharp as a needle.
My dog likes mud as much as he likes his food.
My dogs tail is as long as an ant.
My dog does not like having a bath.
My dog likes going for walks.
My dogs name is Becky.

Jordan Jones (Age 9)

My Scary Experience Poem

It was a sunny cloudless day in August
I was playing in the calm green garden
My friend Lewis and I were throwing a ball
When poof appeared Aladdin on a magic carpet

His monkey aide was talking gibberish
When the Power Rangers appeared
They shouted something about a dragon
And we were shoved on the magic carpet and were gone

In the desert a wall of red yellow and orange
There was a big fiery fierce mighty dragon
That was breathing the flames of hell

The Power Rangers attacked but were burnt to a crisp
Aladdin and the carpet were melted away
Lewis sprinted away but was frazzled
His rapidly decaying body stared up at me

I dodged the flames leaped and ran
But I tired and slowed
A fireball hit me in the head
And I woke up.

Gareth Jones (Age 11)

It Was So Noisy

It was so noisy that
I couldn't hear a fire engines loud siren
It was so noisy that
I couldn't hear the baby's crying mummy
It was so noisy that
I couldn't hear a wolf howling loudly
It was so noisy that
I couldn't hear a CD player booming
It was so noisy that
I couldn't hear the cars racing along very loud!
It was so noisy!!

Elliott Jones (Age 8)

Dragons

I am a dragon
I soar through the air
I am very scaley
But I really don't care

I blow red hot fire
I'm either red or green
I love shiney gold treasure
I'm also very mean

When I swoop I see the town ablaze
When I fly I'm the king of the sky
When I glide past all my dragon friends
They say we want the people to die

Shelby Jones (Age 8)

A Day At School

Long summer days,
Nothing to do but laze,
Play on the beach,
Sit and eat a peach,
Juice dribbling down,
Mother looks with a frown.

Digging to Australia in the sand,
Funny, I never did get to that land!
Sit in a hole,
Mum must think I'm a mole!

Paddling in the sea,
Got my trousers wet -it's free,
Seaweed tickling my toes,
Briney Breezes twitching my nose.

Now the tide is coming in
The battle I must win,
Build a barricade with sand and stone,
As the waves break through, mum shouts 'home!'

Anthony Jackson (Age 14)

My Best Friend

Leonie is fabulous
With sparkling blue eyes
She walks in the sun
With her light brown hair shining

She makes me laugh
Wherever we are
So warm and tender
I am glad I have her.

If I am sad,
She will come to my rescue
With a big smiley face,
That makes me happy.

All in all,
She is the best person I know,
Nothing is too much trouble,
That is why she is my best friend.

Lauren Jones (Age 11)

Happiness

Happiness is rosy pink
It is the taste of golden pears
Happiness smells like succulent strawberries
It looks like dashing mares
Happiness sounds like a gospel choir
Singing with sheer delight
Happiness feels warm and gentle
It is like soft feathers on my skin

Bonnie Jackson (Age 12)

Getting Around

The car is loaded like a mule,
I hope we don't run out of fuel.
Traffic's crawling like a snail,
It might have been better to go by rail.

Gatwick as usual is like a zoo,
Where do we go? I haven't got a clue.
The plane's engines are lions roaring,
Now we're in the sky and soaring.
Two hours of boredom and then we land,
Not long now until I'm on the sand.
Then we go to get our bags,
Dad's off to duty-free to get some fags.

We're on the coach to catch our ferry,
Mum's had a cocktail and is feeling merry.

The boat is bobbing like a bouncy ball,
But I don't feel sick at all.
The sea is a carpet of luscious blue,
I think I'll like it here and so will you.

Matthew Johnson (Age 12)

The Harsh Winter

The crisp, coldness bites into the flesh of walkers,
Blades of grass are like tiny spears, each sharpened,
Flowers are destroyed and decayed by unforgiving frost,
Trees drop their leaves before the savage ice attacks.
Water cannot escape and perishes from the merciless frost
Each droplet solidifies as a result of uncontrollable, punishing ice,
Ruthless ice invades every surface, looking for victims,
Every roof top is whitened and glistening, triumphant.
As the ice conquers all, every surface is attacked,
Every branch of every tree is besieged by tiny crystals,
Icicles plunge and shatter like a broken mirror,
Each piece sharp and jagged like vicious knives
The earth is imprisoned in raw, bitterly cruel glass.

Zoë Joyce (Age 13)

Travelling Into Space

3,2,1, blast-off
Into airless orbit
Accelerating up
Approaching space
Moonlit stars
And sunlit flames
I can see Earth
Jupiter and Mars
With the glittery stars
The moon shining as bright as can be
Making everywhere look like ice

Clare Juby (Age 14)

Bonfire Night

Bonfire, bonfire, bonfire night,
The fireworks noise gave me a fright,
Bonfire, bonfire, bonfire night,
People talking with all their might.

Bonfire, bonfire, bonfire night,
The fireworks made such a sight,
Bonfire, bonfire, bonfire night,
The sky is filled with lots of light.

Bonfire, bonfire, bonfire night,
The smell of soup is such a delight,
Bonfire, bonfire, bonfire night,
I couldn't wait to take a bite.

Bonfire, bonfire, bonfire night,
The wind and I had a fight,
Bonfire, bonfire, bonfire night,
It felt so cold as it was night.

Bonfire, bonfire, bonfire night,
The hot-dog tasted alright,
Bonfire, bonfire, bonfire night,
The soup warmed me up to my delight.

Rhian Jeffery (Age 11)

Ten

Ten singing cats digging in a mine
One hit his toe and then there was nine

Nine singing cats one had a date
They went off and then there was eight

Eight singing cats going up to heaven
One slid down and then there was seven

Seven singing cats, one bit itself
And then there was six

Six singing cats singing to a jive
One had a sore throat and then there was five

Five singing cats singing more
One collapsed and then there was four

Four singing cats in a love tree
One fell in love and then there was three

Three singing cats one went to the loo
It got stuck and then there was two

Two singing cats met a nun
One went with her and then there was one

One singing cat hi-jacked a plane
Flew to America and was never seen again

Rhiannon Jones (Age 10)

Hello, Hello

Hello, Hello,
Shouted a man who played the cello
He played real nice,
But at the same time he could roll a dice,
Until he became mellow.

Rachel Jones (Age 10)

He Might Get You

The mad bad man from the scary street,
Slunk right out to bite my feet.
His house is hidden in the trees,
The diet he has is kids and cheese.

Then he went and gnawed my toes,
A dung - like whiff got up his nose.
He coughed and spluttered until his death,
At least he didn't smell my breath.

If you think you're safe and sound,
I'll warn you now he's still around.
And if you doubt my story's true,
You never know he might get you.

Edward Jones (Age 9)

Recipes For A Dolphin

The dolphin caught:

The rubbers from a pencil case,
To spread out on its skin,
With a moonlight twinkle, to shine and gleam,
From the salty blue waves, that crashed against the shore.

The two midnight buttons, that were grabbed from the sky,
Like two black, salty drops of oil,
That had fallen down - from the sun,
Especially to see through the wonderful deep sea.

And then she grabbed all the flippers,
From all of the divers, down, down,
From under the sea, to help her move around,
To flow along the deep blue sea, to be free,
To see all her friends under the sea.

Now all she needed was a brain,
So she went to the school, and stole all of them,
She popped them right in, and was now complete,
So she ran to the shore, and swam down in the sea.

Natanya Jaeger (Age 10)

The Battle

I see the blood spurting out of fellow soldiers bodies
I see Richard III galloping towards my ruler Henry Tudor
I hear a lot of screams as bodies fall to the ground,
I hear myself killing people in anger.
I touch my silver blade as it chops a person to death
I taste the fear in my body
I feel so happy after that terrifying war but we won

Chris Jenkinson (Age 10)

The Iron Man

Oily joints down the street,
Speeding up hear the beat.
Crashing, smashing into town,
Then, oh no! he's falling down!

Flashing, crashing then CRUNCH!
Then, oh no! MUNCH!
Sitting down, slowly does it,
Then, CRUNCH! he's eaten a bit

Getting sleepy, laying down,
Then he falls straight to the ground.
Puts his head down, very sad.
Then he gets up and goes MAD!

Naomi Jackson (Age 8)

The Real Writer Of This Poem

The writer of this poem
Is as clever as a brain
As keen as a monkey
As strong as a chain

As bold as a cricket ball
As sharp as a pin
As clean as a bar of soap
As smooth as a pint of gin

As fast as a blast
As tall as a tower
As handsome as Anmol Jain
As humorous as a joker

The writer of this poem
Never tells fibs for attention
He's one in a billion trillion
Or should I mention . . . .

Anmol Jain (Age 11)

The Birthday Party

Noisy children running riot,
around a wrecked room.
Sheet's of crumpled wrapping paper,
scattered everywhere.
Colourful balloons,
bobbing about in the air.
Half-full fizzy drinks,
shoved onto every available surface.
Happy kids gorging themselves,
on plates piled high of junk food and sweets.
Party games such as Twister,
left on the floor.
State of the art birthday presents,
broken already.
Worried parents,
watching helplessly at the sidelines.

Esther Jones (Age 11)

A Quick 'Pop'

A shotgun is a spider with a deadly bite.
A shotgun is the start of a war.
A shotgun is a shrill sharp cry.
A shotgun is a flash of bright light.
A shotgun is a quick death.
A shotgun is a terrifying thought.
A shotgun is a quick 'pop' then silence.
A shotgun is a deadly weapon in the hands of the enemy.

Kevin Jolly (Age 12)

Lost

She sits there in the corner,
She thinks that no one cares.
Her eyes: a wash of broken lies,
Her words silenced by memories.

With every gesture made,
And every comment passed,
She shuts them out, although made in kindness.
Dreams shattered from the past.

With every breath and every thought,
Nothing can be changed.
Her life will never be the same,
Her hopes, her dreams. Lost forever.

Elizabeth Kember (Age 16)

A Green Piece of Something

He saw it,
A green piece of something.
The right leg swung up,
Kicked it away,
And he forgot about it.

There it skulked,
In the obscure depths
Beneath the bed,
Amidst the long forgotten games,
And it lingered.

Patiently it waited
Because it knew
That one day in the future
Its chance would come
And it would seize it.

And the right leg
That right leg
Would pay.
Revenge, it thought
Is sweet.

Jack Jarrett (Age 13)

I love You

I love you lots
You give me the hots
You're the only one for me
As we both can see
I'll give you a hug
And you'll give me a kiss
And our love won't be a miss

Faye James (Age 12)

Dinner Time!

Garbage can lids fall to the ground
A glimpse of red reflects from the soft, silky fur in the moonlight
A passing car's horn makes the creature flee back to the darkness
He waits for silence, a chance to collect his daily meal of scraps for his cubs
His beady eyes watch the road like a hawk
Deserted, now is his chance
He dashes from cover and flees from the road

He sprints back to his cubs in the marshy corner of the park
They await his return in anticipation
Six eyes light up, dinner!
The waiting is over
They're little paws rip the chicken bones apart
Scavaging for any scraps of meat
Nothing, they whimper
The wait begins again

Samantha Johnson (Age 13)

In A Witch's Purse There Was . . .

A few dead frogs and rats
Some pussy warts turned a sickly green
Some deadly spells
A green lipstick
A miniature black cat
Three shrunken headmasters in jars
A book called "How to be a Witch"
A small jar of blood and
A FOOTBALL!!!

Kallie Johnson (Age 11)

Death Of The Child

Into the darkness she ran,
for what reason we'll never know.
Taking only a sketchy whisper
that echoed softly through the untamed trees.
Her hair huddled neatly as she stopped
only to find a surprising coldness from her skin.

The night surrounded her,
she could feel nothing as the moon shone,
for all her ideals were teased away from her.
Her breathing was faint and
wind stole the air that she needed.
The rain fell to ease the wind,
but she lay on the ground dying.

And as the sun rose to greet the day,
her remains melted into the dewy grass,
leaving no trace for me to find.
Then how could I know this, you ask,
she was my innocence.

Kristi Juve (Age 15)

The Dolphin Dream

The curling sea
The dolphins come to me

I love the soothing, gentle sound
I know right now what I've found

The sea is just so beautiful
By now I must have seen it all

I look again and see his eyes
The next time he is by my side

There is just a peaceful wave
That draws me near to a big cave

I love dolphins
I love dolphins

Emma Jeffery (Age 10)

The Iron Man

The iron man is running to the super market
Bashing, crashing,
Clang, squeeze, squash
Suddenly stopped
Found some metal thing
Run back to the junk yard
Getting faster faster
Bashing and crashing
Then getting slower
Bang
Squash
And finally sat down.

David Jones (Age 8)

Owl

Swiftly flying through the air,
Swirling, diving without a care.
And now and again,
Ducking lower as if to avoid the moonlight frame,
Swooping down upon small prey,
With glider wings that never fray.
Soaring above its forest home,
Hunting silent always alone.
And therefore to be exact,
Look back on this fine owl face,
Always pay respect to few,
The ones that awake in the black not the blue.

Sarah Jones (Age 10)

The Forest

The forest stood murky, moody,
Dark and dull like an old abandoned house
The leaves were like a carpet beneath,
With trees, tall all around.

The moon was like a spotlight on the leaves
I walked on while the branches, seemed to grab me like a spindly old man.
A heart stopping hoot sounded, an owls hoot,
Like long nails scraping down a blackboard.

My shadow seemed to be staring at me,
The trees were thinning, I was near the edge,
I started to run, there was a rustling behind me,
Like someone was chasing me.

But then - I got out, safe and free,
The rustling stopped, I looked back,
The forest stood, murky, moody
Dark and dull like an old abandoned house.

Eleanor James (Age 11)

The Rollercoaster

The big red rollercoaster
Its magnificent and fast
People scream loudly
Everyone's excited
The ride is over
Everyone is sad
They'll be back tomorrow
To go on it
Again!

Adam Jordan (Age 9)

My Sweetie

His hair a bundle of liquorice laces,
His skin as pale as milk,
Dandruff on his shoulder like sherbet traces,
His face as soft as silk.
His tread so soft, his step so light,
His voice so sweet and mellow,
I won't give this boy up without a fight,
My soft and sweet marshmallow.
My Mr. Perfect, he's all he seems,
Lips that you could bite,
The boy of my dreams my peppermint creams
Oh my Turkish delight!

He's all adorned with chocolate money
He's so sweet, sweeter than honey.

Chloe Jordan (Age 13)

Stone Cold!

His music blares as he walks to the ring
His opponent wants to cry
He's big he's strong he's bad he's mad
He's Stone Cold Steve Austin
He has beer in one hand and a HHH in the other
Steve Austin thinks he's not worth the bother
He ends his match with a big and mighty crash
As we watch in a stare
Trish Status gives us an evil glare
Steve Austin has won once more
We stare in amazement
As mum slams the door!

Andrew Jones (Age 12)

Snow

The snow is thick it is floating
Down like cotton wool.
It is tingling your hand
It shines brightly,
It is cold.
Your baby brother sticks
Out his hand
The snow touches it
He,
JUMPS!

Carl James (Age 9)

The Sun

The sun is a flaming ball of fire,
Burning away on an invisible stick.

The sun is a yellow dinghy,
Floating on a calm blue sea.

The sun is the yolk of an egg,
Being fried on its own without a white.

The sun is an orange,
Rolling around a sky blue plate.

When I see the sun it is to me as if,
It is a golden apple,
Hanging on a branch on a tree,
Swinging back and forth,
Alone in the light blue sky.

Melissa Jackson (Age 11)

Winter

Winter's cold so go inside
Warm yourself with a sausage fried.

Sit by the fire that glows bright red
If it is too cold go to bed.

Look out of the window and watch it snow
See the temperature, oh so low!

We go outside to skate around
Where all the kids shout out loud!

We make snowmen, feeling cold
Give him a pipe to make him old.

When together they have such fun
Night has come and the day is done.

Ben Jelfs (Age 11)

Listen . . .

Silence is when you hear things
Listen:
Do you hear the tanks go by?
Machine guns killing innocent people
Listen:
Do you hear their hearts trembling?
The sounds of soldiers running towards the enemy
Listen:
Do you hear the exploding bombs?
Is peace so difficult to hear?

David Johansen (Age 10)

Do You Still Think It's Glorious

It's noisy, it's muddy we're cold, we'll be here till we're old
Back we go for a rest to be safe,
We leave the noise, we leave the mud, we leave those dead to rot.
"Away, away" I hear the boys say,
I looked at the men all ragged and slow, why I say can't they send them home.
"Get your masks on as quick as you can"
They struggle they moan, they've got them on except for one, he's gone for good!!
The gas is thick, I cannot see, where are the men, will they shout out to me?
I see the man, the one without the mask,
I'll never forget the memory, it will always last.
How would you feel to see a friend die, struggling, dying inside
You walk with the cart, the man inside,
He looks so helpless, what would you do, imagine a man to drown on land
To cough up blood, the wagon jumps up and down, can you hear the sound,
If you had seen it you wouldn't say it was glorious to die,
You would be upset you would cry and cry
Do you still think it's glorious?

Claire Jones (Age 14)

The World In The Distance

The rain hits me hard in the face,
As I stand on the cliff
A never ending sea of trees,
Cover the forest floor

The trees create a giant umbrella
Shielding the shrubs underneath
The mountains in the distance
Look so small but are so large

The leaves and branches swaying,
Like the sea bobbing up and down
The wind so strong
Hitting me hard in the face, but still I stay

The rivers going in every direction,
Flowing over waterfalls and rocks
The world seems so beautiful,
But yet has many problems

It's so large,
As I am so small
I can see for miles
At what seemed such a wonderful place

Darren Jones (Age 13)

My Wrestling Teacher

I have a wrestling teacher
Her name is Mrs Peacher
I think she should be on telly
She's got a big belly
Whenever there is trouble
She comes to the rescue
I think her favourite footballer
Is Dan Petrescue

Adnaan Javed (Age 10)

Birds

In Spring
I like spotting the birds
Coming out to sing

Sophie Jackson (Age 8)

Autumn

Autumn is the season of fun,
You can go trick or treating with everyone,
Don't eat too many sweets it will make you feel sick
Be careful, which door should you pick.

Autumn is not just about Halloween,
But the plants and trees that start to lean,
The plants drop dead, in the flower bed,
It's the circle of life don't think it's mean.

It reaches November
When the fireworks start which you may remember
Sitting round a scarlet fire, glowing hot and red.
That makes you feel at home, snuggled up in your bed.

Joanne James (Age 12)

How I Got My Golden Wellies

I wore my stealing hat, as I stole the Cheshire Cat
Wearing my violent, Vauxhall, Volvo visor.
It grinned at my shirt and said its name was Kurt
As it jumped on my magnificent, Monday, moulded mackintosh.
Kurt looked at my watch and started to sprint off
In my cool, cyber, coloured combat-trousers.
It trod on my sock, which turned into a thin, gold rock
And I sculptured a pair of wacky, wonderful, Warrior's Wellies.

Ben Jones (Age 11)

The Blue Sash

Before dinner on Sunday my sister displayed
The brand new blue sash that my mother had made.
The middle was navy the edges were gold
And there were no creases, not even a fold.

The next day she took it to show at our school
And our nasty teacher then and there made a rule,
"No-one's to touch dear Sarah's new sash
Any children who do will receive a sound thrash!"

So me and my friends hatched a daring new plan;
To soak Sarah's sash with a paraffin can!
But to our surprise, then sincere regret,
It was set alight by a dropped cigarette!

And then through the smoke trains and scatters of ash,
I saw the remains of my sister's blue sash!

Simon Joyner (Age 10)

Sea

Sea waves, curve like rubber,
Swiftly, swinging up like a fountain rolling,
And splashing back down again with a fizz.
Sea as straight as a sword until it,
Cries as it crashes against a rock then,
Calms as it faintly flows back again.
Sea as calm as a flute,
Singing its way past every horribly, hectic country,
Then settling in a different place.
Sea storms, as its dislike appears,
It strikes and crashes over and over again,
Then it stops, with boredom or success
Sea evaporates as though it's just visiting a friend
And then, floatily flies back to the endless beginning!

Vicky Johnson (Age 12)

What Is One

One is a lost fish
An injured baby kangaroo
A penguin crying for its mother
A lost dormouse's wish.

One is a squashed orange
A last tree standing
A tornado swirling round the world
A damaged bird landing.

One is a dog's heartbeat fading
A dead fox laying with no fuss
A squirrell's nest
Destroyed by us.

Kellie Jacques (Age 9)

Freddy And Neddy

Freddy was voted to guard the palace
But Freddy was never ready, steady,
And was always in beddy!
But Neddy was fitter than Freddy,
And was always ready and steady,
So soldier Neddy called on Freddy
But he was not ready.
So he waited in his sheddy.
And soon Freddy was ready.
Neddy asked Freddy whether he
Wanted to go out for tea
It took Freddy time to get ready
So Neddy put a speed tablet
On Freddy's bready
And Freddy became ready and steady
All because of Neddy
And was put to guard the palace.

Adam Jones (Age 10)

Moods Of The Sea

The sea is a
Fierce leaping tiger

The sea is a
Growling bear,
Growling for its prey

The sea is a
Leopard
Waiting for its juicy prey

The sea is a
Giants bag of salt

The sea is smashing
SMASHING
On the beach.

Henry Jamieson (Age 6)

Ice Cream

I play ice-cream with my friends,
One person is turning round
The other people are running,
Oh dear one person
Has bumped their head.

Rhiannon Jones (Age 8)

The Sea

When I see the sea
I fill with glee
When I play in yellow sand
I feel very grand
When the ocean is wet
I catch fish in a net
When I see the sea
I fill with glee

Ellie Jones (Age 6)

Please Sir

Please sir,
I lost my pencil, I need my pencil,
Help me sir.

Borrow this one then, go get one from your den.
Please do not ask me. Whatever's coming next,
What will it be?

Please sir,
I've not enough paper, I need more paper,
Help me sir.

There's more on my table,
But get it yourself 'cause I'm not able.
Please do not ask me. Whatever's coming next,
What will it be?

Please sir,
I've made a mistake, I need to change something.
Help me sir.

Start all over again, rub it all out.
Please do not ask me. Whatever's coming next,
What will it be?

Philip Johns (Age 9)

Spring

Trees swaying birds singing,
Plants growing rivers flowing,
Wind blowing cattle lowing,
Sheep bleating clouds appearing.

Sun shining miners mining,
Daffodils sprout children shout,
People scream the sun gleams,
Everyone sings it is Spring.

Christopher James (Age 8)

Poem On Birthdays

Center Parks was quite amazing, cycling, bowling, swimming, skating.
The swimming pool with all those slides, I was in for a huge surprise!
Little did I know it, but all my friends had made a plot.
A chocolate cake for all to see, was sitting waiting, just for me!

The animal park was long and wide, we went on the trailer for a ride,
To see the animals they had there, a gorilla gave us quite a scare,
By banging on the cages and going into rages.
The day, it ended, we were in the car, now we had to travel far.

The swimming party was a great success my sister wore a lovely dress,
Of pink and white, red that glistened, not one single person listened
To what I had to say, they were all busy singing Happy Birthday!
I'm growing older, next I'm twelve, I keep all my presents on my shelves.

Hayley Javeleau (Age11)

The Lady

Have you seen the lady
With a cold, bombarding smile
Upon an illuminated face
Scanning with intensity
With deep swallowing eyes
Walking like a tiger
Across a moonlit sky

Dressed damp and ragged
Always told a lie
Hands all rippled and bent
Nails all timid and blunt
Have you seen the suspicious lady?
Have you seen the lady?
All bent and dried.

Ben Jarvis (Age 10)

The Alien School Boy

I have a alien friend,
He goes to our school,
Although he's quite a fool
He beats me at football
And doesn't cheat at all.
He mainly eats slugs and snails,
And hardly ever tells tails,
when he eats slugs and snails,
It makes me cringe my teeth
He lives beneath our cellar,
And is a nice fella,
Would you like to know his name?
His name is Silly Trevor.

Ryan Jones (Age 9)

Jordan Jenkins

Jordan Jenkins, so intelligent,
Really cool, very brave,
Brown eyes, hardly cries,
Not tall, doesn't behave.

Sporty person, likes football,
Two cats, tries hard,
Likes spaghetti, neat writer,
No hats, makes card.

Hairy arms, rubbish drawer,
Blonde hair, likes himself,
Likes music, likes friends,
Plays fair, good health.

Fast runner, drinks fizz,
Soft skin, Leeds fan,
Woolly jumper, Nike trainers,
Not thin, one pan.

Jordan Jenkins (Age 8)

Chocolate

Chocolate, chocolate
It's so bad,
Lots of people like it,
But it makes me mad.

Chocolate, chocolate
It's so bad,
Lots of people like it,
But it makes me sad.

Chocolate, chocolate
It's so bad,
Lots of people like it,
But it makes me glad.

Jason Jenner (Age 9)

Computer Madness!

"Ticka" "Ticka" "Come down at once!"
"Ticka" "Ticka" "In a minute!"
Computer Madness!! Computer Madness!!
Come again another day!!

"Boom!" "Boom!" "Zap!" "Zap!"
I'm on table Aliens!
"Boom!" "Boom!" "Zap!" "Zap!"
I'm on Chair Martians!!!

"Ticka" "Ticka" "Come down at once!"
"Ticka" "Ticka" "Please mummy, PLEASE!
Computer Madness! Computer Madness!
"I HATE YOU!

Philip Jury (Age 9)

Matilda

My new baby sister,
I've only just kissed her
Her name is Matilda
Eight pound six ounces is her build yeh!
Her big blue eyes and her wee little fingers,
Her shiny straight black hair is to bring us,
On to her cuteness
Oh such buteness,
With so so soft skin,
And a nose like a pin
With such small curly wurly tootsies,
And a cry like whimpering puppies,
How could you resist her,
My new baby sister

Katherine Johnson (Age 8)

The Door

Go and open the door
maybe there's an ocean and people
flying on carpets.

Go and open the door
maybe there's flesh eating aliens,
and there is a giant rocket
flying into space.

Go and open the door
you could be on top of the world
you could be flying into space
in zero gravity.

Go and open the door
maybe there's a haunted mine
maybe there's a dark damp prison
and maybe you're back home.

Adam Jama (Age 9)

Spring

In spring we see the baby lambs
Jumping in the fields and grass.
Daffodils pop up from underground.
Around the trees and along the paths.
Baby chicks are being born on the farm.
The weather gets better and we play outside.
Bunny rabbits are hopping in the grass.
Bees are collecting pollen to make honey.
I like spring it means summer is coming.

Chloe Joseph (Age 7)

What Is White?

White is a swan swimming under the clouds
White is milk in a baby's bottle
White is an iceberg floating on the ocean
White is ice in the freezer
White is paper in a pile
White is a polar bear on the ice
White is a school t-shirt
White is a clock on the mantlepiece
White is a diary in someone's bedroom
White is rice that people cook

Alex Jourdan (Age 7)

Bears

Once I saw a brown bear
It was looking straight at me
I knew what it wanted
It wanted ME for tea
I was very very scared
what ever could I do?
I couldn't think of very much
So I shouted BOO!
He ran to the left
And I ran to the right
I never went to the wood again
I didn't want a fright

Sophie Jenkin (Age 6)

Machines Go Bump

Machines machines roll over there
Bumpty bumpty bump
Why do they bump?
Because my fields are bumpy
Bumpty, bumpty, bump.

Aurea Jones (Age 6)

Animal Ways

Two fluffy bears looking for food
                munch, munch
Four grey elephants squirting water at each other
                splash, splash
Six crocodiles snapping in the river
                snap, snap
Eight giraffes munching on the tree
                munch, munch
Ten tired tigers all fast asleep
                Zzzzzz
Twelve squawking parrots sitting on a tree
                squawk, squawk

Megan Jones (Age 7)

Colours

Yellow is the vast glimmering sun high up in the sky,
Or hot and sunny beaches full of shiny shells,
Or the shiny peel of a juicy lemon,
Or a fluffy young chick at Easter time.

Red is the silly noses we wear on Comic Relief Day,
Or my heart beating fast after I've been running,
Or wet dripping blood falling from my cut knee,
Or the sizzling sun sitting in the evening sky.

Black is my school shoes shining in the light,
Or the night sky interrupted by glittering stars,
Or a big dark hole that never seems to end,
Or the ink thrown at my school.

Ben Joseph (Age 9)

Haiku

Tough machines play fierce
Fighting for the ball
Yes! I scored a try!

Dominic Jones (Age 10)

Silence

Silence is a dog sleeping
Silence is a cat watching a mouse
Silence is a snake wrapping around a tree
Silence is an ant crawling
Silence is an elephant sleeping
Silence is a hedgehog creeping through some leaves

Jake Jefford (Age 6)

T-Rex

It has sharp claws
And big big jaws

Eyes very very small
I've heard it was tall

As tall as a house
MUCH bigger than a mouse

It's favourite food is meat
What else could it eat?

Long ago there weren't skips or chips

Ryan Jones (Age 6)

Sea

The sea is a wonderful place
Filled with mystical things, there's
Fish with gleaming fins, there's
Shark which look like hammers
Coral that's rainbow colours
All of these in the deep blue sea.
But my most favourite thing is
Something that is cute,
It's skin is silky soft
Have you guessed it?
A Dolphin

Sienna James (Age 10)

Feeling Bad

Yesterday I had a cough
I was feeling really rough

Today I'm feeling much better
Even though it's wetter

Tomorrow I will be as right as rain
And go back to school again

Annie Jones (Age 10)

My Hero Is . . .

My hero is very strong
My hero is very kind
My hero helps people
My hero's name is Goku
And he's got a son called
Gohan and a wife called Chechi

Cory James (Age 9)

The Goat

A nasty starer
A big creature
A grey sniffer
A deadly charger
A fast runner
A grass eater
An angry looker
A tough fighter
A high leaper
A slim lander

Marcus James (Age 7)

Alley Cats

Alley cats mean,
Alley cats keen,
Alley cats oh here comes Dean,

Alley cats dash,
Alley cats bash,
Alley cats oh you have a rash,

Alley cats shaved,
Alley cats behaved,
Alley cats oh you are badly behaved.

Daniel Jesudason (Age 7)

Storm

Ghostly noises all in a pack
A train running on everlasting track
Bangs and flashes whizzing around
A ferocious dog ready to pound
Flashes streaking across the sky
People not stopping to say hi
Animals howling to get in
Wishing that they were more thin
Destroying poppies all in rows
Then after night it all goes.

Alex Jones (Age 8)

Feelings

I have feelings good and bad
Sometimes good and some quite sad,
Sometimes I'm down in the dumps
And then I get the horrible humps.

Sometimes I'm very happy and bright
And then I sleep all through the night,
When I wake up I'm feeling quite chuffed
The night has gone I've slept enough

Steven Johnson (Age 10)

Mermaids

Mermaids have beautiful tails,
Each one has lovely scales,
Riding on a sea horse,
Maybe she will win the sea course,
A lovely kind of breeze for her,
I like her pictures sir,
Did you know her shells on her head were nice,
She had very cold ones like ice.

Sophie Jewsbury (Age 6)

Listen

Listen to the sea waves
Sssssssssh.
Listen to the children playing,
Ha! Ha! Ha!
Listen to the palm trees,
Swish, swish, swish.
Listen to the bird's song,
Flap! Flap! Flap!
Listen to the coconuts,
Bash! Bang! Bash!
Listen, listen, listen.
Just relax and listen.
To EVERYTHING!!!!

Charlotte Jacques (Age 9)

The Magic Box

I will put in my box
A friendship that will never end with a best friend.
I will put in my box
A summer's day play with a best friend.
I will put in my box
A star to give a best friend.
I will put in my box
A best friend to remember for ever.

Georgia Johnson (Age 9)

The Battle

I see dead bodies lying on the floor with arrows in the heart.
I touch the cold steel armour in my hand
I smell rotten bodies lying on the floor.
I hear swords clashing and people shouting.
I think I'm going to win this battle.
I taste salt in my mouth
I see a spear flying through the air it's in my heart
I fall on the floor

Adam Jarvis (Age 9)

When I Grow Up . . .

When I grow up I'm going to have a red Ferrari
I will be driving round the streets while my mum's writing a diary.

When I grow up I'm going to be a football star.
My dad will be watching every game - whilst drinking in a bar.

When I grow up I'm going to have a black and white bunny
And it's going to cost loads and loads of money.

So when I grow up I'm going to have one massive life
With three kids and a wife!

Callum Jenkins (Age 11)

3 O'Clock Friday

3 o'clock Friday away from it all.
On Monday they kicked me and
Threw my ball over the wall.
On Tuesday the gang and big boy Lee
Called me names and stole my food
Also pushed me over and hurt my knee.
On Wednesday the nightmare hit
They took my cash and my credit cards too
But the worse thing was they threw me in a pit.
On Thursday they threw my coat in the bin
They just laughed and then they poked me with a pin.
On Friday it's time to go home I'm safe for two days.

Katy James (Age 9)

Topsy-Turvy World

If the butterfly courted the bee,
And the owl the porcupine;
If churches were built in the sea,
And three times one was nine,
If the pony rode his master,
If buttercups ate the cows,
If Mum sold the baby
To a gypsy for half-a-clown;
If a gentleman sir was a lady,
The world would be upside-down!
If any of these wonders
Should ever come about,
I should consider them blunders,
For I should be inside out!

Laura Jackson (Age 11)

Earthquake

Rising
Falling
Crumbling
Banging
Buildings collapsing
School children praying
The earth quake comes
Destroying everything in it's path
People running
Children running
Panic and chaos all around
People buried under the ground
Only moments ago we were having fun
But now only terror the damage has been done

Eleanor Jones (Age 10)

The Wind Is An Unstoppable Robber

The wind is an unstoppable robber,
Smashing walls to get at anything.
He cracks glass and climbs through,
Eager to get inside.
He slips down the tiniest gaps,
Intent on seeing in.
No-one can see him so he takes whatever he can.
He howls with glee at his treasures in the skies,
Making all the people take cover.
The wind is an unstoppable robber.

Neil Justice (Age 10)

The Dog

The dog went for a walk.
The dog went for a walk with his owner.
The dog went for a walk with his owner and ran away
The dog went for a walk with his owner and ran away, his owner soon found him.

Anna-Louise Johnson (Age 9)

Bush Baby

Her eyes are more glowing than the moonlight,
She's more silvery than the morning mist,
She's stripier on her tail than a zebra's back,
She swings like the wind.

Emma Kessell (Age 7)

Four Seasons

When the spring is in full bloom,
It is a storm of rainbow flower feelings.
When the spring is dancing through a mellow sky,
It is the touch of a bright green leaf blasting from a branch.

When the summer is humid and flamed,
It is a devil, screaming, with purple sticks of fire.
When the summer is bursting with joy,
It is the cry of a flower being stung by a bee.

When the autumn wind is hurrying through an open door,
It is a tree letting go of a handful of multi-coloured leaves.
When the autumn is carrying seeds through the air,
It is a squirrel, scurrying through a field, looking for a place to hide its nuts.

When the winter is spraying snow across the ground,
It is the patter of a mouse crawling through a basement.
When the winter is heaving coughs and colds,
It is a bear growling at an evil eagle's chatter.

Laura Karadakova (Age 10)

The Cow

Eating sweet grass at the light of dawn,
The cow soft and warm,
And helping her calf learn how to walk,
Gently lifting him up.

The cow moved closer to her young baby,
As he started eating the morning grass,
Then the farmer came to milk them.

Matthew Kerin (Age 7)

My Auntie Spotty

My Auntie thought it was nice
To skate upon very thin ice
Poor Auntie Spotty didn't listen to my warning
And went skating every morning
Goodbye my lovely Auntie Spot
'Cause the ice was thin but she was not

Keshia Knight (Age 11)

The Writer Of This Poem

The writer of this poem
Is as clever as a brain,
As wise as an owl,
As strong as a chain.

As fast as a hare,
As sharp as a hawk,
As powerful as a President,
As bouncy as a cork.

As rich as Richard Branson
As proper as a butler,
As handsome as a prince,
As brave as a wrestler.

The writer of this poem
Is so bright, makes anyone blind,
Sparkling eyes, a glistening smile,
He's certainly one of a kind!

Imran Kassam (Age 11)

Orange Is Mine

Orange is the colour of a sparkling sunset
Orange is the colour yo will never regret
Orange is the colour of treacle and honey
Orange is the colour of lots of money

Orange is a colour that may be very old
But its the colour that is very bold
Orange is the colour of fresh corn
Orange is the colour of a new French horn

Orange is the colour of evil fire
And is the one everyone would like to hire
Orange is the colour of pure danger
Orange is the colour of a baby's manger

Orange is the colour of a boiled sweet
Orange is the colour of hazardous heat
Orange is the colour of a hot sandy beach
Orange is the colour of a juicy peach

Rupert King (Age 13)

Around The World In Two Hours

Across the dry, desert land
Then souring through the sky
Creeping through the palace grand
Watch as we go by

Into the jungle
Up the trees
Flying on an eagle
Chased by bees

Around the world tour
With time to stop for a cuppa
But now I'll go home
So I don't miss my supper

Stephanie Kimpton (Age 11)

Glorious?

Me and the lads are tired of fighting, living in conditions with no heat or lighting.
Leaving the noise which we have, day in and day out, I need the rest, I can't even cry or pout.
We're grubby, sore and acting drunk, no boots, feet bare and rotting, they stunk.
We're staggering and crawling, we didn't realise bombs were falling.
The gas is coming - I yell and shout go! We struggle for the masks but one is too slow,
He mutters and cries as the gas drags him below.
The gas is thick, like my mum's pea soup, we didn't know if we were going round in loops
The one without the mask came towards me, the gas fills his lungs but I can't see.
You don't realise what it's like to see people die, you're sitting at home eating home made pie.
While we're out here fighting for the King, the war is an ugly, stupid, pointless thing.
The wagon carrying the injured, jolts all around, my friend is drowning but he is on the ground.
The blood and mucous is drowning him, but the experience is drowning me.
You say fighting's glorious but can't you see people are dying for you and for me.

Rachael Kett (Age 14)

I Luv U - Y2K + 1

Some1 said he liked hr,
but she was nt so sure,
he'd laughed @ her + pointed,
verbal interaction such a chore.

She'd pressed the bttns smoothly,
+ held her breath so tight,
snt it sd + snt she rd,
hr heart beat hi in flight.

His phone had squawked so crudely,
1 msg was received,
txt snt from hr aching heart,
deep in her phone conceived.

She knew wot he had typed,
though brkn, strng + tru,
his finger tips had spoken,
and whispered i lv u.

Raechel Kelly (Age 15)

The Mistress' Reply

Had we met before, I'd say yes,
But I've found a new love nevertheless,
He treats me with respect and with love,
He is extremely tranquil like a dove.

But, you tried allocating me to your place,
And tried to smother me to a trace,
Then you tell me about your marble vault,
Telling me being a virgin is my fault,
And where the worms will make me rot,
That cryptic note made me very hot.

Now therefore, my love caresses my thigh,
And then I allow him to go high,
The, he cups my delicate bosom,
Describing me like a flower that blossomed.

Krunal Kahar (Age 15)

Why Did They Kill Me?

I was carrying that heavy cross
People yelled at me
A lady put a cloth on my face
Why did they kill me?

They threw me down on that hard ground
And nailed me to the cross
Forgive them Lord forgive them please
Why did they kill me?

I looked below and there she was
My poor sweet mother Mary
With gentle tears upon her cheeks
Why did they kill me?

The pain it hurt so very much
As I began to die
And then I said some simple words
Goodbye world, goodbye.

Rachel King (Age 9)

Lonely And Angry

My bed lay before my eyes,
My sister's bellowing vibrated into my ears,
My bare feet were soft against the carpet,
I wish I was popular

My stepfather stood in front of me,
Shouting noises vibrated into my ears,
His cold hand on top of mine,
I wish my dad was back.

Kathryn Keenan (Age 10)

My Birthday

My birthday is May 6th.
Last year I was 9.
I went to London Aquarium
With Callum, Adam, Tom,
It was cool!
We saw lots and lots of fishes.
We saw sharks, jelly fishes and eels,
And lots of other things.

We went around and around
For two hours.
It was great, but now my birthday is over,
Adam is gone,
But Callum and Tom are still here.
They stayed for a sleepover,
We stayed up late!

Erol Kucuk (Age 9)

Sunshine

The sun gives out golden rays of light,
children play in them with delight,
singing and dancing with enormous glee,
charged by the sun's life giving energy.

Without the sun the grass wouldn't grow,
neither flowers nor seeds the farmer's sow,
the temperature would drop and it would be so cold,
we would have to wrap up warm even the soldiers bold.

The sun and the rain together they play,
making a rainbow of colours bright not grey,
red and yellow, pink and blue,
all colours that lift the gloom,
orange and purple and even green,
all the most beautiful colours ever seen.

The sun is the most wonderful thing,
of God's finest creations I have ever seen!

Laura Kemp (Age 11)

The Wild Sea

The wild sea is dashing up the beach
Biting at my toes
Trying to pull me down into the dark depths of the ocean
The wild sea
The sharks are swaying
The dolphins are whistling at the moon
Fish dart about hiding from their enemy
The killer whale
The worlds biggest sea creature that ever swam the sea
The killer whale is like
A huge slow moving, swimming elephant

Rachel Kelly (Age 8)

Space

A silent pathway through the sky,
Many shooting stars streaming by,
Huddles of massive meteorites,
Flying off into the night.

A golden sphere gives the cosmos life,
Without it there would be much strife,
A silver ball we see at night,
Among the stars of shimmering light.

The planets orbit around the sun,
Moving past it one by one,
One day the sun will not be here,
And the universe will disappear.

Nicholas Kenny (Age 11)

The Terrible Three

Class 16 are an awful lot,
Especially the three that never get caught
They never to anything right,
And always end up in a fight.

They run about, yell and shout,
Throw things in the air and don't even care
If they spill paint on the floor,
Or even on the door.

They put bugs in people's hair, but only do it for a dare
And of course they don't even care,
If they get a detention, or two,
For putting mud in someone's shoe.

Oh when will it ever end,
The mischief drives me round the bend!
If only the teachers knew,
About the terrible things that they do.

Nadia Kouhi (Age 12)

Use Your Senses

Listening to the cars splashing in the moonlight
Listening to my mum and dad chattering like a crowd of people
Listening to my mum wrapping up presents as the wrapping paper crinkles

Looking at my stars on my ceiling glow up like lightning
Looking at the wind blowing people back blowing their hair
Looking at the patterns in my head and all the beautiful pictures

Smelling my egg sandwiches
Smelling Peeking's clean fur as clean as a polar bear
Smelling the fresh cover on my bed

Touching the gold bars on mum's warm bed
Touching my wall and drawing patterns with my finger
Touching Peeking's silky fur and running my hand down him

Emma King (Age 6)

Dolphins

Dolphins are cool they can take you all
Over the world and back, everywhere you,
Like, they will
Pull under the sea
Hiding in the reeds or trying to find you
In the sea is the
Habitat
Swimming on their back and you will have loads of fun

Alice Knight (Age 10)

Hippos

Hippos are white, hippos are blue
When they see puddles
Hippos splash through
Hippos play in the paint store
Down at the zoo
That's why
Hippos are white and hippos are blue

Hoppos are white, hippos are blue
Sharing a mud-bath
Hippos are two
Hippos dance round by the water lake too
So hippos are white and Hippos are blue

Hippos are white, hippos are blue
Coming to think about it
Hippos are too
Easy to see
So why don't we say
Hippos are best when hippos are grey

Joseph Kelen (Age 6)

The Sporty Snake

Hi, I'm snakey
I'm viscous not friendly
I've got a mate called Jaky
But he's a shark not a snake

Once I played footy
I was the slithery striker
The goalie was Booty
He's an electric eel

Twice I've played tennis
I won then lost
I've played against Dennis
He's a big fat menace

Last year I played golf,
It was a bit windy
I played against Roly
And Crazy Boly

Shoaib Khalid (Age 11)

Red

Red is hot burning everyone's skin
Red is embarrassment when you're changing
Red is a sign of danger
Red is the anger when your plant pot smashed
Red is blood when you cut your knee
Red is fire when it warms up your toes

Daniel Kingshott (Age 7)

The Tree

Crispy golden leaves falling off the trees
Flittering leaves flying around the branches
Massive roots at the bottom of the tree
It stays in one place and doesn't move
Spikey branches falling on the ground
Huge and giant trees standing anywhere
Birds build their nests in trees
Brown dirty leaves on the road
Hard green trees growing in my garden
Giant thunder hitting the branches
Bananas grow on trees
Apples grow on trees
Monkeys jumping on the tree
Squirrels live in trees
Crunchy little leaves falling on my car
Wasps build their nests in trees
Twigs stand on trees

Aamir Khan (Age 10)

Poem

We've got a new born in the house
It's just a little baby mouse.
It's such a fragile little thing,
Just as much a clever thing
He can even tell the weather,
And never say never
Because he is so clever

Crispin Kirby (Age 12)

Beach Comber

On Monday I found a trophy,
gold and shiny.
So I gave it back to the waves,
so they could boast.

On Tuesday I found a comb
white and plastic.
I gave it back to the sea,
so it could comb its waves.

On Wednesday I found some body armour,
black and strong.
I gave it back to the sea,
to protect itself from sharks.

On Thursday I found a filter,
big and clean.
I gave it back to the sea,
to get rid of pollution.

On Friday I found one million socks,
odd and waterproof.
I gave them back to the sand,
to cover up cold seaweed.

Oliver Kozlik (Age 11)

Ghost!!

The ghastly ghostly, spooky shadow,
Shivered through the room,
The ghostly silent spider
Wailed around the walls
Crash, bang!
The spirit sighed
Suddenly a smash,
What was that?
A ghost, a bat or shadow.
A bat against the window is what I saw,
No!
Suddenly a shiver of silent spirit,
And gone was that ghastly ghost,
That wailed through the walls!

Louisa Kirk (Age 14)

My Silly Cat

My cat
Is really fat
It catches a mouse
And lives in my house
It is nice
But it likes mice
It lays on a mat
And sleeps in my lap
It likes it hot
And eats in a pot

Tasmiyaha Khatun (Age 9)

A Fairy

I wandered down to the apple tree,
At the end of my garden.
Without a thought or care in my mind.
Through the wild flowers and daisies
And under the sun beams I skipped.

I laid down amongst the long green grass.
Where I found a tiny fairy,
No bigger than a buttercup.
Her face glowed with sweetness,
While her wings fluttered in the wind.

Her delicate little wings were injured.
So I took her in the palm of my hand,
Inside where my quaint doll house stands.
I placed her gently on the miniature sofa,
Where I nursed her until her wings sparkled with health.

I wandered back down to the apple tree,
At the bottom of my garden.
Where she flew like an angel out of my hands.
Into the sky with the summer seeds spinning.

Isabel Keppel (Age 15)

Date Me! I Like Mummification

Hi, I'm Bob, what's yours?
Well obviously you can't reply,
It's a recording.
But I would like to know
You.

What interests do you have?
I'm into helping my community,
I'm also a member of the local rambling club.
Perhaps you share my interests,
Meet up some time.

I'm a bit of a recluse actually . . .
I only do a lot of community work because
I have no friends.
I'm very independent.

Sorry, I'm told my times up, I have to finish.
We've only had a few minutes.
There's so much I haven't told you,
Like my religion involving
Mummification.

Robbie King (Age 14)

The Spice Girls

My bedding has lots of colours
Blue, pink, purple
Lots of spice Girls pictures on covers
Posters will go on walls after mummy decorates
I've seen their concert on TV
I watch their video and dance in my bedroom
I play with my Spice Girl dolls
Baby Spice is my favourite
I have sparkly trousers like them
I have a dark blue spice Girl bag

Justine Kirby (Age 12)

Dinosaurs

D inosaurs lived long ago.
I wish I could see them.
N ow they are extinct.
O h why, why, why!
S ome dinosaurs survived.
A lligators are part of the dinosaur family.
U sing books you can read about them.
R azor sharp teeth and claws.
S ome were vegetarian, some were meat eaters.

Cameron Keeler (Age 7)

Friendship

Friendship is like glass,
it shouldn't break.
It's something special
you have to make.

Friendship is like a tree,
strong and built to last.
Painful words and arguments
should be rooted to the past.

Friendship is like clean air,
it's hard to live without.
You love your friends whatever
even if they're stout.

Friendship is eternal,
there is no conclusion.
It's not something to chase,
and it's not an illusion.

Friendship is life and never to be restricted.
It's a memorable aspect
in the world, that happens
even when you least expect . . .

Rosie Killingworth (Age 12)

Britain

Floods homes,
Just close the dome,
Tony Blair spends a lot of money,
Funny another one doesn't get any,
So get rid of drugs,
Get rid of road rage,
For God sake let them have their own way
Foot and mouth takes lives of farmers
Down the street the woman's got lamas.

Michael King (Age 12)

Bad Sonnet

Shall I compare thee to a rubbish pile?
Thou art more foul smelling and more unclean.
I hath seen more cleanliness on the Nile
And thy body hath more stench than some beans
Sometimes, thankfully, rubbish is cleared out
Maybe someone hath disposed of good stuff
However, thou'st shall never leave me
Somehow, I must endeavour to stay tough
Thou art more bad looking than a putrid snail
And hath the intelligence of a flea
I hath been insulting you without fail
Yet still, thou shalt not even desert me
As long as thou can live with this sonnet
Thou shalt remember to look upon it

Adib Khondkar (Age 11)

He Who Drew

When the artist looked across the scene,
Black and lifeless, dark and drab.
He used his talent with no lean
Painting horizons left to right.
That line he drew to pick apart
The darkness from the blinding light.
With gracious blue he stroke two marks,
One the heavens and one below,
This he drew with all his heart.
The ocean blue, the waves so brisk
The mystery! and that's not all . . .
With all his strength,
With all his might,
He carved the mountain, valley and hill
And then realised it's missing, none slight.
He, with talent above all ours,
He, who made the gracious stars.
With paint that served for any task,
Life so picturesque, that betrayed him so.

Nigel Kaye (Age 13)

The Mysterious Garden

The garden lay still but yet to delight
Any soul who wandered into its light
It shone and blazed all who could see
The garden was as beautiful as beauty could be
It sparkled and glazed the leaves shone bright
A beautiful green that was such a delight
The bushes shone bright like I've never seen
And the flowers so pretty a pink but still green

Michael Khalsa (Age 13)

Space

S tars, galaxies, moons and
P lanets
A ll of these
C an be seen in space
E specially with a telescope

Jonathan Kellie (Age 10)

Bullying

There he is sharp and tall,
Makes you think he's so much more.

Run away he's coming here,
There's no time to stand and stare.

He wants my money,
He'll always get it.

So what shall we do about him?
We should stand-up and not make him win.

Know we're in control,
Oh no have I become a bully just like him?

Shereen Khan (Age 11)

The Sun

The calm sea tickling the rocks,
The sea running over the delicate beach,
The sun shining down on the beach.

The sea touching the cliffs
Like baby's fingers,
People sun bathing all day,
Gently the tide nibbles at the beach.

Liam Knights (Age 9)

Swan Poem

You are, my swan,
As smooth as a frosted snowflake,
As graceful as a flowing wedding gown,
Your beautiful neck pours like cream
From a fragile jug.
As you glide in the lake you are,
A snowdrifts glow,
A doublet of a thousand lillies,
A jacket of white roses
Sugar tipped feathers glisten in the moonlight.

Rebecca Kemp (Age 10)

Thunder And Lightning

Thunder and lightning are like two naughty children fighting in the sky.
Getting angrier and angrier because they can't have their own way.
They shout at each other, making other people scared.
Getting louder and louder as they charge around the heavens.
They rumble and grumble and flash out nasty comments.
They go on like this for a long time. Will they ever stop?
But finally they get quieter and softer, running out of things to say.
Maybe, like most children do, they have given up their argument

Chrissy Kett (Age 11)

Numbers

10 is a knife and a plate without a fork
11 is two adults flying without wings,
12 is an adult and a baby separating
13 is a B with a hole in the middle
14 is a square with three lines either side
15 is a t-shirt hanging out to dry
16 is a semi circle with a circle in the middle
17 is a right angle triangle
18 is to turn around to make 81 stick together to make a line with wheels,
19 is a circular table
20 is an upside down 20 with a circle and half a circle

Eleanor Lucas (Age 10)

Money!

There was once a man called Chris Tarrant,
Who gave millions of pounds to his parents,
They thought it was good,
And spent more than they should,
To think it was down to Chris Tarrant!

Jeremy Koh (Age 10)

Lightning

Flash! Flash! you wake up in the middle of the night,
And there's a bright light outside your window
You hide under the duvet but still the light,
It flashes,
Still you try to sleep all night,
But oh! The lightning is so bright!
Ha, ha! I'll use my secret weapon!
Tiptoe down the hall,
I'll get my mum,
Let's go and call!

Alanna Koh (Age 7)

I Had A Nightmare

I had a nightmare
During the night
I thought it was daylight
But instead it was night
I woke up and shouted
It gave me a fright
Just then mum came in
And said everything's going to be alright
It was just a dream.

Charlotte Kelly (Age 7)

Night

Night is spooky cats pouncing
Night is fascinating bats hunting prey
Night is a shiny moon glowing through your window
Night is stars twinkling brightly in the sky
Night is spooky owls screaming

Matthew Knight (Age7)

Use Your Senses In The Car

Smelling the coconut air freshener like it is from a tropical island,
Smelling the fumes from the gassy car as it goes along the rippty rappty road,
Smelling the warm smell of my dad as warm as the baking sun in the silky sky.

Listening to the loud car starting up,
Listening to the mad man on the radio,
Listening to my best brother's heart beating softly like a cat sleeping.

Tasting my lovely lunch from yesterday afternoon,
Tasting my Capri-sun because I am hot and sweaty as hot as the sand on a summer's morning,
Tasting the breeze sway swiftly past.

Touching the warmth of the car rug running up my back like a space rocket,
Touching my freezing old car seat,
Touching the squelchy mud that has been brought in.

Looking at the other cute cars speeding past and racing my car,
Looking at my brilliant dad driving the car,
Looking up through the hole in the roof to see the clouds floating by.

Katherine Kaczmarczyk (Age 6)

Weather

I like weather
All sorts of weather!
Sun is hot
Snow is cold
Rain is wet
Clouds wobble
Thunder is noisy
Lightning is scary
Wind is blowy
In fog you can't see . . .
I like weather
ALL SORTS OF WEATHER!!!!

Nicholas Kearton (Age 6)

My Friend

My best friend is snowball the mouse
He lives in a little blue house
He is beige on top and white underneath
He has little red eyes
I give him a very good life
He climbs all up my arms
He gives me red marks from his sharp claws
He has a brother called mousey
He has a white patch on the bottom of his back
He's got red eyes as well
They're the greatest mice you ever have seen
And I love them so much

Harley Keenlyside (Age 7)

Without Any Water

Without any water, there wouldn't be drinks
There wouldn't be grass
There wouldn't be sinks,
Without any water, there wouldn't be lakes
There wouldn't be ducks
There wouldn't be drakes.
Without any water
Without a drop
The land would suffer
The world would stop!

Becky Kocerhan (Age 9)

Fog

Engulfed in a thick mist
The land is silent
The sun has just risen

Wearing a shimmering cloak
She glides up and down
All the streets
Leaving a blanket of mist

Cars and houses disappear
Gloom hovers above her
Making everyone miserable

Hours pass, the sun is high in the sky,
Slowly and quietly she disappears
Leaving the land as silent as before.

Sophie King (Age 11)

My Best Friends

While I am sleeping in my bed
There is something fluffy tickling my toes
With her little wet nose,
She curls up into a ball
When she goes to sleep,
And opens her eyes for a quick peep
To make sure I am still asleep,
There is also another
Who is her brother,
They play together and
Look after each other!!

They are my best friends!!!

Aydin Konche (Age 7)

Night And Day

The night brings peace and silence,
Everything is still and sleeping
The leaves don't rustle and the wind has dropped,
There isn't a single ripple in the pond
Everything is relaxed

The morning brings energy and noise
Children talking, cars roaring, everything is awake
The wind blows the leaves across the lane
And noises echo through the wood
Everything is alive again.

Laura Kneebone (Age 10)

Untitled

It's not alive
To do with Royalty
And to do with God
Try and kidnap the king
You will have to be very patient
Use strategy
Be careful what you do
What am I?

Steve Keal (Age 10)

Springtime

The winter was gone
The spring has come
The birds build nests
To raise their young
The plants wake up
And start to grow
The yellow daffodils
Blow to and fro
The baby lambs
That run around
Out in the fields
They can be found
In the pond
The frogs will call
To each other
To have a ball
When Easter comes
We have such fun
With chocolate eggs
And hot cross buns

Thomas Kite (Age 9)

The Playground

Children running
Mouths chewing
Voices calling
Arms waving
Standing talking
Legs walking
Legs running
Hoppers hopping
Laughers laughing
Footballers cheering
Machines growling
Children shouting
Accidents always
Bell comes
Finish game
Bell rings
Back to line
Back to school

Laura Kenward (Age 8)

Battle Of Bosworth Senses Poem

I see the other army coming like ants
I smell a smell I don't want to smell
I think I hear the other army
I touch the red rose on my shield
I want to run all the way home
I hear the other army trudge closer
I charge at them with my spear boldly
I know I've met my death

Alex Keech (Age 9)

My Experience As The Thing

I woke to a shout . . .
I couldn't believe a shout could,
Follow my exquisite dream,
I was in a room with a million stacks of food,
It was deserted, OR SO I THOUGHT!
Slowly I yanked open my eye,
There in front of me was a monster,
18,000 feet tall,
I stood up and . . .
I ran . . and ran . . .,
Round and round
I could see no means of escape,
Until I saw a door ajar
I didn't think twice, I zoomed to it and hid,
In a tiny box full of different cloths
My tiny bones rattled in my body,
But my body was secure against the cloths,
But still they trembled with fear,
I could hear them blowing into my ear,
As I listened to . . the draygums (as I called them)

Mariam Kauser (Age 10)

Imagine

Imagine me as cute as a bee
Imagine me as small as a pea
Imagine me as tall as a tree
Imagine . . . . . . Imagine
Imagine
Imagine a cat as flat as a mat
Imagine a mat as round as a hat
Imagine a mouse as big as a house
Imagine . . . . . . Imagine
Imagine
Imagine me as your tea
Imagine a pig wearing a wig
Imagine a dog as still as a log
Imagine . . . . . . Imagine
Just imagine

Jessica Kenward (Age 10)

My Hobbies

I love to read books
I always care for looks
My parents are glad
I've never made them mad
I like to go to school
I've never acted fool
I like to discover creatures
In school I like all teachers
My favourite animals rabbit
I also like their habit
I like to celebrate Eid
I also like to feed
I have a lot of friends
My talking never ends
I love to drink milk
My favourite material's silk
I like to eat sweets
I eat them as a treat
And that's all I could say
Just for today

Sonia Kauser (Age 10)

A Witches Spell

A pinch of salt a wolf's bladder
A hedgehog's spike stirred with a ladder
Horses mane a crab shell
A starfish wrinkled a sprinkle of hell
Some panda fur a lion tail
A teacher's spot a fin of a whale
An owl's hoot a toad's eye
A hunter's tongue a child's lie
A snake's sliver and its scale
A lizard's liver a hair of a male.

Loiuse Ketley (Age 11)

School

The clicking of computers as people type
The munch of barbecued crisps
As people eat their lunch
The scribbling of pencils as people write
Reception kid getting told off poor little mite
A very badly behaved child opening a tin
Dirty litter not thrown into the bin

I enjoy dinner
For fruit there's
Apple, orange, lime,
Bananas, kiwi and pear
We all love what we eat
Ice cream, jelly it's a treat
But now we go out to play
What a lovely lunch today

William Kendall (Age 9)

The Coldest Season

The snow falls,
Everything freezes,
No life is left,
Among the trees.

No laughter,
No sunshine,
Just snow,
And icy temperatures.

The world is waiting,
For the coming of the sun,
How much longer,
Can we all hang on?

Finally,
The first few blades of grass,
The first few rays of sun,
March is upon us.

The seasons start,
Again and again,
Spring, summer, autumn,
Then winter again.

Rebecca Kew (Age 14)

Hickory Dickory

Hickory dickory tall
The mouse is very small
The clock struck ten
He ate a hen
Hickory dickory tall

Beatrice Lovell (Age 6)

School

The green grass
Swishing in the wind
Next to the whitely
Also next to the bin,
As the daffodils drop
In the cold,
And the daffodils
But not so bold,

I like dinnertime
We sit in a bunch,
I like to get out of crime
When I eat my lunch,

At the end of the day
I get my bag,
And I am glad we don't have to pay
Then I get in my jag.

James Keens (Age 9)

Colours

Orange is a juicy satsuma in a fruit bowl
Or the sun setting in the sky or a pointed tasty carrot
Or a halloween pumpkin glowing at midnight.

Blue is the colour of the sea on a summer day
Or a shallow stream with otters, or dolphins leaping
Or a swimming pool with floats

Red is the sun setting in the sky
Or a red red rose growing on a bush in spring
Or a red blob of tomato ketchup on your plate
Or a summer flower growing in the garden

Silver is frost on your car
Or a silver spoon
Or the mirror in my bedroom

Yellow is the sun rising in the sky
Or a piece of cheese in the fridge
Or a banana skin
Or sweetcorn growing in a field

Green is spring leaves hanging from the tree
Or a flower stem or a bunch of grapes
Or as grass in a meadow

Zoe Knight (Age 8)

Scared

Scared is dark blue and black
Scared smells like fire and smoke
Scared tastes like spiders and flies
Scared sounds like a nightmare in your sleep,
Scared lives under your bed

Katie Kelly (Age 9)

Bring Us Peace

The people cry in desperation,
Stop this war now!

Mother's weep, daughters cry,
End this crime!

Father's fight with big black guns,
God have mercy!

Little boys in pit holes,
Pray for them!

Families long to be united,
End this devastation!

The coffin makers never stop,
Give them a rest!

God end all wars and start peace forever!

Louise Kendall (Age 10)

Taking Control

Every time I try and watch TV
It turns into a wrestling match between my dad and me.
When my program just starts,
Dad says time for darts.
Sometimes we end up in a big brawl,
Because he's turned over again to watch football.
I try and tell him about my views,
But he says "Not now I'm watching the news!"
My programmes start at two,
But dad turns over to watch pool.
But worse of all when I'm watching showbiz,
He says "Time for bed", and that's how it is!
I guess one of these days I'll understand,
That the remote control is glued to dad's hand!

Emma Knight (Age 9)

The Storm

Thunder bashing,
Lightning flashing,
Rain lashing,
Splashing, rushing,
Flooding.

Wind whistling
Through the house,
Bending trees,
Crashing, roaring,
Breaking everything.

Jordan Kirk (Age 8)

Mum Helps Us

Orange is her favourite colour
Tea drinker
Heat hater
Endless cleaning
Remembers everything
Helps everyone.

Mahmuda Khanum (Age 10)

Colours

Orange is a juicy satsuma sitting in your fruit bowl
Or the sun setting in the sky when the sun sets
Or a tasty pointed carrot
Or a halloween pumpkin glowing at midnight

Blue is a dolphin splashing in the sea
Or the colour of the sky on a sunny day
Or a swimming pool glittering in the sun
Or a deep river with fishes swimming in it

Red is the sky when the sun sets
Or Santa Claus delivering presents on Christmas Day
Or a red box to put letters in

Rosie King (Age 8)

Desert, Desert

Hot gleaming desert
Sidewinding snakes
Sand storms blowing violently
Shivering shimmering wind
Getting dehydrated
Thirst getting worse
A mirage in the distance
Temperature rising
More and more tired
Just want to collapse
The golden crisp sand
Desert, desert

Paul Kelly (Age 11)

My Imaginary Friend

My imaginary friend is the best,
He is better than the rest,
Why?
Because he is brilliant at football,
Brilliant at running,
Also he is brilliant at umping
When we sit for dinner,
My sister nearly sits on my friend,
But I say stop my friend is sitting there.
MY FRIEND IS THE BEST,
HE IS BETTER THAN THE REST!!
I found my friend,
Under a dusty bed.
Then I pulled him out and said,
I know you can be my best friend

Huseyin Kurt (Age 10)

My Horse

My horse likes to gallop
My horse likes to play
My horse likes to be groomed
And petted every day

My horse likes to eat
My horse likes to sleep
And when I forget to play with it
My horse begins to weep

My horse is very special
My horse is very sweet
My horse is very beautiful
And very very neat

I love my horse

Abby Keohane (Age 8)

Ten Tongue Twisters

One octopus offering orange oranges
Two troublesome tadpoles tying their toes together
Three tiresome tigers tugging tender trees
Four fierce flies flying far
Five fidgeting fairies frightened from foolish faces
Six slithery smelly serpents struggling to survive
Seven silly snails starting sea swimming
Eight envious elephants eating everything
Nine naughty nits nibbling nuts
Ten tall tinned tomatoes talking to talented teachers

Emily Knibbs (Age 9)

What Is?

What is thunder?
A fight between wind and lightning
What is rain?
Thousands of crystals splashing from the air
What is Fog?
A sudden gust of glittering smoke
What is snow?
A shower of soft, cold cotton

Neeha Karamchedu (Age 11)

Why Does The Sun Shine?

Why does the sun shine?
Why does the evergreen have pine?
Who made the computer?
Why is a nose called a hooter?
Why are sounds heard?
Why is a word a word?
Why is the pig pink?
Why does a pen write ink?
Why do I have a best friend?
When will the world end?

Rebekah King (Age 11)

The Dragon

There's a dragon in my house,
It comes creeping up the stairs,
"Oh no, what a scare!"
It's blue and green, it looks awful mean!
It has huge claws that touch the floor,
It has massive feet that stomp everywhere,
It has a big tongue licking his lips,
I think he wants me for tea with a plate of chips.

Natalie Kershaw (Age 9)

The Rainforest

Think of the rainforests being cut down,
Think of the trees leaving the ground.
Think of the rainforest in twenty years time,
Think of the people doing the crime.
Think of the time when forests were big,
Think of them now, people just dig.
Think of all the things we are losing,
Oxygen and our rainforests.
Think of the people just wanting more money,
Think of the days when rainforests were sunny.
Think of the animals losing their home
Think of the rare animals being alone.

Megan Kemp (Age 9)

Spring

I see the golden sun reflecting on the cool, crisp see through water
I smell the fresh green grass and flowers growing
The air blowing towards me making me feel relaxed
I feel peaceful and happy
I feel determined to do well
I feel as though I am floating in thin air

Anna Knowles (Age 10)

Dragon

Blazing fire shoots out of his nostrils
Bone crushing teeth, a forked tongue
Hanging out of his drooling mouth.
Fierce, hot breath that could burn you away.
Mega sharp spine with steel hard scales
That could break any sword in two.
Spitting lava hot breath,
His shining wings flap him home
To guard the gold and silver in his cave.
He sleeps behind sharp spikes sticking out of the ground.
Never to awake?

Elliott Kozlik (Age 9)

A Stormy Sea

Waves crash against the shore as the sea fills with hate and anger.
The sky grows dark and the waves grow fierce.
The wind blows through my hair and howls ferociously,
The sky spits hail, snow and rain in my face.

The sea is like a great hand slapping the beach
Waves whirl, spin, roar and splash.
The great hand grows bigger and comes in closer,
Grabbing hold of pebbles and litter, dragging them in.

Sea gulls try to fly away in fright,
Putting up a good fight against the giant's hand.

I think I prefer my home.

Jenny Kemp (Age 11)

The Circus

I'm going to the circus
I can see the big top,
The aroma of popcorn, hot dogs and candy floss
As I am shown to my seat
The show begins with a spectacle
Of performers, animals and floats.
The ring master enters with a top hat, whip and tailed coat.
The trapeze artist, jugglers, lion tamer,
Chimpanzees and liberty horses executing intricate movements.
But now my favourite act the clowns
Who squeeze into tiny cars, walk on stilts, tell jokes
And perform short silly numbers.
With roars from the crowds and applause all around
The circus comes to an end.

Sammy Kelly (Age 12)

Dear Mum

While you went out
A plate fell and broke itself
A crack happened in the black vase
Your old one Grandad gave you
From Mr. Ling in America
Somehow without me touching the cooker
Flames came out
A muddy hand print came on the new blue carpet
I don't know if we'll ever find out
How the dog turned on the oven
Especially from inside
Or how sister's mouse thought the sink hole was a mouse hole
I was scared when as if by magic
Footprints came on the wall
I was being very good
Honest
Knowing you are going to shout
I've gone to Gran's for a bit!

Rozina Kauser (Age 9)

Sunset

The shining orange floats in the sky, beating on the ground
Shimmering on the calm blue sea, bringing warmth to all around
But the time then comes to give up its kingdom, the kingdom of the sky,
And then it falls, a rosy apple, down from its branch so high
It colour washes the bright blue sky, and changes it to gold,
And opens up a brand new world of colours waiting to unfold.
The shades then change from gold to red, and from red to orange to pink
They merge so freely, swimming about, as water does on ink.
At last the colours fade away, it shows that night is here,
And now the sky is calm, as it watches its queen disappear.
The sky is now bleak and black, after its blazing show of lights,
But, as we all know, day must give way to night.

Priya Kumar (Age 10)

My Sister

Mess maker
Strawberry thrower
Milk shaker
Bike braker
Trouble sender
Oven baker
Baby sitter
Dish washer
Clothes changer
Baby sleeping
My sister

Omera Kazmi (Age 10)

Our Town

R edditch is cool
E njoy having a baby
D anger Mouse went on a ride
D anger look out
I went to a pool
T oday I went fishing
C atherine was going swimming today
H elen was playing

Andrew Knight (Age 8)

Tea With Grandma

I'm going to tea with Grandma
I wonder where it will be?
Maybe it will be at Kyle's house,
Just wait and see
We might have chocolate pud,
Come and see

Rebecca Lennon (Age 6)

I'm A . . .

Nut cracker,
Wheel spinner,
Sand digger,
Cage chewer,
Cardboard knawer,
Great escaper,
Water hater,
Bottle sucker,
Hand ducker,
Soft cuddler,
Cute twitcher,
Cat loather,
I'm a!

Hamster!!

Nathan Kelly (Age 10)

Our Town

Our town has lots of shiny cars
And all the men go to the bars.
The birds go round and flutter by
In the sunny, bright, blue sky.

I wait for the ice-cream van to come,
Then I lick my ice-cream in the sun.
Mums and dads go round and round,
While children scream along the ground.

We throw our rubbish in the bin,
After we have eaten our yummy din,
And in the river the fishes swim,
Along the wet and muddy brim.

We live in big houses or flats,
That have lots of bright coloured mats.
And all this deep down,
Is my special town.

Mary Liu (Age 7)

The Easter Bunny

It was a dark night
When the moon was bright.
The easter bunny came
And played a game.
The bunny left an egg
Under the table leg.

Zoe Liptrot (Age 8)

Iron Bridge Youth Hostel

Blood on the window sill, was it true?
I couldn't help but stand still
A banging sound,
Was coming from the ground.
I looked out of the window,
There were some boys,
Making loads of noise,
We went ot bed,
And the teacher said:
"Don't worry,
It will be over in the morning"
When I woke up I was yawning,
The boys were throwing a stone,
Aimee couldn.t help but groan.
It was time to go home,
Now we weren't going to groan,
Goodbye to the blood,
Goodbye to room thirteen,
Goodbye to the stone,
Because we were going home.

Sophie Lock (Age 11)

Inside Is What Counts
(To someone no-one understands)

I know a girl who is quite fat
And she knows she is too
But if you look inside her heart
She is just like me and you

She has a heart, ears and nose
And tongue and mouth and eyes
And the more you bully and call her names
The more this poor girl cries

She does her work and quietly too
And gains confidence every day
And puts up with names Miss Fatty and Fat
And she just learns to walk away

She must be brave and confident too
To come to school every day
And to put up with the comments in the street
And the people that get in her way

So when you see a person in the street
That isn't as pretty as you
I hope you look inside their heart
Because they are just like me and you.

Rosie Landragin (Age 14)

Being Left Out

Oh woe is me I'm all alone I don't even have a mobile phone!
Nobody to talk to feeling down,
Sad and lonely nobody to help,
No friends, really sad,
I just sit there all of break
Every day all week.

Alastair Kerr (Age 9)

Love

A stolen glance toward your face,
Arms entwined in a warm embrace.
My heart begins to flutter,
A trembling voice, words do stutter.
Birds singing in the sky so blue,
Initials engraved in a tree, me and you.
High upon the canopy of trees,
The wind carries our love upon it's breeze.
We live our lives to the limit,
Taking chances to reach loves summit.
The radio plays our favourite tune,
A sign to us, we must leave soon.
Gather our senses and desires around us,
Keep us safe, that is what love does.

Robert Lees (Age 12)

The Monster

My wings are waves,
My eyes are like diamonds sparkling in the sun,
My tongue is as soft as a new piece of leather,
My claws are as sharp as knives,
My breath is like the wind,
My voice is as sweet as song birds at dawn,
My tail is slippery snake,
I've seen them laugh, I've seen them cry,
I've heard voices like angels,
In anger I howl like a wolf,
They call me the monster.

Lucy Lindsell (Age 13)

My Teacher

My teacher is really mean,
She always like to shout and scream,
My teacher loves to pick her nose,
In class when she plays with her toes,
She always shouts at me,
My friend she does not see,
I'm always in trouble,
I feel I'm trapped in a bubble,
My teacher is mean,
My teacher is mean!!!

Kirsty Layzell (Age 13)

Life

L istening to the grass grow
I s what I like to do
F inding peace and qiuet,
E njoying the view

Clare Letley (Age 13)

The Sea Monster

He gobbles up the pebbles and sand,
Then rumbles and returns back to his hole,
With the fishes and crabs.
He ripples quietly...
And lays silent and still for a minute,
But not for long as he cries and roars fiercely,
Clashing and clanging against the rocks.
White frothy bubbles appear from his floppy lips,
Then he slurps it back in.
His tears trickle down the rocks.
The monster murmurs and mumbles.
The wind blows his tears dry.
His tears are dry and his lips closed,
Waiting for the next time for the wind to blow.

Rachel Levene (Age 12)

Glee!

Glee is silver,
It taste like warm chocolate,
And the smell is like freshly cut grass,
It looks dazzling yet calm and floaty,
It sounds like a peal of bells,
And feels like cool water trickling down my throat.

Kate Ladkin (Age 12)

Untitled

I don't know how
Dragons sleep,
Walk and talk and eat.
And I don't know
How they get
Hairy teeth and eyes.

Billy Lewin (Age 4)

Happy And Afraid

Happy is smiley,
Afraid is aggh,

Everyone can be happy and afraid,
Even me!

William Leyland (Age 6)

School

A is for art which I like the most,
B is for best though I'm never one to boast.
C is for the canteen where I've got the food,
D is for dinnerladies their always in a mood.
E is for excitement at the end of a school day,
F is for football that the boys all like to play.
G is for grumpy like miss can sometimes be,
H is for help that the teachers give to me.
I is for intelligence which some of us may look,
J is for school jumpers, what a load of tack.
K is for Kati oh by the way thats me,
L is for late oh why is it always she?
M is for music thats one subject I hate,
N is for noisey when the teachers shout out Kate.
O is for orange which I have for lunch,
P is for P.E, cor their a crazy bunch!
Q, R & S is for quickly, running, straight,
T is for the teacher, chasing me with bait.
U, V & W is for undoubtfully very wet,
when I was outside with all the work I was set!
X is for Xaustion when I'm almost in deep sleep,
Y is for yawning when dreams are at their peak,
Z is for zzzzzzzzzzzzzzzzzzzzzz

Kati Leverett (Age 13)

Dream!

I had a dream......
That I took a trip to Saturn.
The aliens had three eyes on their nobbly heads
Two toes and were a vivid purple.
I had a dream......

I had a dream......
That I took a trip to Saturn.
The houses were hexagonal shaped
They glowed eerily in the blue haze
I had a dream......

I had a dream......
That I took a trip to Saturn.
The circle that surrounded Saturn......
Was star shaped and misty
Creating a mysterious atmosphere
Then I awoke......
Cosy in my bed at home
I had a dream......

Emma Linford (Age 11)

My Cat

My cat is young and rather sweet.
Her small grey paws are tiny feet.
She likes to run around the grass
But soon, alas, this youth will pass.

My cat is old and slightly fat,
Her fur is dry and tends to mat.
She spends all day upon her chair,
And somehow I am also there.

Jack Lister (Age 15)

Shadows

The shadows lurk where they can't be found,
Forgotten spirits they wait around.
Not quite alive yet they follow at a distance
One step behind, they hide from the sun
Strongest when hidden
They fear the light.
For with it comes goodness, the breath of life.

Trapped between planes
Not earthly, neither spectral
Flat and lifeless, yet strangely alive
They thrive on darkness,
They dwell in the blackness, left by life
Hollow, faceless, selfless, mindless
The shell of what was left behind.

Tom Lowe (Age 13)

My Big Ugly Bunny

Black bunny, when I held you in my arms
And stroked your long, black ears
As you grunted at me, glinting
Pure white teeth, and I felt
The 10lb weight of you on my elbow
As the long black hairs you moulted
Stuck close to my white fleece.

Black Bunny-I told all my friends that definitely
You did not bite or jump! But truly
I had no certainty, and no hope, only wishing
To hold you for that thrill,
Which left
A long wake of pleasure, as the straw rustled
And you faded into the darkness
Of grass and carrots, and I returned,
Smiling and haunted, to a dark morning.

Toria Lambert (Age 13)

Love Is Sweet

Love is sweet like a teddybear.
Love is messages in the air.
Flowers are sweet just like you,
I love chocolates, do you?
So I love you and you love me,
So I think you and I would make,
A perfect match.

William Lim (Age 12)

Everything From Nothing

First there was nothing.
The nothing rumbled.
The nothing exploded.
The nothing was filled by something.
The nothing and the something expanded.

The someting swirled around.
The something collected.
The something formed stars.
The something changed in the stars.
The new something with the old something
Formed planets, which became everything.

The everything evolved from the something.
The something evolved from the nothing.
Will the everything evolve into the something?
Will the everything collapse into nothing?
Will the everything disperse and die?
What are the nothing, something and everything?

James Lilley (Age 13)

When My Sister Comes Home

Thinking of you and me,
What a nice thought.
If only we could be,
Close together not far apart.

When you come home surprisingly,
My face lights up with joy.
We hug each other sisterly,
And I feel warm inside.

We talk and laugh,
Of how we have been.
Rejoice and relax,
In the pub with our friends.

But soon a week,
Can seem like a day.
When she starts packing
Her clothes again.

Today is the day,
She goes back home.
A single hug goodbye,
And then she is gone.

Helen Lee (Age 15)

Autumn Leaves

Autumn leaves falling
Like glittering butterflies
Autumn leaves falling like brown jets
Autumn leaves falling like a loopy kite

Eliza Lauchlan (Age 6)

Spring

I wake to hear the sounds of the birds' melodious whistles,
The sound of their feet tapping gently on the branch of the acorn tree,
The uncomfortable feeling of the blazing, hot, sun beating down on my back,
And the soft touch of my pillow as I lie half asleep pondering.

I sit and gaze out of my window,
It's a beautiful sight.
The new-born lambs bounce happpily around the large, open fields,
Playing along with their brothers and sisters.

Then I look at the old oak tree,
To see it's grown bright green leaves again,
Along with the wonderful rose and scarlet flowers,
I remember from last spring.

I can smell the invigorating aroma of the freshly mown lawn,
It stimulates me.
I lay upon my bed again,
Wishing for a great day ahead!

Danielle Lillington (Age 13)

The Beauty Of Evil

Divine the beauty I beheld,
Lithe and languidly spread, spiralling,
The strength picturesque.
An arrowed head lay resting,
While the vulpine lengths left the sweeping dust abridged.

Lying there sibilantly heaving,
Sinewy curves licking the ground,
With a mouth of lightning, ruptured rosettes seething,
There lay the creature,
A stained glass window with shining tessellations.

It lay there so mild and serene,
Frozen in the sands of time,
I watched unloving in worshipful awe,
The chocolate brown and stagnant black, placid, pulsating,
Knots of woven shapes and patterns.

No fire in the golden eyes,
The flames flicker unblinking, softly dormant,
A pulsing, sleeping death.
Unable to wake, unable to die,
The devil's reincarnation.

Michael Lamb (Age 12)

Friends (Acrostic)

Friend in the playground having lots of fun.
Tolling round in the mud with my best friend Spud.
I hate it when my friend is ill and off school.
Every day he's away is so lonely.
Nowhere to hide.
Don't hit me, I get bullied when I'm on my own.
Shooting down the street, running home, wishing Spud was well.

Nicola Lindop (Age 9)

The Dolphin

Here is a dolphin
So slimy and skinny
Splashing around and in
The water so happy.
He is cheerful
I swim with the dolphin
He is so playful
So I can hold its fin.

Victoria Louden (Age 13)

A Dragon In My Classroom

A dragon in my classroom,
It's skin all made of scales,
His colour is all purple,
And has daggers for his nails.

A dragon in my classroom,
His tongue all slimy green,
When you look at him,
He does look rather mean.

My teacher said, "What a good creature you are,"
"To visit us you must have come far?"
"Me good? NO," he snorted,
SNAP, SNAP! He roared through his jaw,
And chased our sprinting teacher down the corridor.

Eleanor Lasota (Age 10)

Tiger

I wait for my prey every day,
I watch it run for the last time in it's life,
I can roar like thunder in the night,
I chew on my meat fiercely,
I am so well camouflaged.
I am as fast as a car,
I come from Asia, that is far,
I am a dark orange colour.
My black stripes are like thunder bolts,
I am going to sleep,
I turn into a heap.

Louise Laidlaw (Age 8)

Midnight Snowing

White droplets of water falling from the sky,
Swirling and whirling and then they die,
Like petals falling from thousands of trees,
Riding on the midnight breeze.

A winter's night full of nothing,
Except gleaming snow and moonlight bluffing,
The moon smiling with its golden shine,
The stars twinkling in a beautiful line.

The soft tufty snow settled all around,
Watching and gazing without a sound,
But then comes footsteps munching and crunching,
And some faraway voices grumbling and mumbling.

The snow crystals quietly and delicately sing,
Finishing falling at the end of the evening,
And then silence, stopping and making its mark,
Can you hear the snowing and whispering in the dark?

Harriet Lockyear (Age 11)

My Diary

From the mountains the wind would blow,
As the night would fall so does the snow.
When I look out of my window pane,
I see wild horses running down the country lane.

As I sit by the fire to warm myself up,
And to my lips I bring my cup.
As the moon starts to rise and the stars start to sparkle,
I can feel the heat from the burning charcoal.

I like to sit and gaze for a while,
My dreams and thoughts they make me smile,
I'm shutting my diary to go to bed,
So fresh, new thoughts, can flow through my head.

Annie Lawrence (Age 10)

Shimmer

It was very peaceful,
Nothing to be heard,
But the wooshing of the sea,
It was getting dark,
And we now could,
See the shimmer of the sun.
The sea had many ripples,
Whish, whish, whish,
The sea washed upon the sand,
The tide was nearly in,
It was though the sun was fading away,
From my eyes.

Johannah Lee (Age 10)

My Pets

My dog called Guinness is a black labrador,
He was born in Thame and now he is four.

He likes to jump in puddles and get soaking wet,
But he shakes like a leaf when he goes to the vet.

He's crazy about food and he loves his walks,
I love him so much I wish he could talk.

My rabbit Flopsy is one of those types,
He likes romping about and playing with tights.

He loves carrots, I feed him every day,
He lives in a hutch lined with hay.

My fish called Socks is orange and white,
He can see in the dark so he must have good eye sight.

I never clean him out, whoopsie,
But when he swims along he must go 'whee.'

Rosie Lynch (Age 8)

Use Your Senses

I smell the strong smell of my monster munch,

I smell my mummy's perfume when she sprays it on.

I feel like touching the christmas star when I dream.

I feel like touching the sun when it rises.

Looking at the late night taxis cram like black beetles down King's Street.

Looking at my delicate baby brother.

Tasting the lovely chocolate spread that is on the T.V.

Tasting the lovely dinner that my mummy cooks when I dream.

Christopher Louch (Age 6)

The Easter Bunny

The Easter Bunny pays a visit
Don't stay up too long or you might just miss it
At night if you lay down to rest you legs
In the morning you could wake up to some beautiful eggs
I love the Easter Bunny
He is really funny
With his floppy pink ears
I burst into tears
His little brown basket and his lovely eggs,
His white fluffy body and his white fluffy legs.

Rachel Leigh (Age 10)

Fire

Slowly the monster awakes,
The red, orange, yellow, purple monster reaches for his food,
His tongue wiggles around, his grey breath circles,
He stops and shrinks,
But we have not seen the last of him.

Graeme Lye (Age 6)

Any Dog

It creeps it leaps
It loves to eat
It rolls it pulls
It pushes you down
It's oh so hard
To stay on the ground
You call it stays
It always gets its way
It barks - you answer
You're sad and lonely
It's always there for you
It's any dog!

Lizzie Lucas (Age 7)

My Body

First the skull all thick and bold,
Then the clavicle all yucky and cold.
My body's gone through torture and pain,
I've broken my bones and burst a vein.

I'm in a weelchair all alone,
I can't do anything but reach the phone.
I go to hospital every day,
They always fuss, I guess it's ok.
I always feel left out,
When I meet new people I feel the doubt.
I can't do anything for myself,
I can't even reach the bottom shelf.

Tara Lehane (Age 11)

Fire

Fire flickering through the night
Say your prayers and whisper goodnight
For if you don't you'll get a fright
From fire flickering through the night

The fire flickers on and on,
In a second you'll be gone,
It plays a tune that is anon,
The fire flickers on and on.

Christopher Lambeth (Age 7)

Computer

Can you tell me why
My disc has not tried to fly?
Can you tell me why?

Rebecca Lambert (Age 8)

The Are Coming

They are coming! -They are coming!
The bladed ships. - The bladed ships
They are coming! - They are coming!
They are here! - They are here!
Run for cover. - Run for cover
Up the tree and under cover
They are here! - They are here!
Now coming to get me!
Running, running, running running.
Hiding, hiding
Behind the tree but they will see
Oh no! - Oh no!
They can see me!

Jamie Lewis (Age 10)

Poetry Of World War One

My eyes will barely stay open,
My knees are going to buckle under my weight.
I stagger away, I'm leaving the noise behind me.
My head throbs, but I am relieved, back to safety.
My boot comes off; I don't care.
We look like a group of haggered, drunken old men,
I barely recognise them, I didn't know them anymore, their smiles had left them.
The gas suddenly covers my eyes, I shout out, desperate.
I fumble to put my gas mask on,
Except one, he cries as the gas gets into his lungs.
I can't see, the gas is thick, green
My friend comes, staggers towards me, I'm helpless.
He coughs, he is going to die, imagine, what would you feel like?
I am disgusted carrying the dying man behind the cart.
He is black and covered in deep, red, blood.
Listen to the dying man, drowning on dry land,
The cart jolts, he coughs up blood and mucus, listen to him,
Is it glorious to die for your king and country?
Were you there?
Think, Is this really glorious?

Tessa Leonard (Age 14)

Anger

Anger can be shown in many different ways
For me it's a tornado ram raiding through my head
Biting my lip I go bright red!
I feel like giving my brother a knuckle sandwich
He cries
I can't take it any more,
I'm going crazy.

Alex Lilburn (Age 11)

Tick Tock Tick Tock

Tick tock tick tock goes the stop watch
At seven o'clock I wake up and go down for breakfast
I must eat fast
Tick tock tick tock goes the stop watch

I must get dressed fast or I will be late for school
Tick tock tick tock goes the stop watch
I put on my watch
Tick tock tick tock goes the stop watch

Buzz buzz stop the alarm clock
Tick tock tick tock goes the stop watch
Tick tock goes the Grandfather clock
Tick tock tick tock goes the stop watch

Tick tock goes the clock tower
Tick tock tick tock goes the stop watch
At 12:30 I have my dinner
Tick tock tick tock goes the stop watch

At 5:00 I have my tea
Tick tock tick tock stop the stop watch!

Samantha Longmire (Age 9)

Gossip With Friends

Gossip in classroom,
Oh, what was I going to ask you

My friend Jessie
Is so messy

My other friend Kat
Is in love with rat

My friend Vicki
Doesn't like Nicki

Art and PE are the best
RE and English are not like the rest

Jessica Levett (Age 9)

The River

As still as a statue
glistening in the radiant sun,
it makes its way swiftly
down to the excited waves.
Crashing and crashing
to the sea bed.
Where the sand is
as still as a statue.

Ruby Limbrick (Age 10)

Seasons

Winter is a time of
Black smoky clouds
Snow as white as a dove
Rain as transparent as glass

Spring is a time of
Birds popping out
Trees growing green as apples
Grass growing huge

Summer is a time of the sun
Burning like fireflies
Birds singing brightly
Singing and laughing

Autumn is a time of
Trees with no leaves
Leaves luring yellow, red and brown
Wind blowing in your face

Catherine Linsell (Age 10)

The Elephant

Elephant hiding in the trees,
Animals fleeing everywhere,
Man with guns and scraggy hair
The elephant is endangered

"We'll chop off his tusks!"
They shout "Will be rich!"
They don't know what they're doing,
They only think of themselves.

"The feel of his skin, nice and rough"
"The lovely feel of his long tusks!"
"This is a big one!"
"It weighs 5 tonnes!"

"Here comes the herd guns at the ready!"
"We've got quite few we're lucky we got any."
Elephant looking from the trees, everything's gone quiet,
Men with guns and long hair, making a silent exit.

Blood on the ground,
The smell of gun powder,
A baby elephant stands on its own,
Most of the herd was taken.

Georgina Lennon (Age 11)

The Death Wish

I should like to touch the Earth's Core,
I should like to smell the lava of hell,
I should like to hear the call of the dead,
I should like to take home the bones of an un-dead warrior,
I should like to understand the fear of a man's death,
I should like to be the Red Devil.

Mark Lampshire (Age 10)

When I'm Older

When I'm older I'm going to be a groovy gran,
And have nail varnish on each hand,
And I'll take my 20 year old boyfriend on a date,
And I'll spend all his money,
And make myself feel great.

I'll spend all my money,
On sweet things like honey,
Have little fluffy cats,
And big clashy hats.

I'll play with Barbies all day long,
And walk with my stick and sing a song,
I'll stay up nearly every night,
And give the teenagers a fright,
Even though they will laugh at me each day,
And I will make them run away
I'll look really wacky,
Even though I'll look tacky.

Heather Lilley (Age 11)

The Wind At Play

It's swiftly flying through the air,
Calmly changing course with care,
Flying over all the trees around,
Peacefully gliding not making a sound.

I watch it fly and then sit down,
It's so fast it deserves a crown,
It heads away to the north, so then I run,
To watch it fly so gracefully is quite fun.

But then suddenly it quickly falls,
Deeply downwards near some walls,
I catch my breath and run to it,
People look at me, stand up then sit.

A crowd of people gather round me,
All shouting do you want some help dearie,
Someone runs off to a phone,
I reach it first, I'm all alone.

Then the other people come,
It's just a plastic bag, they think I'm dumb.
I glance at them, they just give me dirty looks,
I look up and down then stare at some rooks!

Rachel La Bouchardiere (Age 10)

Spring

All the colours have a meaning
It tastes like juicy apple peeling
It sounds like birds in the skies
It looks like blossom falling from my eyes
It smells like sweet cherry pie
It feels beautiful in the sky

Katy Lynch (Age 8)

Football! Football!

This is a poem about football,
The game I love to play,
On Saturday I go training,
And play matches on Sunday.

I play for Hordle Spurs,
In League Division 22,
We usually win the game,
But sometimes draw 2 - 2.

I like to pass the ball,
And sometimes score a goal,
I support Man United,
And like to watch Andy Cole.

We play seven aside,
And our kit is yellow and red,
I run around lots and lots,
And come home ready for bed.

Adam Lavis (Age 9)

I Didn't Want To Write This!

I didn't want to write this poem,
But mummy said I had to.

I'd rather play my gameboy,
Or play on my computer.
I could have practised cello,
Or read some Harry Potter!

I could have played with Furby,
Or tidied up my room.
Or played with Dad's best C.D player,
And made it really boom!

I do like playing with Sophie,
The girl who lives next door.
I might have played with Lego,
And spread it round the floor!

But now I'm glad I wrote this poem,
I wish I could write more!

Charlotte Little (Age 9)

Pig (Pinky)

I am a pig,
I'm not so big,
I'm not so scary,
I'm just right,
I grunt,
I grunt all day,
Hay!

I am oink,
I do not swim,
Because I will sink.

Larissa Last (Age 11)

I Spy

I spy with my little eye,
Something beginning with C.
Is it key?
No! I said C silly!
Is it Clouds? Car? Castle?
Yeah it's castle, your go next.

I spy with my little eye,
Something beginning with S.
Hey look, there's Tess!
Have you guessed my S word?
Is it satellite?
Yeah, right!

Spy an E word, B word, K word,
Spy a cow, a dog, a lake,
Spy on your ex-best friend, your sister,
Spy on your mum and dad in bed,
Spy through a keyhole, a chink, a window,
Spy for your country, spy out the land.

Spy on anyone, anywhere, anytime,
Just don't Spy On Me!!

Sophie Lovick (Age 10)

Faces

Scary faces,
Silly faces,
Sad faces,
Baby faces,
Happy faces,
Mischief faces,
Great faces,
Jelly faces,
Sleepy faces,
Cute faces,
Horrible faces,
Cool faces.

Nikki Lam (Age 7)

Hell

Hell, the place the Devil dwells,
Where dark souls conspire, surrounded by fire,
The evil reign, thriving on pain,
Every minute one more death, in the time you can take a simple breath,
A lurking, dark figure dressed in a cape,
Warty, grotesque demons, stopping any chance of escape,
Shaking, quivering, trembling with fear, hoping this terrifying world would just disappear,
You can scream and shout, but there's no way out,
Hell, the home for all who have done wrong,
For men with weak souls, and not those with strong.

Jack Holden (Age 11)

Loneliness

A blanket of loneliness swept over me
As I slumped in my room alone,
No-one to speak to, no-one around,
Silence is the only sound,
Sadness is crying out inside of me,
Minutes feel like hours days feel like weeks,
Fun has left my heart forever
I'm crying sobbing hour after hour
Waiting for the phone to ring or a knock at the door
But nothing happens,
Why is loneliness happening to me?

Rebecca Lee (Age 8)

Winter

The dripping icicles hang from the door,
Look there's some more.
Snowmen all around the street,
Look at their little stick feet.

It's going dark, better put on the light,
Doesn't that seem so bright?
When the sun starts to shine,
Isn't the weather just fine.
I start to shout with glee!
"YIPPEE!"

Heather Lord (Age 9)

Sunset

The milky light fills every gap between the sagging trees,
Pinks and purples mixed together to make the perfect sky
Birds chattering edging away
No interruptions
Tranquility!

The pink clouds fluffy and like cream,
The yellowy ball in the sky dropping out of sight
The relaxation trickling on and on . . . .
Balls of pink fluff running away revealing the most magical sight
Nothing to ruin the peace.

But what's this, a little yellow star hurtling across the surface of the silk
Dark drawing in, curling in around the tranquil easing in bit by bit
More stars, more black sheet, the last majestic sight peeling away.
Now here I am
Waiting for the next

. . . Sunset . . .

Rachel Lester (Age 11)

Hidden Tiger

A crouching tiger is a hidden dragon
Searching for its prey, looking this way, looking that way,
It meets an antelope, starts at a run, it looks like fun.
It brings it down, another tiger coming for the kill.
Defend the kill or the other tiger will take it and make it his own.
The other tiger goes and when he's eaten he leaves too
Then the vultures and hyenas move in.

Conor Lennon (Age 8)

The Dog

I pull heavy sledges
Over very hard snow,
I am as white as paper,
I am as smelly as a skunk
As some people say
But if you know me I am not all the day

I will be very good
And play all the time,
I come from a big family
Called Canine which includes
Wolves, jackles and foxes.
I do not see my family much
They come out at night and I do not.

I sleep very softly
And pretend I am a runner.
People think I am a man's best friend
But I am not.
People do not know what colour I am
Because when I am out in the snow I am white
But I am black when I am in the woods.

Daniella Lennon (Age 9)

Wartime

Sick people crying for help,
Bombs dropping every night,
Sirens screeching,
People hurrying into the shelter

Houses getting hit by bombs,
Blood and insides all over the place
Soldiers sinking in the boats,
Pilots crashing into houses

Ack ack guns shooting down planes
Everyone so tired and weary
Trying to doze off in the shelter,
But can't because of all the noise.

War is bloody and horrible
Tanks going off into the horizon
War is so so horrible.

James Longley (Age 8)

The Mermaid

The mermaid, mermaid, splashing away,
For she has come from far away.
She has travelled for days, and days,
And has often lost her way,
But she still carries on her journey.

Elizabeth Lewis (Age 10)

The Friend I Will Not Forget

My friend is the best,
He is better than the rest
Why?
He is amazing, fantastic,
He is everything to me.

His eyes glisten in the starlight,
While wagging his tail from side to side,
His fur is light brown which,
Turns dark black in the water,
He has got white spots on him,
Dribble comes from his mouth
Like rain falling from the sky.

My friend is the best,
He is better than the rest,
Why?
He is amazing fantastic,
He is everything to me,

That is why he is my friend!
He is the best
He is better than the rest!

Billy Langford (Age 11)

Stranger Of The Rocks

Early one morn when the moon is done,
I saw a rare sight upon the sun,
On a rock she was leaning for all to see,
But what was this stranger, who could she be?

I looked once more at her pale white face,
She seemed to be staring right up into space,
On a rock she was leaning for all to see,
But what was this stranger, what could she be?

She stretched out her arms full of grace,
And she swam away with her beautiful face,
In a second she was gone in the glistening sea,
But what was this stranger, who could she be?

As the days and weeks and the months went by,
I failed to see the stranger pass by,
Where she was and who could she be?
This was all such a mystery!

If only the rocks could speak and tell,
Where she is and if all is well,
But what was that stranger, where could she be,
Will that stranger come back to me?

Charlotte Lander (Age 10)

Just Another Day

A normal train, a normal day
People think everything's OK
But they don't know what lies ahead
And they don't know 13 will be dead
But then it comes without warning
It's too dark to see, it's early morning
A crash comes as you hit a land rover
You think that's it, and it's all over
But then a shake of the rail
And it's another tragic tale
You hit a train coming the other way
And the rest is too sad to say.

Madeleine Lawrence (Age 10)

Jumbling Doggy

There was a little boy
Who had a cute dog
And he taught the dog to beg
And that cute little dog at tea times
Would stand on one leg.

One day to his master's great surprise,
The cute little dog said "Here goes!"
And he stuck his hind legs in the air
And stood up on his nose

Maaia Loza (Age 9)

The Magic Box

I will put in the box
        the leap of a dolphin
        the growth of a plant
        the moon in the night sky.

I will put in the box
        the swish of a unicorn's tail
        the flap of a bird's wing
        the dazzle of a firework.

I will put in the box
        the glassy design of a snowflake
        the treasure of a tomb
        the whiskers of a puppy.

I will put in the box
        the words from an ancient book
        the message from a bottle
        the breath of the breeze.

My box is fashioned from wood
that's seen the world.
With wishes in every corner.
The hinge is made with a line of time.

Emma Lindop (Age 10)

Spring

Spring is a time of year,
When you begin to hear,
Birds singing in the trees,
Bees buzzing as they please.

Daffodils showing
Their yellow heads,
The new born lambs
Snug in their beds

Jaid Limbert (Age 7)

The House

The house is haunted
Full of spectres and ghosts
With unwashed windows
And banisters dusty
And the fire from the fireplace dead

With crumbling chimneys
And the hearthrugs ragged
The carvings surrounded with cobwebs
The smells of all rooms are musty
The mantel piece full of faded portraits

Sara Lands (Age 10)

The Big Question

Why are the planets so far away?
How old is out planet?
Why are we part of the Milkyway?
How does gravity hold our bodies down?
Why are there so many different climates around the world?
How can some creatures fly?
Why can't animals talk to us?
How are we able to see, smell, taste and hear?
Why do we not all have the same colour skin?
How can people do such amazing things?
Why can't it be hot in this country all the time?
How does the earth rotate?
Why is air invisible?
How are we able to talk and walk?
Why are the stars so bright?
How big is out world?
Why do all the planets look round?
How did the world start?
I know some of these answers,
But one day will I know them all?

Fiona Lane (Age 8)

The Halls Of Blood

I can step where you cannot,
Legs boil then feet rot,
As you step some will splat,
It is as mysterious as the black cat,
As you look upon the walls,
Death hangs as blood falls,
Many dead lie in the flood,
These are the halls of blood.

Ricky Lawless (Age 11)

The Aliens Spacecraft

Lights flashing round and round,
People driving in their cars,
Thinking there might be life on Mars,
In the spacecraft aliens controlling it,
They look out to study Earth and it's life,
They grab people one by one.
Smells gooey,
Put them on the scanner,
Ready with their laser guns,
To kill and destroy,
Put them in them in the cloning room,
Make clones,
6ft long things all squishy,
Hypnotising people to destroy Earth,
Zooming through the night sky,
Looking at the planets nearby,
Coming from a different planet.

Mark Langton (Age 9)

The Little Kitten

There was a little kitten
Who always plays with a pink mitten
Her name was fluffy bell
She was a little white kitten
She had a sweet little pink nose
With little blue eyes
With a little fluffy tail
With small paws and a small head
With small little ears
She was a sweet little cat girl
She always had her hair in little bows
She was only a baby kitten
She had a lovely basket that she slept in
And a lovely warm home
With a wonderful owner
She was a very stylish kitten
She was a very small kitten
She was a nice little kitten
She was a very cute little kitten
She was a very fluffy kitten

Lucy Lynch (Age 8)

The River

I start up in the mountains
Small and shallow,
I begin my journey,
I get bigger and deeper,
Going down the waterfalls,
Through lakes and making valleys,
As I get closer to the sea.
I am getting bigger, faster,
Stronger and wilder.
Nothing can stop me
On my journey to the sea.
Crashing on banks
Going in a v-shaped valley,
And now I am in the sea.

Sam Long (Age 9)

Hope

Hope is the colour of silver
It smells like victory
It tastes like glory
It sounds like trumpets in a band
It feels like victory
It lives in your heart

Stress

Stress is the colour of yellow
It smells like a burning fire
It tastes of anger
It sounds like shouting
It feels like a burning fire
It lives in your head

Dominic Lee (Age 10)

All Day Long

I wake up in the morning and get rushed along
And while I brush my teeth and hair I sing a lovely song.
I put my uniform on sleep still in my eyes, talking to my mum but I don't wear any ties.
I pack my bag and clean my face I put my shoe on and tie my lace.

I go to school and play with Max and Kit, I play a game of chase I'm sure I won't be it.
Then when we came in, all in a line, and sit down quietly children divine.
We do some English, writing I like lots, then we do maths with dashes and dots.
Then it's time for lunch, hungry am, I the sun is so sunny like a yummy custard pie.

Talking to my friends, and eating very slow and after that, it's playtime as you do know.
Playing chase again, Stacy joining in, running very fast, I can beat her and Kim.
The scratching of my pencil, the rattling of the papers,
The screaming of the teacher as her patience tapers.

Stuck on something, teacher losing her temper, put my hand up for her, because I can't find the centre,
Then it will be clearing up time desks very tidy, people are running "watch out behind me".
It's home time out we go, people packing bags but I'm very slow.

Bliss Lewis (Age 8)

Fear

Fear is dark blue because it sounds dark and scared
It smells like smoke and fire
Fear tastes like pepper and slugs
It's a sound like creeping and fire burning
It feels like hot concrete
Fear Lives

Chloe Lineker (Age 9)

Babies

My name is Lucy I'm a baby.
No-one likes me when I want my things,
When I'm winging they just ignore me.
When I want some then I have to be noisy,
I hate being bad, but the only way is to scream and shout.
Because they don't understand my goo-goo's and coo-coo's!

Rachel Laidlow (Age 7)

Sunshine

I made a young girl take off her jumper,
I made leaves go golden and crispy.
I made flowers pop up from the soil,
And helped them to germinate.
I am as hot as a dragon breathing fire!
I am a million times bigger than the earth,
I sleep in my bed until dawn.

Katy Liddell (Age 8)

The River

Splash and splish, splosh and splash.

The water is playing in the river,
The river is going in the lake.

Splash and splish, splosh and splash.

Fish are playing in the water,
Fish are eating in the river.

Splash and splish, splosh and splash.

Amaury Levisalles (Age 7)

My Friend Across The Sea

My friend across the sea,
She really misses me,
I really miss her too,
Please see me friend I really need you.

You can get there somehow,
And I want to come now,
Sadly I can't come today,
But I'll get there some way.

I'm as happy as a lark now,
She came on a boat somehow,
We're like monkeys in the trees,
Me and her are like linked keys.

Now we are together,
Together forever,
I'm back with my friend,
Until the end.

Zoe Lynes (Age 9)

Clouds

White puffy clouds.
Floating through an azure sky.
Drifting carelessly, go
Thick clouds,
Thin clouds,
Dark grey clouds poised over the ocean blue.
With rain like mini-meteors,
Falling down from the clear atmosphere.
They are a big beard,
That has grown over the years,
With shaving foam scattered all over.
Like candy floss.
I can see pictures, a monkey up a tree!
What a silly place to be.

Craig Lye (Age 9)

It Was So Noisy

It was so noisy that
I couldn't hear the teacher talking loudly
It was so noisy that
I couldn't hear the play time bell buzzing noisily
I was so noisy that
I couldn't hear the dog barking madly
It was so noisy that
I couldn't hear my mum yelling loudly
It was so noisy that
I couldn't hear my radios booming

It was so noisy!!!

Alisha Lloyd (Age 8)

After School

I come home from school, my tummy rumbles
When's dinner on the table? My brother grumbles
My Mum's in the kitchen, cooking my tea
My brother's in the lounge, annoying me
My Dad's in the garage fixing the car
My Mum calls from the kitchen, "Can you open this jar?"
I'm sitting in the lounge watching TV
Mum says "Can you set the table for me?"
Knives, forks, plates, enough for four
I'll eat all my dinner tonight for sure!
Dinner's over, salt, pepper, sauces put away
I ask Mum "Can I go out to play?"
"30 minutes" she said is all I've got
Then out with your books, time to swot
School work done, I'm tired and fed
I think it's time to go to bed!

Amy Loader (Age 8)

Snow Poem

I woke up one Christmas morn
I looked around and gave a yawn
Last night the wind was blowing
But "Wow" today it's snowing
I went outside and gave a look
It looked so good just like in a book
Then I thought it looked like:
A ball of cheese falling from the sky,
Lumps of lard falling down, down
And lands like a feather,
Or a white dog moulting.

Sophie Large (Age 10)

A Steam Engine

Pistons spinning lower gear shaking up and down
Steam pointing north like a blow away gown
Rattling up and down the smooth track
Shunting trucks into sidings
With everybody's likings
Pulling the Express and no stopping
From the steam there's a lot of coughing
Waiting at platforms near and by
Passing big storms and little . . .
Suddenly slowing down and down
Coming down the end of the line . . . stopped

Alexander Lozinski (Age 8)

My Friend

My friend is good she is not bad,
My friend is kind when I am sad,
But when she is away I cannot play,
With my friend any more.

Victoria Lewis (Age 9)

My Biscuit

A biscuit is a round flat cake,
I saw it flowing down the lake,
My mum said it wasn't properly baked
So I said I'll buy an Ice-cream with a flake.

A biscuit is a round flat cake,
I saw it flowing down the lake,
It wasn't properly baked
Because it looked like a flake.

A biscuit s a round flat cake,
I saw it flowing down the lake,
It did not look like a round flat cake,
I put it in the oven to bake,
It came out of the oven exactly like a round flat cake.

Adam Laher (Age 9)

Jungle

Tigers roar in the name of the law.
Birds tweet in the burning heat.
Cheetahs run, I bet its fun.
Parrots squawk, like we talk.
Elephants sway through the day.
Rhinos charge but some barge.
The monkey swings as it sings.
The hippo swallows as it wallows.
The giraffe laughs as it follows its path.

Charlie Large (Age 8)

Angel Of Love

I should like to touch the warm feeling of love,
I should like to smell perfume drifting towards me,
I should like to hear my wall telling me my secrets.
I should like to take home everything around me,
I should like to understand that warm feeling of love.

Tristan Laity (Age 10)

Food

I like strawberries because they are nice and juicy
I like sweet juicy bananas
I like hard crunchy sweets
I like chips because they are nice and squidgy
But I don't like horrible sweetcorn
Because they get stuck in my teeth

Amy Lowe (Age 7)

Thunder

I boomed and made all the animals scamper back home,
I scared a small boy out of his wits!
I made my cousin zap the telephone wires.
I crashed down and scared everyone into their houses,
I wondered what was happening to me.
I was turning into a hum as gentle as a bee.

Stuart Locke (Age 8)

The Crocodile!

As it swims with grace, its tail slashes like a blade in the open water
As it kills its prey with sorrow, it glides back into the water.
As the suns light reflects off its blazing teeth, you begin to see reality.
It plods across the land to bathe on the shore.

Its skin feels like freshly laid tarmac.
Its claws are as sharp as the red roses thorn.
Its eyes are like dazzling red rubies.

It settles down to wonder about what tomorrow will bring.

Roza Large (Age 11)

My Perfect Happy Day

A happy day with a happy surrounding
People are joyful as the seagulls squawk is resounding
As my family paddle and play
I watch them from the bay

This is my perfect happy day

Glistening, sparkling waves so calm
The perfect peace works like a charm
The golden sand beneath my feet
I get a sun tan in the heat

Sarah Lowings (Age 11)

Untitled

Silently sleeping, dreaming away
Going to work, it's just another day
all of a sudden you wake with a crash,
You hear the brakes pull and then a noisy bash
Panic arrives, you look around
People have fallen to the ground
You hear the people shout and cry
These people are going to slowly die.

Kate Lamb (Age 10)

Guess Who?

She brightens up Sweden,
With a smile of golden love.
She is a rose,
Shining in the sparkling sun.

She is a tiger, beautiful, but viscous,
She is a vanilla ice-cream,
And she travels to venus,
To bring back love.

Matthew Lee (Age 11)

Battle Of Bosworth

I smell gunpowder ready to fire,
I see the captain talking to us all,
And in the background lots of men crying.
I think they have cannons ready to fire.
I hear the sound of men cheering,
The sound of a horse running.
I want to go home and be warm,
I touch the sweat running down my face.

Andrew Logan (Age 9)

The Garden

Out in the
garden
I smell the
smell of a
sunflower a
daffodil
and a crocus
they all smell
beautiful

Philippa Legg (Age 7)

The Boy Called Mike

Once there was a boy called Mike,
He once rode his bike
He lost his wheel,
And had a thrill
And went rolling down the hill
And then he did not have a thrill.

Kathryn Alison Lamb (Age 11)

Kangaroo

Speedy,
Strong back,
Good jumper,
Tremendous tail,
Big feet,
Baby carrier,
Malodorous.

Ffiona Lewis (Age 11)

Playtime

P eople playing,
L eaping high,
A lways asking,
Y esterday yet
T rouble time,
I s,
M ade
E asy.

Iain Lovell (Age 10)

A Good Friend Poem

F riends are truthful
R ight as always
I want a friend that's loyal
E asily believes me
N ever snitches on me
D oubts all Rumours about me

Jack Longman (Age 11)

My Kenning About A D.J.

A rapping raver,
A music maker,
A disc scratcher,
A dancing diva,
A top of the charts geezer,
A millions maker,
A groove shaker.

Rachel Lee (Age 11)

Fiddle Diddle

Fiddle daddle
Fiddle daddle
Bish bash
Plip plap plop
Riddle gaddle
Dish gash
Glip plap glop
Diddle fiddle
Lish bish
Dish tash throo
Diddle riddle
Mish gish
Dim lam goo!

Calum McGoff (Age 7)

Hey Frog

Through the pond
The frog goes
Jumping through the trees
With a yellow stripe
And green skin
Eating crickets with his big tongue
Hey - don't behave like that.

Adam McMahon (Age 7)

Flowers

I like flowers
They are pretty
They're everywhere
In the gardens
In the fields
Lots of colours
Lots of smells
Flowers, flowers
Beautiful flowers.

Carla McCarthy (Age 5)

Kittens

K ittens are cute and furry,
I n the night their eyes glitter like a coin.
T iptoeing up to their pray,
T ill the break of day.
E ating by the fire laying on a chair,
N early everywhere you go kittens on the loose.
S itting by the table, eating by the fire.

Chelsea Lynch (Age 9)

Snow

I covered people's houses, cars and trees
Like a pure white blanket.

I made children play outside wrapped up in scarves and hats,
I froze up windows with icy frosty fingers.

I made the whole world turn white and cold
I made teeth chatter like casternets.

I made my flakes sparkle at night,
The sun turned me into slush, all sloppy and slippy

Chloe Lam-Moores (Age 9)

The First Christmas

A star glowing in the midnight sky
The angels singing with joy over Jesus
Some Shepherds guarding the sheep as they sleep
Long, long ago

Jesus growing as the days go on
Mary and Joseph watching Jesus sleep
All the animals watching as they sniff and snort
Long, long ago

Everyone watching as the baby awakes
When the baby Jesus is in the manger
The baby is a star, the baby is the King
Long, long ago.

Sophie Mortimer (Age 7)

Recycling

Recycling is a great thing to do
Newspaper, bottles and drink cans too!
We can cycle instead of using cars
We need to take care of this world of ours.

Our rainforests are shrinking day by day
The trees are disappearing and humans will pay
For the destruction of the ozone layer in our sky
Will mean that some of our plants and animals will die.

So PLEASE help recycle before it's too late
Go to recycling centres, make it a date!
Think about others as well as yourself
And maybe we will benefit from better health.

Alexandra Eve McCluskey (Age 7)

Sun, Sun

Sun, sun oh glorious sun
Please oh please shine till the
Day is done
Sun, sun oh glorious sun
Please oh please shine till the
Day is done
Sun, sun oh glorious sun
Shine on the hills for
The flowers shall grow
Please oh please sun
Shine on the earth
Because the flowers need you
Not just one not just two
They all need you!

Louise McKenner (Age 7)

What Is White?

What is white?
White is a swan sailing
On the lake
White is paper blowing in
The wind
White is the colour of
Our shining teeth
White is a snowman
Standing in the cold
What is white?
White is the colour of
Cream on a chocolate cake.

Chelsey Makinson (Age 6)

Babies

Babies
Wriggle, wriggle, wriggle
Until babies giggle.
Babies are sweet
They might like a treat.
Jump, jump, jump
Until there's a thump.
Cry, cry, cry
The baby is shy.
Bedtime, bedtime, bedtime,
Bye bye for now baby
Until next time.

Kitty McWilliams (Age 7)

Number Poem

Ten fat tigers making a cup of tea
One fell over so that left nine
Nine naughty nannies throwing glass around
One smashed a vase that left eight
Eight enormous elephants rolling down the hill
One hurt its head so that left seven
Seven silly snakes tickling each other
One dived down so that left six
Six silly elephants climbing up a tree
One broke a branch so that left five
Five sick tigers went to the doctor's
One was frightened so that left four
One tripped over a stone so that left three
Three frightened chicks throwing eggs
One slipped over so that left two
Two tired turtles rolled down the hill
One fell down so that left one
One shark called to another
But it was too late as it had already blown up.

Thomas Mitchell (Age 5)

At The Supermarket

At the supermarket
Trolleys are squeaking
Tills are bleeping
First the cream
Hey look! There's David Beckham from the football team!
Now for the cake
Oh no, they're all fake!
Let's have some ham
Oops mustn't forget the Sunday roast lamb.
We need some tea
Oh look, it's free!
Let's get you a treat
What about a sweet?
Go and get the butter
Look at that man, he's beginning to mutter
That's enough
We've got far too much stuff
Now where's the money?
Oh no, it's at home, isn't that funny?

Emily McFiggans (Age 8)

Orang-utan

The Orang-utan was formed.

He grabbed the candescent golden sunrays
And the reflection of the metallic silver moon
To form his orange coat.

To make his coat soft he
Grasped the petals of balmy white
Daisies and red roses.

He stole the swing from ropey vines
And the swings and monkey bars
That ecstatic children play on in parks
To form his movement.

For the texture of his hands and feet
He stole an agile slimy skin of a
Black Mamba

He stole the cuteness of a baby
And the grin of a child
To form his face.

Nicholas Mills (Age 11)

The Storm

The distant padding sound,
Gets nearer and vivid lightning flashes,
The lion roars as he grabs the sky and rips it,
The defenceless sky pleads for mercy,
Sending thunder claps as the lion roars again,
The sky cries pleadingly.

Charlotte Mead (Age 7)

In The Dark Of Night

The wind whistled and the dead night howled,
The owls hooted and the wicked wolf prowled.
The lonely girl approached the lonesome street,
She was apprehensive and scared of who she would meet;
Her footsteps echoed and her rapid breathing was heard,
Misty smoke filled the atmosphere but nothing stirred.
But then, at once a mysterious carriage appeared,
It carried a hidden figure that the little girl feared.
The air was damp and dreary when it started to rain,
The frightened girl struggled in vain.
But suddenly, death's dark cloak ensnared her with an evil, cold stare,
The scared girl screamed, but the devil did not care.
Oh where did the little girl disappear to and where may she be?
Many tried to find out, but nobody could see.
Nowadays nobody dares to enter the eerie silence of the wood,
With its deep and dark secrets I doubt if anyone could.
Entering the black forest is now considered an offence,
Because the little girl died in an act of defence.
If I could only see the lonely girl again then I would say,
Anything can happen in the dark of night, any how and any way.

Ella Mahrenholz (Age 12)

Cricket

Cricket is my favourite sport,
I play it rather well.
Bowling is my strong point,
But I can bat as well.

People say it's boring,
I don't know what they mean.
When I'm running round, having fun,
I never come home clean.

I think some people are scared,
Of the really hard ball.
But if you're a good cricketer,
You'll have no problem at all.

I wrote this poem to tell you,
That a brilliant sport is cricket.
And if you say it's boring,
Then perhaps you should try it!

Richard Manthorpe (Age 14)

Rain

Diamonds trapped in spiders' webs
Gleam and shine
The rain is racing down the window panes
Little tiny ripples in the puddles
The colourful umbrellas have shiny raindrops on them
Heavier and heavier it falls
It bounces off puddles, then they overflow
The world is freshly washed.

James Montague (Age 7)

Family

I have brown flat hair,
Fair skin and nothing bare,
I have brown eyes,
I have a wider grin and grey socks.

My brother has brown flat hair,
Just the same as me,
Brown eyes, very cool,
That's my brother, Oliver.

My mum has black curly hair,
Very nice and very beautiful,
Very polite and very mad about chocolate,
That's my mum, Cheryl.

My dad has jet black untidy hair,
Very good at building things,
He tries to get all my mum's chocolate,
That's my dad, Antony.

William McKean (Age 11)

The Darkest Night

As you sleep in your cosy bed
A visitor lurks around you
Going through doors and windows
He casts a spell on all the city

Although he's silent, no clues left behind
He will search all around you but nothing
He will find
And if he does he will always come back
Because he is night and night is greedy.

All he wears is a black silk robe
No body to be seen
Nobody sees his invisible eyes
The way moves always floating

As the gleaming sun rises from the east
The night gets scared
And floats back home
In the depths of the underworld.

Andrew Moore (Age 10)

It Was So Noisy

It was so noisy that I couldn't
Hear my washing machine buzzing loudly
It was so noisy that I couldn't
Hear the TV booming like a rocket
It was so noisy that I couldn't
Hear my mum screaming enormously loud
It was so noisy that I couldn't
Hear the dog barking out annoyingly
It was so noisy that I couldn't
Hear the cleaner buzzing round sharply.

Sophie Mitchem (Age 7)

Free Barabbas

Pontius Pilate asks the question
Of life or death
Free Barabbas, free Barabbas
The crowd shout
My followers cheer
Pontius Pilate declares that Jesus will die
And that I will live
I sigh in relief.

I attended the crucifiction
But I hid away
As soon as Jesus' head dropped
The sky went black
And it really rained
If there was one thing I remember
It was the crying
But I didn't care.

Lewis Murphy (Age 9)

The Big Match

I play for Manstow Football Club
We play at Filham Park
I play out on the left wing
There is no one to mark

Our shirts are green and yellow
Our shorts are shiny black
We all wear studded football boots
And numbers on our back

We always have a referee
To make sure we play fair
And if we make a bad mistake
He whistles in the air

We try to score a lot of goals
Get the ball inside the post
The winner of the football match
Is the team that scores the most.

Tom Moody (Age 9)

I Wish That Spring Was Here

Outside it's windy
Cold and dreary
The traffic moans
And the trees groan
I wish that spring was here.

The mud is dirty
It's dark and murky
The people are talking
And the birds squawking
I wish that spring was here.

Holly Millard (Age 7)

Night

The sun slowly fades away
And I wish for a minute that it could stay
The night begins to spread it's big, black cloak
Over the land and sea and boats
Nearly all the shops have closed
And not many cars are on the road
The world is a different place when it's dark
Children don't shout and dogs don't bark
The only people that walk on the street
Are the homeless people looking for something to eat
But if you look hard then you might see
The small, creeping cat or the hungry rat with fleas
And when I wake up on a spooky night
The dark sometimes gives me a fright.

Livvy Myles (Age 10)

My Moon, My Star, My Sun

My mum is my source of life
She took care of me from when I was young
She's my idol, the one I look up to
She's my moon, my star, my sun.

My dad is the highlight of my life
He's not boring instead he's fun
He's jolly, he's joyful and happy
He's my moon, my star, my sun.

My sister has great fashion sense
Her hair is always in a bun
She's the ruler of our bedroom
She's my moon, my star, my sun.

My brother is a little terror
He's scared of me and will run
And still he looks up to me
He's my moon, my star, my sun.

All these people are my family
I love them tonnes and tonnes
Not forgetting my dog Toby
They're all my moon, my star, my sun.

Joanne Mullaly (Age 11)

Creation

On the first day, he created light,
Separated darkness, making day and night.
On day two, he was making pies,
Whilst making the heavens and sky.
On day three, he separated the seas,
Making dry land and sea.
On day four, he made animals,
Reptiles, beast and mammals.
On day five, he created plants,
For creatures to eat such as ants.
On day six, he made Adam and Eve,
Who dressed up in leaves.
On day seven, he rested in peace,
Dressed in trousers and woolly fleece.

Grace McCatty (Age 11)

What Is Weather

What is thunder?
The crashing water of Niagara falls.
What is hail?
Tiny marbles being thrown down by Zeus.
What is rain?
The teardrops of God from up above.
What is fog?
An opaque wall of dark, evil blanket.
What is sun?
A blinding light bulb looking straight into someone's eyes.
What is the breeze?
Nothing but silence.

Peter Mumford (Age 11)

A Trip Into Space

One day I went on a journey
To far away space
I was so excited, but I was still learning
But I forgot to keep the chase

I flew past giant asteroids and meteors many
Until I came across a planet with spots
Shining just like a new penny
What a memory, a picture, a shot

I found an alien wandering about
With a big yellow nose and eyes on stalks
It gave me such a fright, I had to shout
And when I asked him where we were he said we
Were on the planet Malks

Then I was afraid I had to go
So bye bye now I'm off back home
The alien had one last thing so say
Which was, "Goodbye and go to the planet Zog."

I was no way going there
But if I did I would not say
So you will have to find out .....

Sarah More (Age 9)

Teachers

T eachers are terrible, teachers are bad
E ver so boring
A nd ever so mad
C inemas are better
H ouses are cosier
E veryone hates school and teachers
R ules are made by teachers
S trict is their motto!

Madhumathi Murali (Age 9)

The Writer Of This Poem

The writer of this poem is as curious as a cat,
As silent as a mouse and as small as a rat.

Her eyes are hazel and always stand out,
Her hair is silky and smoothly straight.

She's not very organised for many important times,
The reason for this is because she's always kind.

Her friends think she's nosy but I don't think that's true,
Running to the door just waiting to go to the loo.

The writer of this poem is as groovy as a zebra,
Singing and laughing and her cousin is called Debra.

Mirella Mortellaro (Age 11)

Seasons

Spring:

Trees put on their fluorescent coats.
The grass shoots up like water fountains.
The bushes put on their spiky green coats.
The sun's shine is popping out to say hello.

Summer:

The trees get brighter as if someone's throwing up bright paints.
The grass is getting taller like a person growing.
The bushes are getting thicker like a person eating too.
The sun shine getting stronger like a strong man growing muscles.

Autumn:

The trees take off their bright old coats.
Like a building being demolished the grass starts dying.
Like a person getting weaker the bushes start to die.
Like a fading sky the sun's worth flies away.

Winter:

White rabbit skins the trees put on.
White snug blanket the grass puts on.
White fur coats the bushes put on.
The sun's warmth falls out of the sky.

Jordon Marsh (Age 8)

Untitled

I'm going to tea with grandma
I wonder where we'll be?
Roast dinner or jelly with ice cream
And a packet of sweets for me.

Carys Mangan (Age 6)

Pants To Poverty

Hi my name is Tim I just thought I'd say
PANTS TO POVERTY!
I saw the poor people
I felt sad and mad
I don't know why
But I saw a lady
She'd broken her limb
I thought long and hard
PANTS TO POVERTY!
Then my brother came downstairs I told him
But he did not care
PANTS TO POVERTY!
I thought that's not fair
Now I'm 9 months older
I've always saved my money
It just goes to show
Nobody knows till you say
PANTS TO POVERTY!
Just you think before you say I want
BECAUSE SOME PEOPLE JUST CANNOT.

James Maxwell (Age 11)

The Big Game

The whistle starts blowing
The players start throwing
The crowd starts to roar
When the players score.

Someone's got to boot
Is he going to shoot?
It's going through the air
The crowd shout "Yeah!"

Everybody clap
What a bad slap
Someone's laughing
I'm gasping.

Everybody's talking
Some people are walking
Someone's beating a drum
A Bristol player hurt his thumb.

There is lots of noise
From the girls and boys
People start singing
The Saracens are winning.

David Morley (Age 8)

Owls

I love owls
I love owls
All I can think of is owls
Some are big and some are small
None of them are like another
I don't know why
Go ask your mother!

Adam McQueen (Age 6)

The Sandy Desert

The sandy desert is full of sand
The lizards are very short
Cactus spikes begin to grow
Nothing's there that can be bought
What alot to know!

The sandy desert is made from yellow sand
The sandy desert is alot of land
What alot to know!

The white clouds are big
The sun shine shows
The tree branches hang out very low
The cactuses grow
What alot to know!

The sandy desert is made from yellow sand
The sandy desert is alot of land
What alot to know!

Rosie McCall (Age 8)

In My Memory Box

In my memory box I have put

My hand print I made when I was five
My cuddly toys Wille and Spot
My first day at school.

In my memory box I have put

The feel of dad's spiky beard
Mum's soft skin
My first tooth coming out.

In my memory box I have put

My favourite foods, tomatoes and sausages
Mum cooking my favourite dinner
A sausage waiting to be eaten.

In my memory box I have put

My lucky England shirt
A chess set
A play station and game.

In my memory box I have put

A picture of Tottenham winning the F.A. Cup
A picture of my grandpa
The warmth of a fire on a cold winter's night.

James Mullender (Age 11)

Clouds

As I look up to a cloud
My mind is spinning round and round
With a long bright shining horn
It looks just like a unicorn
But then I start to laugh aloud
Because, of course, it's just a cloud!

Kate McGarry (Age 8)

Brothers

Brothers hit you,
Brothers punch,
They even eat all your lunch.

Brothers ruin footy,
Brothers take the ball,
They won't leave until they score.

Brothers take your P.S games,
Brothers take your aftershave,
They just won't leave until they get something.

Brothers give,
Brothers share,
After all they really care.

Jordan McCatty (Age 11)

Underneath The Silence I Can Hear ...

Underneath the silence I can hear ...

The grandparents whispering as their voice fades away
The squeals of my adopted baby dolphin in the ocean
The father deciding what to name the baby child
The laughter between my friends as I tell them a joke
The loud shouting to see who is the loudest

Underneath the silence I can smell ...

The fresh bread from the bakery
The French perfume smell as my mum kisses me goodnight
The smell of bacon, sausages, mushrooms, toast and juice for lunch
The fresh cut grass far away in the field
The golden chicken cooking in the oven.

Underneath the silence I can feel ...

The purple smooth velvet blanket
The smooth soft babies bottom
The soft spongy cake with frosting on top
The soft cuddly warm rabbit running up my hand
The friend holding onto my arm as she goes away

Underneath the silence I can see ...

Sindiwe Mvubu (Age 9)

Winter

The lifeless fields stretch out towards the distant horizon
Animals scurry away from winter's frosty fingertips
The gaunt trees stand lifelessly
Their branches scraping the pale blue sky
The chill breeze whisks through the dusky night
The soft hooting of the tawny owl breaks the deadly silence

Jack McLean (Age 10)

The Battle

Bang! Bang! Phut! Phut!
Goes the noise of a gun.
See the soldiers moving forward
And diving, then run.
Hear the men screaming
And then fall to die.
Hear the noise of a machine gun,
So many people cry.
Bodies lying all around-
Like looking into the eyes of hell.
Buildings now like leggo pieces
Scattered all around.

Boys like me, we play with guns,
And war seems so much fun.
Real war is cruel and callous
And should never be begun.

Andrew McMaster (Age 9)

If You Want To See A Witch

If you want to see a witch
You must go down to beloing cave

I know a witch
Who's living down there
She's green-headed, long-nosed and scary-faced

Yes if you really want to see
A witch you must go down to beloing cave and say

Witch
Witch
Witchhhh!

Then she will come
But you must RUN.

Kirsty McCathie (Age 7)

Red Nose Day

It is red nose day to day
People buy and pay today
Spend lots of money for red nose day
And lots of other things to buy
Red nose is like a rose so I
Like things to buy!

Isma Munir (Age 9)

The Sweet Little Butterfly

Look at the sweet little butterfly
It's pretty wings are fluttering
What a polite little butterfly
Look at the graceful little butterfly

Jessica Lindsay (Age 9)

The River

The river flows day by day
Splashing the banks on its way

The fish are dancing merrily
In and out of the pebbles we see

As it winds gracefully in and out
It meanders quite quickly without a doubt

The men came along and polluted it
I wish they would stop doing their bit

In the end it reaches the sea
To be enjoyed by you and me

So remember when you sit, drinking your tea
The water you're drinking's from the river you see

So please keep it clean as can be.

Richard Mumford (Age 10)

Dear Mum

Dear mum
I saw a wolf
Who started to puff
Along came a hunter with his gun
And he started to eat his big fat bun

Dear mum
I saw a cat
Who was chasing a rat
He got his claws
And scratched his paws

Dear Mum
I saw a bird
Which I heard
His body is yellow
And he's a very good fellow!

Umar Moghal (Age 10)

The Challenger

Shuttle left the launching pad
Heading towards the station
Up into the world above
Testing times for the nation
To step right out of the 'Challenger'
Leave my past behind
Each step I make is history
Space walk is the first of its kind

Jim Morris (Age 11)

Polly

I have a black cat called Polly
Who thinks she is the farm dog collie
She runs riot round the farm
And into the barn
And rounds up my dolly Molly.

Catherine Morris (Age 8)

The Tides

A line of soft foamy white cotton wool,
Slowly creeps up the golden sandy beach.

Sky blue waves grow tall like fierce monsters,
Before quickly crashing onto the smooth floor.

Large grey rocks stand tall like guards,
As the water washes over them.

A large rippling sheet of shining blue paper,
Glistens in the fiery sun's path.

Finally the sand and all the waters rest,
As the moon silently takes the tides away.

Kathryn Moran (Age 10)

Exam Nerves

I stand outside the hall, waiting for the *test*
I lean against the wall, I'll be worse than all the rest.

The children enter the room,
I stumble through the door.
It fills us all with gloom,
Tests are a *real* bore.

The teachers look around
Like a hawk at hunting time
A chair scuffing the ground
Is like a church bell chime.

The tests are handed out,
Face down, so no one cheats.
I turn to look about:
We all turn to our sheets.

We all start, pencils dart,
"Quiet please this is a test
Now everyone, *do your best.*"

The test is over the hard work is done
Time for a breather, time for some fun!

Clare Morris (Age 11)

Chocolate

C hocolate is creamy and chocolate is thick
H appy faces smile whilst having a lick
O h how I love your velvety feel
C an I eat you instead of a meal?
O h why can't I eat you every day
L icking you and eating you in every way
A nd when you melt inside my mouth
T he joy you bring, you see
E very day in every way will always be with me!

Hannah McDougall (Age 9)

Underneath The Silence

Underneath the silence I can hear
Swirling ashy smoke creeping into every corner,
Every space, accomplishing its deadly mission
The torturing plots of the wicked flames
The works of a cunning mind, boiling away amidst the heat
Evil taunting of the flames as they encircle him
Swift silent speed of the blades of flame slice through the screams
The pounding of petrified hearts ... silence.

Underneath the silence I can feel
The engulfing smoke, strangling, choking
Intense heat breathing down their necks, scorching their skin
Fear and blinding panic in the helpless victims
The embers still glow like rubies, a reminder of the horrific nightmare
Peace as the gentle breeze blows on my face, rippling my hair
A silence, knowing their pain and suffering is over.

Stephanie Modak (Age 10)

The Vets

Seven o'clock Saturday,
Time to shut the vets,
You wouldn't believe,
How many pets.

I've had to treat here,
All today,
Including animals,
Which are strays.

I have seen horses,
Dogs and cats,
And even someone's,
Sick green gnat.

It's lovely to know,
You're stopping a pain,
It feels as if you're,
The person who reigns.

All over the seas,
All over the skies,
From every elephant,
To every fly.

Rachel Morris (Age 9)

Spring

In the day the bluebells grow
In the day the butterflies fly
In the day the fruit grows
What a beautiful day today.

James Matthews (Age 6)

The Writer Of This Poem

The writer of this poem is
As cocky as a parrot,
As witty as a boffin
As yummy as a carrot.

As cheeky as a monkey
As tall as a tree,
As sporty as Giggs
And everyone likes me.

As angry as a beaver
As crafty as a fox,
As busy as a bee
As chatty as a chatterbox.

He never seems to change
In everything he does,
People say he is annoying
But he really is a buzz.

Joseph McNerney (Age 11)

Fire

Fire, the blazing monster
Fire, the eye of heat
Fire is the devil of brutal beasts
The fumes sneaked up my nose
Then ignited into amazing fireballs
The suffocating smoke
The stuffy air of nature
The smoking fire
The fire is breathing and is
Getting bigger, mammoth sized
The temperature
Is a scorching ninety-five
Degrees
The heat smashes the thermometer
With its amazing heat
The intense inferno could burn
Down all in its path!
Nothing can stop
The raging barbarian fire!

Spencer Moss (Age 11)

Wendy The Witch

Wendy the wicked witch,
Had a
Wonderful home in a ditch,
Where she would
Brew up her potions
And change people's emotions
With the help of her cat called Mitch
Wendy the wickedest witch of the West
Would always try to do her best
But one day it come upon her
That she could no longer
Create chaos like she wished
She went off to her Dad's
Who said he would be glad
If she changed from evil to good
That is how she is known as:-
WONDERFUL WENDY THE WITCH

Leanne Morriss (Age 12)

Tranquillity Time

My mind's at rest, don't bother me
I feel no tension, but tranquillity
I know there is some work to be done
But I must stay here, just rest, no fun
But somehow in my wondrous dream
I play and sing in the hills and the stream
I applaud the dancing butterflies
And hear the trees whisper a compromise

As I travel through my world of calm gaze
I think of chores which end my daze
I move my hands and wake up from my dream
It's back to work and chores it seems!

Kimberley Moore (Age 10)

Rush Hour

It is half eight,
Rush hour's about to start
Noisy traffic passing,
Spoiling the quietness,
The quietness of the town.
It is 10 o'clock
The noise dies down,
It is peaceful again.
We can relax,
And take quiet walks around.
In six hours time
The rush hour will start again.
People will be rushing home,
It's time for your tea and for your family.
Children start coming home from school
Rush hour's now over,
The day is over, the town dies down.
The only noise is the birds,
Peace and quiet until tomorrow,
When the next rush hour starts.

Kirsty Maciocha (Age 13)

The Storm

The rain's getting harder
The wind's getting stronger
The sea's getting rougher
The storm is starting

A boat has crashed
Three boats to the rescue
One has crew
The other two cargo

The rain's turning to drizzle
The wind is dropping
The sea is calming
The storm is stopping.

Keeley Metson (Age 11)

The Midnight Fox

A sound like a baby crying
My heart pumping like a ball and a bat
When will I see you again?

I heard the thunder in the sky
My heart stopped
A shudder came over me

BANG! My heart had a sudden pain
Where's the fox?
I felt like a knife had just gone through me

He missed!
How great but a silence was still in the air
Why?

Hara Morgan (Age 11)

A Day In The Life Of A Teenager

In the morning, I wake up.
Dad comes in with a cup.
I get ready, it's a drag.
I go downstairs and fill my bag.

I walk to school, it's so tough.
Some days I think I've had enough.
I'm at school it's so boring.
Someone in the back is snoring.

Yippee it is lunch.
Me and my mates hang round in a bunch.
Our school has nothing decent.
It was made into a prison quite recent.

Kids smoking in the loos.
Teachers still have nothing to do.
Teachers think they're real funny.
Cos they get paid loads of money.

I get home, nothing on telly.
The cat's here, he's really smelly.
Dad's gone shopping, I'm all alone.
I call Nicola on the phone.

Lisa McCann (Age 14)

A Panda

A panda is a

Man eating teddy bear
The size of Mount Everest
The fluffiness of a cotton ball
The colours of a penguin
The viciousness of a tiger eating its prey
The softness of a smooth, furry jumper.
Its teeth are the sharpness of knife
Its eyes are the size of two giant marbles

Kim Mehmet (Age 12)

The Show

Finally the night has come after weeks of preparation
The audience are waiting with great anticipation
Our make-up is done and our wigs are on
The costumes look great, we're having so much fun.

The curtain has risen and the spot-lights are turned on
We begin to repeat our scripts and songs.
The audience are laughing and everything is going great
Nothing has gone wrong yet, lets hope it stays this way.

We sing and dance with great ease
We're doing tremendously well, our director was very pleased!
My dance is now finished so I've to go off stage
And wait to come on again at the very end.

I walked on proudly to take my bow, everyone clapped as we all marched on
We all started singing again and again, we really didn't want it to come to an end.

Bethany McIlroy (Age 13)

The Horse

Horse,
Wild creature of the forest,
Galloping around,
The leader of the herd,
Stallion, mares and foals together.

Wild creature in the forest,
Tame friend in the stall.

My pony,
You are my friend,
Winning together,
Trophies and medals,
No sign of your wild past,
Until you are free in the field.

Wild creature in the forest
Tame friend in the stall.

Horse,
I do not know you,
When you are free,
Your hooves thundering,
Your mane flowing,
Horse?

Hollie McManus (Age 13)

Murphy The Horse

Murphy is a black horse,
A black horse with white socks.
I like riding on Murphy.
Murphy has a star on his nose,
Murphy is a mischievous horse,
I love Murphy
And he loves me.

Lorna Marland-Flint (Age 12)

Manners

Coming from a foreign land,
I'm widening my perspective,
I'm offering you my hand,
But what for, a stuck up finger,
A threatening glance, and,
Hopefully you will walk on by.

Don't get me wrong, I don't,
Just complain, for where,
I come from it's a,
Whole lot worse, with,
Guns and knives,
Thugs and thieves,
I am lucky, I came out alive.

So all I have to say,
Is please, a little common,
Courtesy, goes a long way,
So when you see someone new,
Extend a hand, give a wave,
And next time you're alone,
The favour might be returned to you.

Luke McCulloch (Age 16)

Spring

The Spring is here
Summer is near
Flowers are blossoming
Children playing
Animals are being born
Girl then boy
Farmers leap
Filled with joy
Cows moo
Birds sing
Everyone is happy
Thank God it's Spring.

Natalie McCalmont (Age 12)

The Darkest Night

As night returns to curse the world,
People lie peaceful in their simple homes.
He raises from the deep dark shadows,
Then curses the world with his staff.

His face crackles in laughter,
As a shadow covers the helpless world.
Then he roars with eternal pain,
As he sees the light appearing.

So he fell back down to the shadows,
Where he rests before cursing the world again.

Samuel Morris (Age 11)

Bang, Flash, Boom

You're all cosy in bed,
Unaware of anything doing on,
When the breeze turns into a fiery wind
And a few minutes later, a tree creaks and cracks.

A bright frightening flash fills your window,
Boom! Boom! Was that thunder?
Slowly you hear the clouds bursting with a waterfall,
Gradually you start the countdown to get out of bed.

Lightning hurls itself into a nearby field,
You leap through the air,
Thunder grips your fear, it's just too scary,
FLASH, FLASH, BOOM!

You fall to the ground,
The earth won't stop spinning,
Lightning heading for your window,
Thunder breaks the lightning.

The lightning gradually fades into harmless stars
Thunder graduates into a hushing wind
The rain only a pitter patter
It's a good thing too - You'd had enough BANG, FLASH BOOM!

Charlotte Maybury (Age 10)

Old People

I often walk down the street
And there's a lot of old people you often meet
I always wonder do they eat tough meat
Or is it soft because of their teeth?
So next time you walk down the street
Look at the people who have false teeth!

Dionne Maynard (Age 12)

Dolphin Moments

As the sea shimmers in the night, the
Dolphins rise to the surface with their streamlined bodies.

They glide through the water with elegant movements,
Suddenly one leaps from the water with a
Playful jump. Others, enjoying the game
Copy with excitable leaps.
Sparkling spray, splashes from the
Dolphins, as they cut through the surface of the water.

A breeze blows the clouds, revealing a full, glowing moon.
As if by magic the water is calm.
All that remains are the moon's reflections
Glistening, silently on the gentle waves.

Philippa McMaster (Age 11)

Autumn

Autumn.
One thing I really hate.
The moany old leaves,
The junky smell.
I despise Autumn.
Every leaf, every tree,
Every puny colour
Hates me back.
I get ready,
For a punitive trek
Through the leaves.
I kick, I crush,
I totally stomp
What life is in the leaves.
I look at a mangled leaf in disgust.
The trees, to me
Are stupid big stumps in the ground,
With mouldy bark on them.
I decide that I have had enough.
And trudge home.
I take one last angry look at Autumn
And slam the door.

Max Morton (Age 9)

Big Bad Wind

Wind,
Whistling like a steam train.
While whimpering like a fat dog.
Howling and screeching,
Ripping and screaming.
Speeding along like a Red Arrow in flight,
Smashing into houses and trees.
Taking pleasure in rustling leaves.
Then with a screeching like brakes it stops.

Alasdair Morrison (Age 11)

World Of Colours!!

Um, um
There's too many colours
In this colourful
Big old world

How many colours
In the world?
I don't know!
The only colours
I can think of are:

Green, blue, black
Pink, grey, red
Yellow, orange, peach
Turquoise, gold, silver,
Brown.

Craig Moore (Age 14)

Animal

There he runs, completely free;
Broad chest, full eyes, small head and nostrils wide,
Away from chains, away from whip and spur,
Spiritual
Free.

Quick but elegant,
Innocent but brave,
Pure but strong,
Willing but independent,

Beauty comes in all forms;
Some tall, some short, some broad, some not, but they,
All can withstand the threat from man and keep,
On standing,
Proud.

Friendship without envy,
Beauty without vanity,
Giving without taking,
Loyalty without question,

- The Horse.

Sara Mulvanny (Age 13)

My Dreams

I don't dream of winning the lottery
Or having everything I want,
I just dream of trees and animals,
And lovely countrysides.

I don't dream of boys,
Or popstars and celebrities,
I dream of things in real life,
Funfairs, parks and slides!!!

Some times I dream at night,
Or in the morning sun,
I like to dream of pretty things,
Ponies, slides, swings and fun!!!

Lianne McMenemy (Age 12)

Cats

Some cats are sleepy cats,
Dreaming all day of mice and rats.
Curled in any chair or lap,
For their continuous daily nap.

Some cats are greedy cats,
Who are most likely fat.
They rub round your ankles waiting for food,
And make you change your mood.

Some cats are rather vicious,
And make you feel quite suspicious.
They tear your face, make you squeal,
They scratch your leg and bite your heel.

Jenny Morrison (Age 12)

My Mum

My mum is the best
She makes me lunch
And then she rests.
She cooks me roast
And I like it the most.

And then I sit in a chair
And put food in my belly
And my mummy said that's not fair
Whilst watching the telly.

My mum stopped moaning
When I went out of the room
And started groaning
Because of Josh's moaning.

But then I came back
And she gave me a smack
Because of the paint in my hair.

Kayleigh Macklin (Age 9)

Through The Door

Open the door and you will see,
Dogs and cats and a bumble bee.
Open the door and you might see,
Dragons, giants or a magic key.
Open the door and you may sight,
A prince or princess or a black knight.
Open the door and you will find,
Scientists with a clever mind.

Max Marcheselli (Age 11)

Races

A wicked witch's broom,
A beautiful bride's groom,
Who is the last one,
To get to the moon

A tail of a dog,
A cute little hog,
Who is the last one,
To get to the log

The greedy little fox,
And the girl Josephine Cox,
Who is the last one,
To get to the box

The big fat bear
And the tiny little hare
Who is the last one
To blink when they stare

Well the hare of course
Because the big fat bear
Ate the tiny little hare.

Jade Mahoney (Age 9)

The Beach

The mega hot sun
Burns the cold sand,
As the sea's waves
Clash about.

The fish wave
About as the
People swim.

Ants search for food
As the sun goes down.

Saffron Mackie (Age 8)

Contrast Of Autumn

I'm running, running, running
Towards the ancient oak tree
I see the leaves swaying this way and that
Like a group of butterflies
Coming towards me
Rusty red, dark brown, golden, yellow
Fall gently to the ground
Like a river of jewels
Lie before me!

I'm running, running, running
Nowhere to hide
The howling wind chasing behind me
Rain like bullets surrounding me
Here I am hiding under
The old oak tree
Nowhere to hide, nowhere to go
Suddenly I trip into a pile of leaves
They shoot up into the air
Like confetti.

Kizzy Matthews (Age 9)

My Snoring Grandad

My snoring grandad snores so loud
That the dog next door
Howls so to tell him to shut-up!

My snoring grandad snores so loud
That the walls next door
Go smashing down.

My snoring grandad snores so loud
That if there were first prize for
Snoring the loudest he would win.

Rachel Mairs (Age 9)

On The Beach

On the beach the children have fun
Sometimes they lay
Sometimes they play
With the exhausting water slides
And the everlasting roller-coaster rides

In the big blue sea the children splash, splash, splash
Some children are on donkey rides
Others are going down water slides

The mums and dads are peacefully relaxing
Some taking naps
Some taking snaps
Others are reading books

Along comes the great ice cream van
In the van is the popular ice cream man
On the beach the children have fun.

Alexandra Mann (Age 8)

To Hear You Sing

I am deaf, so what,
People think I'm special, but I'm not,
Others have an advantage over me,
For I can't hear the roaring sea.

Thunder never comes, but lightning's struck before,
And I still get to see the things I adore,
Still there's something missing from inside me,
Something missing that no one can see.

I hear people through their hands,
It's as though I speak a language from far off lands,
Our worlds are similar,
But I will never be at all regular.

I've seen the world, although there's much to see,
And still it's not enough for me,
So it would be a special thing,
To hear you laugh, to hear you sing.

Hannah Millest (Age 11)

The Sweet Shop

I have £1.00 and 50p,
The sweet shop is where I'd like to be.
The shelves are full of different colours,
Lots of different kinds of sweets.
Bubble gum is tasty,
It can be fun,
By blowing bubbles on your tongue.
But gooey, chewy toffee,
That tears out your teeth,
Just simply can't be beat.
Cadburys chocolate is so scrummy,
Especially when it's in your tummy.
Willy Wonker chocolate,
That makes your mouth go pop.
Beueno chocolate bars,
Which have a creamy inside.
I'm really stuck,
They're all so scrummy and very yummy,
So which one shall I choose?

Jessie Meaney (Age 10)

Spring

Spring time is a new beginning,
When all the bells are ringing,
Little lambs are trying to walk,
Lots of babies are trying to talk.

Flowers are sprouting,
Children are shouting,
Ladybirds are coming out,
Mums and Dads are rushing about.

Lots of leaves are out on the trees,
Now people are on their knees,
The stream is clear,
Spring is here!

Helen Medlock (Age 9)

Saidey From Haidey

There was an old lady from Haidey
Her name was very old Saidey
She lost the plot
When I smashed her pot
And now she's the real Slim Shady

Gary Mawers (Age 10)

The Tiger

Mine is the howl,
That sends terror and fear,
When humans are close,
Mine is the ear.

Mine is the eye,
That gleams in the sun,
When my prey is near,
Mine is the run.

Mine is the fur
So stripy and bright
Mine is the fur
For which I must fight.

Alex Miller (Age 11)

Underneath the Silence

Underneath the silence I can see ...

The swirling hot sand in a desert sand storm,
The baby laughing and smiling at me,
The Whales darting in and out of the salty sea,
The beautiful sunset, like runny caramel disappearing into the shadowed hills,
The crackling fireworks as they shoot into the deep
Blue star filled sky.

Underneath the silence I can smell ...

The freshly cut grass in the meadow on a hot spring morning,
The beautiful scented flowers in my nan's garden,
The breakfast being cooked on a Sunday morning,
The sweet smell of my mum's perfume as she leaves the house to go to bingo,
The fear of a stranger as they are pierced with a dagger.

Maxine Macklin (Age 11)

Blob The Cat Is Back

I remember, I was five,
I saw a cat,
Just a toy, but he was real to me,
I knew I would always love him.

He, as I had chosen, had two ears,
And two glowing eyes,
With a wet glistening nose,
That said, I love you.

It was in a lonely tea room,
That I saw him on a shelf,
What was it like for him,
To leave his other friends.

He still the same today,
Two ears, two eyes, a nose,
Even if he didn't have them,
He'd mean the same to me.

His name is Blob the cat,
He will always be the same,
With his tiny glowing eyes,
And his sticky, wet nose.

Alex Masters (Age 10)

Tyrannosaur Poem

Dinosaurs are big and small
Dinosaurs are high and tall
Hunting in the dark of night
Giving everyone a great big *FRIGHT!*
Everything it looks at
This dinosaur is very fat.
As fast as lightning
And is very frightening
This dinosaur is called Tyrannosaur.

Jean-Philippe McClintock (Age 8)

Lessons!!

(Maths is fun)
Which is more than I can say
For english (torture)
We have every day.

P.E. is great
I.T. too
But R.E. and history
Equals boo.

But I like play times
Play times rock,
But you won't catch me out there
Wearing a frock!!!

Kathryn Miller (Age 9)

When I Saw The Sea

When I looked at the sea,
What did I see,
Beautiful navy blue waves,

But they didn't look like waves,
(Well not to me)
They looked like horses to me.

Their tails were swishing,
Their manes were flaring,
White as the face of the clown.

I went back the next day,
And saw them again,
But this time different than before.

They had sea people on their backs,
Calling out to me,
"Come here, come here, come to our home."

So I did,
And there I lived,
With a seahorse of my own.

Jaide Massey (Age 8)

The Lost One

Once there was a boy
Who ran away
Far, far away
His parents searched and searched
There was no sign of him to be seen
And maybe one day, one
Single day, he might return
To his searching parents.
His parents felt so sad
That their only child had gone missing
The child was lost
He didn't mean to leave
He was just jealous from one person.

James McCarthy (Age 10)

I'd Rather

I'd rather have the measles
I'd rather eat a rat
I'd rather meet a vicious dog
Or be extremely fat
I'd rather smell a sewer
I'd rather have a skunk
I'd rather have a bath in beans
I'd rather be a drunk
I'd rather be a lonely tramp
Or touch a diseased toe
I'd rather do most anything
Than have my Gameboy go!

Jamie Macpherson (Age 10)

Treasure Box

I will keep in my treasure box

A sun ray from the world's first sunrise
A wish from the wand of the most magical fairy
A dewdrop of moonlight.

I will keep in my treasure box

The beat of a humming bird's wings
A necklace of snowflakes
A yetty's footprint.

I will keep in my treasure box

The first dive into cool, calm azure water
My morning cuddle from my little sister
The happiness in my best friend's smile.

I will keep in my treasure box

The excitement on a Christmas morning
The blissful taste of a freshly roasted potato
The crackle of the flames burning in the hot fire.

I will keep in my treasure box

The delicate scent of a freshly peeled lycee
A lick from my puppy's soft pink tongue
The smell of the fresh sea air.

Rosalind Mayes (Age 10)

Nonsense Poem

Disty pisty the windows are misty
Ritter ratter the rain goes splatter
Flower power it's a shower
Split splot time to stop!

Robyn Moynihan (Age 10)

Fish

He snatched the gleam out of gold
And the colours of the rainbow to
Form his silky scales.

He snatched the blowing of the
Waves to form his swift tail.

He snatched the blinking of an eyelid
To form his sleek lips.

He snatched the S from a snake
To form his flickering movements.

He snatched the darkness of a gloomy hole
To form his starless eyes.

Finally the fish has been formed
With all five features.

Lizzie McCluskey (Age 10)

Blind Date With A Vampire

He e-mailed me on Thursday,
He wants us to finally meet,
He's taking me to the cinema,
And then a bite to eat.

From a distance he looked strange,
And closer even stranger,
He ought to get his teeth checked out,
Or kissing could be a danger.

We sat down in the movies,
To watch a graphic thriller,
His pale, bony fingers pulled me close,
As the vampire went to kill her!

We then went out to dinner,
He ordered a rare steak,
It really made me sick to see,
The pool of blood upon his plate.

Then he walked me to my home,
And I don't think we'll date anymore,
He went to kiss my neck on the porch,
And I shut his face in the door!

Hannah Munday (Age 14)

Galaxy Bar

As smooth as silk
A scrumptious chocolate square
Melts in my mouth
Silver foil crinkles up into a glittery ball
Delightfully warm chocolate
Slides down my throat
Every piece enhances my contentment.

Robbie Meikle (Age 10)

My Day

Can you hear the wind whistling
Past the window?
Can you hear the rain banging
Down on the roof?
Can you feel how cold it is?

Can you see the sun, blinding
If you look?
The day is going quickly
I really must hurry
The sun is starting to descend now
The day has nearly passed
The sky is starting to go yellow,
No, now red, then orange

What a day I've had!!!!!!

Jonathan Meldram (Age 10)

My Funny Poem

If you meet my aunty, you wouldn't like her

All she likes is a big wet kiss! That's the problem

It's all wet and slobbery, horrible and disgusting. (Like a monster's)

You wouldn't like to meet her. Every time she comes, it's just

KISS, KISS KISS!

That's the thing *I DON'T* like about her.

I always try to hide, but she always finds me

Instead, I would rather be drowned or cooked

I'd do anything to get away from her *ANYTHING!*

And that's what I have told you about my aunty.

Kira McLean-Ash (Age 8)

Homeless

I see the homeless on the floor
I wish they were behind a door
I see them walking down the street
I wonder why they have bare feet
I have seen them living in a cardboard box
And they don't work in posh office blocks.

I hope in the future we could do something to help
But all I can do now is to pray and to yelp
Perhaps a willing school could have their say
By holding a fund raising for 'shelter' day!

Christopher Mundy (Age 9)

No, No, No

"It's time for bed." "No, no, no."
Up the stairs I go shouting, "No, no, no!"
"It's late," said mum. "Late," shouts dad
I know but I still don't want to go!

I want to watch T.V.
I want to phone friends
I want to play outside
I want to surf the net!

"Time to get up," said mum. "No, no, no!"
"Time to get up," shouts Dad. "No, no, no!
I want to stay in bed
I want to read"
"BUT YOUR FRIEND IS COMING OVER, SO GET UP!"

"NO, NO, NO!"

Charlotte Moore (Age 9)

Drat That Cat

Hey don't climb on the tables
Get off the rug and the mat
Never jump on the chairs,
You naughty, naughty cat.

Scat out of my house
Go outside and play
Or I will take away your mouse,
Just please get out of the way.

This cat is so fluffy
Just so easy to please,
I know they are so cute
With such different colour suits.

Hey, don't climb on the tables
Get off the rug and the mat,
Never jump on the chairs
You naughty, naughty cat.

Holly Martin (Age 9)

Beach Days

B ig waves lap over the sand
E ach morning they have gone
A wave jumps in my hand
C ome over and swim with me!
H ooray we're in the sea

D ancing in the waves
A ll the waves fly onto me!
Y es summer in the sea is fun
S ummer day in the sun.

Claire McKenner (Age 7)

Revolting Recipes

How would you like to eat
Apple pie with feet
Or mud meat
And antiseptic sweets?

How would you like to try
Strawberry flavoured flies
Or a very burnt pie?

This will make you cry
If you eat black pepper eye.

I hope you never eat
Apple pie with feet.

Suzi Money (Age 11)

My Cream Bun

There I lay in the blazing sun
Dreaming of a squidgy cream bun

I went off to the shop
With a great big hop

I walked in and to my horror there's no cream bun
So I am still dreaming in the blazing sun

I went off to the shop
With a great big hop

There my cream bun lay
Squidgy, creamy I'm glad I came today

So there I lay in the blazing sun
Munching my lovely big cream bun.

Kayleigh McCrea (Age 10)

Winter

Winter is sparkly and bright
It tastes like cinnamon hot apple crunch
It sounds like eggs sizzling in a pan
It looks like ice glistening in the sun
It smells like bacon cooking in a pan
It makes me feel happy and free.

Georgia Marcus (Age 6)

Girl Talk

Me and my mate, right
We were looking really great, yeah
Saw this flexy girl
One cute and sexy pearl
My mate he said, "Go ask her out,"
I said, "Her lips will pout,"
"Hey lady," I shouted out loud
"Come with me, make your mum proud,"
Thwack! I got slapped
And guess what, my friend laughed.

Stuart Mitchell (Age 10)

Loss

The thoughts so deep inside you
The pain that she went through
The upset friends and crying relatives
Wishing it wasn't true

The gravestone in the graveyard
The coffin lying deep
Like a never-ending tunnel
The light you cannot reach.

Amy Mills (Age 11)

The Dragon

The baby dragon is lying awake,
His pointy eyes look like a snake.

His scales are cold, silver and green,
Nobody is sure because he is not seen.

He lives in a dark cave near the wood,
Where he echoes a howl from where he is stood.

The fire from his mouth is red and golden,
From the coins and sweets which have been stolen.

The smell from the dragon is musty,
From inside the cave where it is dusty

Inside the cave it has bright red walls,
From the blood of people and distant calls.

Jennifer Middlehurst (Age 11)

The Winter King

Slowly the old king gets out of bed fluttering icing sugar on the grass
He dances down the stairs scattering daggers,
Opening the door to the winter's day,
Scatters snowflakes over the droopy plants,
While freezing the pond hard,
Slowly the old king in his cloths went into the forest,
When in the forest he was scattering snowflakes,
Slowly wandering back to the castle.

Catherine Meek (Age 10)

Snow

I made the grass turn icy and frozen
I made icicles from drains and gutters
I made the rivers freeze ... the ice as hard as rock
I made snow as white as polar bears' fur
I made children play out wrapped in scarves and hats
Eventually I turned into sleet ...
Soft and quiet like a million leaves.

Andrew McGrath (Age 8)

When I Die

When I die, I wonder if
My mum will cry or clean my room and give it to Tiff.
I need to know before the day comes
So I can mess up my room and so I assume
Tiff would be miffed.

I need to know I shouted to my mum
What would you do when I die
She said she'd be upset
But I think she's under threat
BUT I NEED TO KNOW!!!

Jessica Merrell (Age 11)

277

From A Shark

You think of me as a rival
But I'm not
All I want is something to eat
I think of you as a turtle or a fish
Playing, swimming
That's what they do, you know?
I don't want to hurt you
If you think I want to.
Then sit down and think about it.
Why do I stop?
Because I realise you aren't a fish or a turtle
So, next time you see me accidentally biting someone,
Please don't kill me!

Hannah McCaully (Age 11)

Georgina's Pets

In my bedroom I keep
Ten gerbils with long tails
Nine ponies with long shiny manes
Eight bears that roar and growl
Seven mice that eat my cheese
Six butterflies that flutter and like butter
Five naughty foals that never obey me
Four slippery snails that live in my back pack
Three fluffy pandas that wreck my room
Two tame lions that sleep with me
And one, guess what, big fat penguin.

Georgina Mind (Age 9)

I Will Keep In My Memory

I will store in my memory

The photo of my grandad,
The kiss of my nan,
The hug of both,

The thought of our holiday,
The sun heat on the back of my neck,
The sight of fish darting around me,

Being tackled for the first time at rugby,
Riding my bike for the very first time.
The mud slipping off my body

The touch of my dad's rough stubble
The hush of my mum,
The laugh of my brother,
The bark and feel of my dog's fur,

The crunch of my first biscuit.
The churp of a chick,
The cluck of a hen,

The cry of a new born baby,
The last word of someone old,

I have now filled up my memory (for now).

James Mills (Age 10)

Teenage Romance

The first time I ever saw your face,
I lost all dignity and all grace.
I can feel your skin around my bones,
But yet the old mountain never moans.

How is it that you're never here?
I feel mislaid and shed a tear.
I don't want to tell you that I care,
I feel scared and I'm in despair.

I have now walked inside of your heart,
I can't bear it when we're apart.
Maybe I'll let you know how I feel.
If you say no, I'll forget my deal.

Katharyn Mann (Age 11)

Winter

Sitting by the fire is you and me,
A cat's curled up by a
Christmas tree,
People ice-skating on the ice,
While I watch with a bowl of rice.

Snowballs flying through the air,
Then I saw a furry bear,
A little robin in his nest,
I looked at his lovely breast.

Rebecca Millard (Age 9)

Black

The darkness of the night sky
The colour of the alleys
The darkness of death
The colour of murderers
The darkness of the dark evil spirit.

Daniel Mitchell (Age 11)

My Swimming Week

Monday I go swimming,
It's really, really fun,
I only wish it was holiday,
So I could lie in the sun.

Wednesday I go swimming,
It's not really ever good,
So I'd rather be walking,
In a shady leafy wood.

Thursday I go swimming,
I work really, really hard,
It always tires me out,
So I want to scream and shout.

Jaclyn Messer (Age 11)

I Wish!

I wish I could fly to the moon
And have no gravity,
I wish I could go to the beach
And swim in the cool sea,
I wish I could eat a pizza
And crunch the yummy base,
I wish I could be a queen
And wear silk and lace,
I wish I could meet Harry Potter
And cast a magic spell,
I wish I could know the devil
And send hatred to hell,
I wish I could go to the zoo
And see the meerkats,
But I wish more than all of these
That I do well in S.A.T's.

Carol Meteyard (Age 10)

A Dull Day

A sad dull day,
All the birds are out,
Looking for their morning meal,
A sorry, sad day,
You can feel the wind blowing,
The swings swaying back and forwards,
The clouds stick together,
Like they are a family close together.
What would happen without clouds, without wind?
What a day,
It seems as if the clouds are weeping.
On this dull, dull day.

Jake Maloney (Age 10)

Snowdrops

Signs of Spring
Come to tell us
Winter is near
But Spring will come

Little sharp plants
Come out of the ground
And peep at the earth
And light up the ground

Little army of plants
Marching with spears
Out of the dark
And the earth wakes up

Like a collection out of the sky
Pure and white
Like the clouds in the sky
Smelling like Winter
Cold and clear
With yellow velcro
And like snow out of the sky.

Robert Macintosh (Age 9)

Birthdays

I woke up in the morning,
Feeling special deep down.
When I came out of my bedroom,
There was no one around.

I crept downstairs
And everyone was there,
With a huge pile of presents,
I could feel their care!

On another occasion
It was not mine,
To tell you the truth,
It was a disastrous time!

Lying in bed was my poor old Dad,
I must admit I was there too,
I could not help thinking I'd spoilt his birthday,
I had given him the flu.

Sara Manaton (Age 11)

Cat Dog Bone X-Rays

Cat dog bone x-rays
Dog man sun days
Hour minute second first
Winner tired drink thirst
Water lake river damn
Reservoir floods field lamb
Sheep herd shepherd stick
Old boy football kick
Throw jump run sprint
Quick fast food mint
Tiny midget small large
Canal water lake barge
Boat motor engine money
Equipment disco stereo sony
Television lounge table cupboard
Box cell cage leopard
Cat dog bone x-rays

Richard Massing (Age 12)

Unexploded Bomb

U nexploded, lying in a crowded place
N ext to tourists and the human race
E nergetic people living life
X marks the spot!
P recision in
L aying the bomb
O h, is this so fun
D evastation, this may cause
E nding lives and also
D isastrous effects on local houses.

B ang, off goes the bomb
O bstreperous people scream and shout
M ercy, lord have on us. Is this the
B eginning of World War 1?

Vishal Mistry (Age 15)

Child Abuse

Scared, helpless little children,
Mentally and physically being abused.
Too frightened to tell anyone,
About their problems.

Believing that no one loves them
Crying themselves to sleep
Their bodies being distorted,
By bruises and cuts

I feel so sorry for children,
Who get abused,
No matter how much others try to stop it.
We all know that there are still children being abused.

Nobuhle Mumba (Age 13)

Summer Holiday

The sun was rising on the shore,
The sea was gleaming like the sun,
They lay on the beach for days and days,
People come out to soak up the rays,

Brightly coloured parasols cover me,
Heads are bobbing in the cool, calm sea,
Queuing for an ice cream in the blazing heat,
The boiling, burning sand, burns your blistered feet,

The crashing of the broken waves,
The spraying of the smooth, salty sea,
People strolling along the stretched pier,
Looking out at the view from here,

The sun was setting on the shore,
The sea was black, bleak and grey,
People go home after days and days,
Of soaking up all of the beautiful rays.

Rebecca Meynell (Age 12)

Boil, Boil

Boil, boil, eagles toes
Blood of cow, snot of nose
Tail of mouse, leg of crow
Dead corpse from the snow
Skull of horse, phlegm of toad
Make sure we add a load.

Boil, boil lizard's tongue
A human body that's been hung
But make sure it's gone insane
Maggot from an apple, poisoned fish
Serve it all up on a large round dish!

Ricky May (Age 13)

What Is Love?

Some say it's a bird, some a tree.
Some say it's beautiful, some think it's nasty.
Some say it pierces you deep in your heart.
Some say it stays with you, never to part.
Some say it's an illness you can never beat.
Some say it tastes strange, bitter yet sweet.
Some say it sings like a bird in its nest.
Some say it's something you can never forget.
A special thing, upon which the sun will never set.
When I asked them, some simply turned away.
Some said, "Maybe another day."
But how will I know what to do?
How will I know if it's really true?
This feeling I have, growing inside.
Do I turn and run, or hide?
Please tell me,
What is love?

Jenny Morgan (Age 13)

Roadworks

Roadworks, roadworks are such a pain
Sometimes I think they will drive me insane
They pop up at night and early morning
Beware watch out for signs they are your only warning.

Roadworks, roadworks when will they end
Watch out, watch out there's one round the bend
Sitting in the queues make the train seem so appealing
While sitting there for so long I've lost all feeling.

Machinery, traffic lights and always there's cones.
It's so frustrating that everyone moans
Roadworks, roadworks when will they go
Oh joy! They'll be somewhere else tomorrow.

Adam Millington (Age 11)

The Writer Of This Poem

The writer of this poem,
Is as clever as can be,
As tall as a mountain,
As loud as the sea.

He's as bold as a lion,
As smooth as silk,
As wise as an owl,
With teeth as white as milk.

As strong as steel,
As handsome as gold,
As sleek as a cat,
As profound as the old.

The writer of this poem,
Is as good as it gets,
He's going to win the race,
So come on, raise your bets!

Max Maisey-Curtis (Age 11)

The Song Of The Sea

Murky blue waters on a desolate beach,
No one there but me.
The world so silent,
Only the echo of hollow waves
Singing the song of the sea.
Aqueous horses of foam,
With frozen oyster pearls for eyes,
Never blinking,
And tails of chilling spray,
Fizzing midnight blue,
They're whirling through the ocean waves,
Dancing, prancing, frolicking,
Never wanting to cease, craving for more.

I stand and stare,
The numbing wind stings my face,
My eyes smart from the raw wispy wetness,
The breakers slowly lap up by my feet,
Drenching my skin,
Dragging me down,
To sing the song of the sea.

Anna Marsland (Age 14)

Someone Who I Admire

He is like a very bright light,
He's like a cosy coat,
He's like a clear bright morning,
He's as fast as a meteorite.

He's as wise as an owl,
He's as strong as a bear,
He's like a sunny day,
All he ever does is care.

He speaks as smooth as a flute,
As loud as a trumpet,
He speaks quite fast and fluently,
And only speaks good things.

Nathaniel Mendies (Age 11)

It Wasn't Me

It wasn't me!
Who knocked over this chair?
It wasn't me!
Who snapped that ruler?
It wasn't me!
Did you shout out?
It wasn't me!
Who hit him?
It wasn't me!
Did you screw up your paper?
It wasn't me!
Miss, it wasn't me, I didn't do it, it was
Someone else, the other boy hit me first.
OK IT WASN'T YOU!

Craig Moore (Age 12)

The Wind

The wind whips round you,
Wrapping you in a blanket of coldness,
Your nose turns pink,
Your eyes begin to water,
The wind picks up speed,
Tree branches sway.

Leaves swirl around, swimming through the air,
Litter dances round you,
You can hear a whistling in your ear,
You can tell the wind is here.

Wind chimes tingle
Like the sweet sound of chirping birds,
Your hair blows in your face
The cold is almost unbearable,
Milk bottles smash,
Then the wind stops blowing,
There is silence all around.

Helen Metcalfe (Age 14)

A Red Balloon

The balloon tugged and pulled
Trying to slip through my fingers
It blew into the sky
And flew
Until I could barely see it
We put a message on
Hoping they would read it
And write back
Will we get a message
Or not?

Aaron Mullett (Age 6)

Love Says Everything

I tried to endeavour
As love is forever.
My heart was on fire
But you started to tire.

You said it was over
At the white
Cliffs of Dover.

I cried and cried
But you only sighed

I declared love
Forever, but you said
We couldn't be together

You left me on my own,
It was the first
Time I'd ever felt

Alone.

Samantha Moore (Age 12)

I Dive Into The Water

I dive into the water,
Down into the sea,
I hear a whale's calling,
Is he calling me?
I float below the surface,
Where beautiful fish swim
I see a sunken ship,
How do I get in?
How peaceful it is,
Beneath the ocean,
Who would think up above,
The waves make such commotion.

Daniel Michalik (Age 10)

The Jungle

The crocodile swims in the sea,
Hunting for its tea
The snake curls up the tree,
The spiders all flee.
The lion's mane,
Getting drenched in the rain,
None of them are tame,
They think they have a heroic name.
Tiger's eyes
Look up in the skies
They can even energise
The eagles' beaks,
Its prey it seeks
It soars over the animal seas
Its prey it sees.
The warthog
Hides behind a log
It's as smelly as a smelly sock!

Connor Manning (Age 9)

Why Oh Why My Son

Why oh why does my son have to die,
He has done no harm.
But now I stand, breathless and crying,
As he, my son, walks in pain to Golgatha.
Why oh why my son?

He is the one who did good deeds,
And helped others in pain.
But now he is going to be put to death,
Because everyone called for Barabbas but why?
But why oh why my son.

Now pressed in the face with a cloth with love he still fears,
How sad I feel for I will never again have a son like Jesus.
While carrying his cross he no longer feels like the son of God,
And just feels sad and helpless.
So why oh why my son.

Katy Merrison (Age 9)

Kangaroo Watching

Kangaroo watching
People playing
Children laughing
People talking
Boy running
Monkeys aping
Kangaroo watching

Kangaroo watching
Crocodile snapping
People chomping
Babies crying
Everyone looking
At him
Kangaroo watching

Kangaroo watching
All alone
No friends
No family
Kangaroo watching.

Joshua Marshall (Age 8)

The Orange Spotty Ball

So much depends upon
An orange spotty ball
Sparkling like silver glass
Beside the old tree

Jessica Macivor (Age 9)

Colours

The sky is blue,
The water is blue.

The sun is bright yellow,
The stars are shiny yellow.

The grass is green,
The leaves on the trees are green.

The fence is brown,
The tree trunk is brown.

At night the sky
Goes
Black

Kiran Majid (Age 8)

Why Is The Sky Blue

Why is the sky blue?
Why do cows moo?
How does hair grow?
Why does the wind blow?
Why do butterflies fly?
Why do trees have bark?
Why at night is it dark?
Why do snakes bite?
Why do bears fight?
Why do fish swim?
Why do bees buzz?
Why are shoes made from leather?
Why are leaves as light as feather?
Why do pens have ink?
Why do people blink?
Why is the sun yellow?
Why is the moon so bright?
Why do stars come out at night?
Why is the world round?
Why do we all live on the ground?

Abigail Marsh (Age 9)

The Fish

My fish is as shiny as gold,
He always does as he's told.
My fish is as proud as a peacock,
He swims in and out of his little rock.
My fish is as happy as a king,
He wags his tail like a wing.
My fish is as cute as a teddybear,
He swims around as fast as a hare.
My fish is as handsome as a prince,
My first smile has made him happy ever since!

Zeenat Mahmood (Age 10)

It's Spring In My Garden

It's spring in my garden
The sun is shining down
It's spring in my garden
There's frog spawn on the pond
It's spring in my garden
There are yellow daffodils
It's spring in my garden
There are red tulips
It's spring in my garden
The buds are growing on the trees
I like spring in my garden

James Mitchell (Age 7)

It Was So Noisy ...

It was so noisy that I couldn't hear
My tea cooking
It was so noisy that I couldn't hear
My grandpa shout
It was so noisy that I couldn't hear
My cat meow when it chases a mouse
It was so noisy that I couldn't hear
The traffic roaring down the road
It was so noisy that I couldn't hear
My dad snoring in the armchair
It was so noisy!

Danielle Maskell (Age 7).

My Hat - My Cap

My hat
Is a cap
It's got letters
I put it on my head.

It's got a peak
And it's got a tag
And I wear it cos I do
Cos the other one was old.

Luke Martinez (Age 4)

My Brother

I've got a brother Sam
Who plays with me a lot,
He is growing up so fast and
Sleeps in a bed not a cot.

I've got a brother Sam
He goes to nursery
And when he comes home
He has his tea with me.

Ben Mansfield (Age 5)

Rain

Falling raindrops all around,
Bouncing sparkling drops underfoot,
Surprised spiders with diamonds that shine,
Gleaming drops racing down the window,
As the glistening drops fall down into the shiny puddles the small ripples start,
Passing cars make a swishing sound,
It is a clean and new world.

Isabel Moore (Age 8)

Sunshine

I made a young woman take off her coat and pullover.
I burnt the lush green grass to a crisp, crunchy brown.
I shone my rays on the old people and made them come out and sunbathe.
I made beautiful flowers wake up, from a deep, deep, sleep.
I brought children out who began to play games with each other.
I made birds start to sing a twittering, cherruping song.
I became a sunset, soft and gentle.
I decided it was time to go to bed.

Rachel Meacher (Age 8)

Sunshine

I made the children take off their coats in a hurry.
I made the flowers flop to the grass with my rays.
I forced people to go inside from sunbathing by burning their skin.
I shrank large puddles into nothing at all.
I shone on the grass making it yellow like straw.
I slowly started to fade ... until I became a small red glow.

Rebecca McErlean (Age 8)

Battle Of Bosworth Senses Poem

I feel my hands as I clutch my sword
As I get ready to fight.
I hear the shouts of my sister in her smelly room.
I smell the smell of my companion's sweaty armpits.
I see the blood on the newly cut grass
I want to run away back to my nice warm house.

Charlie Meade (Age 9)

My Family

My brother is called Bert and he likes to wear a skirt,
My sister likes to sing and she wears a shiny ring.
My mum is so much fun and she likes to drink her rum,
My dad is glad that he's so sad.
My pet is called pig and he wears a silly wig,
My mum says I yap but all I do is RAP!

Joseph McGarry (Age 11)

Leaves

Leaves floating in the air,
Wind is blowing in my hair.
When I look at the ground
I see the leaves drop slowly down.
I feel a leaf so light and brown,
I see the leaves drift from town to town.
They smell as sweet as a chocolate bar
And when I let go they run so far.
As time goes by it's time for bed,
And as I rest my sleepy head
I think what I did today
And I remember that I saw the leaves sway.
From every village and every town
Each little one will come right down
To the floor and on my path
And make a pattern on the grass.

Anna Meadows (Age 9)

I'm Sorry Miss

I forgot my homework,
Oh yes it's true
I really don't know what to do,
I've got a good enough excuse
His name is Biscuit, he's always on the loose,
He stole it, he took it
And now it's in bits
My dog ate my homework
Yes, I admit

I really shouldn't tell any lies,
Sometimes I have to try and disguise.
I really should tell my teacher,
I have tried my best,
I've tried to please her.
I cannot do it any more,
Yes, I admit I've broken the law

Chloe Madigan (Age 11)

Oh Great Tornado

Oh tornado, why do you spin so fast
Why do you swallow everything in your path?

"It's the fault of the weather forecast!"

But why do you create destruction where ever you go?
Ripping roofs of the top houses!!

"My power's too strong, I even rip up flowers!"

Where ever you whirl you cause fright!

"I make most of my power while the sun is blocked!"

When you go, will you send me a postcard?

"Who knows when I will reappear
But when I do I'll give you one next yearrrrrrr."

Rhys Mackay (Age 10)

Poem Of Love

You don't know me
But I know you,
I'm not in your world,
But you're in mine.
I see you every day
But you don't.
I think of you all the time
But you don't at all.

Do you know who I am?
I most certainly know you.
We can hug each other in the playground
And chase each other as we run around.

Next year you can give me a card
Think of who I am, it's not that hard.

Sally Meineke (Age 11)

Loneliness

The young boy stands motionless in one corner of the playground,
Another long day of misery and torment has just begun.
No one knows about the fear and loneliness that he feels inside.
He looks around to see children playing games, which he has been excluded from.
All of a sudden the ball hits him with a thud,
That's the third time this week.
No one apologises they just laugh and say "hard luck."
He feels uneasy and tense as the tall boy comes to pick up the ball.
Before he goes away he slyly punched him for no reason.
The feeling of rejection shows on his face as he wipes away a tear.
He asks himself, "What have I done to deserve this treatment?"
"Why me?" as he drowns in a pool of tears.

William Martindale (Age 9)

The City

The sun shines but the rays don't reach the ground.
Big skyscrapers and large buildings block them.
People bustle and race to get to the shops.
Children cry and scream.
No wildlife can be seen along the cobble streets.
The small bird twitters from a distant tree.
Clouds close in over the bustling city.
Rain begins to fall but the sun still shines.
A rainbow stretches across the sky.
Like a multi-coloured elastic band.
Men and women, children, teenagers.
They run to shelter.
From the spitting, drizzling rain.
The city calms after 10 o'clock.
It lies quietly until morning.

Lizzie Mayne (Age 12)

The Lemon Sherbet Sweet

Lemon Sherbet Sweet
It blows me off my feet
With it's shiny yellow coat
Like a car it lashes out
It's lush flavour of smooth lemon juice
Down it zooms down like the sound of music
It runches and pops and bangs altogether
It's brilliant!time...for...another...I...think...Don't you?

Lee Morgan (Age 13)

Hospital

The screaming of people fills the hospital with noise.
I walk through, looking around
I see people lying on beds asleep, lying as still as soldiers.
Then I see young kids rushing around, pushing and shoving.
Through the cubical curtains you can hear the
Machines working, making the sounds, beep, beep, beep, beep!
Porters pushing patient's beds and trying to cheer them up
As the reception desk is crowded with people
Shouting they were next.
The waiting area is full of injured people waiting to see the nurse,
And the relative's room is the dreaded place where
You wait and wait, very tediously, till late,
To hear your relative's fate!

Sophie McIntosh (Age 13)

Bully Bunter

Still and quiet, no one daring to speak,
That's how our playground was every day of the week.
The children were bored, they wanted to play and wear themselves out,
Saying and doing nothing, is not what play time's about.
People are scared of Bully Bunter, because he's in year 7,
And beat up a boy who was in year 11.
My friend Monique thinks he's dumb, stupid and weak,
And that he wears ugly shoes, when he walks they squeak.
She always teases him and calls him a geek,
"Hold on, Bunter is not the bully. Oh no! It's Monique!"

Chanel McPherson (Age 12)

What Am I?

A food-bolter,
A lunging-leaper,
A bullet-sprinter,
A silent-creeper,
A total-lacerater,
A hunting-killer,
A moose and deer-eater
A huge-clawerer,
Add them up and I'm a...

Tiger

Peter Moffat (Age 11)

The Mole

The mole is a worm crunching
Beast which uses its razor-sharp teeth
To munch on its lunch

It is a blind giant, rumbling
In its underground world

It is a J.C.B. digging
At the saturated earth

Its babies are big worms,
Blind and helpless -
But not for long!

Charles Morfoot (Age 11)

The World

The world is a wonderful place
It's a huge beautiful crust round
A gorgeous lovely gigantic place
A giant nice green blue place
The wonderful place
Babies being born
Animals being born
Such a good life
It is good, good, good, good.

Walter Murphy (Age 8)

My Science Poem

Why are pans made of metal?
Why do leaves turn brown?
Why is paper made from trees?
Why do we mix mixtures?
Who made thermometers?
Why do liquids change to solids?
Why do we have sweet?
Why does yeast make bread?
Why do we have mayors?
Why do matches light fires?
Why do we have fizzy drinks?
Why is chocolate bad for us?
Why do we have salt on our chips?

Sam Major (Age 9)

Daydream

Mum thinks I'm doing my homework
But no
I'm either jumping out of a plane
Or I'm getting the biggest swimming medal ever
I really wished the daydream was real
But it was a daydream
Mum thinks I'm doing my homework
But no
I'm really sliding down the biggest waterfall
It was great
Or I'm running in the athletics competition and won it again
I love it
But it was only a daydream.

Jessica Martin (Age 9)

My Baby Brother Makes So Much NOISE

My baby brother makes so much noise.
Even when sleeping with my teddy bear.
He even broke my favourite toys.
He tried to pull my hair.
He tried to kick some boys.
But the worst thing of all, he makes so much *NOISE!*

Nathan Mann (Age 9)

Darkness

Darkness is evil and bad and dull
Darkness is a miserable sad and black shadow
Darkness is a thunder cloud bursting out and anger
Darkness is a damp wintry night
Darkness is a murky maroon moon
Darkness is a sleepy gloomy night
Darkness is like a dark devil sitting in the corner
Darkness is an eclipse blocking out the light
Darkness is an owl hooting during the night
Darkness is a sleeping sad miserable murky night
Darkness is *BAD!*

Ryan Mace (Age 10)

Dark Poem

Dark is a meaning for death and hell,
Dark is a creepy thing.
There are shadows lurking everywhere even in a haunted house.
Dark is a meaning for baddies such as Darth Vader.
There is a cloudy sky as a sign of evil,
There is gloom of mysterious murder,
A tunnel is a spooky place full of murky oil.

These are the things you will learn if
You come across darkness.

Sean Maguire (Age 10)

Jungle

Mighty jungle is a hectic and busy city.
Hungry cheetah is a new-fangled car.
Large leaf is a decayed man's back.
Cruel tarantula is a brand new book.
Dry earth is a cool tiled floor.
Glistening dew drop is a gorgeous diamond lace.
Bright red flower is a red nose.
Tall tree is a sky scraper.
Glittery greenery is an impish child's hands,
Shining yellow flower is a blazing golden sun.

Sophie Maddern (Age 10)

The Raging Sea

The sea rolls onwards powerfully towards the land.
The waves getting bigger, stronger and faster.
The sea rolls crashing onto the black rocks.
Shooting up a fine mist of spray and white froth.
The noise was terrifying like thunder.
The ground tremor'd like an earthquake.
Then the water rolled back again into the dark sea.
Hissing like a snake as it disappeared.
There was a moment's silence but don't worry.
It will be back again raging like a bull.

Ryan Mitchell (Age 10)

My Bed

Here I am, in my bed,
Thinking of something in my head,
Dreaming of something that I've read.

Then my brother came in,
And poked me with a pin,
And threw things out of the bin.

Megan Mackay (Age 8)

Winter

Winter coming,
Pond's frozen over,
Under thick ice,
Down in the depths,
Fish rest,
Snow starts to fall,
The clouds become overcast,
The storm begins,
Cars blocked in,
The snow carries on falling,
The temperatures drop,
The spring is near,
But there is still,
Time in winter,
We wait.

Oliver Marks (Age 10)

Advice

When I get teased at school,
Then on my way home
I drag my stone filled feet along.
The weight of my heart is remarkably heavy,
I go straight to my Granpa
Sitting calmly in his chair.
I tell him I have no real friends
But he pulls me on his knee
And tells me who my best friend is:
My best friend, it is me!
So now when I get teased at school
I don't even care, because I always know,
My best friend is deep within my heart!

Lauren Makin (Age 10)

Puzzle

Puzzle my pony, a beautiful mare,
Patches of white and chestnut hair.
Looking at me with her shining bright eyes,
At 12.2, just the right size.

She stays in her field and happily grazes
Munches away at fresh white daisies,
Comes in at night to her cosy warm shed
Chews on her hay all night in her bed.

When she walks she does it nicely
Breaks into trot very precisely.
Given the chance she goes over the jumps
She canters all round missing bumps.

Claudia Meller (Age 10)

A Poem About Kate

There was a young woman called Kate
She is always extremely late
The manager got cross
And told the boss
The sack was the fate of Kate.

Thomas Marshall (Age 9)

The Labrador Dog

I move like lightning,
Cos I'm only a puppy.
I can open a door to get in and out,
I am never just lying about.

When I want my food I will jump like a
Baby elephant, and when I get my food I
Sometimes eat like a pig and, I can't possibly
Taste the food and my favourite is eating the kitchen!

I am supposed to be a man's best friend,
But I can be your best friend,
If you take care of me!

Nathalie Mannion (Age 8)

The Poppy Field

The field wears like a garment the
Golden sunset lapping over the rows of
Poppies blooming happily.
Whilst in the distance you can hear the
Wind whistling through the woods,
While the trees murmur silently to each other.
The beauty of the evening took my breath away,
As I watched the golden sun melting into the
Poppies as they swayed to their sleep.

Sarah Meyer (Age 9)

Frogs

Frogs are green
They like to lean
They like to be green
They like to swim
All day and night
They eat flies
They leap like flies
All day and night
They like to lie

And that's how
Much they
Like
To
Lie.

Leigh Middleton (Age 9)

What Am I?

I have two wheels,
I am driven by feet
I have different speeds I can be as slow
As a snail or as fast as a cheetah,
I have red and white lights to help you see,
I have a chain to make me work,
I have two flat peddles attached to it,
I also have a seat to sit on of course,
What am I?

Kerri Marshall (Age 10)

I'll Be Just Me

In the future I will be
An acrobat or a chimpanzee
I'll swing through forests far away
And try to glide as high as the sky
I'll be an actor or a superstar
I'll be athletic and run a million miles
Actually I'll be an astronaut
And discover life on mars
I'll be a magician and pull a rabbit from a hat
Or maybe I'll be a superhero
Actually I'll be plain old me.

Jay Matthews (Age 8)

The Fearless And Deadly Dragon

My wings are sharp daggers of ice
My eyes, glowing crystals
My tongue is a red hot chilli pepper
My claws, sharp steak knives
My breath is flames of fire
My voice, a devil's sigh
My tail is an angry porcupine
I've seen brave men run away like scattering sheep in a field
I've heard animals pleading for its life like a baby crying for its bottle
In play I breath fire like flames from a flame thrower
In anger I swish my tail like a whip
They call me the predator of all predator.

Andrew Murray (Age 13)

Summer

Hot summer sun beaming down on the ground
Sound of bees buzzing all around
Trees swaying gently in the cool summer breeze
Ice cream van selling 99s and fruit lollies
Lawn mowers mowing the fast growing grass
Tomatoes ripening in the house made of glass
Children's laughter rings through the air
Playing in the garden without a care
I love summer sun and I'll tell you what's more
The great smell of BBQs I simply adore
Of all the seasons, winter, spring, or fall
The season of summer beats them all.

Ashlea McGregor (Age 12)

It Was So Noisy

It was so noisy that I couldn't hear the ice cream van's lovely music
It was so noisy that I couldn't hear my father yelling at my big sister
It was so noisy that I couldn't hear my baby cousin crying loudly
It was so noisy that I couldn't hear the cars zooming on the main roads
It was so noisy that I couldn't hear my dog barking madly.

Rhiann Middleton (Age 7)

Will You Be Mine?

Lying here upon my bed
Loving thoughts going through my head
All I want is to be with you
To become one and not two
I want to take you in my loving arms,
Along with all my loving charms.
Will you be my shoulder to cry on?
I will become one you can rely on.
I will never let you down.
My love will always stick around.
Do you want to be my teddy bear?
I promise to take you everywhere.
I know that you're the one for me
And nothing will come between me and thee.
Tell me that you feel the same
For I can no longer play this game.

Kelly Morgan (Age 16)

Achievement

A ctivate your brain
C onverse with human life
H ear the sound of quiet muttering
I nvite brain waves into the mind
E ngage yourself to learn
V igilant brain
E nergise your hand to write
M emory
E nergy
N othing can stop you now
T ime to achieve.

Adam Matthews (Age 11)

The Zanzibar

The fishes swam to the bottom of the sea
When they came up they frightened me
My face turned red
I bashed my head
I thought I was in the park
Then I saw a shark
The lightning flashed
The thunder crashed
I started to cry
The fish were shy
GOODBYE!!!!!!

Terri Murphy (Age 12)

Midnight Folk

A tree's fingers slither
Around its snake-skin trunk
Glowing white cats' eyes
Flicker around the junk
The twittering of an owl
Going on its nightly hunt
The sly fox's paws
Creeping silently out in front.

Hannah Morris (Age 10)

When I Fell Down The Stairs

I was winding up my sister
On a beautiful day,
We were getting naughty
Because she was annoyed,
I slipped right down the stairs
And kicked the pillar at the bottom
And broke my toe,
It was agony.

Richard Medlock (Age 9)

Owl

Outside among the moonlit sky,
Sits somebody brown with freckles.
Out on her branch she watches closely,
For something small that can't fight back,
A field mouse or a rabbit perhaps.
Something for her and her family to eat.
Squawking with pleasure she flies overhead.
Mice run for cover and hide away.
But one mouse always loses.
Mean, mean is the brown bird with freckles.

Jenna Manning (Age 10)

The Magical Dream

One night I had a dream,
Of strawberries and delicious ice cream,
Of chocolate and peaches and fabulous cream,
To fill my tummy with yummy food.
Oh, what a wonderful dream.

One night I had a dream,
Of teddies sailing down the stream,
Of rabbits sliding down my slide,
Their faces full of pride,
Of Toffie the hamster cartwheeling down the lane
Oh, what a wonderful dream.

Lucy Mayo (Age 9)

Red

The power of red,
Of civilisation,
The colour of blood, pain
The colour of death.

Kirsty Majeika (Age 11)

Weather

What is rain?
-God watering his plants.

What is wind?
-A howl of a wolf crying at the moon.

What is snow?
-An adult's white teeth.

What is sun?
-Aphrodite dancing in the skies.

What is a rainbow?
-Colours of a happy child's painting.

Kirsty Mackinnon (Age 11)

My Brother

Hair-puller
Never-duller
Bruise-maker
Sick-faker
Fist-puncher
Steal-luncher
Eye-poker
Silly-joker
Girl-hater
Boy-mater
That's what he's like most of the time
But usually he is really fine!

Jordan Masters (Age 9)

Space

Shooting off in a rocket,
We're going at mega speed,
Racing, blasting, zooming, flying,
We're starting to proceed:

Shooting off in a rocket,
"Look, we're almost there."
Going, going nearly gone,
We're floating in mid-air.

Elena Matthews (Age 10)

The Whale I Saw

Once I saw a whale who was as big as can be
It came up to the shore and met me by the sea
The whale looked at me with his big round eyes
And I looked at him with my small round eyes
Although he was big and I was very small
I think we are just the same because God
Made us all.

Abbey Martin (Age 8)

School

School, school
Boring, boring
In the night it keeps me snoring

School, school
Fun, fun
My homework must weigh a ton

School, school
Home time, home time
Finally it's home time.

Rebecca Male (Age 9)

The Sounds Of The Garden

The wind in the trees and the buzz of the bees
Singing birds can be heard

Dogs barking and people laughing
I dropped the watering can and it made a big bang

The engine of the motorbike is a sound I don't like.

Emma Matthews (Age 7)

Spring

S pring has gone and buds peep through
P retty daffodils yellow and crocuses blue
R ain falls gently helping flowers grow
I like midday when I see the sun glow
N ewly hatched ducklings in a nest by the stream
G littering dewdrops make the grass gleam.

Fiona Mills (Age 7)

Alcohol

Deadly alcohol is a tiger waiting for its prey,
Fatal alcohol is a murderer waiting with its weapon,
Poisonous alcohol is a problem solver (so every victim thinks),
Cruel alcohol is a death leader for all the addicted ones,
Sickly alcohol is the meaning of the word hatred,
Fearsome alcohol is the lonely one's friend.

Bailey Meyer (Age 10)

Monkeys

Monkeys swing from tree to tree
And eat bananas when they're free
They lie around high in the trees
And make their beds from great big leaves
They play all day and sleep at night
They like to play both day and night
If you stumble across them they'll give you a fright
They run around like great big fools
And they drink water from the pools.

Robyn Meredith (Age 8)

Dinner Time

The bell rings it's time it's time,
March them in here at the double,
Boil and bubble, toss and turn,
March them in here at the double.
Horrible food yuk, yuk, yuk,
Get me out of here, quick, quick, quick,
Horrible food they must have made it wrong.

Laura Martayn (Age 8)

The Flamingoes

The Flamingoes pink
Was enough to make you wink!
With their feathers beautiful and big
Their legs are like a long thin twig
Their hooked beak
Which definitely couldn't be weak
The long beak rests
On its pink chest

Hannah Morris (Age 9)

One, Two , Three, Four

One, two, three, four
Knock on the door
Five, six, seven, eight,
Little plates
Nine, ten, eleven, twelve
Lots of work to shelve.

Sally Moran (Age 11)

Colours

Bluebells are as blue as the sky,
The sun is golden when it sets,
Leaves turn yellow, orange, brown and crisp,
These are the signs of Autumn.

The sheep are as white as snow,
The shades of colours are really pleasant,
From white to pink,
These are the signs of spring.

Helena Majek (Age 8)

A Nonsense Poem

I went for a run.
I eat a bun.
I saw a mouse
My brother was eating jelly
I said you have a big belly
He said shut up and watch the telly.

Ayshia Mahmood (Age 10)

Lion

Mine is the ear,
That hears the sound.
When danger is close,
I'm not around.

Mine is the eye,
That seeks my prey.
I climb up trees,
And that's where I stay.

Hannah Major (Age 11)

Tate's Late

Hi I'm Tate, I'm great. I support Arsenal because they are cool.
Got to go to school or I'll be a fool.
I'm glad I caught the bus or I'll be in a right fuss.
Good I'm at school now I'm going into class.
Just finished French, dejeuner time now, oh sorry, it's lunch in French.
Munch, munch, munch, now I've finished brunch.
(Three hours later) it's home time got the bus, later I'm at home.
BYE.

Tate Matthews (Age 9)

I Once Woke Up

I woke up,
And I found myself in the bottom bunk,
I must have been sleep-walking in the bottom bunk,
By the way, I did have a dream
But sleep-walked into the bottom bunk,
Well that solves it!

Adam Maddock (Age 8)

Freedom

Once I had the freedom,
The freedom of a bird swooping low soaring high,
Once I had the freedom in my plane.

But now the only thing I see is four walls around me
No space to move no space to breath.
The four walls coming in crushing me.
Why Oh why did this happen to me?
The food is little the water is drops and stale at that
How can I live?
I can't, I can't live in here, I have to go, go now but how?
A glider I will build, I'll glide above the ground, silently I'll fly,
No more will the four walls kill me
Nor will Germans starve me
For I shall have my freedom,
The freedom of a bird.

Miguel Nance (Age 12)

Abandonment

As the sun disappears behind the deserted houses,
And the dark of night tightens it's grip on the town,
A black car speeds away down the clouded, empty street.
The only thing left is a small girl carrying her only possession,
A small, filthy stabbed rabbit.

Wearing only a short, strappy summer dress,
· And a pair of trainers with a hole in the sole,
She slides down the graffiti covered wall and sits, silently on the ground,
Her eyes wide with fear and her arms wrapped tightly around herself.
As the night goes on, her eyes slowly close,
As she drifts off into an eternal sleep.

Sarah Nelson (Age 14)

Red Nose Day

It is Red Nose Day
You need to wear
Red clothes today
I got a nose it looks
Like a rose
You have to
Pay 20p.

Husna Mahmood (Age 9)

My Bunny

I am in love with a bunny
I stroke it every day
I have love for this bunny
That's what I always say
She hops on my bed
And curls to my ted
She eats all the honey
And she is very funny.

Alexandra Nolan (Age 7)

Spring

Spring has bright pretty flowers.
Tulips, daffodils and crocuses.
Lambs skipping in the fields.
Bubbling streams everywhere.
All the people are smiling
All the birds are singing
It's SPRING!

Liam Danny Nichols (Age 8)

My Pen

My pen is sharp and inky,
It gives me a blue mouth,
It never stops wobbling,
And it keeps ending up in my mouth.

Tom Newcomb (Age 9)

The Sun

The sun is rising in the morning,
It rises up with red sparks,
The rays shining very bright,
I just can't wait for it to come,
Wishing that I could touch it,
On tip-toe reaching tall,
Trying not to fall,
Suddenly afternoon comes,
The sun settles down.

Tabitha Norris (Age 8)

The Ghost Lover

The wind was a pack of wolves biting at the trees,
The moon was a bright firefly floating in the breeze,
The path was a long silver serpent writhing and wriggling,
And the Ghost Lover came floating-
Floating-floating
The Ghost Lover came floating up to the old stone grave.

He had torn black trousers at his thigh, a grey hat on his head,
A collared shirt of flannel and a coat of beautiful red,
He was a poor young country man and the name of him was Dave,
And in the clearing down he lay-
Lay-lay
And down he lay and set the flowers at his grave.

He knelt for a while, on the floor looking rather sad,
But he decided to go; now feeling a bit glad,
So he rose slowly from the ground,
And floated away without a sound-
Sound-sound
Rose slowly from the ground, floated away without a sound.

Jack Newton (Age 11)

The Flowers In Spring

In spring the flowers bloom
And all the people have a happy tune.
But when winter comes and the flowers go,
And all the people say oh no!

Mark Nicholas (Age 7)

Lost Colours

A stranger called this morning dressed up in black and grey,
Put every colour in a bag and carried them away.

The tongue-tingling red of the strawberry ice lolly,
The pink frilly dress of the small pretty dolly.

The bright green grass that sparkled in the sun,
The cold icy blue that gave me so much fun.

The black and dull grey that's gloomy in the sky,
The white of the clouds that slowly pass by.

The burning yellow sun that once filled the sky,
Replaced by the darkness that leads me to sigh.

The small purple flowers that used to be so bright,
Now there is no colour not even a speck of light.

The orange of the fruit I will never forget,
The brown on the T-shirts of the working men.

When will I see the colours when will they all come back,
I don't want to see the greys or whites and really not the blacks.

At last the man arrived with the big brown sack,
All the colours in the world have now come back!

Kelly Napier (Age 11)

Elephant

I am an elephant big and grey,
Hiding in the trees,
In the wind my trunk will sway
In the soft and gentle breeze.

I am hiding from those humans,
Who want to kill me,
But I'm going to put up a fight,
To save my ivory.

Sometimes I wish I wasn't an elephant,
Oh so big Oh so grey,
I wish I could change my life,
In every single way.

Georgia Narey (Age 11)

Sea Blue Lorry

Once upon a dreary day,
I saw a sea blue lorry coming my way,
Stopping and stalling here it came,
To rest beneath my window pane.

And there it sat for half an hour or so,
Just below, so below,
Then started it's journey once again,
No longer beneath my window pane.

Kirsty Nolan (Age 11)

"Oh Dear" Grandpa!

When my Grandpa goes shopping,
First I say "no stopping."
But when he sees a shop,
He has to pop-in.

When I see the jewellery,
He sees the pants,
Don't go shopping with your Gramps,
He pulled me in the pants shop.

I said to him "no way"
Finally we got out of the shop,
Now it was my turn to say "stop!"

So here I am,
Having a great laugh.
Looking for things,
To go in my bath.

I turned around,
He had gone away
"Oh no"
What a day!

Tamsin Noyes (Age 10)

Snake In The Playground

Snakes in the playground hissing around.
Scaring everybody it weighs just a pound.

Snake in the playground slithering about,
It's frustrating parents gushing down the spout.

Snake in the playground everyone thinks it's cool,
But only the kids in the pool.

Snake in the playground everybody knows,
Sliming on the floor but sliming round toes.

They call him Hiss! They call him Rattle!
He lives by the reptile shop he lives near cattle.
Who told you that? Cake hole! Zip it!
I've known that snake since he was a midget.

Snake in the playground we'll catch him soon,
Leave it to us, unless he goes to the moon!

Snake in the playground what's there to do!
400 children, headteacher too,
Chasing the snake, chasing everybody,
I know that snake his name is Noddy.

Dominic Nott (Age 9)

Spring

Spring has the colours of pink and yellow,
I can taste easter eggs coming to my door
I can hear sizzling marshmallow
I can see chirping birds coming to my floor
I smell the golden birds glow
Spring makes me feel like I want more

Frances Nutt (Age 7)

Beast

Concealed by a barrier of long luscious grass,
The sun belting down.
In the distance the song of the Indian tribesmen can be heard,
And the beating of the drum.
Any animal who crosses his path must move quickly,
As he prowls the jungle.

Stripes of death cover the beautiful but deadly beast.
Deep green eyes watching.
He spots a herd of antelope, down he crouches.
They have no idea the beast is near.
In the background a cascade plummets towards the raging rapids,
Creating an explosion of froth.

As he gets into striking distance the monkeys' shrill voices call out,
A warning which sends the antelope in a panic.
In the mass escaping mania a pregnant female trips on a tree stump,
She succumbs to the beast.
He drags her into the bushes where the gorging proceeds.
Soon vultures begin to land on the branches.

Arthur Nares (Age 10)

Excuses, Excuses

You haven't got the measles,
Or the mumps,
And your face isn't covered in strange bumps,
So why haven't you got your homework?

You don't have a headache,
Or the flu,
You're not feeling sick,
So where's your homework?

"The dog ate it miss'
After I was abducted,"
Yeah really,
"Where is it?"

Excuses, excuses I know them all,
My baby dribbled on it,
My cat chewed it all,
Come on where is it?

Excuses, excuses they never work,
In the playground you will lurk,
Doing your homework,
Until the teacher comes!!!!!

Aron Nedd (Age 10)

The Psychic Person

When I go down the street,
I know lots of the people I meet.
I see by their faces
That under their laces
They have horribly smelly feet.

And when I look up at their eyes,
I see that they like to eat pies.
And on their eyebrows,
I see that they like cows,
And that they like telling lies.

Sarah Nussbaum (Age 10)

Untitled

Wings are as strong as steel
My eyes, as bright as fire
My tongue is a shooting arrow
My claws are as sharp as knives
My breath, as hot as the sun
My voice is as loud as thunder
My tail is coiled like a snake
I've seen goblins and fairies
I've heard laughter and tears
In play I play hide and seek
In anger I terrify the villagers with my fire
They call me Great Dragon.

James Ness (Age 12)

She's Bullied Me

She's bullied me since I don't know when,
Slapping me or kicking me now and then.
No one believed me she was teacher's pet
Even though once she wrote me a death threat.
I wanted to die, cried myself to sleep at night
I was always in the dark and never saw daylight.
Off to the headteacher I went, time and time again.
It was always her fault and she just went off giggling.
3 years later, we became friends
She looked so cool with all the latest trends.
Then she moved away
Said she'd write to me every day.
I waited by the letterbox, and then I understood,
She didn't want to write to me, I didn't think she would.

India Norchi (Age 10)

Indian Earthquake

In India, a terrible earthquake and thousands of people die,

Only two towns were mainly hit.
People living in stones and rubble,
For about a week they lived in it.
Until some men come to rescue them.

Rumble, rumble the earthquake,
It's like a big shaking slide,
The ground just opens there's a big dark hole,
Some people lay up-side down,
A destructive quake, a town destroyed forever.

Adam Nicoll (Age 10)

I Went To See Grandpa

I was going to see Grandpa, I went on a train and guess what I saw?

Over the way I saw a goat, over the way I saw a boat.
Over the way I saw a lad, who was being bad!
Over the way I saw a car, over the way I saw a jar.
Over the way I saw a train that wasn't working what a pain.
Over the way I saw a pet that was very wet.
Over the way I saw a flower that grew, over the way I saw a car brand new.
Over the way I saw a drum that had a good hum.
Over the way I saw a seat that was very neat.
Over the way I saw a bin that was very thin.
Over the way I saw a pool that was very cool.
Over the way I saw a hive that had five bees in.
I found a book that was about Captain Hook.
There was a good top in a shop.
Over the way I saw some smoke that was only a joke.
Over the way I saw a skirt that had lots of dirt on dirt.

Sophie Northmore (Age 8)

What I'd Like To Be

What I'd like to be when I grow up,
I could be a rescue worker feeding a pup!
Or maybe a teacher that helps in art,
but everything I'd make would fall apart.
Maybe even an electrician,
no way I'd rather work in demolition.
Maybe a job at the local market,
probably not I'd muck up the carpet.
What about a mornin' paper round,
if I did no newspapers would be found!
I could be a famous cook,
I'd cook from Kebabs on a barbecue,
to pouring sauce on a duck.
I wonder what the best job is for me,
I don't have a clue at the moment,
so I'll have to wait and see!!

Harriet Nolan (Age 11)

If You Want To See An Alien

If u want to see an Alien,
You must hop down to the shop
I know an Alien who's living down there
He smells, he's fat, pink, brown, black and he is ugly.
Yes, if you want to see an Alien,
You must hop down to the shop,
Go down fast and say,
Big Alien,
Big Alien
Gig Aliennnn
And he will run up to you
But you must run, run as fast as you can!

Michael Nicholson (Age 9)

The Thing

It had teeth,
It had bones,
It had forces that could crush bones,
And it also has a comb.

It had a pet,
It had a big wound in it,
It had a big debt to pay,
And it was happy.

It could change colour and go far,
It could live in the sea,
It could live on land,
And it could fly.

It's the most fascinating thing in the world,
It's coming very slowly,
It's got a ball pint pen,
And that's all I've got to say.

Lee Newby (Age 8)

The Childhood Secret

For eleven years you lied to me
For eleven years I was left in the dark
For eleven years you never loved each other
For eleven years I was the one who looked up to you

In a split second my heart broke
In a split second the truth created pain
In a split second you both became strangers
In a split second my reality became my nightmare

If you ever tell me to love forever,
I will throw it in your face.
If you ever tell that I am a failure,
I will throw it in your face.
If u ever tell me I am a struggle,
I will throw it in your face.
If you ever want me to be your little girl,
Just remember the news I heard at fifteen.

Rebecca Norman (Age 15)

My Favourite Possession

My favourite object, a strange sight to see
Is a red rocket lava lamp, belonging to me,
I watch it when bored and see it bounce,
A blob nearly touches, so gets ready to pounce.
They all join up in one huge bubble
Then crash at the top causing chaos and trouble.

Harry Nelson (Age 10)

An Acorn To An Oak

An acorn is such a tiny thing,
To become an oak is such an amazing feat.
Roots spread out like a network of spies, exploring, investigating.
As owls advise and squirrels jest around his feet,
He grows.

Like a prince, he rises in power, unaware of doomed existence
His holes become cottages, an estate for his court.
They serve, and will serve him well.
And as he carries on with great persistence,
He grows.

A majestic old king, a monarch of the woods.
Early morning mist like a fur-lined cloak;
Gnarled branches, like arms., whose fingers
Turn from green to brown, become bare.
As they wait for spring he appears dead, yet still
He grows.

His age begins to show, once there were fifty in a row,
Now he stands alone.
As the chainsaw bites in, ripping his flesh,
The city grows.

Mark Newman (Age 15)

Our School

Our school is full of stuff,
Including our hamster called Fluff,
He sleeps all day, and is awake all night,
And he would give any burglars a very big fright!

We have lot's of books and lot's of toys,
In our school we have lots of boys,
Many girls, quite a few teachers,
Lots of classrooms, lots of features.

Our class is the art room,
The cleaner comes with her broom
She doesn't like us that much
Because of the mess in Fluffs hutch!

Daniel Noy (Age 13)

Food

I like rosy, juicy apples.
I like soft fish.
I like fat squishy peas.
I like tomatoes and cheese pizza.
I like juicy tangerines.
But I don't like egg sandwiches,
Because they are smelly!

Louise Norton (Age 7)

Winning

If I won £50...

I'd make my friends sad and gloat,
When I show them the fifty pound note.

I would be filled with glee,
I wouldn't spend it all on me.
I'd spend some,
On my mum.
Depends how much I had,
I'd spend a little on my dad.
I would give some to my brother Paul,
But he doesn't deserve anything at all.
I am so kind, people would say,
But I'd end up giving it all away.
Then again, I might change my mind,
And maybe I wouldn't be so kind.
With all the things I'd have to pay,
Perhaps I won't give it away.

I may be sad and all alone,
At least I'd have a new mobile phone.
You all thought I was so nice,
Guess I lied once or twice.

Stacey Newman (Age 13)

Untitled

When Fred went to bed,
On a cold stormy night,

His curtains fell down,
And gave him a fright.

He yelled to his mum,
There's a ghost in my room,

Come up here now,
And bring a broom.

She hurried upstairs
After hearing his cries,

She went into his room,
And to her surprise,

Fred was not there
He could not be found,

He was under his covers,
Safe and sound.

Jimmy Neal (Age 12)

A Busy-Buzzer

A busy-buzzer,
A happy-hummer,
A colourful-creature,
A nectar-nicker,
A flower follower,
A tulip toucher,
A pollen picker,
A silent stinger.

Katie Nash (Age 11)

Sport

The enthusiastic player
Achieved so much so far
Succeeded in scoring two goals
The score is two nil
Competing in the game,
He's proud to wear the kit
The venue is superb
The final whistle's blown
Arsenal are the champions
The exhausting match is over
Arsene Wenger's gaping
Other players are hugging
They'd beaten Man-Utd!!!
The United players are crying
Sir Alex looked stunned
Arsenal broke the record.

Paul Nagle (Age 11)

Feelings Within Thoughts

The sun shone on the scorching golden sand
A piece of clear glass caught it's gaze
A beam of light flashed and hit the sea
The clear ice cold bottomless sea, breathed.
It caressed the brim of the sand
And frothed with envy as finger touched finger
A footprint lay cemented on the deserted island
No one had been there for so long
The lonesome trees smiled like a child's face at christmas
As a rainbow coloured Toucan rested it's drained body on the trusty branches
The clouds danced across the sky beating like an aroused heart
A snake slithered out from it's heaven hole and brushed it's head against a leaf.
A noise was heard in the distance, a murmur of life existence
A fresh wind like a blink of a tired eye
Awoke what seemed to be a lifeless sixth sense
The sun intensified and the sea howled like wolves
The noise in the distance grew louder and powerful
The world shook in someone's careless and misjudged hands
And then there was calm, like a click of a finger
A long slender click of a finger.

Lauren Newton (Age 13)

The Milkman

Clink, clink, clinkety clink,
The milkman's on his rounds I think,
Crunch, crunch on the milkman's feet,
Closer and closer along the street,
And then clink, clink, clinkety clink,
He's let some bottles of milk to drink.

Shafiya Najib (Age 10)

The Cat And The Rat

The cat sat on the rat,
The rat went splat!
The rat ran off to his hiding place,
The cat picked up a mace,
The rat was eating a bun,
The cat pulled out a gun.
The cat hit the rat with the mace,
Then they had a race.
The cat was in the lead,
And he made the rat bleed.
The cat pounced at the rat,
The rat was hiding under the mat.

David Nicholl (Age 10)

Winter

Winter rain is falling, drumming on the ground,
Soldiers are marching down from their castle in the clouds.

Winter wind is howling while you are tucked up in your bed,
For outside is a crying wolf who is searching for his pack.

Winter thunder is banging on the window, shouting to be let in,
Throwing a tantrum of fury at being left out in the cold.

Winter snow is falling, the earth is covered in a thick blanket of snow,
Warmer than the duvet on my bed.

Winter fires are glowing, warmth is spread around the earth,
Warming cold hands and icy feet.

Susie Newman (Age 11)

The Tiger

In the immensity of the jungle
The black striped and orange tiger lives
Silently he moves
And gives the soft sound of his padded feet
Back to the silent night
The cool wind blows,
And tree tops bend from side to side
And sway beneath the cold, grey sky.
And where the water falls,
Freezing from the forever going heavens
Then he crouches low to drink.

Sophie North (Age 11)

The Snake

There is a snake with livid eyes
Down a hole the creature lies
His long thin body is full of scales
When he moves it trails and trails

He has a pair of long sharp teeth
Just one bite and the victim will cease
And that is when he gets his dinner
And now the snake is no longer thinner.

James Nightingale (Age 9)

Tick Tick Bang

I like tick tock Bang
I can hang tick tock Bang
I can dance to tick tock Bang
I can sing to tick tock Bang
Who is tick tock Bang?

Daisy Oatham (Age 6)

Giant

Brushing my hands along the tops of dense,
Broccoli shaped trees

Slithering snakes lead to lego houses

Longing to be played with,
The sun glimmers like a golden ball

Remembering sports day as I hurdle
The snow-capped mountains

Spying for fish in the rock-pool lakes

Bleating white clouds at ground level
Scatter nervously as I pass.

Charlotte Norman (Age 10)

The Ghostly Train

Old remains of the railway
Are slushy and enclosed
The hedges and nettles are tangled
It's grassy and gravely also

Old sleepers rusty by the side
Some old leaves and cogs too
Then the slight imagination
It leaves me wondering,
The whistle of the train, then back to reality.

Simon Newe (Age 10)

The Seaside

The sand is gold,
And it feels so cold,
The waves are big,
I watch them as I dig,
I take my bucket and I take my spade,
It's so hot I have to sit in the shade,
When I first got to the seaside,
I ran straight to the slide.
It's getting dark we've got to go,
But oh no I've got sand in my toe.

Joshua Nudd (Age 8)

Dogs

D ogs can run
O n the grass
G rowling at cats and
S lobbering over a bone.

Anna O'Connor (Age 8)

A Winters Day

Naked trees blowing gently with the wind,
Snowflakes landing softly on the ground,
Steamed up windows from last night.

Rabbits curled up in their luke warm burrows,
The frogs swimming in vain breaking water,
Snow melting on your feet.

The ice glistening in the frosty sun,
The foot marks in the snow,
Layered on top of the crispy grass.

The snow melts as the day is over,
The beautiful scene melts away,
To come again next year.

Laurence Newberry (Age 9)

The Quiet Meadow

In the meadow rivers are flowing,
And mowers are mowing,
Farmers are working,
Children are smirking.

Horses leaping, people sleeping,
Cows peeking, sheep are sneaking.

Pigs are rolling around in the mud,
Then somethng goes thud,
The lambs are starting to choke,
Then there's smoke.

Horses leaping, children sleeping,
Cows peeking, sheep are sneaking.

Dogs are sad, hens are mad,
The bulls are chomping, oxes are thomping.

Horses leaping, children sleeping,
Cows peeking, sheep are sneaking.

Conan Osborne (Age 8)

Red

Red is the colour of luscious lips,
The colour of love and bloody ships,
It is the colour of death and war,
Yet happiness, joyful and the earths core,
It is the colour of a cosy, warm fire,
Red is the colour of explosion lead from a lead wire,
It is the colour of terrible danger,
Also Jesus lying in a manger,
Red is the colour of blooming red roses,
As well as winter's red, cold noses,
It is the colour of flushed red cheeks,
Like the colour of relaxing in cosy red sheets.

Marty Nardelli (Age 13)

War And Peace

War is like a T.V show, but the guns do the talking,
Peace is like a butterfly, it flutters by fast,
War is like hell, with dead men walking,
Peace is like a chocolate cake it never lasts.

Peace is like a roaring cheer,
War is like a C.D it never stops,
Peace will never stay unless it's just gun shots you want to hear,
War will never go untill every last man drops.

So, remember the war heroes remember them well,
Remember the legacy they befell,
Remember the men who made this country great,
By trying to keep it that way before its too late.

Lauren O'Neill (Age 10)

Witches Spell

Witches smell and deadman's shiver,
Werewolves heart and lizard's liver,
Deadman's eye and rabbit's tail,
Blood from a bat and leg from a whale.
Eyes from a frog and toes from a eagle,
Hair from a cat and blood from a needle.
Ears from a pig and foot from a bat,
Nails from a blackbird and wax from a cat.

Nicola Nay (Age 10)

Noise Poem

Smash went the plates
Crash went the saucepan
Stamp went my foot
SHUT went the door
Bang went the cupboard
Wallop went the pen that I broke
ERRR went my voice

Shhh went the caterpillar
Then somebody picked up all the things.

James Otieno (Age 5)

The Graveyard

Evil graveyard is a sorcerer's den,
Grey gravestones are mountains waiting to be climbed,
Deceased flowers are dead bodies waiting to be buried,
Rusty gate is a lid to a dark, damp coffin,
Dead grass is gravy spread all over the ground,
Old church is the end of life,
Rotten graveyard is the gateway to hell.

Thomas Oliver (Age 11)

Cat

I am as soft as butter,
And as cuddly as fur!

I am as bouncy as a ball,
But not very tall!

I am a big bundle of fun,
With soft, shiny, silky fur!

I am as fast as a cheetah,
So people can't catch me!

I am as swift as a Tiger,
And as amd as a Tornado,
And I hate snow!

My Name Is Max!

Megan Oldfield (Age 11)

What Makes A Good Friend

A good friend is always there.
A good friend shares everything with us: laughing and crying
A good friend is reliable.
A good friend is confident.
A good friend understands why we cry or why we laugh.
If we need help, a good friend is helpful.
If we need patience, a good friend is patient.
If we are happy, a good friend is happy.
A good friend shares chocolate into two pieces.
A good friend gives you the last piece of something.
A good friend phones you when everything is O.K.
A good friend doesn't forget you in their greatest moments
A good friend is loyal.
A good friend is a friend of your friends.
A good friend is never jealous.
A good friend is generous.
Everybody cannot have a good friend
Only a good friend can have a friend
This poem cannot be understood by everybody
It's only written for good friends.

Lara Ors (Age 13)

My Poem

The Lion is ready for another feast,
It's stalking a deer, here it goes,
Its muscles moving, its legs speeding,
Nearly there, getting closer and closer,
"GOT IT!"
The Lions finally having its feast.
The feast is over now,
But it will all happen again soon,
Very soon.

Joanne Oliver (Age 12)

Winter's Adversary

A calm breeze stirs the topmost branches of an old oak,
Causing them to swing and sway simultaneously.
Gnarled trees droop like hanged villains,
Isolated from the harsh coldness of the world.
Frozen thorns curl like venemous snakes,
Twisted and interwoven.
Flowers and shrubs drown in a perilous white ocean,
Concealed and forced under the glittery white mass.
Trapped behind a cloudy wall the sun hangs solemnly,
Useless against his merciless foe.
Starry-eyed children gaze out at the one coloured wilderness
Hypnotised by its two-faced appearence.
The whole world is still and quiet,
Like an ancient clock that has ceased ticking.
Finally the sun breaks free,
Ripping the clouds apart with the powerful rays,
And restoring the land to its former glory.

Robin Orman (Age 13)

Cats

Cats are small
Cats are tall
Cats sometimes crawl

Cats are grey
Cats are white
Cats are sometimes striped

Cats sleep in the day
Cats hunt at night
Cats sometimes fight

Cats have tails
Cats have claws
Cats love to sleep in drawers.

Charlotte Ogley (Age 7)

Who Is She?

She has a magic mind,
And a tropical climate,
She is a sly fox,
And a gleaming opal,
She is a daffodil glittering in the sun.

Her sky-blue personality lights up when
It's dark and dull,
She is a Mercedes,
Driving on the planet Saturn,
Her sunny smile makes the rain go away,
Her laugh makes the sun come out.

Lisa Newton (Age 11)

Pictures From My Mind

Pictures from my mind are about
Such horrible things as drought
Or maybe monsters under my bed
Or creepy crawlers around my head
The sound of gun shots
BANG! BANG! BANG!
Or maybe screaming people lying down.

Pictures from my mind are about
Walking around on a sandy beach
Eating ice-cream,
Mucking about with my friends
And that is the end.

Danielle Orme (Age 11)

The Wonders Of Space

While floating through the galaxy,
I can see the planet Mercury,
It seems such a mystery,
But it is my destiny.
To float and dance,
To look and prance.
While floating through the galaxy.

While floating through the galaxy,
I can see the planet Uranus.
It seems so mysterious,
But I am so curious.
To leap and bound,
To look around.
While floating through the galaxy.

Samantha Ore (Age 11)

Rob

My best friend is Rob
We have,
Two mini scooters
Two game boys
Two wicked bikes
Two game boy games
Two T-shirts
Two pairs of socks
Two P.C games
Two beds
Two squigy pillows
And one great friendship.

Michael Owens (Age 10)

School

At school, in the playground,
All the children run around.
Some play football,
Some get put against the wall.
Some play with the alphabet snake,
While some eat a chocolate flake.

Now it's time for lunch,
That's when we all munch.
Then we won't be hungry anymore,
And I found an apple core.
As I chew my food loudly,
Miss is not proudly.

Aimee O'Gorman (Age 9)

Two

Two good friends,
Make up a pair of
BEST FRIENDS!

Me and my friend
We go out and shop,
We shop till we drop!

If we ever break up
We always make up!

We are the bestest of friends!

Meg O'Reilly (Age 10)

The Storm

The wind was flashing
Leaves were wooshing
In the sky
Trees were whistling,
The door were banging
People were cooking
Trees knocking on the window
Swish swish
Go the leaves
Howling goes the wind
Through the forest.

Paige Osborne (Age 8)

Colourless

What is colourless,
Is colourless white,
Is colourless the difference
Between dark and bright?

Is colourless transparent,
A trick of the light,
If something is colourless
Is it out of our sight?

Is colourless clear,
Does colourless smell,
Does it have any taste,
Can anyone tell?

A rainbow of emptiness,
The expanse is clear,
A brightness of nothingness
The vision is sheer.

Claire Paish (Age 17)

The Desert

In the empty desert, I see,
The shimmering, glittering, golden ocean
In the burning, I feel,
Beads of perspiration, sliding down my cheek
In the dry desert, I smell,
The tantalising aroma of the restaurant, found only to be a mirage
In the blistering desert, I hear,
The whistling of the wind through the oasis
In the sweltering desert, I see,
The whirling durbish that is eternal fury of a sandstorm
In the increasingly dangerous desert, I feel,
The throbbing of my heart as I run, fleet of foot, across the barren wasteland
The desert has a mercurial temperament that I never want to witness again
THE DESERT

Michael Orvis (Age 11)

Out And About

When Dad and I are out and about
We call and wave and even shout!
To people who pass along the way
Hello, good morning a lovely day.
People often call back to us
Hi how are you.
Sometimes the days go with more
Of a swing when you say hello or good morning.

Nobody knows how the word goes.
Nobody knows how the word flows.
It takes some time to say goodbye
And that is when I wish to fly.
All my friends say don't be silly.
And all I say is wait until that day.
GOODBYE!!!

Katie Oaten (Age 9)

I Love Spring

I love spring because the sun comes out,
Blossom grows and the plants start to sprout.
I love spring because it's sunny and bright,
It's the opposite of winter where everything is white.
I love spring because birds come to me,
They sing me a song that goes tweet, tweet, twee.
I love spring, children everywhere,
Laughter, joy and happiness in the air.

Kathryn O'Gorman (Age 8)

The Countryside

As I gallop through the wood
With the daisies by my side,
I fell with a stumble and a glide
And landed beside a small oak tree.
Then a small golden key caught my eye,
I looked at it being very suprised.
Hello, Hello has anyone lost a key I cried.
My voice it echoed through the wood,
Until at last a voice replied
That must be mine I would like it back if I could.

Sure I said but where are you?
Don't worry I'm on my way
A moment later a boy appeared
With ginger hair and a small beard.
He said might I have it back please

I handed it back and walked to his cottage,
As we passed the view was pretty with hills and nature.

Morwenna O'Brien (Age 10)

The Wobbling Rainbow

Why does the sun shine so bright?
Why does daylight turn into night?
Why does a tortoise go into its shell?
Why do people ring a bell?
Why do flowers smell so nice?
Why do people eat sugar and spice?
Why does the wind blow?
Why does the sea flow?
Why do we cry?
Why do we eat pie?
Why does the wind howl?
Why do bears growl?
Why are trees so tall?
Why are mice so small?
Why does a ball bounce so high?
Why do areoplanes fly in the sky?

Yvonne Olang (Age 11)

My Big Day At The Zoo

I went for a day out at the zoo,
On Monday, Tuesday and Wednesday too
I heard a load roar, and looked around,
What did I see a tiger looking at me,
The tigers lovely, brightly, coloured
Cats, all fluffy and warm fur.
I turned again to my excitement I saw
Some monkeys, swinging too and fro,
Up and down and around they go,
Them funny Monkeys where will they go
Big Grey Elephants they seem the best
Swinging their trunks better than all the rest.

Nicole O'Brien (Age 8)

The Snow

As I sat at the window
And stared out,
One snow-drop fell-then more and more.
As I stared out of the window
Onto the countryside,
The snow danced in every direction.
As the wind blew the snow
It swirled and twirled
Then settled on the grass.
All that could be seen was white
For miles around
As though a white carpet had covered all in its way.
As I stared
It got slower and slower.
Then I stretched out my hand
And caught the last snowflake.
As it fell in the light of the sunset sun
And melted in my hands
I sat at the window
And stared and stared and stared.

Heather O'Gorman (Age 11)

301

My Uncle

Raggedly and crooked he moves,
Moving hastily towards you
With a shaking hand
Yet bent and torn
With a hungry eye,
Watching
Watching closely
With a spiteful grin
On his short fat face
Have you ever seen my Uncle?

People looking in astonishment
As he walks within metres touch.
People backing away,
They see him as the monster.
Have you ever seen my Uncle?

William Owen (Age 10)

It Was So Noisy

It was so noisy that
I couldn't hear my little sister crying out sadly
It was so noisy that
I couldn't hear the school buzzer buzzing out loudly
It was so noisy that
I couldn't hear the traffic zooming by
It was so noisy that
I couldn't hear my teacher talking happily
It was so noisy that
I couldn't hear Mrs James smashing the cymbals.

Victoria Orchard (Age 8)

Swimming

I like swimming because it's fun
The chlorine makes my eyes blurry
It's horrible when my ears pop
It's exciting when you D
I
V
E
Off the diving board.

Dan O'Brien (Age 11)

Rain

Soft gentle rain runnning off the the window panes,
Tiny sparkling drops bounce off puddles,
The world has been washed,
Spiders sit in their diamond webs,
Rain shining on the ground,
As I look up rain softly funs down my face,
Heavier and heavier it gets,
I'm walking on a diamond path.

Kelly Osborne (Age 8)

The Shadow Man

At night-time
As I climb the stair
I tell myself
There's nobody there.

But what if there is?
What if he's there-
The Shadow Man
At the top of the stair?

What if he's lurking
There in the gloom
Of the landing
Right outside my room?

The Shadow Man
Who's so hard to see
What if he's up there
Waiting for me?

At night time
As I climb the stair
I tell myself
There's nobody there.

Kerry Oderdaal (Age 10)

Mission To Mars

Gotta get ready setting off to Mars, gotta call yesterday, Big Man said "Kid you're going to Mars."
So here I am putting on the suit, Mum comes along and says, "Son, you're cute"
I climb into the rocket, whoa! look at all the dials, I go up to the driver, ask how far it is, he says about 27 miles
"What do you think you are? Mars aint that near, your barmy, your nutty, we're not going to the pier"
"Kid calm down, now climb into the back, I need to set our course, so we go along the track."
10...9...8...7...6 "Hold the countdown we gotta change course so we go down town"
We're off at last, I'm not floating yet, either we're not out of orbit or this aint real, I bet.
Wahoo I'm floating, just went past the moon, we're going very fast so we're going to be there soon
Thump! I'm on the floor, through the door comes the driver "Kid this aint real," I'm dreaming for sure
"You're on T.V for the Mars Bar advert, now when you step out please don't divert"
I hold the Mars Bar out, I'm famous, I'm a star who's waking me there's no-one there, all there is is the rocket car.
"Wake up, wake up, stop dreaming please, you're late for school again, *WAKE UP!!*"
Shame it was a dream I really thought it was real, how real it did seem.

Craig O'Callaghan (Age 9)

Underneath The Silence

Underneath the silence I can hear...
The angry sobs of a farmer as his greatest possessions waste away,
The whistling of the whirlwind as it makes each house a pile of rubble,
The heavy breathing of an Asian individual as he runs desperately away
From a crowd of racist hooligans,
The screeches of a pain-inflicted fox as the hunter reloads and fires
Another speeding bullet into his back,
The crackling and roaring as the firework takes flight,
The cries of despair as the childs mother sits close by to her injured child.
Underneath the silence I can feel...
The beating of my heart while I stand frozen to the spot,
The perforated ship rocking from side to side, a mind of its own,
The heat of the flames burning my face,
Panic rushing through my body, cold shivers going down my spine,
The raging rain ricocheting off the car windows.

Simon Osborne (Age 11)

Blue Is...

Blue is a tremendous blue that's splashing with fright.
Blue is a very cold day.
Blue is a person all miserable.
Blue is scrumptious blueberries.
Blue is the sea lapping against the shore.
Blue is just blue.

Harvey Owen (Age 7)

I Can't Be Bothered

The trouble with me is that I can't be bothered to think,
I can't be bothered, I can't be bothered and I can't be bothered to think
Why, why, why, why
Why do I have to think?

Alison Oram (Age 11)

Sports Thoughts

Foootball you need a ball,
Be careful you don't fall.

Tennis you need a bat,
Don't play if you're very fat.

Cricket you need pads,
And be friendly to all the lads.

Rugby you must be fast,
Get the ball and don't be last.

In netball you need a post,
To win the game just sore the most.

Get the gloves on
And punch till they have gone.

Ice hockey you need a puck,
It might give you good luck.

Keep the arms going
And it will keep you flowing.

Keep those legs at the same pace
Then you might win the race.

Rhianne Parsons (Age 11)

Fire

F ighting
I n a
R oom . . .
E scaped!

Richard Pearce (Age 11)

Trumping Terrapins

Once I had a little monkey but he became very chunky
After eating bacon from a peaceful plump pig
My very hairy cat was squashed by a big fat rat
Then got eaten by a ballistic boney budgie
I have a very silly turtle that sometimes turns purple
But turned green with envy when it saw my famous friendly fish
Some stupidly ignorant iguanas like to eat green bananas
And so does my terrible trumping terrapin

Jonathan Oliver (Age 11)

A Garden Poem

In the morning I look at the grass and everything is dripping wet.
The petals curled, the steam bent, the worms wriggling, the birds chirping.
The cockerel sings it's daily song, the misty mist on the grass like a jungle of the past.

James Owen (Age 10)

Smile!

A smile,
A warm red smile,
Is all it takes, to make the sun come out
From behind the dull clouds,
Those clouds of grey.

A smile,
A warm red smile,
Is all it takes,
To make everyone happy
To make everybody's day.

A smile,
A warm red smile,
Is all it takes,
To dry those tears away.

A smile,
A warm red smile,
Is all it takes,
To make everybody happy
Everybody gay.

Vicki Pashley (Age 10)

Night

In the night the sun goes down,
The moon comes up, the stars are about,
I hear the owls hooting in the sky,
While the lions are lying by,
I hear the naked trees moving in the breeze,
While I look out of the window I see the view of the trees.

Lucie Oaten (Age 9)

What Am I . . .

I'm the leaping leopard
Jumping from tree to tree.
I'm the wet rain cloud
That pours down to the earth.
I'm the waving grasses
Swaying in the wind.
I'm the tasty carrot
Lying in the ground.
I am baby blue
Sitting on the wall.
I'm the fresh cool water
Sparkling in the glass.
I am the soft sand
On the sun struck beach.
I'm the leafy plant lying in soil.
I'm the talkative parrot
Nattering on my perch.

Caitlin Parker (Age 10)

Wood-Louse

When you see me crawl through your home,
Don't throw me out I just like to roam,
I'm only a little wood-louse.

When I'm in the kitchen, nibbling on some food,
I don't mean to be unhealthy or to intrude,
I'm only a little wood-louse.

In the garden when your feet thunders about
You make me scared when you scream and shout,
I'm only a little wood-louse.

I'm always frightened, scared of you,
Please don't poke me or prod me with your shoe,
I'm only a little wood-louse.

All I want is a warm cosy home.
Made of fluff, wool, cotton or foam.
As I'm only a little wood-louse.

Rebecca Pike (Age 11)

The Weird Guy

He was mad, he was a dad
He was crazy and very lazy
He was weird, he had a beard
He was funny, he had money
He was cool, he fell in the pool
He was hot, he had a pot
He was good, he had a hood
He was alive, he was forty five
He was a man, his name was Stan

Jonathan Pardoe (Age 10)

Science Inspection

Let's take a look at Science
Einstein and photons
Forces and motions
Fission and fusion
Gravity oh! and evolution, what a confusion
Science, Science
Modern illusions
Light
Heat
Water
Air
Gases
All unearthed by some famous people
Flanklin
Fleming
Newton
Darwin and of course Louis Pasteur
And this is my visit of science.

Matthew Peel (Age 10)

Ten Dancing Dogs

Ten dancing dogs working in a mine
One bumped his head, then there nine.

Nine dancing dogs, one had a mate
One went off, then there eight.

Eight dancing dogs going to heaven
One fell down, then there were seven.

Seven dancing dogs eating weetabix
One ate too much, then there were six.

Six dancing dogs, dancing live
One fell off stage, then there were five.

Five dancing dogs asking for more
One went off, then there were four.

Four dancing dogs up a tree
One fell out then there were three.

Three dancing dogs, one went to the loo
One got stuck then there were two.

Two dancing dogs eating jam buns,
One fell asleep, then there was one.

One dancing dog having fun,
It ran off then there were none.

Lisa Price (Age 9)

Colours

Orange is a juicy satsuma sitting in a fruit bowl.
Or the sun setting in the sky, or a tasty pointed carrot.
Or a Halloween pumpkin glowing at midnight.

Blue is the waves swaying in the sea.
Or ink pouring out of a pen or the sky on a sunny day,
Or a dolphin in the big ocean.

Red is a balloon floating in the sky.
Or a ladybird flying through the air.
Or blood streams running through your body,
Or red ink flowing out of a pen.

Silver is tinsel of a Christmas tree
Or a disco ball on your ceiling on your birthday.
Or silver glittery new shoes.
Or big diamond earrings in your ears.

Yellow is sand lying on a beach.
Or yellow paint waiting to be used.
Or a big yellow jumper waiting to be worn.
Or a daffodil in your garden in the Spring.

Green is the grass in the forest
Or a colour of the rainbow, or a bunch of grapes
Or green wrapped sweets that we eat

Kelsey Playford (Age 9)

Sea

Pea green, sparkly blue are some of the sea's colours.
Fish are some of the fascinating creatures which inhabit it.
Islands are like spots compared to the sea's gaping mouth.
Boats large and small cover the sea like birds.
Divers explore small, uninhabited crevices to try and find more.

Jonathan Pierce (Age 10)

Flowers

F lowers have got pollen inside
L ovely beautiful and elegant flowers stand tall.
O nly the best of all.
W hen it is night it closes up.
E ven when it is morning it opens up.
R oses are very prickly and elegant.
S o flowers are the best thing of all.

Sally Paine (Age 7)

Interesting Water

The water is so calm and peaceful,
Reflecting everything around it.
It makes me very sleepful,
The pond is so wonderfully lit.

It is very gooey below,
Are there any hippos sleeping?
Now I'm going to follow,
The vegetation weaving.

Can I see frogs leaping,
From lily pad to lily pad?
There is a shadow in the clearing,
Which was in a dream I had.

Talfryn Provis-Evans (Age 10)

Dad, Being Far Away

You love him,
But he lives far away,
You are unable to see him every day,
But every moment spare he is constantly in your thoughts,
And he knows he is loved and thought of all the time,
Never forget being apart means always in your heart,
Even if you can't see him, there's a picture in your mind of your dad all the time,
And that he is loved,
So never forget just because you're out of sight, you are not out of mind,
The love a daughter has for her dad is forever,
Never forget this 'Dad'.

Claire McCarthy (Age 16)

In My Box

Into my box I will put,
A freshly grown daffodil from springtime,
A blade of grass from a summer's day,
A leaf just fallen on an autumn's evening,
And a piece of crystal like ice that will never melt.

Into my box I will put,
My wristband from when I was born,
My first pair of glasses,
My small blue diary,
And my grandmother's engagement ring.

Into my box I will put,
A photo of me on my first birthday,
My first ever toy,
My first tooth, that fell out,
And my first present given to me.

My grandfather made my box,
He made it from fine oak wood,
He engraved our family tree on the lid,
On the inside of the lid it said "To a special granddaughter".

Carolyne Palmer (Age 13)

Me And My Horse

I love to work with horses
I have one of my own
I ride as often as I can
Whenever I'm at home

They are so strong and gentle
I love, mine very much
My sister helps me all the time
To bed and feed and such.

My horses name is lady
She's such a soppy thing
She likes being cuddled all the time
As I ride her round the ring

And as I take her out each week
To gallop round the fields
She more than pays for what she costs
With the happiness she yields

Anne-Marie Palfrey (Age 12)

Nature's Army

The silent sea sleeps as the fishermen plough their way through
BOOM! Everything awakens and the sea is frustrated
The once light blue sky turns to ebony and is as dark as a Winter's night
Whirl winds twist and twirl and curl and whirl

WHOOSH! the waves are getting angry
The sea now becomes more like an army
CRASH! BANG! SMASH! THUD! SLASH! GUSH! CLASH!
The small frigate is under heavy fire from the attack

The pendulum is swinging and the momentum is building
They go in for one last pelting, exploding attack
It's going to be mean, cruel and full face!
The attack is aborted and the army has fled

Bhavish Patel (Age 12)

Love Sonnet

Thy fiery eyes, beautiful but so firm
Thou so sweet, but still thou art aggressive
A face so lovely but always so stern
It is thy love that makes me want to live
Thou art so sweet and tender as a rose
Though thorns surround thee and keep me at bay
I am the artist, the poet who knows
Thy love is what keeps me alive each day -
Never crying, always denying
That thou hast done nothing worthy of thee
But what hast thou done? You lie there crying
Why hast thou come back? Thou came back to me
And we shall grow old, always together
Thus hand in hand our love dying never

Kyle Payne (Age 13)

Animals

Some animals are fluffy and very friendly,
They like to play but very mentally.

Some are tall, some are short,
But not really the tall sort.

Some are thin, some are fat,
Like mice are not as fat as cats.

There are lots of different types of animals,
But like parrots they make funny calls.

I love animals and I hope you do,
Like animals love us, so we do too.

Sophie Packer (Age 12)

Putting It Away

Freddy was a greedy boy
Who like to eat all day
His friends were all amazed
At the amount he put away.

His favourite was egg and chips
With pickles, sauce and peas
Followed by a bag of crisps
And cake and fruit and cheese.

He always had a store of snacks
In school bag hidden deep
At night time there was no escape
He dreamed food in his sleep

Though he always ate and ate
He never got much fatter
Not even eating ice cream, cake
And Mars bars fried in batter.

One day he fell down on the floor
As dead as dead could be
A growing worm inside his guts
Had ate his food you see.

Stephen Potter (Age 13)

Stray dog

The dog is a very peckish little thing,
It never will stop to play,
Nibbling the bits thrown away,
Raw or cooked,
He does not mind,
He eats everything he finds.

Fred Powell (Age 8)

My View On Life.

Endless brawling,
Fighting and mauling,
The tempest is calling,
To get me on my way.

It is now raining,
The sun is still waning,
With no thought of gaining,
So why am I here today?

Those who brought me,
Shopped and caught me,
Bullied and fought me,
They will have to pay.

So now when I try,
I don't have to lie,
You know I'll get by,
And you'll do what I say.

Stuart Powell (Age 16)

Always Be There

You'll always be with me,
Never fading, never ceasing to be,
Doing nothing, yet everything, at once,
My confidence, strength and courage.

The fire burning within me,
The inner peace when anger ravages my being.
The cool and hot, the night and day,
Always there, doing nothing, yet everything.

Never leaving me,
The calm, the anger,
The storm, the summer's breeze,
Everything, yet nothing.

In waking, or sleeping, you're with me.
There for me when I need you,
Taking a back seat when decisions must be my own,
Allowing me the space I need, whilst always being there.

You'll always be with me,
The fire within,
In waking, or sleeping, you're there.

Harriet Pinel (Age15)

My Poem

Once long ago on a very dark night
Darkness sneezed and knocked over light
The sun began falling head over heels
And slowly unwound as an orange peels.
The moon stared in horror, her silvery eyes
Lifted their lids up and swallowed the skies.
The king of the teapots was singing again
Of goodwill to God and peace to all men.
The mountains exploded and crumbled to dust,
The moons tears corroded away the Earth's crust.
The light struggled up and as one well may
He picked up the darkness and threw him away.

Rosa Petherick (Age 15)

The Car

The car is a lovely red
It gleams as it goes past my house.
On hot days it goes past
With the roof down and I wish
I was in the car with the
Wind blowing through my hair
Going down country lanes
With everyone looking at
My lovely red car
It goes really fast
And the trees must look like a blur
As it speeds down the country lanes
And I wish I owned that red car

Mark Pretty (Age 12)

Me And My Shadow

One hot afternoon in summer
As I was drinking tea
I saw a shadow stare at mum
And then he looked at me

He glared at me then smiled
I did not trust that grin
I tried to run away from him
But I just could not win

I ran around the garden
And then climbed up a tree
I breathed a sigh of relief
For him I could not see

I waited for five minutes
Then jumped onto the ground
Using the oak as a shield
I looked all around

Where has my shadow got to?
Oh where could be he?
I walked into the sunlight
And he was following me!

Alastair Prince (Age 10)

The Beautiful Garden

The daffodils, the roses,
The trees, the posies.

In a beautiful garden.

Worms wriggling give them a chance,
Bugs do their dance.

In a beautiful garden.

Squirrels climbing trees,
What a nice thing to see.

In a beautiful garden.

Bees buzzing, birds tweeting
Shhh! Moles are eating.

In a beautiful garden!!

Joseph Potter (Age 7)

Monkey Man

I am a monkey man
Who found a banana

I am a monkey man
Who found a banana
Who ate it in jamas

I am a monkey man
Who found a banana
Who ate in jamas
Who lives in a tree

I am a monkey man
Who found a banana
Who ate in jamas
Who lives in a tree
Who doesn't like peas

I am a monkey man
Who found a banana
Who ate in jamas
Who lives in a tree
Who doesn't like peas
That sleeps on a branch.

Jake Potter (Age 10)

Craziness

Craziness is lots of bright colors together because it would look weird.
Craziness smells like a cacophony of rainbows.
Craziness tastes like a mixture of sweet juicy foods.
Craziness sounds like a partying noise where everyone is wild.
Craziness feels tingly and jumpy because it would feel ridiculous.
Craziness lives at a party or at an excited place.

Sarah Preece (Age 10)

Yellow Digger

I have got a yellow digger
I play with it every day.

Tom Pearce (Age 13)

Space Rocket

Is it true that in space no one can hear you scream, Or laugh or cry or shout or sigh as that is how it may seem
Me and my friends one day wanted to prove this fact, We thought we'd send poor Billy up that murky tract

We thought we'd make an aircraft, a beautiful shining thing, With a cardboard box, an elastic band and a cereal packet wing
We opened the door, pushed Billy inside, he began to cry, That was good we needed the noise to hear up in the sky

We pushed him in the fireplace, crunching new burnt logs, I changed into my launching suit my favourite sunday togs
We checked the airborne thrusters made sure they're working fine, Four washing up bottles should be enough, Bill's only three foot nine

We walked back a few spaces and hid behind the chair, I didn't want to burn my clothes or singe my curly hair
We started up the countdown, ten, nine, eight, seven, six, And then lit up the fuse, three burnt out candle wicks

Fumbling with the matches we got to number five, And then we heard a car crunch up the gravel drive
Footsteps started marching towards the patio door, We pulled Bill out the rocket and left him on the floor

We thrust the box into the stores the rest into the bin, And stood beside the doorway wearing a saintly grin!

James Pennington (Age 13)

Peace Poem

Today, I had this blade of grass
The only one no but my one
Today I will lose my childhood a baby no more
Going into the big world
Today I will have the world.

Tomorrow the balloon will settle all the wars
The dove will take the diseases away
The dolphin will bring water to those who need it
And it will be the best day ever.

And yesterday? yesterday
I had the moon on a stick shining at me
Yesterday I saw my moon
Say goodbye as the sun sailed over it
Yesterday I saw the cat give birth and the kittens cry out for their mum.

Ben Parker (Age 11)

What Nonsense

I'm sorry Miss I'm late but aliens invaded,
And took away the school bus so I had to walk.
And the teacher said "What nonsense".

I'm sorry Miss I'm late but a crocodile took my school bag,
I tried to take it back but it ended up as tug of war
I won of course!
And the teacher said "What nonsense".

I'm sorry Miss I'm late but an 'orrible monster
Was in my road and it tried to eat me
We chased and chased until I hid behind a tree
And teacher said "Help"
"A giant gorilla is trying to kiss me!"
And I said "What nonsense".

Becky Quinton (Age 10)

A Puppy

It is a puppy that is a fury fluffy ball, bouncing around the house.

It is a puppy eating in the house, a puppy went out to chase a bird.

It is a puppy having a drink outside, in the sunshine enjoying very much.

It is a puppy that is enjoying it very much out in the dark.

Hannah Pomfret (Age 8)

The Sea

The sea is a light blue, green jungle demolishing the earth bit by bit.

It is an animal running from its enemy, bashing the earth, disturbing the animals in the jungle.

It is the rushing wind, blowing at the trees, demolishing the earth.

Rebecca Pomfret (Age 10)

Gone

Hush the baby's cries,
Cease the children's laughter.
Prevent the waves from breaking on to the shore,
And bring him back to me.

Stop the wind rustling in the trees,
Hold the rain from falling onto the grass.
Block the sun shining over the desert,
And let me hold him again.

But never will I touch his face,
Or hold his hand.
Never will I hear his laugh,
Or whisper in his ear.

He is gone,
And he has taken my happiness.

Kate Monaghan (Age 17)

Everglades

Earth owns nothing more beautiful.
Life would be dull without it.
The silent lapping of the swampy water rings in your ears.
At dawn animals stir from their night hibernation
The marsh land eventually gives way to the exotic trees,
With egret chicks silent,
Daring not to break the folding silence.

Adam Portsmouth (Age 11)

What Are Materials?

Plastic cars whizz around on the ground,
Metal rails on the wall, and the hall.
Wooden chairs around the table and inside
The stable, and my woollen vest is the best.
SO NOW I KNOW WHAT MATERIALS ARE.

Robert Price (Age 7)

Run Sun

I like the *SUN*
Because I *RUN*
Under the *SUN*
I like to *RUN*
Ooohh *SUN*
Fun to *RUN*
RUN SUN RUN SUN RUN

Alexandra Preedy (Age 8)

My Dream World

In my dream world I would see
A tree that was made out of bumble bees
And next of all there would be
A place where everything is free
Then there would be a chocolate tree
That was put there for you and me.

Although it was Monday everyone was out to play
Hip hip hip hip hip hip hooray
There is no school for all the day.

Suddenly I saw skittles falling from a tree
I got a bowl and filled it up
Then started to eat the whole lot up
Then my dream would start to fade,
Maybe I'll come back another day.

Lindsey Pearce (Age 11)

War

Hear the gunfire
Hear the people dying
Hear the families crying

Doom, death, destruction
War can destroy families

Water turns to blood
War is not good

I wish everyone would get on

Then there would only be one...war!

Steven Powell (Age 12)

South Coast

The raging storm
Beats down on the water
As the water starts to turn
The great white horses run up the beach
And collapse as they hit the wall.

As the storm dies down
The white horses start to disappear
And in the distance the orange sun
Settles down, tucked behind the sea

Everything is calm now
The moon shines it's rays
On the surface of the shimmering water
Like a lamp on foil trays

As the sun starts to rise again
It's like the world is changing
From the morning to night
And back again.

Hannah Page (Age 13)

Red Is...

Red is the passion of warmth and care
Red is the auburn strand of hair
Red is the sunshine waiting to break
Red is the icing on your cake
Red is the rose just burst into bloom
Red is the wine drunk freely at noon.

Red is the blood that flows within you
Red is the pain and suffering too
Red is the danger sign saying *STOP*
Red is the light that sits on top
Red is the fire that shows no remorse
Red is the wound left after its course.

Red is the love we sometimes miss.
Its expression shown by a simple kiss.

Red is evil, murder and death.
Red could...just be...your last...breath.

Nicol Phillips (Age 12)

Football

I like football,
Because I score hat-tricks
I hit the ball really! really! really! hard
And it goes in the back of the net.
And the goalkeeper has to pick the ball out of the net
I like football!
I like football!

Matthew Powell (Age 14)

The Knock At The Door

Knock knock at the door,
Who was it,
I wasn't sure,
It was late at night,
I had a terrible fright,
I started waking, but I was shaking,
My mum got up to see who it was,
But my dad held her back because,
It could be some boys,
Making some noise,
The knocks were dying down,
So I started to frown,
Morning was near and I could hear,
The whistling of the birds that were near.
I woke up with a thud and went outside with my
Mum and Dad and saw *BLOOD!*
It happened to be an old lady who had fell,
Who made a yell,
Who cut her wrist,
And made a hiss.

Kayleigh Patterson (Age 12)

Autumn

Autumn's the time weather is sad
Crisp air turns to a screaming wind
Picks up golden leaves swooping like they are mad
Which come from an oak tree withered within.

Delicate animals ready for hibernation
Dinky mice scurrying gives me thrills of exhilaration,
Haunting halloween not far away,
Bang, pop, whizz go the fireworks in a momentous display.

Wrap up warm in snuggling clothes,
Hats, scarves, gloves made from a woolly sheep
Beside a blazing fire warming your toes
Calm and relaxing go straight to sleep.

Glistening dew on overgrown grass,
Dreaded schools already started don't be late for class
Fiery colours-brown, yellow and red
Once beautiful flowers now feeble and dead.

Andrea Poole (Age 12)

Friends

Friends will be there for you,
Whenever you need them,
They will give up their time to comfort you,
They will give you any advice you need,
They'll be there whenever you need a hug,
Everyday if needs be,
They wouldn't miss your birthday,
Or talk behind your back,
True friends you can rely on,
Like the sunshine in the sky,
Jokes to share, secrets to keep,
A friendly smile, a gentle hug,
Laughs and giggles galore,
All these are found in friends,
Friends are like jewels,
So precious, to cherish and to keep.

Sarah Purtill (Age 11)

Prisons For Children

Schools are prisons for children,
Schools are nightmares that haunt you,
Schools are ant hills with millions of ants inside,
Schools are waiting rooms where you sit all day,
Schools are torture chambers where you dread to go,
Schools are camps where they line you all up,
Schools are cages where you waste your life,
Schools are bedrooms where you're sent when naughty,
Schools are demons that whip and sting you.

Stuart Prescott (Age 12)

Dolphins

In the water moving fast
Under the surface, what could it be?
A school of Dolphins
Swim through the sea.

Swimming together, side by side
Racing each other as they glide
Gracefully cutting through the sea
A wonderful sight for you and me.

Eyes coloured black and skin silvery grey
They seem to smile as they play
A fin on their back and a long snout
Changing direction as they flit about

Sticking together through thick and thin
Catching fish as they swim
These beautiful creatures a sight to see
Swimming with them I'd like to be.

Victoria Plummer (Age 11)

In The Shadows

I was in my bed,
Snuggled up tight,
With scary thoughts,
In my head.

I was like a jack-in-a-box,
Getting up and down,
With shadows sweeping past my window,
Like an owl catching its pray.

One shadow was scream,
The other was like a massive dragon,
In the shadows,
Snuggled up tight.

Natalie Phillips (Age 12)

The Dying Town

Cold bows the wind through the town hall Square.
Laying the town dwellers' spirit bare.
Stone-hearted tyrants digging to power.
Watch the decaying town from a tower.
Boarded-up buildings, bloodless and bleak.
Loveless liaisons, wasting and weak.
Voices of violence, wordings of war.
Tidings of terror, too many and more
This is the future, this is to come.
Soon they will marry ghetto and slum.
Don't look away, you must understand.
This town is dying and with it the land.

Lee Pownall (Age 12)

A Better World?

Looking back I recall how my life used to be.
Graceful, gigantic rivers gushed ardently in my soul.
Leaves, like frantic fireflies skipped radiantly on the breeze.

Birds, foxes, rabbits and sheep, I sheltered them from the enraged elements.
I stood alone, strong and supportive, like a swan guarding its young.
I was a director of nature, putting on an act I thought could last forever.

From my perch like an owl I kept vigilant,
Contemplating the vast adjustments materializing within my body.
Colossal, coal-burning chimneys covered the skyline,
Producing a snake of smoke, slithering predominantly into the atmosphere.
Bulldozers like bears, ruthless and reckless ripped the hairs from my chest.
I am being engulfed by a thunderous silence of modern activity.

The sun was my mother, warming and nurturing me with her luminous rays
Mighty, majestic and now, mournful
As it witnesses me turn from glory to misery and from birth to death,
At the hands of men, merely visiting strangers to this world.

I am only a mere skeleton of what I used to be,
My stage is destroyed, my actors and musicians departed.
Never more will they perform.
So I ask you, what is there left for the children of today?

Sarah Petchey (Age 15)

The TXT Generation

What u up 2 l8r?
Do u fancy going out?
Da parT will b jumpin,
Just give me da shout!

What u say ur busy!
How can that b rite?
When I saw u earlier u said:
"I'm home all nite."

Gr8! I'll meet u by da river!
Da 'rents will never know.
Don't worry, it'll b worth it,
Cmon u've gotta go!

Sorry bout da parT,
It wasn't so great afterall,
But how was I supposed 2 know
There'd b a drunken brawl!

Sian Purath (Age 16)

Untitled

He had to get away,
He hadn't listened because she hadn't heard,
Now the dark roads were deserted,
As he sped through the night,
Replaying the row.
Glanced at the clock.
His wife would be worried, the baby awake,
Was it time to go home, accept his mistake?

She slammed the front door,
She hadn't tried to understand because she felt misunderstood.
The streets were flooded with silence,
As she hurried down the lonely roads,
Considering the confrontation.
Brushed off a tear.
Her parents would be wondering where she'd gone,
Was it time to go back, admit she was wrong?

A piercing scream,
A sickening smash,
A hollow thud,
A blinding white flash.

Rachel Oldman (Age 15)

Alliteration

As I hosed the horrendously huge horse
And unmatted it's magnificently mangled mane,
As I combed his copper coloured coat, course
And thick to touch, terrible to tame,
I remembered riding Robin come rain or shine,
A gentle giant galloping gladly on the grass,
Now he neighs and nods, he's nearly forty-nine,
His pretty, prancing, pacy days are past.

Georgina Poulter (Age 10)

Things I Like

I like fast cars
I like eating chocolate bars
I like lots of toys
I like playing football with the boys
I like playing on the computer
I like beeping the car hooter
I like Arsenal Football Club
I like going to the pub
I like riding my bike
I like my dad's friend Mike
I like a hot day
I like going out to play
I like shooting pool and most things as a rule
But there's one thing I don't like -
I DON'T LIKE SCHOOL!!!!!

Joshua Price (Age 9)

What Happens If . . .

Ask me no questions, I'll tell you no lies,
Now go and play on your game, the star-ship enterprise!

But . . .

What happens if the world ends next week?
What happens if Daddy turns into a monster freak?

Child, child I do not know, now leave and lie low!

What happens if the sun suddenly died?
What happens if the teachers have all lied?

Child, child leave me be, run along and play now . . . down by the sea!

What happens if the gravity all stopped?
What happens if the seas all dropped?

Child, child you're making me mad, you'll have to stop being so bad!

What happens if there's no more rain?
What happens if there's no more food again?

Child, child we'd all die, now look you're making me cry!

What happens if a lion eats me?
What happens if it's a tiger's time for tea?

Child, child go and play, anything just GO AWAY!!!

Gracie Pease (Age 11)

Riddle

It can be any shape,
You can see it with a naked eye,
It is weightless,
When you put it in a barrel,
The barrel becomes lighter,
So, what is it?

Aakash Patel (Age 11)

I Need My Mum

Mum is always there
Mum is always here,
I need my mum.

If I shout "Help" mum would hear,
When I was scared mum was there
I need my mum.

When mum is going out and I am ill,
She wouldn't go she would look after me
Mum is there.
Mum loves me and I lover her.

Rebecca Page (Age 10)

The Recipe Rap

Recipes are cool,
Here's one for a classroom,
At school.

Take 15 desks,
And thirty chairs,
Find your place,
But don't get stares.

In the corner a bookshelf oh so fine,
For you to read books,
And exercise your mind.

Visually a white-board,
Equipped with rubber and pen,
Teachers write instructions down,
Not to help get detention again.

Sorry kids,
It has to be done,
A teacher,
Is essential at school,
They can be dragons,
But mine's cool!

Natalie Pluck (Age 10)

Aztec

The Aztecs are brave
They fight like soldiers
And they fight like evil
They lived along time ago
They wore armour to protect themselves.
Who ever is bad they cut off their heads.
Then they put them in the skull rack

James Parritt (Age 8)

Magical Creepers

Silent, tiptoeing through the woods
Magical creepers are, as they should
Pine trees rustle as the red squirrel glides over
Foxgloves tinkle as the weasel scurries by
Ants march purposely to their kingdom
A deer is munching the mellow grass as the new day breaks
A magpie is swooping low trying to catch its prey
Red and white toadstools shading a miniature shrew
A great oak waving to the sky above
The badger snuffles around for worms and slugs
The sly fox CREEPING, CREEPING. . .

Tamsyn Pack (Age 10)

My Great Gran

My Great Gran she couldn't eat
And she couldn't sleep.
My Great Gran she couldn't walk
And she couldn't talk.

I was so sad when she couldn't eat
And couldn't sleep.
I felt so bad when she couldn't walk
And couldn't talk.

My Great Gran is better now
She can eat again,
And sleep again,
She can walk again,
And talk again,
Now she is up in heaven.

I'm so happy my Gran can live a nice life again.

With God right by her side.
I hope she lives a peaceful ride,
Up in heaven,
With God right by her side.

Imogen Plumridge (Age 10)

Spring

Spring is here it is good
Sunshine is bright
Trees are coming alive
Buds are working their way out
Chicks are running all around
Listen closely not a sound
Tulips are dancing in the breeze
Blue bells are sparkling
Green grass is growing
I am so happy spring is here.

Sophie Plumridge (Age 7)

Playground

Out in the playground
we have lots of fun.
Eating our snacks
maybe crisps, apples or a bun.

We play lots of games
such as tag and football.
Skipping and running
oh, mind you don't fall!

When the bell is ringing
playtime is over.
It's back to our desks
where we sit and wonder.

Craig Powell (Age 9)

The Lion And The Mouse

There was once a lion who was mighty,
But sadly his trousers were tighty,
He was the jungle king,
Better than anything,
And he gave most mice a frighty.

One Sunday when he was stalking,
He heard some animals talking,
He said, "You gave me such a fright, you're not nice,
But you are only little mice,"
And then he carried on walking...

Suddenly in a bundle of hay,
Some men were going to get a lion in a bad way,
The mouse saw him in fright,
So he saved him and the lion said in delight,
"You just saved my day!"

They were best friends forever,
And ever, and ever, and ever,
And ever, and ever, and ever,
Oh, did I say that they were friends forever?

Benjamin Porter (Age 10)

Cats

Creeping, crawling everywhere
Different colours, different hair
Black, grey, white, and ginger
Different shapes and different sizes
Big eyes and round faces
Silent steps and fast paces
Inside basements, boxes, carts
They live places you've never been
Cats do things you can't believe

Astrid Victoria Pruitt (Age 9)

Thoughts About Heaven

What will it be like in Heaven?
Will it be anything like Devon?
Where will you live? What will you do?
Is Heaven the place for you?

Angels with halos flying around,
Their feet never seeming to touch the ground.
People never starve; children never die,
In heaven there's no reason to cry.

There are no wars; there is no pain,
In Heaven, do they ever get rain?
The sun and the stars give off a lot of light,
And all those halos shine very bright.

Akis Plaskasovitis (Age 8)

A Day At The Seaside

People go to the seaside for a day in the sun,
The children splash in the sea and build sand castles for fun,
The sand is so hot it burns your bare feet,
The ice-creams and lollies melt in the heat.

The sun starts laughing as its burning your skin,
The calm sea starts racing as you jump in
A rubber ring bounces on a wave,
The life guards run out they've got lives to save.

People get out their towels and start to get dry,
The children start crying as they wave friends 'good-bye'
Bucket and spades lay still on the shore,
The beach will be empty the sun shines no more.

Hayley Pearson (Age 13)

Junk Wars

Junk, junk everywhere
What do we do,
Besides stop and stare
What do we do
With junk everywhere

Junk, junk, everywhere
Ooops! I've dropped some on the stairs
Where could I put it?
Oh! I know in my flares!

Junk, junk everywhere
Why do we leave it everywhere?
What should we do!
With junk anyway
Put it in the BIN!
At the end of the day.

Tammi Palmer-Young (Age 12)

What Love Means To Me

To me love means a fast growing passion,
Something that does not want to go away,
But follows you like a dark black shadow,
You look behind, you look in front, but you still cannot escape,
Even if you know you don't want to love,
You cannot help stop yourself from loving,
Nothing is worse than your love not loving you,
But you can't forget how he makes you weak,
Loosing a love, be it death; is so hard,
You are full of grief, but yet you still love,
If you are lost an arm wraps around you,
An arm from someone who cares, who loves you,
That is when you know you are in love forever,
When you know you will have the same feeling day after day called "love"

Karlina Powell (Age 13)

Bugs Life

The candle burned so bright
Its glow spread up and out,
It pierced the gloomy night
The flame flickered about.

A moth, entranced, flew close
She danced and pranced around.
She needed just a dose
Of the flames that abound.

Alas her life cut short
She flew into danger once more
The colours drew her to court
The death and she dropped to the floor.

Ricci Pettitt (Age 13)

Life

Life is joyful and full of fun even when it's just begun.

A baby waking from its sleep a grown up walking through the street.

If life weren't there where would we be, in darkness, gloom and misery.

Flowers growing in the park, dogs running round starting to bark.

These simple things that happen each day even a just children begging to play.

They all make life what it is so enjoy it now while you still live.

Farrah Pahang (Age 16)

Untitled

Bruised like my knee
A spot of rusty colour
Triangle shape
A teardrop from your eye
Dotty and dimpled
Like my Grandad's skin
Curved stalk
Leaning like a candle wick
A rounded piece of wood

This pear

Ellie Preston (Age 8)

Kosovo

They came in their thousands,
Hoarded out like sheep,
Fleeing like terror,
Into many unknown lands.

Their country's emptying,
Through fear and unease,
Those who escape the killing,
Are left alone and dead inside.

They're gathered together,
Labelled refugees,
Helpless and homeless,
And all praying for peace.

Their lives have been ruined,
Normality destroyed,
Their freedom has been stolen,
All that's left is time now.

The bombing still goes on,
The fighting and evil,
Kosovo's a barren land,
The vulnerable victim of war.

Jessica Pulsford (Age 16)

Sharks

Sharks are big
Like a pig
Sharks dive
Like they're alive
Sharks can see
So let them be

Connor Peart (Age 10)

Sunset

I see a sunset in the sky
as I lie on the sun kissed shore,
the colours orange and red
those colours I adore.

The sunset is dying disappearing
behind the moon swept sea
fading away I can hardly see

It's getting darker now
the sun has gone,
the moon is appearing
stars in throng

The moon is big
and like a pearl
only fit for an Urban Earl

Laura Paine (Age 13)

Steve

My love for him will never stop,
I'll always keep him in my heart,
The pain the grief will never leave my soul,
Until the day I leave this world.

My heart felt like, I had just been shot,
I wish I had at the time,
He was a loved one, friend, and family member,
He will never be forgotten.

My life flashed before my eyes,
It was hard to take it in,
This kind, caring man,
Had died no fault of his own,

For a second when I heard, no-one said a thing,
It was silent,
I felt like crying,
I ran to my room in horror.

He's probably looking down on me,
Trying to keep me safe,
I'll always love him he will never be forgotten,
I think of fun times we spent together.

Michele Powlesland (Age 15)

Winter Is Cold

Bleak, chilly
Cool, freezing
Icy and wintery
Red noses
Red cheeks
Tingling fingers
Frosty mornings
Long nights
Winter is cold!

Natalie Purves (Age 6)

Snakes

These scary serpents slither and slide,
They wait like lions ready to strike,
Crushing and swallowing, killing almost instantly.
With poisonous, sharp, long fangs, why do people
Like these dangerous serpents.

These horrible creatures were made to deceive,
Some of their skins are camouflaged,
So to go unnoticed, to watch their prey
And others to hide from predators.

How anyone can own these serpents,
Is beyond me, why would you want
These dangerous, ugly, poisonous friends?

Claire Page (Age 13)

My Nightmare Poem

The sky was as red as strawberries
I was walking to the bank with my Mum
The floor felt just like sand
My Mum walked up to the ATM
I waited for her round the corner
Then suddenly I heard footsteps
Echoing in my ears
It was a monster
About two times as tall as me
He tipped me upside-down and carried me
To his car, he tied me up and put me in his car boot.
I could not breathe or see
Then suddenly I woke up
The taste was dry and bloody
The touch was wet and sweaty
The sight was scary and dark
The smell was bloody
And the clock was ticking.

Katherine Potter (Age 11)

You

You, my love are full of light,
Your eyes twinkle like stars,
And your hair is like strands of gold,
Waving in the wind and glistening in the sun.
You're the love of my life,
My hearts delight,
And yet I cannot tell you,
How much I love you
Or how much I need your love in return.

Lauren Parr (Age 12)

All Because You're A Different Colour

All because you're a different colour,
You'll probably be attacked,
All because you're a different colour,
People will make your life a wreck.
All because you're a different colour,
They'll call you horrid names,
All because you're a different colour,
They'll make your life a game.
All because you're a different colour,
You'll get all sorts of abuse,
All because you're a different colour,
Complaining is no use.
All because you're a different colour,
You may even be killed,
All because you're a different colour,
Your blood will all be spilled,
All because you're a different colour,
Nothing will be done,
All because you're a different colour,
You're the unfortunate one!

Carl Pendlebury (Age 13)

The Hero Related To Love

It was so romantic,
The beautiful stand out of the heart on the wall,
It makes me feel so ecstatic,
The top of the heart like a dent in a ball,
Oh! Wait! There is my woman,
I licked my lips,
Walked over to her and,
Admired her finger tips,
Oh! No! There is the trooper duper man,
Don't touch the woman, I say,
He had a gun,
Or what, he would say,
He looked tough chewing his gum,
So now I am rumbling in my tum,
I'll make you sad,
I will, I'll hit you with this eating pad,
He staggered to the ground,
I was rewarded 1,000 pound,
What could I say,
I am a hero anyway.

Joshua Perkins (Age 11)

My Pets

I have two pets
One rabbit, one bird
My rabbit runs around the house
And my bird flies around the cage
My rabbit is sweet and doesn't bite
But my bird is nice but he bites.
My bird is orange, yellow, white and grey.
My rabbit is brown all over,
I'm glad I have two lovely pets
Even if they are pests.

Katie Palmer (Age 13)

I'm The Fox

I'm the fox that runs away,
I hunt at night and sleep at day.
The horses come with the hounds,
I flee I run in leaps and bounds.
People hunt me for my fur,
Though it gets caught in burr.
I'm the fox that runs away,
I hunt at night and sleep at day.

I'm the fox that soon will die,
I'll look on my family and make a great sigh.
I know it will happen to me one day,
But foxes are saying not me no way.
I guess I'll always definitely say,
I loved my cubs in every way.
I'm the fox that will soon die,
I'll look at my family and make a great sigh.

Lisa Potter (Age 11)

The Fox Cub

The fox cub cried out like a lonely puppy
Calling out through the deep dark trees
Calling desperately for its mother
I'll never forget that cry of despair

There was a sound of thunder from the west
I knew that something was turning bad
As I looked over the narrow brook
The sound of clashing and thumping

Then a sound of a drum filled the air
A gun shot flying through the air
The quick, sharp sound of a whip
Like a quick boom of a beating drum

Then a sudden silence filled the air
No sound, just silence
As a breeze goes around and whistles
Around the trees and over the flowing river.

Amanda Pearson (Age 12)

Dragon

My wings are sheets or guards
My eyes are burning fires
My tongue is a red hot piercing knife
My claws are blood red sharp
My breath is like warm air
My voice is as deep as glass
My tail is as shaped as a swans
I've seen clear white bones
I've heard screaming and screeching
In play I chew and chop
In anger I roar like a twister
They call me the shadow of the wind

Daniel Patten (Age 13)

School Dinners

Never eat a school dinner a girl once said . . . .
She did and unfortunately now she's dead,
What is it made of?
I don't think you want to know
But I'll tell you anyway here we go,
The tomato soups made of beetle juice
That brown stodgy lump is supposed to be mousse
Mashed potatoes made of bits of fat,
Greens and cauliflower all boiled in something
That smells like cats.
The apple pie has a filling of - I'm sure it's flies
I mean I'm positive you could die
You never know what you may try
So don't take a chance not even a glance.
So stick to your packed lunch,
I'm sure you'll agree
That they're much, much better to munch

Lauren Patterson (Age 11)

Loneliness

Invisibility,
That's what it feels like,
No friends,
Loneliness has spun its web
And caught its prey,
Me
A message in my heart
Sent by those I hate,
'You don't deserve,'
'You don't belong,'
'You don't have a right'
A simple walk down a street,
The crowd splits,
And the jeering starts,
'Loner', 'Loser', 'Weirdo',
My ears cannot hear,
My thoughts cannot be heard,
I am trapped in a soulless mind and body.

I want to be seen and heard,
But for now I shall be invisible.

Olivia Pay (Age 13)

The Jungle

This jungle of creatures,
The size of preachers
Lions and snakes different sizes
The jungle is a crisis
Squawking parrots
Rabbits eating carrots
The jungle I'd like to see
FOR ME!!

Rebecca Pugh (Age 9)

Lightning

A golden streak,
Goes shooting by.
Flashing,
Dazzling across the angry sky.
Appearing then disappearing at once.

A golden streak,
Flashes by.
Blinding as it shoots.
As jagged as the corner of a book.
It crackles through the sky.

A golden streak,
Goes streaking by,
On an icy cold night.
It flies through the dark,
Screaming as it goes.

It ends . . . .
Disappears completely.

Zoë Pollard (Age 10)

It Was So Noisy

It was so noisy that
The tables crumbled to the ground.

It was so noisy that
The board thundered to the fierce carpet.

It was so noisy that
The mountain exploded with a gigantic shake.

It was so noisy that
The windows crumbled to nothing.

It was so noisy that
The paper folded up frighteningly.

IT WAS SO NOISY!!

Sian Parker (Age 7)

I Will Follow You

I'll follow you through the park
When the children play
I'll follow you down the slide
Where you slide down
I'll follow you when you're playing football
Netball and other kinds of sport
I'll follow you up and down the climbing frame
I'll follow you
I'll follow you
EVERYWHERE

Sarah Pegg (Age 9)

Back To The Shops

Off to the shops mum said,
I'd rather see myself drop dead.
This is the most horrible time of year,
When mum says hurry on dear.

Off we go, in the car,
Can't we slow down a little bit ma.
Waiting for food, takes all day,
We've only filled up half a tray.

Off we go down the street,
To the butchers, to collect the meat.
Back down to the car,
Off we go burning tar.

Up goes boot,
Out comes loot.
Sun burning hot,
Unpack the lot.

Ben Pearce (Age 10)

Pollution

Why, why, why do we pollute this Earth?
Is there any need?
Is there any worth?

When will the Forests and the fields be free?
When will there be no pollution in our seas?

Will the Earth benefit if we walk?
Will e-mail take over our talk?

Let's make the Earth a better place,
And give the Environment a bit more space.

Let's try and stop polluting this Earth
Because there really is no worth.

Stephanie Parkin (Age 9)

Friends

F riends are very helpful
R eal friends are great
I love all of my friends
E very day I play exciting games with them,
N obody likes horrible friends
D o you have friends?
S ometimes we break up but we don't normally because
we are all BRILLIANT FRIENDS

Sarah Parish (Age 7)

The New Teacher

The new teacher came to our school today
She did seem a little bit weird,
She liked Miss Wilkins' cooking
And she even had a beard!

One look at her hair and you would faint
(It had a bright green hue)
Quite strange I'm sure that you'll agree
And her skin was bright blue!

She hasn't got things quite right yet
She once bowed down to a kettle,
And once she said to us in class
That blackboards are metal!

When she wasn't teaching
She was sleeping like it was night,
She kept saying "what is that?"
And her name was . . Miss Knight.

Michael Patrick (Age 10)

Summer

A big fire ball
Heading your way
Sand burning and
Covering your feet

The sea lapping
On the beach
Running up to
The top of the beach again

Running down to the
Sea
Feet sinking
In sand

Pulling them
Back up.
The sand
Will not
Give your feet back.

At last you get
Your feet back
It starts to go cold again.

Laura Paxford (Age 8)

The Black Dog

My nick name is Jake
I am very very loud when I growl
I can jump very high
And swing from the sky
And then I run like a bullet
I like people to tickle my tummy
I am as black as the night
And as shiny as silk.

Sarah Padgett (Age 10)

Waves

Waves are so great
But still they cause fate
They crash, bang and kill
Some are higher than hills
They whip at the rocks
And scare all the flocks
Some though are small
But they still make rock pools
Some are calm and sleek
But you still hear them shriek
They role on the sand
But still hit your hand
They crash up the caves
Like they're chasing Pharoah's slaves
Waves are so great
So don't start to hate

Tom Perry (Age 12)

Animals

Firm purrer
Happy sleeper

Bird swallower
Beef eater

Wall climber
Lawn mower

Mouse frisker
Piano player
Put these together what am I ????

Adam Patterson (Age 11)

Dragon

Hellfire breath.
Burning scales.
Treasure cove within the mountain.

Glintless eye.
Empty heart.
Guarding gold with fiery wings.

Whip-like tail.
Spiny back.
Shows no fear while facing men.

Crushing legs.
Slashing claws.
Mirthless laugh when destroying towns.

In your village.
In your town.
I'm after you.
You'd better run.
'Cause I'm the Dragon King.

Sam Perry (Age 10)

Bubblegum

Bubblegum's chewy, bubblegum's sweet,
Bubblegum's stickin' to the soles of my feet,
I love bubblegum . . .chew . . .pop . . .BANG!
The scrummiest sweet in all the land.
It sticks to my fingers it sticks to my nose,
It sticks to my face, it sticks to my clothes
Bubblegum's yummy, it's my favourite treat,
It definitely is my super sweet!!

Lieha Parry (Age 10)

Colours

Orange is a juicy satsuma sitting in the fruit bowl
Or the sun setting in the sky
Or a tasty, pointed carrot
Or a halloween pumpkin glowing at night.

Blue is the big calm ocean
Or the sky on a beautiful day
Or ice is melting in the sun
Or the school uniform that I wear.

Red is the blood that comes out of you
Or a big red nose
Or a massive blob of ketchup on the floor
Or paint on the wall

Silver is the snow on frosty days
Or a silver smily sticker
Or shiny tinsel on the christmas tree
Or coins in your pocket

Mark Paxton (Age 8)

I Will Place In My Special Box

I will place in my special box,
The feather of a new born bird,
The crunch of a chocolate biscuit,
The taste of an eggy soldier,
The softness of my duvet cover.

I will place in my special box,
The sight of a magical rainbow,
The sound of waves crashing on rock,
The sound of thunder cracking in my ear,
The feeling of sun beaming onto my neck.

I will place in my special box,
The sound of my rabbit thumping the floor,
The look of my fish swimming round in circles,
The sound of my hamster rustling sawdust,
The squeak and squeal of my guinea pig,
That's what I'll put in my special box.

Matthew Pearson (Age 10)

Teachers

Terrifying with their awkward frown
Even the homework is a monster
Annoying when they chatter on
About stuff we already know
Horrible ways they have
Evil in their eyes
Revolting habits they have
Shout a lot they do.

Anthony Phillips (Age 11)

Getting To School

I yawn and stretch I'm wide awake.
I'd better get up or I will be late.
In the bathroom I must go
"Hurry up" Mum is shouting
"You're too slow".

Back in my bedroom
Adjusting my tie
I'm looking quite good
I must not lie.

I'm eating my breakfast really quite fast
While mum is busy filling my flask.
Now it is nearly time to go
I must put on my coat
Strap on my bag
Out the door we go.

At the school we arrive
Watching the playground come alive
The bell rings time to go
So "Bye Mum", "Cheerio"!

Laura Phillips (Age 8)

Eco-Day

Eco-day is lots of fun,
Activities for everyone,
Planting lots of lovely new trees,
Attracting animals and honey bees,
Eco-day, what good fun.

Decorating old plant pots,
Using lots and lots,
Of fresh brown soil,
Making mosaic patterns like a coil
Eco-day, what good fun.

Planting flowers to attract wildlife,
Beautiful birds singing like a fife,
Walking round the school grounds,
Doing ecological work to save pounds,
Eco-day, what good fun.

Eco-day was a brilliant idea,
We have been doing environmental work for nearly a year,
We spent all day having fun,
Unfortunately, vandals spoilt it for everyone,
Eco-day, what good fun!

Marc Paton (Age 11)

Sparky The Snake

I am a king cobra,
I have a neck as wide as a house,
When I am cross I eat girls,
I can adjust my jaw,
I have scales as shiny as gold,
I can slide along the floor,
I am a boy,
I can eat my prey in one gulp,
I am the king of all snakes.

Ryan Pinnington (Age 8)

Magic

Don't meddle with magic,
Or it could be tragic,
Don't drink a strange potion,
It might be sun lotion.

Don't mess with a wand,
You might end up in a pond,
Don't try out a broomstick,
It might turn into a glue-stick.

So don't meddle with magic,
Or it could be tragic,
Or you might end up like me,
I turned into a bee.

Harriet Pilkington (Age 9)

Please Mr Taylor

Please Mr Taylor this boy Alex Way
Keeps on hitting me Sir, what shall I do today?

Go sit on the floor dear,
Go sit outside
Go sit on the swing dear,
Go sit on the slide.

Please Mr. Taylor this boy Alex Way
Keeps on kicking me Sir, what shall I do today?

Go sit in the sink dear
Go play the weakest link
Go sit on the floor dear
Go sit by the door.

Please Mr Taylor this boy Alex Way
Keeps singing in my ear Sir, what shall I do today?

Lock yourself in the cupboard dear,
Run away to sea
Do what ever you want my dear,
BUT DON'T ASK ME!!

Aimee Pearce (Age 9)

Heart-Broken Day

The turkey in your throat,
Feeling as though it is going burst,
Keep your tears behind your eyes,
Don't worry yourself,
He will keep warm,
And keep from all harm,
Didn't see him on the day he went missing,
A picture of my one and only child,
Joining the army of homeless people,
I miss him,
My son,
I will keep looking,
It is after all...
Christmas.

Hayley Pocock (Age 10)

It Was So Noisy

It was so noisy that
I couldn't hear a bear roar fiercely
It was so noisy that
I couldn't hear the frying pan sizzle loudly
It was so noisy that
I couldn't hear a fast booming train coming over the tracks
It was so noisy that
I couldn't hear a car engine puffing out smoke loudly
It was so noisy that
I couldn't hear the wall rumble as I hammered in a nail.
IT WAS SO NOISY!

Katie Price (Age 8)

Webster The Call Duck

Out of his house, he waddles to the pond.
He splashes and swims round and round.
Then he ducks and dives,
Getting his silky feathers wet through,
And goes to the edge of the pond to preen.

When he comes out of the pond,
Webster shows off his splendid, rainbow-like feathers.
Blue, green, purple, grey, white,
Are all the magnificent colours.
With a pale yellow beak and orange webbed feet
Webster is a wonderful-looking duck.

He looks after his mate Wilma,
They waddle together.
Their beaks shovelling in the mud,
Looking for a handy snack or two,
Their favourite place to be.

Jacob Prangnell (Age 11)

Happiness Is . . . .

Happiness is sweet like candy floss,
It's orange with delight,
Shines like the sun on a hot day,
Smells like roses new in blossom,
It sounds like gentle singing
It's smooth like silky velvet,
It makes me feel good in my self,
It flies through the skies from people to people.

Rachel Pilley (Age 9)

If You Want To See A Lion

If you want to see a lion,
You must crawl into the green, and gold jungle

I know a lion
Who's living down there-
She's a brown, yellow, terrifying thing.

Yes if you really want to see a lion,
You must crawl into the green, gold jungle.

Go down slowly and say,
"Lion boo
Lion boo
Lion booooo",

And out she will come
But don't stay because
BITE, BITE, BITE!!

Charlotte Poulter (Age 8)

Swimming In The Sea

When I go in the sea,
I put on my goggles,
I dive down into the water,
I see dolphins in the sea,
I ride on their backs,
When they are out of the water,
I feel the water gushing through my face,
It is a wonderful place to be,
I hear their beautiful voices,
It's great under the sea,
I can taste the salt from the sea,
I see dolphins fish and most scary sharks,
I swim as fast as I can,
Will I make it to shore?
Yes I will, I have got there.

Emily Parker (Age 8)

My Mum

I love my mum because she is great,
She's not just mum she's also my mate,
She's always with me through good and bad,
She cheers me up when I am sad.

My mum is special in every way,
She always knows the right things to say,
She's the one that tucks me up in bed,
And brings sweet dreams to my head.

She's proud of me and all I do,
And I'm proud that she's my mum too,
She's always taught me wrong from right,
Not to swear and be polite.

I will always love my mum,
Because she is my number 1.

Olivia Prince (Age 8)

Lilac

The soft silky swish of a cloak.
The blendable shiny gems.
The perfect purple fluff.
The queen of colours.
The magic of a horses tail.
The pheonixes curing tears.
The pleasurable thick creamy swirl.
The fresh airy flowers.
Picked on a full moon.
The lilac sky.

Amanda Pargin (Age 11)

Ladies And Elephants

Ladies and elephants,
I stand in front of you today,
That's why I'm outside,
To tell you about this very good
Theatre Performance on Sunday this week,
All of you are not invited, when you get here.
You can stay at home,
Admission is free,
Pay in cash, not cheques,
We will give you something to eat and drink,
So please bring your own.
We'll give you somewhere to sit,
So sit on the floor,
Remember what I said,
(Pay at the door)

Adam Pemberton (Age 10)

The Cheetah

I'm a cheetah, cunning, fast and sly,
In the long, green grass I lie.
I'm found in zoos, safari parks,
Jungles and deserts I stalk,
When I catch my prey I slowly walk.
They can't see my camouflage coat
I catch my prey and bite their throat,
Then when they're dead I eat them up,
They have a big gash and a deep, deep cut.
Antelopes, birds and rodents I eat,
I have a grin, it's my favourite treat,
I run around all day long
And when night comes
I'm slowly gone.

Lindsay Parnham (Age 11)

My Skateboard

I like my skateboard
My skateboard likes me.
I also like my shoes.
That makes three.

I do lots of tricks.
I do back side kick flips
I also do an Ollie
That turns into a nollie.

Sometimes I slip
I hurt my hip.
But I'd like to play on my skateboard
All day.

Josh Parkman (Age 9)

Spring

The morning starts with the birds singing,
Building their nests to lay their eggs.
The sun shines longer,
The evening is brighter.

The grass begins to grow,
So soon we'll need to mow.
The flowers come,
Daffodils, primroses and tulips.

The trees begin to blossom
As the buds turn pink and white.
The farmer plants the fields,
And soon the tractor will go.
The lambs skip in the fields.
Running up and down.
The sound of spring is here to stay
Spring has come at last.

Nicola Purkiss (Age 8)

Drink

There are so many kinds of drink,
You don't know what to think,
When you try peppered mink
Your breath will always stink.

There are so many kinds of drink,
You don't know what to think,
When you try stinky sink
Your spellings always wink.

There are drinks that are rough,
There are drinks that are tough,
One makes you puff,
Others make you stuff.

Ross Phillips (Age 9)

My First Day At School

When I went to school for the first time I cried
All I could see was strange faces smiling at me
Voices that I had never heard before.

I tried to run back to my mum
But SLAM
The door was shut
And I was flying above everybody

And then I was on the floor again
More strange faces came in
But this time they were crying
I tried to run out again
But SLAM
And I was flying above everybody again.

Christopher Perry (Age 8)

Tiger

Mine is the roar
That frightens men,
In the jungle deep
Mine is the den.

Mine is the fur
Of orange light,
Barred with stripes
As black as night.

Mine are the teeth
That rip up prey.
I eat my kill
And then slip away.

Christopher Pearson (Age 11)

Bubbles In The Air

Bubbles are...
As colourful as splashing pastels
Like a lapiz lazuli splash of paint
Like poppy cherries
As warm as a colourful kaleidoscope
As frosted as primrose honey
Like tangerine stars
As fresh as golden dandelions
Like increasing pale balloons

Gemma Parsons (Age 10)

Grandma Says Things Like:

Sit up straight.
Eat your vegetable.
Remember your pleases.
Wash your hands.
Stand up straight.
Don't drag your feet.
Go to sleep.
Mind your own business.
Turn the television off.
Go to bed.

Jessica Pye (Age 7)

Waiting

Waiting
Why should I wait
When I cannot wait any longer
Fighting my hope to abscond
Fighting my impatience
Hoping to flee from my troubles
Waiting for the beautiful day to arrive
When I can open my graceful wings
And stealthily glide away.

Imogen Pickup (Age 10)

I Should Like To . . .

I should like to hear the flowers grow on the hills,
I would like to see the dolphin dive peacefully into the water,
Or feel the heart beat of Winnie The Pooh,
To see the caterpillar change to a butterfly,
I would like to hear the trees screaming when they're being cut down,
I would like to cut a piece of the sun off and bring it home,
I would like to feel a baby kick inside its mother's tummy,
And to see a calf or a foal being born.

Katie Robinson (Age 10)

Heaven

I know I will never see you again until you come up here.
But every time I look at you, I always feel the tears.

Always remember me and I'll remember you.
I cried when I had to leave and begged to stay on Earth.
But I heard someone say to me "You now belong on heavens turf."

So now I am up here looking down.
I will always remember the day I died
And I'll certainly remember the way you cried.

Stephanie Pereira (Age 12)

Spring

S pring is the best because it brings blossom on trees
P erhaps spring is the best
R un your mum is calling and she says it's spring
I magine spring was the only word you could say
N ice old spring that brings blossom on trees
G ive your strength and we'll do it together

Tom Richardson (Age 6)

Lambs

All of the day, I watch them play.
They dance so sweetly, ever so neatly.
They love to jump, on that huge bump.
They kick their legs so high, you couldn't even try.

While the mums happily munch, they hang around in a bunch.
All day long they stay in an eight, run back to mum before too late.
When she calls them for their tea, that's the bit I like to see.
Come into the shed when it's time for bed.

One has lost her lamb and wants it found, so we look everywhere around.
Then I find him in the dirt, not a single thing was hurt.
Whilst I pour in their corn, I see a lamb being born.
Its woolly coat is full of slime, but not to worry all is fine.

Mum will start to lick him dry, and soon she hears her baby cry.

Jessica Powell (Age 10)

Our Town

Our town is big,
The shops are small.
Our town can be happy,
Our town can be sad.
Our town can be glad
Some shops are a bit of fun,
But soon aren't fun at all.
What a pity!

Rebecca Prior (Age 8)

White Board

White boards are white,
You can draw and write,
With a pen of course,
You can use any colour.

Ian Richardson (Age 6)

The Beach

As the sparkling ocean glistened in my eyes,
And horses galloped across the sinking sand,
The wind blows the sea over my tired feet,
I finally was in peace, no battle.
Seagulls fly over my head like hovering flies,
With their white coating like pearls,
As they dip their smooth heads in the ice water,
They finally have space and freedom.
Cliffs hover over the golden sand,
High like heaven in the clouds,
Rocks falling down, down, down.

Georgina Page (Age 11)

The War

The war was bad
The war made everyone mad.

There were tonnes
Of big bad guns.

Loads of people die
Millions of people cry.

It starts to rain
As in comes the train.

As the evacuees go
To where we don't know.

Michael Peddle (Age 9)

The Fierce Beast

My wings are monarchs of the air and sky.
My eyes they are a vast array of blue diamonds.
My tongue is a coil of razor wire hidden behind a gnashing jaw.
My claws, burnished bronze, will blind you in sunlight.
My breath is an explosive smoky haze which bursts from my mouth and nostrils.
My voice is heard for miles around whenever I am angry.
My tail is a cracking whip flashing green sparks of fire.
I've seen hundreds fall dead at my feet.
I've heard maidens' screams and the clank of armour.
In play I surf the clouds, rescue phantom princess in my palace in the sky.
In anger I lift my head and strike.
They call me...Falstaff the Indomitable.

Toby Pearce-Slade (Age 13)

Hunting

It sniffs around in the dark
It's got grey fur.
It howls and barks,
It does not purr
It's fierce and big
It scares all bats and cats
It's such a pig

A wolf is!

Bethany Palmer (Age 8)

Stormy Night

A storm is a trench,
Howling in pain,
Shouting out orders,
Explosions all around,
Wet all over, cold with fear,
Short bursts of machine guns,
Running around not knowing where you are,
And then the last shots of the guns,
The last throwing of grenades,
It all stops: we know we've won.

Stuart Parkinson (Age 11)

West Ham

West Ham West Ham
Is the team I support
We've some talented players
Like Di Cainio, Joe Cole and Trevor Sinclair.

West Ham West Ham
They play at Upton Park
That is the best ground in the world
And the manager Harry Redknap
Has the best players in the world.

WEST HAM IS THE BEST!!!

Aston Pegg-Smith (Age 10)

I'd Rather

I'd rather do my homework,
I'd rather trim the plants,
I'd rather live on Jupiter
Or even live on Mars.
I'd rather walk blackbeards plank,
I'd rather swim with sharks,
I'd rather eat some mushy peas
Or kiss an old aardvark.
I'd rather be stung by killer bees,
Or have a kiss that's smoochy,
I'd rather do most anything
Than eat raw fish sushi!

Sam Quill (Age 10)

Wishing For A Friend

On the Beach

Gulls, drifting on the light wind
Sound of sandpipers, whistling, "Ek, ek"
Smooth, shiny stones under numb, aching feet
Wishing for a friend.

On the Quarry

Trees, endless, everywhere
Pigeons, chattering babble
Grass and thistles, staining my clothes
Wishing for a friend

Andrew Painting (Age 11)

Robot Wars

Robots smashing
Robots bashing
Robots mashing and clashing.
I like Hypno-Disc,
I like Razer, what about you?
Sir Killalot, Dead Metal,
Matilda, Sergeant Bash and Shunt
Will batter you to a pulp.
Ref bot keeps this lot under control.
And at the end as Craig
Would say "We don't use camera tricks
Or hidden trap doors
The danger's for real on robot wars,
Good night and God bless."

Tobie Phelan (Age 10)

I Could Not Bare It

I was taken by my arms,
With the crown of thorns, tight upon my head,
I was in agony with strings around my arms,
I was weak, no strength or health,
I walked with the heart breaking cross on my back

I bleed and hurt everywhere,
The noise was loud, people shouting and crying,
But I payed no attention,
I just walked with my head on the floor
My arms were in pain, I couldn't face what I could see.

They hit nails into my hands,
In my feet as well, I screamed,
My mother screamed too, but cried as well,
It rained and I died down slowly,
It went silent I stayed on the cross.

Hannah Quinton (Age 10)

Friends

My friend has brown hair, brown eyes his friend is Isabelle
He is quite short but is rather a chatterbox
He can be annoying and a bit of a wimp
But I like him anyway.

He came from Australia and he will go back home soon
I will miss him when he goes
Have you guessed who he is yet?

Jack Pearson (Age 7)

Can I Go . . . .

Mum, you know I've been really good lately,
Well there's a school trip coming up, can I go please?
Where is to and how much does it cost?
Well, it's to France and it costs two hundred and thirty pounds
Two hundred and thirty pounds!!
Do you really think I've got that much money to give out?
Well, you have just got a new car and I haven't been abroad yet, oh please?
No, Way!
I'll do the washing up for three months and wipe it all.
We've got a dishwasher!
Oh please!
Are you going to have any fun?
Nope no way.
Alright then.
Thanks Mum, fun and France here we come!
But you can still do that washing up.
But . . . but . . . alright then.

Danielle Phillips (Age 10)

Numbers

Numbers, numbers are everywhere.
When we look we have to share.
Counting in tens.
We don't use pens.
We use a ruler.
Our teacher says
We work out sums in our heads.
We can jot it down on some scraps.
Just to try and work it out.

Jessica Perry (Age 10)

What am I?

I have no colour but I'm sometimes blue,
It is very hard to hold me,
I can be liquid, solid or gas
I am very important,
You need me to live,
I am refreshing,
I can also clean,
But I can also kill.

I am . . . . .

Water

Matthew Peach (Age 10)

Special Memories

My special memories are

The distant roar of a lion,
A scream from an elephants trunk,
A slurp from an animals water hole.

My special memories are

Riding my very first bike,
Kicking a little football,
Racing our little dog Hattie.

My special memories are

Coming to this very school,
My first time swimming without armbands,
Riding my pony that seemed huge,

My special memories are

The feel of a washed up pebble,
The sound of the sea clattering against the rocks,
The reflection of a sunset.

Those are my special memories

Gus Quirk (Age 10)

Lullaby

Sleep my little one sleep
While we watch the stars leap
Do not fear
While we sleep my dear
Sleep my little one sleep
Dream my little one dream of fairies
Sleep tight and you will be in a land of your own
So sleep in your special place
My little one.

Hellen Parsons (Age 10)

Christopher's Conversation Poem

Hey, Wotsit, get your things out of my thingummyjig

Wots? it?

The thingummyjig!

Thin? Gum? My jig?

Say 'bye to your things'

Bytyathings!

Christopher Pope (Age 11)

Do You Know What Will Happen

What will happen fifty years on?
Will cars be able to fly in space?
Is there going to be mutant people?
Will the ozone layer die?

What will happen fifty years on?
What happens to the milkyway?
What will become of us will we turn mad?
Can technology turn on us?

Jacob Pryke (Age 10)

Rain Poem

The rain is glass shattering as it hits the ground.
It is a powerful ruler taking over the world.

It batters the trees
Its twigs are like arms which steal things.
Its leaves are like its windy hair.

When the rain is snow it lands as a sheet of white powder,
Which dusts the surface of the earth.

Matthew Powdrell (Age 11)

The Wind

The wind is howling,
It sounds like growling.
The rain is tapping,
It sounds like banging.
I went outside the rain went *POW*,
I went inside to grab a towel.
I felt like I was going to cry but mum wiped me dry.
Mummy was kind, she said never mind.
The rain will soon go away then you can go out to play.

Kirsty Palmer (Age 9)

Sea Tour

The sea, the sea, the sea
How nice can it be
Dark little caves
The beach and some waves
How nice can the sea be.

Down in the ocean dark and deep.
A shark saw a fish this is what it will seek
It swims up and grabs the fish.
It goes home and puts the fish on its dinner dish.

David Poulton (Age 7)

School

At school when I'm walking
I can hear people talking
And I can hear the breeze
Going through the swishing trees
And I can hear the dead leaves crunching
And munching
I can hear people
Clicking and typing
Sometimes when
You're on the field
You see loads of space
Then someone comes up to you
With a moody face.

Carl Pritchard (Age 8)

Sports

S port is fun and cool
P laying football is great
O r perhaps you prefer tennis it is fun and great
R ight lets get started score a
T ry in rugby to get 3 points
S port is the best thing in the world

Jamie Penfold (Age 9)

It Was So Noisy

It was so noisy that I couldn't hear the ice-cream yaks annoying music.

It was so noisy that I couldn't hear the builders working loudly.

It was so noisy that I couldn't hear my sister yelling annoyingly.

It was so noisy that I couldn't hear the teacher yelling loudly.

It was so noisy that I couldn't hear a lion roaring loudly.

IT WAS SO NOISY NOISY!!

Carla Powell (Age 7)

Lava Burst

A lava burst,
A rumble first,
A black layer,
A stone sprayer,
A red bang,
A lashing clang,
A scarlet fountain,
An open mountain,
A flame maker
A cloud baker
A catalogue to make a volcano.

Olivia Rudman (Age 9)

Trees For Life And Fun

When trees are put together they provide us with shelter, comfort, food, light and air.
Without them we cannot survive.

Weeping willows sway in time to the wind, providing pillows for the fairy beds.

Oak trees stand big and strong protectors of the land.

Elm trees shade us from the sun keeping us cool.

Siver birch an elegant tree dressed in a silver gown.

Holly trees a reminder of Jesus upon the cross.
The thorns for his crown, the red berries for his blood.

Horsechestnut: bearing fruit to give us toys to play conkers.

Palm trees standing tall and straight with leaves to weave baskets.,
Fruit to nourish us and a liquid to quench our thirst.

William Pollitt (Age 10)

The Storm

I hear a faint rumble in the distance,
It gets dark fast,
It starts getting closer,
It starts banging and lights flash,
The sky starts crying.
Finally it dies down with little flashes.

Julia Ryrie (Age 6)

My Friends

I like them as my guest
When I play with them they are the best
When they come around they are the best
Who is that?
It is Craig.

Alex Rockall (Age 7)

I'll Follow

I'll follow you wherever you go through the wires where the electric goes

I'll follow you through the screen wherever you go
I'll follow you through the cable wherever you go

I'll follow you through the video wherever you go
I'll follow you through the speakers wherever you go.

James Purchon (Age 7)

Nibbles

I've always loved my hamster,
But now I have to cope,
Without him in my bedroom,
I really have no hope,
My hamster is all gone now,
'Cos he's never coming back,
I wish I had him with me,
For I feel my heart will crack.

Amy Rix (Age 10)

Our Class!

In our class there's twenty-two,
Here are some names and the teacher too.

First there's Catherine kind and fun,
Then there's Cathy annoying and glum.

Next it's Sally who is successful all the time
But so is Samantha although she makes everything rhyme.

Then the boys, here are some, Mark the pincher, Joe the jinxer,
Adam the mixer and worst of all Daniel the prankster.

Teachers well as for them I don't think you really want to know.

Charlotte Powell (Age 11)

The Sea Storm

Dark and secretive
With many tales to tell
Gentle yet rough
As you're pulled down into hell
Heavy drowning rain
Pounding on my skull
As the sail rips and the wind blows
I hide for comfort down below
I can feel the daggers of the night times waves
Stabbing at my undying pain
Black night sky and lightning bolts
My eyes are stinging I'm feeling worn
As sea salt splashes, can't wait for morn'
I scream so loud my lungs are burning
Though no-one hears me I keep yearning
I need a hand to guide me near
Although your hand can't stop my fear.

Ruth Read (Age 13)

War

Strong, brave men striding gallantly into the battle field,
Armed with deadly weapons,
Teary eyed children lost on the streets, starving,
People terrified of going out, are the bombers coming?
Gas masks constantly with them,
Houses lost in the dark,
Black out curtains hanging in windows,
No light to be seen,
Helpless women wondering, will I see my husband again?
Families trying to survive with food rations,
Rows upon rows of tiny Anderson shelters in the cramped gardens,
Many people fearing the worst,
Many people homeless, on the streets, dying.
Warning sirens sounding late into the darkness of the night,
Refugees wandering the lonely streets looking for a place to stay,
Strong brave men striding gallantly out of the battlefield,
Why?

Amanda Rule (Age 12)

Thinking Of Animals

I love animals.
They're so warm,
You just want to cuddle them,
But what if you're looking for a pet,
Could you choose.
What's your choice.
A cat
A dog
What, what, what would you want.
A rabbit
A rat,
What, what, what would you want.
A guinea-pig
A budgie,
What, what, what would you want.
A parrot
A mouse,
A chinchilla
See it's hard to pick,
Wait...no sorry I need more time to think.

Katherine Polden (Age 9)

Number Poem

Ten tiny tigers roaring at passers by,
Nine nice newts ignoring the tigers,
Eight angry elephants stomping down the hill,
Seven sensible sheep looking after lambs,
Six silly snakes slithering down the hill,
Five fishing frogs not doing very well,
Four fat fish flying in the air,
Three fire flies kissing,
Two tortoises being naughty,
One octopus playing.

Alison Ratcliffe (Age 6)

My Nonsense Poem

Yesterday I went to the shops,
And came home last week.
Had tea for breakfast,
Breakfast for lunch,
And lunch for tea.
Slept under my bed,
With my hair polishes,
And woke up on the roof.
Jumped out of the car with a parachute,
And landed in the sky.
Met Piper Billy on a cloud,
Who was making a cup of tea.
When I got home,
My dog was ready, to take me for a walk.
We went to kids kingdom,
And had a cup of wine.
Soon it was time to get up.

Amy Reade (Age 10)

The Raven

I stand alone, I stand alone on the cliff near my death,
I stand here waiting forever waiting, for the sea to take me to my final resting place,
"Take me, take me" I cry, but no-one hears me.

As I stand there all alone, I hear a tap, tap tapping in my chamber door,
I go to the door, cautioned I open it . . .
Darkness there, and nothing more,
I close the door but in the silence of nothingness I hear the tap,
I open my chamber door and in flew the raven, perched, perched and sat on my chamber door,
Quoth the raven "never more!"

Surely this bird, this bird sat on my chamber door,
Is the window to my unhappiness,
I stand on the cliff waiting, forever waiting,
But they don't come.
Just the raven who quoth never more on my chamber door,
On this midnight dreary,
While I pondered weak and weary.

As darkness walked onwards,
Forever onwards,
Towards my everlasting fate . . .
Never more.

Roxanne Royer (Age 13)

The Football Flies Across The Pitch

The football flies across the pitch,
rolling down a little ditch.
The crowd are screaming,
and the lights are beaming
half time has finally come.

The players have a little rest.
The crowd are shouting you're the best.
The players walk on,
half time has gone.
They'll have to score,
or they'll draw.

Shaun Rice (Age 12)

Fire

Fire, flickering bright, giving off fumes
It erodes the forest eating trees on its way
Cutting off humans from their possessions.
The fire blazing hot scalding all who trespass it
While humans suffer intense pain.
Fire, igniting all in its path
Its taunting flames strikes us all with scorching pain
The fire is a courageous beast which is uncontrolled
Even beating water its main enemy
The fire is in heaven until the fire fighters put it out,
It then becomes as dead as stone.

Charles Rose-Nokes (Age 11)

Dreaming

I went to the museum to see a painting
But it was not there!
I went to the cinema to see a film
But it was not showing!
I went to the zoo to see a bear
But the night before it died!
This is what I did on my weekend
But all the places I went
I did not find because of the places I went!

I didn't get the things I wanted
At the places I went!
The places didn't appear as they seem
Because it turned out to be a dream!

Christopher Richards (Age 12)

Dreaming

Dreaming is like swimming with dolphins, priceless,
Dreaming is like floating underground
Dreaming is like a pen, it has to stop.
Dreaming is like an alien, it's out of this world
Dreaming is like a leaf blowing in the wind.
Dreaming is like the devil, hurtful, horrible.
Dreaming is like a bird, it has its ups and downs.
Dreaming is like a drug, addictive yet killing.
Dreaming is like an electric fence.
Dreaming is like a demon, going to take over the world.

Claire Rymarz (Age 12)

The News

Staccato bullets, rip, pelt and maim, classmates lie prostrate on the cold earth
Life, love and laughter ripped at the seams.
A disillusioned teenager, incarcerated.

Bombs dropped on innocent babies, wrenched from loving arms.
Tiny limbs frozen in time, goals unfulfilled, strewn on the floor.

Starving people, hunting seeds on the dusty ground,
Swollen bellies, lifeless eyes, malnourished, infected, hopeless lives.
Remains of lunch and dinner thrown in a bin.

Blood curdling cries, onlookers sighs,
A mother lies next to her son's twisted form.
He, high on cocaine, felt no pain as his life blood drained away.

Scorching, burning mountains of flesh.
Animal carcasses piled high in eerie funeral pyres.
Pungent aromas of rotting masses, life and limbs askew.

Battered, bruised and torn, her thin frame trembling,
Hit from behind, a glancing blow, purse snatched.
Almost home from the shops, £3.50 gone.

Does it have to be like this?
Good question said the philosopher.

Maryam Rejai-Moghadam (Age 13)

Love

Love is a book, you flip through the pages and never know what's coming.
Love is a bed of feathers, relaxing and enjoyable but generally wears out.
Love is a door to heaven but somehow ends up in hell.
Love is a school term, as the time goes by you gradually learn more and more.
Love is a journey by boat you get to enjoy the view but you could go overboard.
Love is like a pen gliding along the page writing more and more but you have to be careful your ink doesn't run out.

Jodie Royal (Age 11)

Copper

My cat is called Copper
Yes, he is lovely

Can I have another one like him,
As I always take good care of him?
Two like him would be brilliant!

Copper's old though
Always been cute,
Lonely as can be,
Lovely as can be,
Easy to make him mad,
Deaf and blind

Cool still
Oh! He's dead
Poor Copper he's dead
Pray for Copper
England took good care of him
Relying on you God to take care of him.

Lee Russell (Age 11)

The Animal Chorus

Dogs barking,
Cats meowing,
Horses neighing
This is The Animal Chorus.

Guinea -pigs squealing,
Lions roaring,
Snakes hissing,
This is The Animal Chorus.

Toads croaking,
Birds chirping,
Dolphins squeaking,
This is The Animal Chorus.

Elephants thundering,
Monkeys screeching,
Parrots singing,
This is The Animal Chorus.
The Chorus of Life

Kim Ramsey (Age 11)

The Forest Nightmare

The forest was watching me
As if the shadows had eyes
All the wolves were howling
Like they were calling DEATH

The wind was whistling loud
Like it was warning me
Of a hidden danger
The branches were moving
Like a man was grabbing me

The forest has a predator
And I was its harmless prey
The creatures in the night
Were creeping and stirring about

The moon and stars were my light
My only guide through the night
The footpath wound through the grass
Eagerly followed to home

William Richards (Age 12)

Peace

A child breathes in dreams like a sweet aroma,
A single cloud flits over a crescent moon.
A snowflake dances on a ray of light,
A father tells his daughter that he'll be home soon.

Silent music plays in lovers' hearts,
The dew congregates on blades of grass.
A small eye opens for the very first time,
A church bell gives a single chime.

Magic pours from the moon on a sleeping old man
And finds its way inside his breath.
The man finds what he's sought for a long, long time,
A still hand clutches death.

An angel soars above the sky
And drops to earth a single star.
When sadness seems to overwhelm
Peace is never far.

Hannah Rickman (Age 12)

The Seasons

The year starts with spring
And the birds begin to sing
The colors range from yellow to pinks to greens
You start to grow peas and beans
Spring is the best season

The next season is summer
It's definitely not a bummer
With sun and loads of fun
In this season you can laugh and run
Summer is not a bummer

Then you have awesome autumn
When it even looks nice in Taunton
Brown leaves green leaves, leaves of every colour
Autumn is where the trees are bare

Last is wonderful winter
Where the snow is sometimes there
And trees are still bare
Animals are gone
I love winter

Terry Rudge (Age 12)

Leopards

L eopards leap leopards hunt
E ven at night they hunt
O pen their mouth ready
P repare for a big fright
A very big type of cat
R acing to catch their prey
D angerous cats all around

Phyllida Robinson (Age 7)

War Again

The soldier shouts at an old man
People stare,
The old man stares back.
The soldier points.
The old man is terrified.
War in Jerusalem
In the year 2000.

Miles Row (Age 14)

Spring Poem

The spring is very beautiful
I love it fair and square
That's all I want to talk about
I jump and catch the pears
From the beautiful old brown tree
The blossomy flowers I just love!
And now it is summer Oh! Bye Bye

Poppy Reynolds (Age 7)

Green Is . . . .

The green leaves on the trees
Some green grapes in a bowl
Grass is green with daisies between
Small green bushes on the tracks

Green is . . .
A tomato which is not ripe yet
Green wire netting all tied together
Acorns that are in their cups
Flower stalks with flowering flowers

Green is . . .
Red berry leaves
Wild flowers that haven't sprouted yet

Green is . . .
Green with envy!

Elizabeth Rowles (Age 6)

The Bright Star

At night there are stars,
And normally next to Mars.
They only come out at night,
But they might blind you because of the light.

When there's shooting stars about,
They are beautiful without a doubt.
On the first star in the sky.
I wish I could fly.

The sky is all a glow,
With stars that overflow
How magical it is at night,
When the stars shine so bright.

Toby Ratcliffe (Age 9)

My Memory Box

I will store in my memory box . . .

The last glance of my long lost puppy dog, Luckie,
A special card from my great grandma, Ivy,
The comforting feel of my cat's rough tongue licking my hands

The smell of mum's cooking,
The sound of my friends close to me,
Photos of my sunny holidays around the world.

The taste of a crispy apple crumble,
A smell of a dead fire burning,
The feeling of my cat's fur on my face.

The vision of my puppy dog staring back at me,
The feel of my soft pillow as I lie in my warm bed,
The smell of fresh mown grass as I walk in the sunshine.

The look on my face when I saw the white glistening snow,
The comforting feel of my mum's warm hands hugging me,
And the final swim in the Italian ocean
Every laugh and every cry.

Emily Reed (Age 11)

My Best Friend

My best friend Sian is cool
Especially when we play ball
We like to play
We play all day
Hitting it against the wall.

My best friend Nicky
Said she was sicky
But after all
Now she's quite tall
She went to Paris to see Micky.

My best friend Kim
Said she was dim
I said "No"
She said "So"
And wished she had a friend named Jim.

My best friend Emma
Owed me a tenner
She had loads of friends
That drove her round the bend
Especially Gemma, she was too clever.

Marisa Reid (Age 10)

The Forest

The luscious sods of grass rustle in the breeze
The hidden birds twitter constantly
The bright sun twinkles through the sturdy trees
Dragonflies dive in and out of a glass-like lake
And no mortal knows that such tranquility exists

Lucie Rose (Age 12)

Chocolate

Chocolate chocolate so so yum,
Chocolate chocolate floating down
Chocolate chocolate melting away
Chocolate chocolate in a grin

Saffron Richards (Age 7)

Once A Friend

I once had a friend,
A wonderful friend,
She took over my heart
The minute she came.
And then the sorrow appeared,
The spirit sadness was finally seen,
She was leaving,
Leaving this world and me
To shrivel up,
And become nothing.
She came, she was loved,
And she went.

Lucie Richardson (Age 11)

I Wonder, I Wonder . . .

I wonder, I wonder,
What teachers do
In their spare time?

Do they watch TV?
Do they go to discos?

What do teachers do,
In their spare time?

Hannah Ryan (Age 10)

Orang-Utan

Swinging through the trees,
So gracefully,
Almost gliding through the air
The only sound you can hear
Is the rustle of the leaves

His great long arms
His great long legs
His beautiful black eyes
And his stunning orange coat.

I wish I were like him,
Yes I wish I were like him.

Sam Raison (Age 10)

Sugar And Spice With Everything Nice

Sugar, spice with everything nice
Put these things in the cauldron

Rainbow of a sunny sky
Like the pastry of a burning pie
Teddy bear from a child's bed
Let all the children rest their head

Sugar, spice with everything nice
Put these things in the cauldron

Sun of a clear blue sky
Bun from the bakery
A heart from a Valentine
Let's have a pudding of a tart

Sugar, spice with everything nice
Put these things in the cauldron

Snowflakes from a fluffy cloud
Tail from a little puppy

Children will rest their head
They have a hard day of work ahead
So the children can fall asleep
Let's give them this poison to eat.

Xanthe Roe (Age 9)

The Reign In Spain

There once was an old man from Spain
Who was really a very big pain
He once met the queen
Who asked, "Where have you been?"
Then he left as he thought her insane.

Karl Reynolds (Age 11)

I'd Rather

I'd rather eat carrots
I'd rather clean the loo
I'd rather fail my Sats
I'd rather muck out the zoo

I'd rather get squashed by an elephant
I'd rather go to school
I'd rather take the rubbish out
I'd rather clean and dust the Scout hall

I'd rather get an illness
I'd rather my mum have a shout
I'd rather do most anything
Than eat my brussel sprouts

Adam Robertson (Age 10)

What I Can See

Dream world I wish I was in dream world
If I was in dream world this is what I would dream

First gleaming water, then a spitting water fall
Then fish swimming next to me
Next small pretty shells and pebbles
When I next looked up I could see
Grass, grass, grass
Long thin colourless grass

After that lions prancing for prey
Gazelles leaping for their life
And grass, grass, grass
Is all I can see
Parrots, birds flying over my head
Trees, lots, lots, lots of trees

Then I was on a rock
And animals, animals, animals
Which I had seen beneath me
Then it started to get darker, darker

Then I was back home.

Darcy Ruddock (Age 9)

B.F.G.

Head like an enormous rock
Tummy like an enormous banana
Lungs like spaghetti
Legs like sky scraper
Feet like cones
Six arms like golf clubs
Hair like crisps
Eyes like windows
Mouth like a pumpkin.

Thomas Regan (Age 9)

The Jungle

The jungle is a wild zoo
full of venomous animals
prowling around like scavengers.

The jungle is an overgrown bush
at the bottom of the garden.

The jungle is an explorer's paradise.

The jungle is a pit full of quick sand.

The jungle is a palm tree maze.

The jungle is the noisiest place on earth.

Stacey Riley (Age 10)

The Optimist And Pessimist

The optimist sees the doughnut,
The pessimist sees the hole,
The optimist's on holiday,
The pessimist's on parole,
The optimist sees laughter lines,
The pessimist sees age taking its toll,
The optimist see the beauty spot,
The pessimist sees the mole,
The optimist sees the safety sign
The pessimist sees the obstruction,
The optimist sees a debatable point,
The pessimist sees an objection,
The optimist sees the baguette,
The pessimist sees the roll,
The optimist sees the mole,
The pessimist sees the garden pest,
The optimist's having a rest,
The pessimist's on the dole,
The optimist achieves all he wants in life,
The pessimist misses his goal.

Matthew Paish (Age 16)

My Owner

I had a little owner,
Who was very small,
Sometimes she was very loud,
Sometimes she made no noise at all.

I think she is horrible,
My brother thinks she is kind,
My dad hates her for the world,
And my mum thinks she's fine.

Rhiannon Rice (Age 7)

The Person Who Liked Pigs

His snoozely nose guided his food,
The way he was eating was rather rude.
His ears were pointed and his hands all mucky,
Though he was safe and sound so he was rather lucky.

His house was cluttered with bits and bats,
Bits of this and bits of that.
Mr Snout, got around and about
Collecting pigs of all shapes and sizes.
Anything that caught his eyeses.

He had pinky skin and was hugely fat,
But we'll never know what was to come of that.
He had pig photo frames and teddies and ornaments too,
Pig cork mats and toast racks that were all brand new.

Sally Robson (Age 10)

The First Time I looked In The Mirror

I was only three,
When I saw someone sitting in front of the mirror,
Staring at me looking straight to my body,
At first I was scared.

I saw brown eyes staring ahead,
Little fingers like short sticks,
A bit of hair poking out of its head,
Wearing rabbit pjs just like mine.

I raised my hand,
The person raised her hand,
I nodded my head,
The person nodded her head.

I called for my mum and dad,
I showed them her,
They said it was me,
I didn't believe it.

When I was five,
I understood
That it was me all along.

Elena Rees (Age 9)

Food And Sweets

Food is yummy,
So are sweets,
Fizzy sweets are scrummy,
Hard sweets make them more yummy.

Poppy Richards (Age 7)

The Forming Of The Flamingo!

Flamingo bent over and snatched two stones
to form his knobbly knees
and joined them together with two
dead straight sticks to form and
build his legs.

He stole his vivid colour from
a palette of paints
bright enough to dazzle your eyes.

He seized his attention drawing gaze
from the blackness of the night,
and the brightness of the stars.

Flamingo grabbed his shimmering stillness
from the leaves falling down
in Autumn.

Jason Remmington (Age 11)

Vampire Bat

The bat began
The bat hopped and stumbled,
And snatched the graceful dove's pinions,
He tumbled over and fell in the loamy sludge,
And his wings were made.

For his ears
The bat carried along and flopped in the sky,
He was not prepared for a nasty bump,
He came staggering down and appeared with no scratch,
But six leaves and mud appeared on his head.

The dark devil swooped for some eyes,
His torso was weak and feeble so he stopped at an olive bush,
He grasped for two dark olives and popped them into his sockets,
He squinted for a few minutes and his eyes were born.

The small piece of shadowed night swooped down to earth,
It raised it's small scruffy head and flew over to two small flints,
It began to seep the stones into it's jaw,
And produced two fangs
The Bat was complete

Edward Rose (Age 11)

Chestnut Drive

Chestnut Drive, Chestnut Drive,
Is the place where I now live,
With fresh cut grass and a white front door
And my family I live with.

Chestnut Drive, Chestnut Drive,
Is the road where we now play,
When the sun shines down on us
On a lovely beautiful day.

The Wells live at twenty-five,
The Woods with the big tree,
The Walls lived at seventeen
And the Holmes laughing hee hee hee.

Chestnut Drive, Chestnut Drive,
Is the place where I sleep,
Eating dinner fish and chips
Heap, heap, heap.

There's playing with friends and laughing
Tooting hoot hoot hoot
Till we couldn't laugh anymore
Riding scooters too.

Kelly Richardson (Age 10)

Lightning

I lit the sky like a giant light bulb
I set a tree on fire with my bare hands
I shocked a man just because I touched him
I zig-zagged through the sky like an arrow from Zeus
I faded like a light being turned down by a dimmer switch

Gordon Ramsell (Age 8)

Miss Kelly

There was a teacher called Miss Kelly
Who often got on your nelly
She got in a rage
When you didn't behave
And stopped you from watching the telly.

Emma Rydon (Age 9)

My Dream Horse

I wish I had a horse for a pet
We would go to shows and win a rossette
Crosscountry, Dressage and jumping in the ring
When I finish my round, the bell goes ding.

A very warm and cosy straw bed
She's waiting at the door to be fed
She gallops round the field at night
It's so large she goes out of sight.

She's all black with a little white star
She's an eventer, she goes really far,
And just before I go to bed I stroke her fur
When I go in, I really, really miss her.

Chloe Rickard (Age 10)

Night

Night comes in a carriage driven by
Slaves and lifted by bats

Night is coming down to earth as he
Casts a black shadow covering all in darkness

Passing over sleepers lives with no sound heard
Lifting up shining moon and stars

Putting out the light of the sun

As the sun rises night flees in fright
Down under to haunt again

Luke Robinson (Age 11)

A Girl's Life A Sequel To A Boy's Life

Well, you're really asking
Two questions there:

Do up your hair
Give the boys a glare

Stay in bed at night
So you won't get a fright

From them deplorable boys
And their absurd little toys

Wear your finest clothes
From your head to your toes

Be polite when you eat
LEAVE the High Street

Hold out the little finger when drinking
Unlike the boys who do less of the thinking

Be polite to your visitor
Do not be sinister

Never ever babble
Always be tranquil

If all these things you can do
Well all I can say is God Bless You.

Luke Ralph (Age 12)

What Caterpillars Do

Caterpillars wiggle,
They move up and down.
They tickle and tickle
And they frown.
And they eat some leaves
And fall off tall trees.
Shh! They're fast asleep.

Jemma Riddle (Age 9)

Ruffles The Dragon

My wings are as strong as steel
My eyes, are balls of fire
My tongue is a sharp dagger
My claws are sharp as a knife
My breath smells like toilets
My voice is loud and creaky
My tail is a dash of lightning
I've seen people being chewed up
I've heard children screaming
In play I killed a mouse
In anger I make loud and angry noises
They call me ruffles the dragon

Melissa Reed (Age 13)

Beyond All Hope!

The sky grew dark, as the waves rode high,
Across the mountainous sea,
The thunder crashed and lightning flashed,
As the wave of fear hit me.

My boat though small but sturdy in form,
Had suddenly entered the eye of the storm,
Tossed and turned in every way,
Would we survive to see another day.

Its mast was ripped and torn asunder,
As this great storm tries to pull us under,
Under the raging violent sea,
I prayed that someone was watching over me.

To keep us safe and free from harm,
I would have to chance my arm,
And ride the storm for all its worth,
Or forever be banished from this earth.

But with all my skills to no avail,
Could we escape the storm to sail,
The rocks we hit were unforgiving,
My boat destroyed we both stopped living.

Kathryn Rankin (Age 13)

Love Is A . . . .

Love is a, boat sailing on a rough sea
is it going to make it across back home.
Love is a, hole never knowing
how deep is could behold.
Love is a, very old house will it end up capsizing
to heart break, as it is full of love.

Rikky Read (Age 12)

The Weather

Sometimes it's hot
Sometimes it's cold
Sometimes it's breezy
Sometimes it's stormy
It rustles the tree
It burns your back
It wets your hair
It's sometimes unfair
The weather can change
At the click of your fingers
The wind can blow
And off the roof can go
The snow can fall
Upon the wall
Whatever happens, sun, rain, wind or snow
The weather will never ever go

Steven Reed (Age 11)

After Death

Death is the end,
It means you won't see this earth,
You won't see London, Paris or New York
Ely, Berlin or Perth.

Death is the end,
You won't feel this earth again,
You won't feel the cold or hot or sandy,
Heat, metal or rain.

But why be so worried?
Could be a better place than here,
No wars, tragedies or pollution,
You would never have to fear!

Harriet Roper (Age 13)

Skies

The stars are glitter,
Dusted across the night sky.
The moon is a mirror ball,
Sharing its light across the world.

The clouds are bouncy castles,
Floating across the blue sky.
The sun is the brightest flame,
Sharing its heat across the world.

Lori-Rose Rogerson (Age 11)

I Don't Like . . . .

Messy hair,
A wobbly chair,

The colour grey,
A foggy day,

Smudgy rubbers,
Itchy bed covers,
Shorts too short,
My Auntie bought,

Brussel sprouts,
Noisy louts,

Pessimists,
Bacon crisps,

Poems without a proper ending. .

Joshua Rumbol (Age 11)

The Rock

When I was young I was in the war
Only ever handled a pistol before
The army taught me to be a rock
To never run away from any fear
They showed me how to be a man
And to always be proud of who I am
Then the day came
I was so afraid
I went into war
Now handled a machine gun, before
I fought for my country
I fought for my life
I fought for my family
In the best way I could
But then the day came
I was free from being a slave

Joseph Risseh (Age 13)

Love

Love is like a comet smashing into the earth,
Once you fall in love you can't stop it
And if you take too much steps
Love can turn into a waterfall
When tears clatter on the floor
But when love is like sea waves going up and down,
Your love cannot be between and cannot be matched
So your love will stay a few weeks.

Paul Reilly (Age 12)

Enter Autumn

Clever autumn,
You see what there is to do,
At the start of it all,
Then you do it.

You find the fun
And enhance it,
You catch the sun
And lower it.

You thieve the leaves,
And paint them,
You take the trees
And fill them.

You lotion the corn
And tan it,
You shape the thorn
And sharpen it.

Tired autumn;
You've done what there was to do,
At the end of it all,
Then you leave.

Lewis Rogers (Age 13)

What Is . . .The Moon?

The moon is a light bulb,
Turned on by the Heavens.

It is a lemon,
Often cut in two.

It is a mini fire.
Set by the angels.

It is a golden eye,
Looking down at the world.

It is a large mask,
Worn by the sky.

It is the night-time sun,
With its little children, the stars.

Fiona Rice (Age 11)

The Ultimate Love Songs Collection - Ode To Elvis

You were always on my mind,
I just can't help believin' you're gone,
I'm sorry that suspicious minds got in our way,
Are you lonesome tonight without me?
But now you're the girl of my best friend,
It's now or never, I have to tell you,
Please love me tender once again,
I've got love fever because you torture me,
I surrender my heart, please love me as I'm loving you,
She's everything a man could want, but she's not you,
Only a fool such as I would let you go,
I'm sorry suspicion tormented my mind,
I've kept all our love letters, and I love you so,
Please help me make it through the night once again,
You don't have to say you love me,
Kentucky rain pours above my head without you,
Please be gentle on my mind don't torment me, I beg you let it be me,
Only your Spanish eyes please me, it's only love I ask for,
When you smile the world is brighter and that's the wonder of you,
You're my bridge over troubled water and that's why I love you.

Aisha Rossi (Age 13)

A Spell To Make My Sister Disappear

A thousand spiders to crawl on her at night,
Bats all around her to give her a fright,
Half a newt to make her mute.

Throw her in the cauldron hot,
Dragon's blood throw in the lot,
A head, a leg and an arm too
To help her become part of my stew.

Stir all around to make her scream,
Add tooth of wolf to make it steam,
Read the inscription from a book,
Then hear her go with a 'poof'.

Rhiannon Rauss (Age 12)

The Cemetery

Proceed into the night air only if you dare.
You will approach a fright of old hosts
That look like bold ghosts

The malevolent bat that hangs
On the fence post where below only
Stands the ginger cat
The dull grass filled with ancient stones
Which God made from his own blood and bones

The churchyard dark at night
Which could be a fright.

Alec Rose (Age 12)

A Night To Remember

The baby fox cries,
Like a hungry puppy
The cry just carries on like an echo,
I don't know what to do.

The thunders rolling,
He sounds like a giant,
His big feet hit the ground
With a crash.

The sound of the gun
Is like a sharp knife,
Or a whip that has hit a horse,
Or even a drum stick hitting a cymbal

The sound of relief fills the air
And the silence is as cool as the breeze
You could hear a pin drop,
It was so quiet.

Holly Robinson (Age 12)

My Baby Brother

Locks of brown curly hair,
Big staring innocent blue eyes,
A smile that could melt a million hearts,
Soft skin that smells of baby Johnsons,
A magnetic charm to force you to play with
Him even when you don't have time to spare,
The tiny tear drops that fall from his face when
He doesn't get his own way,
The warmth of his fragile body as he leans
Against me and finally drifts asleep.

Thalia Rolfe (Age 13)

My Horse

With a mane which is black,
In its stable on its back,
With a body which is brown
Coming up from getting down

Seven years old getting old, getting old
All grown up with a saddle on its back,
With a bridle on its face, showing all his grace
Very proud, very proud going to shows which are loud

Eight years old getting older, getting older
Soon he'll be nine being proud and fine,
Then he'll be ten being in fields with his friends.

Christie-Leigh Ryan (Age 11)

Growing Up From My Granny's Point Of View

When you all grow up
have children, get married
live abroad, buy things you can afford
have a wonderful job and don't worry if you
get robbed.

When I grow up
start knitting, read books
wear hairnets and beware of crooks
live all by myself all alone scared to even
answer the phone,
my granny used to go on about this
but when she passed away,
life was bliss!!

Jessica Ramm (Age 12)

The Final Fear

I'm here facing my worst fear
This is my nightmare
My life is whizzing past me
I can see everything that I did wrong
It is too much to handle
I'm going insane and I know it,
I want to throw myself off the bridge
But I know I still have a lot to live for
I can hear people laughing at me
It's like I am part of a game
The sky is turning red with anger
I have two people chasing me
I don't know what to do.

Michael Roberson (Age 12)

The Plane

I was looking forward to my holiday until I had to go on the aeroplane
I was so afraid I saw it and a great fear came over me
I started having hot sweats I thought I was going to faint
When I sat on the plane I was shaking like mad
During the flight I seemed to enjoy the flight
When we arrived at Malta I was proud of myself
I'd over come my fear

Lauren Rushton (Age 12)

Balls Of Diamonds

My wings are like pointed knives
My eyes are big balls of diamonds
My tongue is a piece of crispy sand paper
My claws, are as sharp as spikes
My breath is as hot as a fire
My voice is as croaky as an old lady
My tail is as curly as a shell
I've seen people dying
I've heard children screaming
In play I killed a mouse
In anger I kill people
They call me balls of diamonds

Natasha Reed (Age 13)

Dolphin

The noise of a dolphin splashing around,
The greatness of its echoing sound.
Its silky skin reflecting from the sun
And it flips and twists like an acrobat.
When they smell the smelly fish
Then they know it's time to eat.
The brightness of it's silver cheeks are
Very nice and very sweet.

Heather Rodgers (Age 11)

War!

Destruction, devastation death everywhere, this is war.
War spreads the destruction through the great land, like wild fire.
There is not a hole unturned that has not seen the death and pain of war pass over them.
The war will end, but the only way the armies and destruction will recede
Is if one side is completely and utterly annihilated by the other.
The hatred is fuelled by a millennia of frustration and jealousy
Some eventually don't know why they are fighting, they just do because they are told to.
The war has engulfed millions of people into the hatred,
The resources of a galaxy all gone, wasted, churned up in the conflict.
Soldiers fight to the death, their blood stains the ground like wine spilt on the floor.
Vast complexes destroyed armies ripped apart as if going through a shredder,
Towns cities, even hamlets have been destroyed.

Michael Robson (Age 12)

Safest Option?

I live in a world that only you find attractive,
Unplagued by the realistic nightmares that stalk us.
Dark alley ways are lighter,
The neon lights are brighter,
And all you love are safe in your world.
Those that die, die of good cause
And people all take time to pause
To admire Earth's glorious creations,
Unaffected and unharmed by the minds of men.

Though there are faults to your beliefs.
To be blind to the dangers
That aim to abolish the everlasting and comforting.
To be naive of the force, capable of poisoning dreams
And attacking your personal safe places.
Yes, it must be fun to live in your attractive world,
Until the truth falls as sharp as a knife
Reflecting the last of your attractive life.

Ashley Roberts (Age 17)

Haunted House 2

Ghost and cobwebs by spooky rats
White sheets covering the furniture
The wind through the broken window
Leaves the house cold
The floor is cracking
And it creeks in the night
Cobwebs cover my face
As I walk to the door
Then I run to lamp post and finally . . . .

home

Lee Rolph (Age 13)

Negativity

It's easy to loose sight of it all,
In a world of frustration.
As moments pass us by,
As the cyclone of malicious words scar us.
In a circle of confusion.
Who can you trust?
The picture fades and darkness turns to grey.
The evil of the world dents the soul,
And selfish people trample your dreams.
Cold people live their lives,
Without regard for other people's feelings.
Vicious comments dent self-esteem,
And cruel intentions trample hopes
And what little hope is left.

Kellie Renwick (Age 14)

Spain

Spain is in Europe,
Joined onto France.
It has many features,
And a traditional dance.

It has many mountains,
In the Pyrenees.
And lots of big parks,
Full of blooming trees.

It has a foreign language,
Some of which I know
I can ask for a cheese sandwich,
"un sandwich de queso".

Spain is very hot,
And full of beautiful bays.
I'd like to go and live there,
And live the Spanish ways.

Tom Ralph (Age 15)

Grandpa

When I go out with Grandpa,
He takes me to the beach.
He only lets me sit on his lap,
And always drifts off to sleep.
He always buys me an ice lolly,
And I've never seen him frown.
For his skin's all wrinkly and brown!

Catherine Rhodes (Age 6)

Abstract Infinity

A, B, C and D
have no place
in the intangible infinity
grace of power, elegance of might
voice of truth, dark voice of lies
and light
lost and found, everywhere and nowhere
in the infinity of abstraction.
Alpha, beta, gamma and delta
the water flows like a marble
on a child's helter skelter
virtue, honour, rectitude, righteousness
what value have they
in the metaphysical infinity?
with the water crashing as the open sea
and the winter sunbeams
and the summer squall
how it falls

See the driftwood, gently bobbing up and down
on the water.

Matthew Reynolds (Age 15)

My Future

What will be
Left here for me
When I grow up?

Will there be
Warmth and air
To help us live and grow?

Will there be
Clear water
And will the sky be clean?

Will the sea
Be polluted
Will it be pure and fresh?

Will there be
Fresh bread to eat
Will it be safe?

Will there be
Fresh air to breath?
Will the streams be clean?

Tom Reed (Age 8)

The Candle

I light up the room,
I flicker about.
I need lots of oxygen,
The wind puts me out.

When electricity goes out,
I'm the option to use,
I'm in so many colours,
So many to choose.

Emma Romsey (Age 11)

Favourite Things

My favourite thing
Is my teddy called Ted!
He's cuddly and yellow
And sleeps in my bed.

My favourite to look at
Are baby photos of me!
They cheer me up when I'm sad
And make me happy.

The best time at school,
Is during lunch play.
I can chat with my friends
It's the best time of day.

Alex Rice (Age 10)

Scarecrow Blues

Down by the field
That sways in the breeze
Lives the poor old scarecrow
With crops to his knees

His head's very wide
Which lops to one side
It has an evil grin
And eyes sunken in

He's made from a sack
And has a pole up his back
He tries to scare the birds all day
But they just won't go away

Emma Robinson (Age 10)

My Poem

Once there was a boy called Fred,
He sat upon his lovely bed.
One day he felt very ill
So he walked right up to the top of the hill.
One day he went to swim
When he realised he had a fishes fin.
One day he wanted to have some fun
So he went and got his father's gun.
He shot the cat,
He shot the dog,
He nearly shot a tree trunk log.
Too late, oh no! he is very dead.
He laid himself upon his lovely bed.
He went to heaven,
He went to hell,
He went to ring the dinner bell.
He went to school,
He went back to the pool,
He went to the hill,
Where he met his friend Jill.

Jack Elliot Risley (Age 9)

Dragon

Dragons, dragons scary dragons,
Dragons, dragons ugly dragons,
Dragons, dragons fierce dragons,
Dragons, dragons scaley dragons,
Dragons, dragons huge big dragons,
Dragons, dragons . . . .
      DRAGONS!!

Daniel Robinson (Age 9)

Pictures In My Mind

A space ship glides at warp speed eight,
A pirate ship attacks!
A ghost comes back to haunt you,
The grim reaper is back!

A brave cop trails through the streets,
You better watch your back!
A gangster could attack you,
Look out behind you THWACK!!!

A fiery dragon stomps around,
A damsel in distress,
Brave knights crash and clank about,
Without much success.

We find a fossil in the ground
I wonder where it's from?
Perhaps it's from a time long gone,
Let's think together chum!

Jonathan Richardson (Age 9)

The Summer Bumble Bee

When I go flying,
I hope to see.

A beautiful flower,
Waiting for me.

I hope it's full of,
Nectar, colour, taste and smell.

It might be waiting for me,
I just can't tell!

The nectar tastes like
Melted butter,

The taste just makes me
Need to flutter,

At last when I'm full up,
I fly away to bed.

Curled up in my hive
Resting my weary head.

Emily Rutty (Age 10)

Pancakes

Pancakes, pancakes they're the best,
I like pancakes yes! yes! yes!
They're so yummy in my tummy,
I like panckes yes! yes! yes!

Ben Robinson (Age 9)

Penguin

Best belly slider
His nose dives are amazing
His hobby is fish

Henry Rule (Age 11)

My Teachers

The one and only Mrs Slattery, does the best literacy
Rugby's a sport she likes to do, scrums, trys kicking balls too.

Miss flood is the year group leader, she can't go away because we really need her
Art is something she likes to do, drawing, painting sketching people too.

Spelling his name is such an impossibility so we just call him Mr DC
Having fun is what he likes to do, laughing joking, tricking people too.

Tall, long, thin and narrow all these words describe Miss Barrows
PE is something she likes to do swimming, running exercising too.

Emma Richards (Age 9)

Fairies!

When twinkling, dew drops start to form.
Cats begin to yowl and stalk.
The glistening dream fairies begin to peep
The perfumed flowers start to talk.

Out of the mist, butterflies drift
And fairies leap, dance and flit.
Clothed in magic, starlight and dreams
And a pearly, swirly light is lit.

To announce a starlit fairy ball
Where snowdrops prance with moonlight
And stars send pure white hope to all
Then fairies wish, with all their scarlet might.

That they could ride upon a wish
To a land where mortals laugh with all
Dance and sing and make magic with them
But one jewely night when dreams fall.

Then fairies come in deathly black,
And suck your life from you
Sweep you to a magic land
Where all your dreams come true.

Heather Reed (Age 10)

Dog Rap

Walking around the house all day,
Jumping up and down.
Trotting around the house all day,
All I say is get down!

My friend is Jess,
She's just the best.
She has a dog,
That knows a cat called Mog.

My other friend is Jessie,
Her dog is very messy.

Victoria Runnacles (Age 10)

The Day And Night

The night comes the day falls,
When it's day you hear bird calls.
The night's moon glistens as I watch it,
As I walk past the park I hear the beautiful blue tit.
As night starts I go to sleep,
Nobody makes a beep,
Until day.

Jenna Rattue (Age 10)

One, Two, Three

One, two, three, four,
Knock at the door.
Five, six, seven, eight,
Oh, dear I'm late.
Nine, ten,
I saw a hen.
Eleven, twelve,
Egg on the shelves.

Ersin Sami Riza (Age 9)

Insects

Insects that are big
Insects that are small
Insects that are slimey
Insects that crawl

Insects that slither
Insects are a pain
Insects that fly,
Insects don't like rain

Sam Reeve (Age 9)

Bill

He sits in the chair
White haired, talking
About steam trains.
With his three fingers
Still lingering,
From the wars he knew
He had done wrong,
But fighting for his country was
An honour.
For the medals
He wore on his chest
Were a symbol
Of his bravery
The rifle he still had
That he shot down many Germans
With but
He sits acting as if
Nothing happened.

Daniel Reading (Age 8)

When Will Spring Be Here

When will spring be here
And the gloomy winter disappear
Till I can see the sun and the bright skies
When I can hear the singing birds and the butterflies
I am waiting for the leaves
And the blossom on the trees
With rows of pretty daffodils
Will spring ever be here, this year.

Savini Rajapakse (Age 8)

The Rain

The rain is a ghost
It tickles you in the night
The wind howls at you
And you listen listen listen
You ignore the patting of footsteps
You ignore the pushing at you
It pushes you, it pulls you
And you nearly blow away.

Johann Rohl (Age 8)

The Track

The ancient track is boggy
Lined with tangled bushes
Moss smothering abandoned sleepers
Just covers what is left of the track

Water pelting on the track
The slippery rails wearing a veil of dust
Bushes swallowing up the line
The remains are half covered with mud

Alistair Robins (Age 10)

The Witch's Kitchen

The smell of the bubbling couldron
The tepid air
The witch's kitchen
The snotty couldron mixer
The chewing of the rats
The witch's kitchen
The reliable spell book
The tapping feet of the mice
The witch's kitchen
The rotten eggs
The gone off milk
The witch's kitchen
The creaking of the floor
The cat as black as night
The witch's kitchen
The wind through the door

Emma Renals (Age 8)

Three Weird Monkeys

There are three weird monkeys dancing on my roof.
One's wearing a cowboy hat.
I think he should be called Bill
What is this I see?
The three weird monkeys have spotted me.

There are three weird monkeys eating on my roof.
One's eating my fridge.
I think he should be called fatty.
What is this I see?
The three weird monkeys want to eat me for tea.

James Redgrave (Age 10)

My Question Poem

Why do leaves fall from trees?
Why do liquids take the shape of the container?
Why do cakes rise in the oven?
Why does metal rust?
How do weeds grow?
Why do reeds grow in the jungle?
Why do stars come out at night?
Why is the sun so bright?
Why is steel so hard?
Why does water freeze?
Why is the sea blue?

Rebecca Rowe (Age 9)

Slimy Stan

From my space ship, I can see
The alien who is chasing me.
He's short and fat and very green.
The ugliest alien I've ever seen.

He's chased me along the Milky Way,
And hounded me both night and day.
I've flown three times around the moon.
He's followed me since the beginning of June.

I'm nearly at my destination -
The Delta quadrant space station
HOORAY! I've lost that little green man.
The one I nicknamed Slimy Stan.

Sarah Rickey (Age 11)

Birthdays

Invitations and letters are sent,
To friends and families, to buy presents.

Mums and Dads prepare food and sweets,
And party bags full of treats.

Friends and family come to play,
To join this very special day.

Discos and parties, lots of fun,
The birthday cake, which weights a ton.

Presents, presents, everywhere,
And party poppers crack in the air.

Presents piled up like Mount Everest,
Opening them all will be like a test.

As the party draws to an end,
You say, goodbye to all your friends.

Scott Roberts (Age 11)

Spring

"Three cheers for Spring!
That wonderful, wonderful season,
Where everyone is happy
No-one is gloomy,
For new creatures are born,
Like the lamb,
All skinny and white,
All small and tiny,
But lively inside.
The lark lays its eggs,
Hoping they will hatch.
She whistles a song to her mate,
Telling him the good news.
The ladybird shelters under a flower,
From the April showers,
That come in Spring.
Three cheers for Spring!"

Maxine Ridley (Age 10)

Autumn

In the quiet the squirrels have a conker fight,
hitting and struggling screaming away.
One transfixed at the bang of a gun,
coming round the hibernating tree.

The wise old owl only comes out at night,
using fallen leaves to hide out of sight.
As he glances down at the long fat mouse,
and dives, dives, dives at the horror struck rodent.

Men stand gazing at beautiful colours,
too amazed to hear the howling wind,
blowing their hair and clothes to one side,
as it twists and twirls in the pale grey sky.

Simon Richards (Age 10)

When I Go To Collenswood

I will see at Collenswood
Ten terrific teachers
Nine piles of new maths books
Eight heaps of hideous homework
Seven new naughty kids
Six pens piled up for me
Five fantastic new friends for me
Four classic classrooms which are my favourite
Three great piles of pens again
Two piles of poems that I made up
One great school just like any other

Amber Rose (Age 10)

The Sound Poem

The fox cub screamed out for its mother,
Whinging and whining,
The sound echoing through the creek.
The cub rattled and raged,
It tried to bite through
But it was no use, it couldn't get out.

The crash of thunder
Hit the ground and rolled
In the sky.
It knocked over trees
And made the ground shake,
And made me jump,
As it would hit the ground
With the force of a giant
Falling from the sky.

Laura Robinson (Age 11)

The Jungle

If you're walking through the jungle
And you hear a loud roar
You might have to stop 'cause
You'll see a big claw.

If you're running through the jungle
And you hear a big growl
You'll have to watch out 'cause
The tiger's on the prowl.

If you're strolling through the jungle
And you hear a loud giggle
Don't look now 'cause
Monkeys can tickle.

If you're creeping through the jungle
And you hear a big hiss
Don't turn around 'cause
You might get a kiss.

Josie Rheeston (Age 11)

Love Is The Best

Love is the most wonderful thing
Lurking high and low
It's ready to fight to protect you from hate
Going as far as it can go

Finding the truth in everyone,
That's just one thing it can do
If you love with all your might
It's sure to love you too

Susannah Russell (Age 8)

The Weather

The weather is gloomy and grey
I wish the rain would go away
I wish outside was nice hot sun
So I could go to the beach
And have lots of fun

Natalie Rogers (Age 9)

My Pet

My pet is slimey, slithery and slippery
He lives in his shell
My pet is small and climbs up my wall
It leaves a trail of silver all over the wall
My pet is a snail.

Jamie Roper (Age 9)

The Snail Began

She stole the curvy conch off the beach
She took the gleaming light of the moon
And made her shell

She took the petals of the flower
She took the vision of a bee
And made her feelers

She took the slithering movement of a worm
She grabbed the slowness of a tortoise
And made her movement

She took the silk of a silk worm
She stole the skin of a maggot
And made her skin

And the snail was made . . .

Eleanor Russell (Age 10)

The River

The earth cannot offer anything,
More beautiful than the beat of the
Sun pounding down on the river, but
. . . the river does not move it just
Carries on pattering across the field.

As you sit by yourself on the bank
Of the river, with the company of
The raging sun glistening, shining,
Throwing balls of fire into the
Morning air.

But when it is done the world
Is still except . . . the sun which still winks
One more time then disappears
Behind the large and
Towering mountains.

Leanna Rathbone (Age 10)

The Future

What will the future really be like?
What contents does it hold?
So many questions need answering.
Discoveries to unfold . . .

Will there still be buzzing bees?
And a beautiful butterfly?
Or instead, hi-tech trees
And cars which go flying by.

So many questions to answer,
Why am I asking all these?
What will the future really be like?
Will there still be mushy peas?

Alex Raschke (Age 10)

Friend To The End

Since ten months old,
Through thick and thin,
We always stick together
Saturdays and Sundays,
We go out to swimming or
To the U.G.C. cinema,
We know which schools we are going to
And split up we will be
But we will stay in touch.
As we grow we will be torn apart,
But will always be there for each other,
No matter what he will always be in my heart,
My life long friend Nicky Webb.

Ashley Richards (Age 11)

The Tudors

Henry VIII had six wives,
Three of them lost their lives.

He had two daughters but he wanted a son,
To be the King after he'd gone.

He died when he was fifty five,
Then he was no longer alive.

He liked to play tennis and many other games,
And he liked being called many different names.

When Henry died Edward Became King,
That was a wonderful and glorious thing.

Henry VIII was bold and brave
But now he is lying dead in his grave.

Victoria Royce (Age 9)

My Dad

My dad's an antique restorer
He's very good at making things out of wood.
My dad has has lots of tools on his bench,
A hammer, a saw and a wrench.
He screws and he glues, he planes he sands
He's ever so clever just using his hands.
I went to his workshop it's ever so big
And I met all the people that he works with.
When he sit down for lunch he gives a big sigh
For it's nearly time to say goodbye

Sarah Russell (Age 9)

Video Games

The thrilling thing about the games,
Is the scary lettering of their names
I open the packet and guess what I see . . .
A whole new adventure for you and me.
Deep inside the game when you're all alone,
Is my favourite part of the play.
Under the dark sea,
Or out in the wet of the day.
The wood is quiet,
Then out of the blue,
Jumps the slimy glue,
Out of the emperor's too,
So determined to win over me,
It won't ever happen,
My gun has blast,
Oops I broke the TV.

Laura Richardson (Age 9)

Please Mr. Davidson

Please Mr. Davidson this girl Naomi Write,
Keeps drawing on my book sir, can I give her a fight?
Just go sit on the floor dear go sit outside,
Go sit on the swing go sit on the slide.

Please Mr. Davidson this girl Naomi Write,
Keeps taking my pencil can I give her a fight?
Go work in reception go work in the sink,
Go work on the roof do whatever you think.

Please Mr. Davidson this girl Naomi Write,
Keeps taking the dictionary can I give her a fight?
Move to a different school dear go become a sailor,
Go lock yourself in the cupboard go ask Mr. Taylor

Molly Rogers (Age 9)

The Sun

The sun shone through my window
it lit up my whole room,
it took away the night time
the darkness and the gloom.

It sparkled on the book case
it sparkled on the floor,
it sparkled on the chest of drawers
the wardrobe and the door.

But soon the day is over
the sun has gone to bed,
the moon lights up the sky again
as we rest our weary head.

Ellen Rockell (Age 9)

The Cat

The cat all ginger and warm,
Fur as soft as down,
Pink and wet soft and shiny is the nose,
The collar blue with a shiny circle saying Puss,
What a cat! That's why I like him.

That old Puss with tender ears,
Pink little paw prints trotting along,
Enjoying the peaceful air,
Outside a breeze doesn't bother him,
Soon he will come back and sit with me,
What a cat! that's why I like him.

Jessica Richardson (Age 8)

The Alien Spacecraft

When I stepped in I was amazed,
Buttons everywhere, I felt dazed.
Radars and triggers with alien figures on top
Space laser guns, cages but the tons.
"Hold it", I heard something I picked up a gun.
I was starting to run, then guess what I saw?
An alien tall, purple and ugly,
I aimed the gun fired and ran for my life.
Something behind me snotty and grotty
I started the engines of my spacecraft
I jet propelled back to earth.

Jonathan Rose (Age 8)

Big Jake

Big Jake has a belt,
It isn't a normal one
It is a Karate belt,
A black one,
When people see him they scream and run,
He has no friends,
He thinks it is fun,
He never ends on his ruins
So watch out he might be behind you.

Zoe Rance (Age 11)

Hamsters

H amsters are furry and full of enjoyment
A ll you want to do is play with them
M any hamsters are very playful
S ome friendly some spiteful
T inkering, being cheeky
E nergetic, full of life
R idiculously funny, always playing
S orrowful when they die.

Mark Reynolds (Age 9)

My Friend

I have lots and lots of different friends
But my very best one is very kind,
Always there for me,
Always plays with me when I'm walking around.
When she plays I feel so good, playing it.
Like best friends should.
She is a girl, a pretty girl a very kind girl.
She sits next to me when I'm upset,
She helps when I'm hurt,
Friends forever we shall be
The last thing I'm saying about her is
She's my best friend too.

Robyn Redmond (Age 7)

The Snow Images

Massive great polar bear asleep on the ground
"Oh no he's lost a tooth", God's child has just lost a tooth
Jack Frost has just painted the ground white
And to make it better he sprinkled it with glitter
Someone is grating cheese in the sky and it was melted on the way down.

Sian Ridley (Age 9)

The Not So Beautiful Game

We sit in the changing room listening to our manager,
I look over at my team mate, his face tells me he's as nervous as I am.
The bell rings, we walk through the tunnel filled with fear.
All those joyful faces depending on me.
The whistle howls, the ball is passed to my feet as I run down the wing.
All of a sudden I feel my legs being swooped away
My vision goes black as I watch my dreams fade away.

Taylor Richardson (Age 10)

The Lake

The lake is rushing over rocks,
Hear the splash and hit the banks,
Early in the morning hear it flow,
Listen very carefully and you'll hear it ripple,
And if you look very closely you will see the tiny rocks.
But when it starts raining,
The lake overflows,
Then later the sun comes out,
And dries out all the flood,
Leaving the remaining water sparkling in the sun!

Emma Rogers (Age 7)

Dolphins

Dolphins are grey and white
You can swim with them whenever you like.
Their lovely noses that help them smell
And their beautiful fins that guide them well.
Their little ears you can hardly see
Their ears are as small as a bumble bee.

Laura Rymer (Age 10)

Leopard

Grazing in the sun under an ashbourne oak tree,
Bugs crawling through its plush fur,
Hazel and walnut eyes with a splash of dark iris
Stalking its prey carefully
Subtle yellow coat acts as a symbol
Of pride and glory.

Lewis Rawlinson (Age 11)

I Found A Pound

I found a pound
and it was round
I went to the shop
and I bought a lolly pop
I saw a duck it started to suck
the muck near the brook
I saw a boy and he was playing with the toy
it started to cry and it said bye

Haris Rashis (Age 10)

My Favourite Thing To Eat

Treacle sponge
Treacle sponge
Is my favourite thing to eat,
Treacle sponge
Treacle sponge
It is my favourite treat,
Treacle sponge
Treacle sponge
I will repeat,
Treacle sponge
Treacle sponge
It is my favourite thing to eat
I don't like it cold,
I like it hot,
Treacle sponge
Treacle sponge
It tops the lot.

Daniel Ripley (Age 7½)

The Garden Gnomes

Here we go with our barrow and spade,
And although out of clay, we are made,
When nobody's looking, out we come!
To do our jobs till the day is done!
Yes, some of us fish, and some of us dig,
Some of us are small and some are big,
Then, when we are finished, we'll start to have fun!
And when the sun goes down, off we will run.
To our hideouts and to our holes,
And that is the song of the garden gnomes.

Sarah Richardson (Age 9)

The Football Match

I woke up in the morning and the first thing I thought about was football
I brushed my teeth and washed my face and the first thing I thought of was football
I went down stairs and had toast and Cocopops and the first thing I thought of was football
I ran upstairs to get dressed and the first thing I thought of was football
On the way to the football pitch all I could think of was football
The referee blew the whistle to start the match all I could think of was football
I ran and ran as fast as I could and all I could think of was scoring
I took a shot at goal which just missed the top bar and all I could think of was scoring
I passed the ball to my friends and they scored two goals all I could think of was winning
The game was finally over all I could think of was my next match

Fred Rogers (Age 8)

My Friend

She is a Dalmatian puppy curling up in a heap,
A lemon yellow buttercup in winter she will sleep.
She is a striking bolt of lightning, brightening up a storm,
A big mug of cocoa because she is warm.
She is a blanket of purple velvet embedded with golden stars,
Her planet is the Moon, not Jupiter or Mars.
If she were a toy, she would be a teddy bear.
The night ebony sky would be her long flowing hair.
She is the early morning sunshine with her huge grin.
A future born singer, she does not make a din.

Sally Robinson (Age 10)

My Imaginary Friend

My friend has purple hair,
She is very small,
She wears a purple dress,
With purple hearts in the middle,
She is very nice,
She is my friend,
She is cute,
She is a happy girl,
Have you guessed yet?
Who is it?
MY IMAGINARY FRIEND

Megan Scott (Age 6)

Fat Factory Faulty Fish

We named our new turtle Pokemons Squirtle
When it went swimming by Jamie's dazed dashing deadly dog
I heard my groovy gecko whistling someone's echo
While looking at Mark's photocopied poisoned parrot
When Sammy ate a finch he didn't even flinch
And was sick over a fat factory faulty fish
Our crazy mazy pony likes Italian macaroni
With Robert's delicious deadly dusky duck.

Bruce Risk (Age 10)

Menorca

Menorca is sunny and bright,
The seas with sharks may give you a fright,
The cafes are really posh,
You will need a lot of dosh,
The food is divine,
And so is the wine,
So I guess my holiday's over
And it's back to the smell of clover.

Eleanor Ryan (Age 7)

The Tiger

The tiger prowls silently
Through the forest
Spots a deer
Moves up close
One deer the size of a horse moves too close
The tiger moves into position . . .
. . . Pounce
The chase starts the tiger kills the deer
The tiger only attacked because she was defending her cubs

John Rowbottom (Age 8)

Easter

I get lots of Easter eggs
And I give you some too
And then we are all happy
With our Easter eggs
I hope you get a lot too
And are you happy too?
"Hey what about me"
"Here you are then"
"Now you can get a tummy ache too".

Emily Stacey (Age 7)

I'm A Refugee

I am a refugee,
Homeless no-one to go to,
I am a refugee,
"Frightened?" No not frightened,
Terrified and homeless
I am a refugee,
I see the bombs dropping killing,
I want to die I can't bear the terrible sight of all the manslaughter
I am a refugee,
Born in a barn no warmth no water to wash, no clothes to wear,
I am a refugee.

Siân Rollings (Age 10)

It Was So Noisy . . .

It was so noisy that I couldn't hear . . .
My cat wailing for food
It was so noisy that I couldn't hear . . .
My mum dropping a metal shelf in the shower
It was so noisy that I couldn't hear . . .
The TV when it was at its loudest
It was so noisy that I couldn't hear . . .
My dad snoring like a volcano
It was so noisy that I couldn't hear . . .
The neighbours dog barking like it was the end of the world
It was so noisy!!

Sarah Roberts (Age 8)

The First Christmas

Star burning brightly in the midnight sky, long long ago,
Hillside grasses blowing in the breeze, long long ago,
Shepherds watching over their sheep, long long ago,
Angels glittering and shining, long long ago,
Wise kings bring special gifts from far away, long long ago,
Baby Jesus lying safely in his crib, long long ago,
Sheep weak and tired, long long ago,
Mary watching proudly, so happy, long long ago.

Emma Stephenson (Age 6)

Recipe For Spring

Take a deep blue sky and a golden sun
Add six cupfuls of fluffy white clouds
And three bunches of bright yellow daffodils
Stir in a handful of beautiful butterflies
And two spoonfuls of seeds
Sprinkle six sprigs of damp grass
Add a trickle of rain
Decorate with Easter chicks and baby bunnies
And you have made Spring!

Hayley Summers (Age 7)

My Friend Is

My friend is Jake and
Jake's friend is Jack and
Jack's friend is Sam and
Sam's friend is Alex and
Alex's friend is Craig and
Craig's friend is Paul and
Paul's friend is Sam and
Sam's friend is Jack and
Jack's Friend is Declan and
Declan's friend is Scott and
Scott's friend is Taylor and
Taylor's friend is Charlotte and
Charlotte's friend is Alex and
Alex's friend is Jack

Jake Simpson (Age 7)

Easter

E aster time is nearly here
A nd bringing lots of spring time cheer
S o it is time for the Easter bunny
T o bring the eggs while it's sunny
E very child will receive a special one
R unning around to find them is great fun

Kristy Shears (Age 7)

Food

I like tomatoes red and juicy
I like crunchy chips
I like crunchy cucumber
I like french sticks
But I don't like purple beetroot.

Abbey Sheffield (Age 6)

T-Rex

T-rex is great
I can't believe it,
Aah! T-rex is coming!!
He is stomping my house!
Help! I want to get out!
I am going to get stomped!!
Good luck T-rex missed me!
Run for it, I am going to kill him!
He is dead now so we are safe!

Shogo Suzuki (Age 6)

The School Caretaker

As I lurk by the dark
And slimy stairs
I feel a tickle up my nose
It's those darn curly hairs.

I have a bunch of keyrings
Carved out of little boys
I read all their comics
And play with all their toys.

I have this greasy uniform
I wish I was a baker
But because it's all I'm good for
I am the school caretaker.

Kids aren't in the playground now
They're running down the stairs
I'm loving their sad faces
As they're sitting on their chairs.

As I lurk by the dark
And slimy stairs
I feel so alone but
No-one really cares.

Ben Shergold (Age 12)

I Won't Get Up

I won't get up
So go away
Just leave me here.
I'm here to stay

I won't get up
I'm out of fuel
So leave me here
You uncool fool.

I won't get up
That's my rule
I have got more
But their all too cruel.

Alright!, alright!
I'm getting up
But would you please
Help me up?

Sally Sharp (Age 11)

The Ballad Of the Russian Submarine

This is the tale of a sunken submarine,
Where fifty mariners died.
Some lived through the initial blow,
But not a soul survived.

Trapped inside an enclosed space,
For how long could they hold out?
They were no winners to their race,
They saw what their lives were about.

Time is ticking away,
Oxygen is what they lack.
Fear of an unknown life,
Longing for their hope to come back.

The rescue operation came and went,
They managed to save no lives,
They could only send letters of sorrow,
To the saddened mariners' wives.

White lilies, gifts and pity were given,
But nothing could replace the lives lost.
On the mariners' coffins,
Red and white roses were tossed.

Victoria Sadler (Age 13)

A Sky Blue Carpet

You pad softly over me, walking towards the venomous cabinet,
Year after year after year. You gingerly turn the key in the lock.

But, then he comes out of the shower room. You leap away.
I watch you walk down the stairs with him,
Chatting so much about so little, discretely glancing back,
Until you are at the bottom where I can't see you.

That is your fault. I know why you went to the cabinet.
But I will never be able to tell anyone. I hear everything though.
I hear him say to you 'The wretched sun! It's dried up my plants again!
It must have some sort of poison!' Everyone knows that he is a professional gardener
But not for much longer.

The toast pops up sharper than normal, you jump. Then a knock at the door.
You cautiously go to answer it. It's only the postman,
With a small, carefully wrapped parcel. Your yearly supplies.
You brush away the tell-tale fluff from the sofa, where only half an hour ago you sat
Like we once did, until he has to go and live another life like me.

No-one will ever guess why you bought him a blue suit, with a matching tie.
Really, you bought it because you thought the colour would go wonderfully with your latest
Pale yellow walls. But with his blonde hair you will need to be more sly
Unless you want yellow tufts in your sky blue carpet.

Imogen Stoddart (Age 12)

Miss Miss! Saved By The Bell

Miss Miss it's me Kurk Miss
I'm sitting down ok after all I'm here for the day

Miss Miss! Yes Kurk!
I'm sat down and ready to work.

Hi Sherry! Oh hi Kurk are they . . .let's have a crisp!
Miss Miss Sherry's got a lisp.

Oh Kurk just give her a crisp.
OK Miss, since you insist.

Miss Miss Claire's got a spider on her head
Oh Miss I think it's dead.

Oh yeh you've got dreadlocks
You could of said! I was going to hit it with lead.

Miss, Miss OH SHUT UP KURK, but Miss

THAT'S IT I'm taking you to the nurse
But Miss I'm not ill.

Oh yes you are you're mental, that's mentally ill,
So much I could kill

Mmm that's right I'll take you to Cleeve
He will set you right.

Oh no Miss not him please . . .DING A LING A LING . . . saved by the bell.

Zachary Sweeney (Age 11)

Angry Boys

Young boys fight in the war.
It is said that they will get hurt.
They are angry because their friend is dead.
People watch flags fly.
War again.

Gillian Scrivener (Age 14)

Snow

Snow is nice
Snow is cold
Snow is nice to throw
Snow is nice to skate on
Snow is nice to build

Naomi Shea (Age 6)

Home Sweet Home

Home sweet home, it's the place that I'll miss
The smell of hot chocolate, my mum's goodnight kiss.
My dad's wondrous cooking, his hot curry dish,
From chilli to spaghetti, the smell of chips and fish.

My friends and my family will be on my mind,
Strange sights and strange noises, hope new friends I'll find
At home or the shop, on the park or the street,
True friends and best-buddies, are difficult to meet.

Minstrel my rabbit and Titch my goldfish,
To take on my journey, I really do wish,
But back in their home, their cage or their tank,
They're warm and they're cosy, deep, dark and dank.

Rebecca Simm (Age 12)

My Special Rocket!

Its bonfire night,
Money in my pocket,
Down to the shops,
I want the biggest rocket.

Big silver and gold,
This is will really fly,
Exploding into light,
In the nighttime sky.

Now its the time,
The rocket we must light,
Being very careful,
It flies into the night.

With a loud bang,
And a sparkling ball,
Everyone screams,
As pretty lights full.

Fireworks are done,
People all cheer,
My rocket's all gone,
Until next year!

Gemma Scott (Age 12)

Bee The Pig

There was a young girl called Bee
Who was just as handsome as me
She was shocked to find out
On her face a large snout
And now she gets pigs swill for tea

Alexander Shears (Age 11)

Love

Love is a strange emotion
It tickles from head to toe.
It comes in one swift motion
An arrow from Cupid's bow.
It takes over your mind
Gives you weird feelings inside.
You never know what you will find
You show feelings you normally hide.
When you see your lover
It drives you insane,
You really want to hug her
Being kept away is a pain.
Love is a strange emotion
It tickles from head to toe.

Daniel Spalding (Age 12)

Tiger

In the jungle there's plenty to fear
Especially when the tiger is near
As he opens up his jaw
He lets out a mighty roar
He looked so soft and tame before
I tried to stroke him, be his mummy;
But now I'm deep inside his tummy
So if you hear the tiger's near
Run like crazy
It's dark in here!
Don't be fooled, there's much to fear.
Next time you are in the jungle
And you hear your tummy rumble,
Make doubly sure that it is yours
Or you might end up . . .
IN HIS JAWS!!

Brianna Simpson (Age 8)

The Dog

A bone chewer
A lead tangler
A loud barker
A cat chaser
A rough licker
A short sleeper
A curious creeper
A long walker
A fast runner

Lily Speer (Age 7)

Seasons

Winter, it's turned colder
The year is older
Christmas is coming
Children are humming.

Spring, lambs are being born
Farmers are growing corn
Daffodils are bright
The nights are getting light.

Summer, nice cold ice-cream
A picnic down by the stream
Barbecues in the sunshine
Summer is a fun time.

Autumn, summer is over
The leaves are falling
Clover's dying
Winter's calling

Andrea Spalding (Age 14)

Best Friends

Best friends are
Always helpful,
Because when you
Are lonely they
Come and play
With you,

They are joyful,
And playful and
Always kind too you
I've got a best friend
She's ever so nice

Yes I've got some
Friends have you?

Hannah Sparks (Age 7)

Trapped

Trapped behind bars for hours on end
Locked up in a cage all day and night
People stop and stare
Rudely point and glare
And sometimes even laugh
As the night gets dark
The days get cold
I soon appreciate my fur coat
Lonely I get and I long for a friend
I want to be free
And see the world
Why am I put through such misery?
All I do is prowl around
But my one and only wish . . .
Is to be set free

Anna Somerville (Age 13)

My Family

My family are tall, short, thin and fat,
I have two dogs but I don't have a cat,
My mum's an artist, my dad's a D.I.Y. man,
And me and my sister will just do what we can,
They all make me laugh, but they all make me mad,
They all shout at me but only 'cause I'm bad,
My mum does the washing, the ironing and she's the cook,
If you tell my dad to do it you'll get a strange look,
My sister does nothing except watch TV.
Neither do I, I suppose but I eat cakes and drink tea.
My dogs are always playing and rolling around the floor.
My fish just swim and my birds just gnaw.
I love my family lots 'cause we're different from all the rest,
I mean how many families do you know that are nothing but the BEST!!!

Jenni Shinn (Age 12)

Waiting - The Audition

Waiting, waiting, waiting,
For the sound of your name.
Will it be rejection,
Or the road to fame.

Waiting, waiting, waiting,
They watch you like vultures.
Scribbling and commenting,
As you struggle to impress.

Waiting, waiting, waiting
Good news or bad.
You've done your best
So no need to feel bad.

Jacob Smart (Age 12)

The Meal?

Majestically soaring through wondrous blue sky,
Showing no fear.
Her golden brown plumes glimmer under the midday sun.
She surveys the rolling hills beneath her glaring eyes,
Scanning the hills for The Meal.

A lush carpet of green grass dotted with trees and littered with dens.
Hares scurrying, something's in the air.
Panic! Hares darting everywhere.
Her piercing eyes sitting on top of her golden beak
Have already fixed rigid on a poor unsuspecting hare.
Launching herself like a missile,
Her homing device locked on
Thrusting her dagger-like claws into its helpless frame.

The hunt is over
Tomorrow's another day

Ben Shanmugam (Age 12)

Environment

I think people should think
Before they throw away their stink
Because we need to help the environment
This won't affect people who are reaching retirement
But it will affect me and my generation
This won't just affect England
But the whole nation
We really need to recycle more
Instead of just throwing it out the door.

George Sabatowski (Age 12)

Poem Of My Scary Experience

We were walking through Tesco when I got lost.
I was terrified and scared, trying to find my family,
I saw lots of people busily doing their shopping,
I felt as small as a mouse.
I was very lonely and sad.

Seeing the people in a big crowd,
Trying to find my parents.
I was confused and worried,
I was afraid and very frightened.
I pushed past the busy crowd like a bullet,
I was tearful as I looked down each isle,
And there they were!
Shopping, not noticing I was gone,
I ran up to them and cried.
I had finally found them after what seemed like forever,
I was overjoyed.
I'm never going to get lost again, (I hope!)

Karan Sehdev (Age 11)

School!!!

School is not that bad
Teachers aren't that sad
Education is there for a reason
We do something different every season
So stick it out
And without a doubt
Those F's and G's
Will turn into
A's and B's
In your SAT's and GCSE's

Kelly Schluter (Age 13)

Daydreams

My mum is nagging me,
But I'm not listening...

I'm riding a speedboat,
Across the waves.
And chasing monsters,
Out of caves.

I'm flying through the air,
Like a bird or a plane.
I'm riding a horse,
With it's beautiful mane.

I'm walking through a desert,
As hot as it can be.
I'm lying on a golden beach,
Listening to the sea.

I'm back in the real world now,
My mum is still there.
And she's still nagging me,
But I don't care!

Katie Skinner (Age 14)

Don't Yell At Me

Don't yell at me!
I hate it when you do,
It makes me feel so miserable
I want to run from you

Don't yell at me!
I always get the blame,
It makes me feel so miserable
It was them who called me names

Don't yell at me!
I just want to scream
It makes me feel so miserable
Wake up and it's all a dream

Lauren Sleeman (Age 13)

Huntingdon Life Sciences - A Beagle's Story

I sit and stare and shake and weep,
I do not eat, I do not sleep.
I bleed profusely - hurt and cut
But no-one takes a second look.
Is this the life I have to live?
What is it that I have to give?
Is this the role I have to play?
Not knowing if I'll see another day.
I have no space to play and run,
Why is it me? What have I done?
I get ignored until they need
Another creature to suffer and bleed.
Locked up inside a cage of throes
With no-one else to share my woes.
I hurt, I ache, I writhe, I burn,
Upset, alone - nowhere to turn.

Alison Shepherd (Age 13)

The Last Sunset

The last mountain, the final victim,
A fiery ocean sweeps across the land
Like a golden eagle, beating its almighty wings;
Its head proud, its presence threatening.

A single feather drops from the eagle's breast,
Slowly it falls unwillingly to the ground
A tear drops from its menacing eye;
Paralysing the earth out of all existence.

Darkness falls upon the eagle's lair,
A thousand stars emerge from the cloudless night
Lying on the sky;
Like diamonds on velvet.

A black raven circles the mountain,
Protecting the night
Its wings strong and powerful;
Its presence threatening.

Abigail Southwell (Age 11)

A Glow Of Peace

Someday, a great glow will sweep the land
Illuminating faces that are angry, sad and bland
In Indonesia and Angola, where war threatens
Soldiers and fighters dispose of their weapons
Friendships are patched up and mended
All races, religions and skin colours are blended
Sodden cheeks and flowing tears are wiped dry
The truth is uncovered and no-one tells a lie
Mass murderers cease their evil killing
Self-indulgent billionaires commence sharing
Hate, sadness and anger are running thin
Evil is out, and peace is in.

Louisa Sutton (Age 13)

My Cat

My cat got knocked down not long ago
On her back was a logo
The logo was from a tyre
The accident was very dire.

My cat's eyes were sunk into its head
I don't know how long it had been dead.
Its head was floppy and so was its belly
It looked like it was made of jelly.

As the cat was crushed
I thought its brains must be mashed
My cat was very flat
It looked like my front door mat.

Matt Stephens (Age 12)

I'd Rather

I'd rather - do the washing up,
I'd rather - be sick,
I'd rather - put make-up on,
I'd rather - give up chocolate,
I'd rather - kiss the floor,
I'd rather - read a book,
I'd rather - go to bed at 5,
I'd rather - clean the loo,
I'd rather - do most anything,
But see or pick up a spider!

Rebecca Salmon (Age 9)

Cats

C ats are clever and intelligent
A dorable and sweet
T ame or wild and are
S ometimes scared of mice

Kayleigh Sullivan (Age 12)

Nightmare!

Lydia I wonder if your thumbs grow in when you die?
Wheelchair going backwards by and by
A pumpkin to my head smiling scarily by and by
Screaming being re-wound as if people are dying

BANG!!

In a graveyard with a taste of mouldy chocolate.

A garlicky smell,

Garlic round my chest.

A breath on my neck!

Falling! Falling!!

Ellie Smillie (Age 11)

The Complaining Monster

Mama! Mama! There is something there
Something where
Under my bed Mum
There's nothing there now don't be dumb
Yes there is, with sharp claws and teeth that bite
Yeah right
It told me so I know it's there
Do you know what I just don't care
And so the boy he went to bed
Pulled up the covers, the pillow to his head
During the night the boy awoke
And from the floor the monster spoke
I'm here to complain,
Complain?
Yeah, for one thing you leave your lights on too long
Another is your radio I hate that old song
Oh not to mention those sandwiches too
You've left them there four weeks and they've turned blue.

Alexandra Serebriakoff (Age 13)

Vampire Cat

Vampire cat screaming for blood,
Born in a graveyard,
Ghosts rising from the dead,
Breaking in houses searching for blood,
Back in the graveyard he goes
The vampire cat

Andrew Sterling (Age 7)

Snow

I wonder what those white things are,
That fall down from the sky?
My mum says they are little tiny drops,
Of icy cold snow.

Is that why it is cold?
Why is it cold?
How is it made?
When is it made?
Why does it come - then go?

My mum says it's made from water,
And it's been made with something so cold,
So it is icy,
I don't know whether she was telling the truth,
I don't know if I should believe her.

Maybe I should just forget it,
And think what fun it is.
Here then gone, with the sun.
Firm, then melted like white chocolate.
Hard then soft, crisp - then wet!
Just how much weirder can things get?

Anna Stewart (Age 12)

Which Dog?

"Come on," I said pulling mum by the hand,
Off we went to a wonderful land.
A land filled with dogs of all types,
Some had spots and some had stripes.

Ben the bulldog with a crumpled up face,
"Oh no!" I said as he began to chase.
Dotty the Dalmatian all covered in spots,
I didn't like him, he'd gone all to pots!

Polly the Poodle with a pom-pom tail,
I didn't want her as she looked rather frail.
Morris the Mongrel with lots of shaggy hair,
That would fall out and go everywhere!

I began to think, "Oh this is a bore!"
I turned and headed for the door.
In front of me was a dog with soft golden hair,
All I could do was stand and stare.

It was the greatest dog I ever saw,
It could even give you a paw!
"Mummy, this is the one for me!"
"Oh good," said mum with a look of glee!

Hayley Sommerville (Age 12)

The Train Crash

Travelling train trashes two tracks,
Crumpling carriages and creating cracks,
Plenty of passengers protest in pain,
Railwaymen run in the rain.

Alarms alert to ambulance arrival,
Straight to the scene to help survival,
Massive machines move mangled mess,
Prying people appear from the press.

Vicky Singleton (Age 11)

Dreams

Pictures in my mind.
Last night I had a dream,
Aliens swimming in the stream
Talking flowers, flying trees,
The big yellow sun was in the seas.
Pictures in my mind.
Will I have that dream again,
Dancing policemen, red and blue hens.
Where a rainbow is upside down,
The sky and clouds are on the ground.
Pictures in my mind.
I am so lucky that I can find
So many pictures in my mind.

Georgia Sach (Age 9)

Fox

Fox began.
He took the sharpness of glinting flint
And stole the clunking sound of wood upon wood.
And fox got his bark.

Fox seized the orangeness of the setting sun;
He captured the blackness of coal
And the whiteness of chalk.
He grabbed the roughness of warped tree bark
And got his coat.

Fox took for his eyes
The piercing yellowness of bright amber
And the murkiness of muddy water.

And then Fox swiped
The thickness of a blossoming bush,
The softness of falling sand, and got his tail.

And finally Fox took
The never-ending cleverness of clear running water,
The slinking and winking of the moon
And got his slyness.

So Fox was made.

Jessica Schramm (Age 11)

Black

A dead body left to rot in an old, broken mine.
The coal-bunker degenerating in the death of night.
The eerie wind of darkness wraps itself around the gravestones of an empty graveyard
The light of day has been engulfed by the darkness of night.

Robert Schatten (Age 10)

The End Of The World

Icy cold wind swirled around me
Like a smothering blanket of death,
The cold is so intense
It's like a thousand knives
Being driven into my icy body.

Death swirls around me
Laughing . . . laughing
Like a mad circus clown
I feel so helpless
In the hands of death I suffer . . .

A blinding fiery red light
Illuminated the world and lit me
Like thousands of fiery needles
Death's finger nails prickle into me
Like a spiky thorn bush
The end is here . . .

I Die

Mark Samples (Age 11)

I Don't Write To Win

I don't write to win,
Just be to heard.
I would much rather this ended in the bin.
I don't care if this is first or thirty-third.

I write so that people understand my pain;
I pity those who can relate.
To say goodbye I cannot do again,
Ever to love her is my eternal fate.

She's changed her school and is gone.
Happy endings live only in books I've read.
Even writing this poem feels wrong -
My heart is forever dead.

With an angel bard compared I should never deserve a chance.
The last poem I wrote made her cry.
I stood up, such a rare dance.
Sometimes I feel I should die.

I wish I could ask her please to forgive.
Everybody makes out still loving her is a crime.
Without thinking of her I could not live.
Yet in this sadness and sorrow I still manage to rhyme!

Robert Smith-Brix (Age 12)

School

At school
This is what I heard
This is what I saw
Shoes squeaking,
Doors creaking,
Children peeking,
That's what I heard and saw at school.
At school
This is what I heard
This is what I felt
Stony walls,
Water from pools,
Air that's cool,
That's what I heard and felt at school.
Outside this is what I heard
This is what I felt
Cool breeze,
Swishing trees,
Dinging keys,
That's what I heard and felt at school.

Robert Scoppie (Age 9)

It Doesn't Really Matter . . . .

It doesn't really matter if you're fat or if you're thin,
The most important thing, I think, is what you are within.

A kind and friendly person, who cares for those around
Will always give you good advice, that's genuine and sound.

It doesn't really matter if you're rich or if you're poor,
Listening to a person brag, is such an awful bore.

As long as you are clothed and fed and have the things you need,
Wanting all the latest trends, is imply down to greed.

It doesn't really matter if you dance with two left feet,
Or if you sing like you're tone deaf and always feel defeat.

Everybody has a gift, in their own special way,
So just remember and never forget this lesson learnt today.

That it doesn't really matter what other people do,
The most important thing to be is just simply be you.

Chloe Smith (Age 13)

Fairies

Tiny, delicate wings flutter in the breeze.
Small, exquisite faces of the finest porcelain.
Their eyes are sprinkled with stardust.
Their cheeks are covered with gold.
Their lips are as red as the finest wine.
And their faces shimmer with dew.
They fly high above the forests.
They touch the stars in the sky.
They play with the unicorns and centaurs.
They converse with the gods in the clouds.
They are hardly ever seen by the humans wandering eyes.
They fly faster than a speeding bullet, they disappear into the sky.
Yet some say they have seen them, frolicking in their minds.

Courtney Sklar (Age 12)

Sunset

I stand alone on the hill watching the sunset for the millionth time.
Pinks, reds and fluffy coloured clouds passing
I know it well
But tonight something is different.
A man's figure
Outlined by the sun.
He is tall, strong and handsome.
He is running but getting nowhere.
I feel as if I recognise him yet
I have never seen him before.
I blink once and he is gone.
I know that when I watch the sun set again
I will no longer see his lone face
Running but getting nowhere.

Jenni Smith (Age 12)

War

There they are, watching, waiting
They are ready to kill.
People are scared.
People are forced out of their homes.
I am taken away from my mother
And other children are put in homes.
One of the soldiers watches out for bombs
Which will drop out of the air.
All the rest keep guard,
Ready to shoot their enemies.
Will I ever see my family again?
Will I ever live to see another day?
Or will I die?

Lianne Simpson (Age 14)

My Island

My Island is,
Green, lush and peaceful.
The cock crows,
The trees sway in harmony
With the wind
The day begins.

The birds start singing,
And soon the morning dew is gone.
Burnt out by the crisp clear sun.
Over the hills the sand glistens,
And the sea tinkles,

Where old trunks lay,
Green shoots appear.
Busy bees buzz around me
The smell of roses overwhelms me.
This is my Island.

Richard Smith (Age 11)

The Night Of The Storm

The night of the storm
Lightning struck
Thunder booms
Light fills the rooms
Huge waves
Fills up the caves

The night of the storms
Rain pours
On the roof tops
Falling hard and strong.

Samantha Smith (Age 12)

Neptune's Rage

Neptune twists the sea in his rage,
The waves rise and throw surf into the air,
He stirs the under currents into a stampede.
The waves roll like the rearing of a great white mare.

The thunder rolls, the lightning tears the sky in two,
As the great clouds collide they echo like a drum,
The sky is black fabric slashed by a golden knife,
The lightning flares like a gun.

The great and beautiful ship is tossed over the wild waters,
It is used like a toy in Neptune's game,
The rocks bring their doom closer still to the elegant ship,
The once majestic sails will bow their masts in shame.

No longer magnificent or dignified,
A pile of wood scattered about the traumatic tides,
The storm is over, the deed is done,
Neptune fixes his gaze on the heavens and his ocean swells with pride.

Jenny Smith (Age 13)

My Dog

I have a Golden Retriever,
Sophie is her name,
She is loyal and friendly,
And loves to play a game,
We go for walk in the wood,
And chase squirrels,
Like all dogs should,
She is fat and hairy,
And soft and true,
Without her I would,
Feel so blue,
I tell her all my secrets,
We have lots of fun,
But when it comes to,
Feeding her I leave it to my mum.

Stephanie Smith (Age 11)

Foot And Mouth Poem

Foot and mouth is very bad

Foot and mouth makes people mad

Foot and mouth could be on your land

Foot and mouth is everywhere

Foot and mouth can get everywhere

Foot and mouth is invisible no one can see it

Only the smoke from the pyres can be seen for miles.

What do you think will happen next?

Sam Sturmey (Age 12)

In Ruins

In the middle of the moor,
Stood in isolation,
A castle with out its core,
No means of preservation.

This scene of natural beauty,
Eroding day by day,
Its value does not matter,
So to us why should it stay?

But heritage is precious,
It's not that some don't see,
The aim is to preserve it,
For the future it should be.

The castle stands in ruins,
While all we do is stray,
Destruction of its beauty,
Until it has worn away.

Claire Shere (Age 15)

The Night Sea

The seagulls have gone
And the silence lives on
The sun has gone down
And the colours will drown.
The grey clouds settle
like a lump of hard metal.
The mist becomes thicker
And the silver stars flicker.

Lauren Shelton (Age 12)

December Weather

Down the snow is falling,
Eventually winter is calling.
Christmas pudding, presents too,
Electronic game for me, but by who?
Many people gather by the fire,
But the snow is rising even higher.
Even though I like the summer,
Realising it's winter is even funnier.

Winter is extremely cold,
Especially if you're going bald.
Another wet, cold, snowy day.
Together we watch the white snow lay.
Hearing the birds sing their songs,
Everyone's wearing their long-johns!
Really hope it's not gone by dawn.

Jessica Smith (Age 12)

A Life Gone By

My wilting grasses, living on my shivering skin,
A constant remainder of days gone by,
When the sun shone brightly, bronzing my scared skin.

I remember my tears splashing around my base,
Undercutting my crumbling structure
Revealing my history as an epic story.

Peregrines nested on my dark edges, cowering in my infancy,
Hiding from the extremes of the sky.
Perching precariously on my jagged spits.

I stretched for miles,
The leader of the countryside,
Orphaning the wise oak trees, which lay as a sheet below me.

Heather embedded itself in my pores,
As gentle as a firefly, it explored my decrepit surface
Creeping suspiciously round each contour.

But no longer can I play
I am dead - murdered by the water below, the rain, the frost,
Which saw my face fall into a deluge of scree.

I don't blame anyone - we all must die,
But do you know what it is like?
Never to be protected, always an exhibit, which no one respects.

Lucy Strong (Age 15)

Silence

Silence is a lonely sea hitting the shore
Silence is a dream of mysterious things in your head
Silence is a wind running in the air
Silence is a candle glowing gently
Silence is a leaf fluttering to the ground
Silence is a baby sleeping

Robert Steven (Age 7)

Fate

It's 2 a.m. and all is silent, all the streets are bare
But for the youth kicking up stones, no-one gives a dare

He's just out looking for a fight, or so some people say
They don't know he has a heart, they don't care anyway

A lad of only twenty years with no place to call home
Because of youth he's rejected by all, to face the world alone

There's dirt upon the clothes he wears, and sadness in his eyes
He sits himself upon the wall and no-one sees him cry

He wonders how long it has been since he slept in a bed
He's more depressed than usual, just wishing he was dead

They found his body there at dawn, the policeman stood and sighed
And sleeves rolled up, his wrists were slit. The verdict "Suicide"

Zoey Seaton (Age 14)

Just Another Day

Bleep, bleep, bleep, bleep THUD.
Another day starts at six o'clock,
I turn on the light and suffer from the shock.
I go to the bathroom and turn on the tap,
It's six fifteen now, there's no turning back.
I climb in the shower and start to wash my hair,
School is coming nearer and it just isn't fair.
I'm eating my breakfast, butter and toast,
I hear a noise, it must be the post.
It's eight o'clock now and not much time to go,
If only there was a flood or hail or snow.
It's nine o'clock now and I'm sitting in class,
I've got history, geography, science then maths.

Brrriiiing, could it be, has the time come?
Is the school day really done?
Now I can go home and watch the telly,
And get some real food in my belly.
I've done my homework and it's time for bed,
Now I can rest my tired little head.

Bleep, bleep, bleep, bleep THUD.

Helen Strike (Age 13)

The Final

It was Liverpool to take the lead,
Birmingham felt like a seed,
Robbie Fowler scored the goal,
Birmingham needed andy Cole.

Birmingham then drew level,
For Liverpool what a devil,
That was in stoppage time,
Time to celebrate with some wine.

In extra time,
Things weren't so fine,
In penalties,
Well for Birmingham it was like a disease.

Liverpool won the game,
For Birmingham what a shame!

Luke Smith (Age 12)

My Scary First Day At My New Secondary School

I was nervous when I walked past those school gates,
Seeing all those Year 11 monsters,
When we went to our tutor room,
I was terrified,
Then I saw loads of classrooms,
With teachers,
It was crowded and I felt like a little mouse,
All confused in the lessons.

Then when it was lunch-time,
I went to the canteen,
And saw it was even more crowded,
And I was feeling even more unhappy,
Then when it was time for the next lesson,
I felt a bit happier,
Because there were only two more lessons left,
And finally when the bell went I was overjoyed,
Because it was time to go home.
But I will have to face it again for a very long time.

Aman Sehdev (Age 11)

A Cruel World

I don't know if I'll live to be a teenager,
Or even ten years old,
All I know is that I'm gonna die,
Or so I have been told.
I'd wanted to grow old and have kids,
Get married and have a wife,
But I'd never have guessed that I'd be told,
That I'd have to fight for life.
In this battle of survival I've noticed a change,
In the way that people treat me,
It is as if I have some serious disease,
That all the world can see.
It was then that I realised the saddening truth,
That my life was on the line,
I joined the weak children on the news,
Of a sickness that was now mine.
I wish I could have a normal life,
Make friends, go out to play,
But instead I have to stay inside,
Who'd have thought it would be this way.

Dawn Sambells (Age 13)

Magical Stars

The stars are little blobs of white paint on black paper
They are sprinkles of icing sugar on a dark chocolate cake
The stars are little fireflies twinkling through the night sky
The stars are flakes of snow spread across black mud
The stars flickers of lights lighting up in a dark room
The stars are shattered fragments of a white piece of plastic
The stars are broken pieces of a lightbulb never loosing its power to shine

Carl Spooner (Age 12)

The Moon

The moon is a giant cookie slowly being eaten.
The moon is white chalk gathered in to a circle.
The moon is a juicy apple looking for its stem.
The moon is a white beachball continually being kicked in the sky.
The moon is a white world slowly disappearing.
The moon is a white animal surfing the midnight sky.

Cameron Stiles-Foley (Age 11)

Dreaming

We're in the sky,
We're so so high,
We're passing by,
The fields of sky,
The clouds so white,
Looks like a kite,
Fluttering and swaying,
Up until night.

Joe Sutcliffe (Age 6)

Dream World

Beyond the door of my dreams,
I hear some rustling in the trees,
I see a breezy Atlantic shore,
I think to myself is there more?
As I walk down the sandy path,
I hear the birds chuckling laugh.
I went back to the door of reality,
Oh No! where's the key?

Jon Stimpson (Age 11)

Dolphin

Bottleneck nose
A stone skimming along the surface of a foam flecked wave
Polished skin.

A child at play
A missile coasting in the bow-wave of an ocean liner
A bubble of life and energy.

Tom Stringwell (Age 12)

Senses

Alone on the athletics track,
Until my senses bring it to life,
Listening.
I hear distant starting guns startling nearby birds,
The hooter signalling a javelin to be launched, like a spear during battle,
The click of the electric scoreboard as points are added up.
Looking.
I see a pair of forgotten spikes going mouldy in the rain,
A deserted time keepers block going rusty with age,
The high jump bar falling off the stand in the eerie evening breeze,
Smelling.
I smell smoke from the starting gun clinging to the dampness of my clothes,
The odour of tired worn out bodies in the changing rooms,
The smell of burnt bacon from the closed snack bar.
Thinking.
I'm thinking about becoming a world champion,
Dreaming of a moment I'll never want to forget,
Hoping I'll become world famous one day.
Soon my senses will no longer be senses, they'll be real life - I hope!!!

Carly Smith (Age 12)

Two Dumb Boys And A Deaf Policeman

One bright day
In the middle of the night
Two dumb boys
Came out to fight
Back to back
They faced each other
Drew their swords
And shot each other
A deaf policeman
Heard the noise
And went and arrested
Those two dumb boys

Adam Stratford (Age 15)

Charge Of the Grannies

A minute away, a minute away
That way comes the grannies today
Charge, charge
There they are ready as usual.

Grannies, grannies
Here today what do you want
If your going to stay.

Hey, hey,
You're going to stay
Eat, eat
The lovely meat
Charge, charge
For the jelly that wobbles on the telly.
There they go messy as usual.

Nicola Snow (Age 11)

One Moment In Time

Although it didn't work out,
There is no question of a doubt,
That when I look into your eyes
I always see paradise skies.
Even if it's always going to be
Friendship as pure as the sea,
The adoration I have for you
Will last as long as the sky is blue.
Because when I look into your eyes
I see a true love that never dies.
Whenever you see the sun rise
Remember never to forget
When I was yours and you were mine
For that perfect moment in time.

Nishi Shah (Age 15)ÿ

In My House

In my house I can smell my mum's cooking
As she tries to please me.
In my house I can taste the food
My mum makes me.
In my house I can hear the TV
When my dad watches football.
In my house I can feel my nice warm bed
As I sleep.

In my house I touch my hamster
As it crawls up my arm.

Gemma Stevenson (Age 11)

Like A Candle

Like a candle I burn away,
My flame was lit upon the day,
You said goodbye and left me there,
You were out of my reach and out of my care.
Away I burn and soon to fade,
Without my heart that you once made.
The flame gets smaller every day,
It'll burn out soon and fade away.
So here I stand all on my own,
I should've told you what I've always known.
I love you more than words can say,
You don't feel the same so I melt away.
The flame is hot and shines so bright,
It shows I'm scared and shows my fright.
It also shines on all my regrets,
But you're my love and I'll never forget.
You hold the key to the door of my love,
But now I drift to the stars above.
The candle wax is all that remains,
Now I'm gone and free from the pain.

Kelly Savile (Age 16)

Cat

Wool muddler
Kitten cuddler
Wood scratcher
Milk lapper
Night prowler
Light growler
Moonlight walker
Midnight stalker

Laura Smith (Age 10)

An Evil Breeze

Wind! Where do you come from and where do you stay?
I come from the north far far away!

Why do you blow so wild wind?
And why do you frighten even the strongest man?

Why! Because I am evil, and I'm powerful
And because I can!

Why are you so destructive?
And out of your mouth a force so strong
Where does that power come from?

Because that's who I am and that's no force
It's my song!

But when will you stop?

I shall stop when earth is nothing
And I can destroy not another drop!

Jonathan Smillie (Age 11)

Shipwrecker

Sea, where do you come from and how long will you stay?
I come from a planet so very far away.
When will you stop crashing against our city walls?
I'll never stop until your civilisation falls
Why are you so carnivorous and when will your reign end?
Because I'm powerful and I have no friend.
Why do you gobble every ship that passes on its way?
Because I can and I'm here to stay

Ben Smith (Age 11)

A Picturesque Dream In Goathland

Smoothly flowing water trickles over jagged imperfect cobbled stone,
Hidden beneath the unruly undergrowth never to be known

Can this secret garden be real?
The sensations too thrilling to be true,
Can this idealistic dream be what hopes are built from
Or was this peaceful imagery created to enslave me and you?

Then the deceitful treacherous pebbles show their hidden secret,
But . . . it's too late water flies and soars, falling to the waiting rocks.
It strikes with a cruel infliction enforcing all its strength,
Torment and misery will soon be shown through the stones hurt indent.

It glides away to pastures new sure to grow and mount and swell,
With the rains silent fall or the grasses dew no time to linger and dwell.
It flows swiftly on unknowing of what's to come,
Over craggy stones and animals' bones to the light sound of the dragonflies hum.

Where will it go? What will it see?
The knowledge of this is not for you, or me!
But I'm sure we'll find in years from now the memory of this stream,
And the fresh scent of imagination is still . . . anything but a dream.

Louisa Saunders (Age 15)

Seasons

Spring is the season that starts off the year
The flowers wake up and the bees get busy
New lambs are born and starting to grow
Meadows turn yellow and birds begin to sing

Now summer's the season that the sun comes out
Children are playing and having fun
The parks are full of happy smiling people
Having picnics and paddling in the pools

I think autumn is the most colourful season
Leaves changing colours to yellow, orange and brown
The wind starts to blow and the leaves scattered around
Animals collect food ready for winter

As winter arrives it brings cold frosty nights
And it also brings freezing fog too
Sometimes it snows and children build snowmen
Do you like seasons? Because I do!

Chelsea Stojkowski (Age 8)

Spring

All the flowers start to wake,
The baby lambs appear
Now I know that winter's gone
And the Springtime is near.

Sarah Short (Age 8)

The Pictures In My Mind

When I close my eyes this is what I see,
Winding rivers stretching into the countryside,
Tall, tall mountains as high as the sky,
Fluffy, bunnies, bouncing by.

Glittering blue seas and soft white sands,
Little boats bobbing up and down,
Children splashing and playing in the sand,
Whilst seagulls screech and circle all around.

Flower covered meadows, hills yellow and green,
Majestic houses surrounded by trees,
Swans floating on rivers whilst ducks fly by,
All surrounded by a pale blue sky.

Magical castles with their tall pointed towers,
Steep, scary, slides, twist and fall,
Dangerous dragons, in dungeons dark and cold . . .
So it's not all fun, you need to be bold.

So these are the pictures in my mind,
If you could see inside my head that is what you'd find,
And see all the things I have seen,
As I close my eyes and start to dream.

Annabelle Smith (Age 9)

Lizard

Isn't it weird how a lizard
Sticks out his tongue
Low or high, to catch a fly
Not for fun, it doesn't matter
He just wants to get fatter.

Little bugs dart about
Trying to escape this thing, poking out
Too bad the lizard is quick
Twenty bugs in just one lick
Not for fun it doesn't matter
He just wants to get fatter.

When he's asleep, you'd never know
His eyes are wide open with a certain glow
If any insects come his way
His tongue pokes out straightaway
Not for fun it doesn't matter
He just wants to get fatter and fatter and fatter.

Katie Smith (Age 10)

Labour

Labour are the best,
Better than the rest.
Hague thinks he'll win,
But Labour will just chuck him in the bin.
Hague is the weakest link,
What do you think?

Kimberley Snape (Age 9)

The Fox's Cry

The cry was painful and upsetting
Help it seemed to say,
The mother fox howling to answer,
It hurt me to hear them too.

The thunder reared over the hillside,
And turned the world white for a second,
The sound confused my head,
A tear sized drop of rain rolled down my face.

A gunshot stopped the world moving,
A deafening bang hurt my heart,
My heart beating faster than ever,
I prayed that it missed the fox.

The quiet sounded peaceful but threatening,
The beat in my heart slowed down,
I heard nothing but the silence was lonely,
The silence was broke by the baby fox's cry.

Nichola Claire Shepherd (Age 9)

The Left Out Boy

He was standing in the park he had a sad face
No one to play with he didn't like this place

He was shaking wild
Now who wants to play with this child?

Folks played jokes on the boy his eyes were weary
All of the bullies broke his toys the bullies looked scary

He was shaking wild
Now who wants to play with this child?

He asked his dad to mend his toy this time he was gong to defend it
The bullies crowded round the boy the bullies were very fit

He was shaking wild
Now who wants to play with this child

He was always on his own a sad life he leads
A left out and lonely boy a friend is what he needs

He was shaking wild
Now who wants to play with this child?

Steven Sims (Age 9)

The Dog

There was a dog called Shandy
Who had a bit of brandy

He said, "I like my bone
I found it under a stone"

I wish that bone was really mine
I suppose I will still eat it by that sign

The bone made me ill
So they took me to our doctor Bill.

Jacqui Shipley (Age 10)

When I Go To Collenswood

When I go to Collenswood,
I will see at Collenswood,
Ten terrible teachers
Nine nutty new kids
Eight high heaps of homework
Seven soggy stationery sets
Six worrying work books
Five dying dictionaries
Four throbbing thesaurus
Three ducking ducks
Two hideous head teachers
And one gigantic school with lots of stair cases
Which one to choose?

Victoria Singleton (Age 10)

Pictures In My Mind

There are pictures in my mind,
Of things I remember that I have left behind.
A sunny day, a leafy lane, Blue skies, flowers
And an aeroplane.

There are pictures in my mind
Of things I love and people who are kind
Like my Grandma waving at her door
And a cuddle from mum when my knee is sore.

There are pictures in my mind,
Of sadder times when my Grandad died
I remember that I cried, gave my mum a hug
As my tears she dried.

There are pictures in my mind,
Of so many places I've yet to find
A sandy shore, a rocky cove
And maybe even a treasure trove.

I'm so lucky that I can find
So many pictures in my mind.

Thomas Simmons (Age 9)

How I Get To School

I get in the car
But we don't have to go far
Get to school
To play with a ball
Bell rings
Children sing.
Go to class
To do our tasks.

Stephanie Smith (Age 8)

In School

Me and my friends play at school,
And some of the boys think they are cool.

They run about and scream and shout,
Especially when the sun is out.

We play our games and sing our songs,
And sometimes get our lessons wrong.

Then it's time to eat our lunch,
And some of us are a noisy bunch.

We go out to play,
Then we shout hip hip hooray.

Because it is near
To the end of the day.

Harry Shakespeare (Age 8)

Dance Until Moonlight

Dance until moonlight
Dance till you drop
Dance and skip
Do a dance
    Dance Dance

Dance until moonlight
Dance till you drop
Dance by the sea
Dance with the waves
    Dance Dance

Dance until moonlight
Dance till you drop
Dance with the moonlight
Dance till it's midnight
    Dance Dance

Dance until moonlight
Dance till you drop
Dance with me
And I'll dance with you
Dance together
    Dance Dance

Nancia Sharp (Age 8)

Snowflakes

Round and cold
As white as snow
Lovely snowflakes
Fall to the ground
But don't touch
Because they'll melt
And be gone . . . .

Axl Stone (Age 6)

Books, Books, Books

Fun, fantasy, fiction books.
Boring, silly, uninteresting books.
Crime, children's chronological books,
Real, reading, relaxing books.
Map, murder, mystery books.
Sad, smelly, serious books.
Hip, happy, hilarious books.
Text, terrible trilogy books.
Good, generous, gobsmacking books.
Death, dreary, demanding books,
Love, lively, lingering books.
Nasty, naughty, notorious books.
Wet, witness, worrying books.
Books can be found anywhere
And can be about anything
And are mostly found in a . . . .

LIBRARY!

Daniel Symes (Age 11)

Furniture Poem

She's the only friend I have,
And everyone loves her
As if, anyone, would hate her.
She is a bowl of sharp pencils.

She loves Tigger, in fact she is Tigger,
The best way for her to start the day,
Is with music.
She sometimes has growing pains in her back,
which make me laugh.

Her favourite football team is Man U.
She is obsessed with English and Maths,
NO WAY SHE SAYS!
Her worst nightmare is the boy over the road, David!
Dun, Dun, Duuuuuuuuun!

We get along well,
She makes me laugh a lot,
Especially when she gets hyper!
She loves pussycats,
And her hamster Reg.

Who is she?

Rebecca Sutton (Age 10)

The Glass Of Water

Standing quite still
The ground starts shaking gently
Ripples start to appear on the glass surface
The ground rumbles like an earthquake
A hand comes out from nowhere,
The hand grabs the rippling glass
The glass moves slowly up
A pair of huge lips appear and open
The water swirls like a cyclone
It disappears down a black hole
Never to be seen again

Cal Smith-Sheerin (Age 9)

The Life Of A Fish

Another day in the big bad world,
All day I'm on the move like a hiker only in fear,
Just Waiting to be caught

I'm in constant danger of everyone all the time
Yet I scavenge on any food left over

Some food, no fight in sight this is my chance,
I've got it but I'm racing
I'm out of the water my life flashing before my eyes,
One last look at the world before it disappears

FOREVER

Eddie Swales (Age 11)

New York

I am outside and am being watched by skyscrapers towering over me.
The tops of the buildings reach up to the clouds,
And maybe goes on even further.

I turn to the side, and my eyes meet a tall
Green statue it's the Statue of Liberty,
And the torch, it brightens up my day.

I walk and walk on, to find the empire State Building.
It takes me higher than ever,
Higher than all of the skyscrapers put together.

I suddenly find myself in an open green area,
It's the famous Central Park, ice rinks, regular joggers, squirrels,
All of these make up a part of Central Park.

I then go to Wall Street, where the stock exchange is
The figures are higher than the clouds,
And just about as hard to work out.

I have thoroughly enjoyed my holiday,
The Statue of Liberty, the Empire State Building,
Central Park and Wall Street,
To see all of these makes your eyes wonder.

Frances Smith (Age 13)

The Thundering Dragon

My wings are spiky holly bushes
My eyes, are shiny jewels sparkling in the sun
My tongue is a long tough like snake
My claws, are like daggers
My breath is like a fire roaring all the time
My voice is a grumbling kind of sound
My tail is long with scales of emeralds.
I've seen sky turn black by the sound of my voice.
I've heard the crackle of ice forming on a cold winter's night.
In play I purr like a baby kitten
In anger I strike fast and silent like a leopard
They call me Penndragon

Andrea Shinn (Age 13)

The Dream

First it was the trees behind the kirkyard,
The branches brushing my face,
Snatching at my sleeve,
Tearing at my skin.
Trailing of the leaves as I move among them.
Striding more quickly increasing my pace as they try to pull me back,
Creepers being serpents as vine traps my ankles.
Whispering voices by my ear,
I turn my head but they seem to follow.
Dark grey cloth enclosing from it's stone vase,
Billowing in a breeze which seems not to be there,
Falling across my face now it's wrapped around my neck.
Pulling me down, choking my life away.

Joanne Sydenham (Age 12)

What Is The Sea?

The sea is blue sandpaper
Floating in the air.

The sea is a huge brick
Stuck in the ground.

The sea is a sheet
Gobbling up the sand.

The sea is a stick
With bark coming off it.

The sea is a bed
With animals in it.

The sea is an open book
Being read.

The sea is a blue carpet
Being replaced.

The sea is a box
Flat on the ground.

The sea is a table
Leaning against a wall.

The sea is silky cotton
Lying flat on the floor.

Stephanie Sullivan (Age 11)

Tornado

Furious, hard, tough wind
Blowing houses down
It's getting nearer.

Stormy clouds getting darker
I can't see a thing
It's getting nearer.

Wind getting faster
I'm getting scared
It's getting nearer.

Sucking things up as it goes
Going round and round
It's getting nearer.

Dust flying up as it goes along
Crashing things as they go down
It's here . . . . . . it's gone past.

Tomas Smith (Age 7)

Rain - A Sonnet

Cats and dogs streamed down into submission,
Faster than the soft tears my window cried,
United in both matter and mission,
Gentle whispers in which I can confide.
Memories pitter patter on black slate,
Walls moan through the blanket of confusion,
Omnipotent, omnipresent in hate,
And in love, the heart of life's illusion.
Crystalised drops fall on leaves and petals,
Releasing colour and vitality,
Tapping the ground where they gather and crawl,
Rejuvenating life in urgency.
The essence of our earth moulding our lives,
We give thanks to the skies from which it flies.

Rhiannon Roberts (Age 17)

The Rainforest

Rustling in the tree tops,
The rainforest rainforest
Animals squeaking, squawking, swinging.
I'm in the rainforest.
No planes, no cars, no trains, rain forest,
The rainforest rainforest,
Animals in trees
Rustling like bees
Lush green grass,
The rainforest
Rainforest . . .

Gilly Sutcliffe (Age 6)

Our Town

Our town is quiet
Our town is fun
Our town is big
Our town is small

It's delightful
It's clean
It's beautiful
It's happy and gay

Men go to pubs
Ladies go to shops
Children go to parks
And babies go to bed

Butterflies flutter
Snakes creep in the grass
People tell jokes
And last of all flowers bloom

Katie-Louise Spencer (Age 7)

Dirty Socks

Don't shun me
Because of my buni
ons, my foot.

The powder haunts,
My toes, fidgety,
My socks are confinement,
Bound by wool
Nuggets across the flesh.

Why, why, why, why, why,
My feet are red,
The rash is growing.

When will the disease,
Stop, stop, stop the pain,
Stop, stop, please stop.

Matthew Saunders (Age 15)

Vicki

I never really knew you
We weren't the best of friends
But never did I know how soon this squabbling would end
It's not that we had a change of heart
Though we got better as time passed
I regret the friendship that we had
Was never meant to last
It ended, I still like you
We didn't feud or lie
I can't laugh with you anymore
I never asked you to die.

Kimberley Seviour (Age 15)

My Future

I'm brilliant at football,
Everyone can see
That I'm the best that anyone can be.
See me dribble, see me pass, see me score,
Not first but last.

I score at least five, every game,
All the other players are really lame!
Professional football's coming my way,
I'm sure I'll make it in the month of May!

James Salmon (Age 11)

Earthquake

Earthquakes are bad
Ache is everywhere
Rumbling ground
Terrified children
Horrible atmosphere
Quake started today
Unhappy people
Afterwards rescue teams
Kind and generous prayers
Echoes through the land

In Gularat
Nearly destroyed

Great Sorrow
Underneath rubble
Jagged ground
Almost dead
Rescue me!
A child cries
Time is running out!

Tom Sambridge (Age 9)

The Tempestuous Ocean

Ocean, ocean, who will stop thou? I ask you when, I ask you how?

Grabbing us with its glacial hands as we cower in it's wrath.
The storm above yields thunder at it's disposal, so deafening and destructive,
That I wonder if I will ever see home again, and if I do, how long will it be until then?

The ocean - an immeasurable murderer, the storm a faithful accomplice and blood curdler,
Just one on its own will make our ship groan, but when both of the loom,
We'll be facing our doom.
Murderous, man-eating, ravenous, raging, roaring ocean - you are a killer,
Whirling, whooshing, whipping winds, when will your terror cease?
The ocean's eyes hypnotise us so that we don't see,
The storms mighty weapon strike our mast in the night, and set our ship alight.

On deck it's too hot, down there it's not,
But if we don't stay and perish in the flames,
We'll have to jump down and drown in the hungry waves.

Storm, storm, who will stop thee?
When will you halt, when will you see?

Joe Sellman-Leava (Age 11)

The Sea

The sea is a snorting bull running to get the bullfighter
Rougher and rougher the sea gets chipping at the cliff's face
Sharks snap at the other fish
Squids are tossed about the air
Splash! Splash! Splash!
Go the ferocious waves
Smash! Go the jaggedy rocks
The sea is a snorting
Boats go Smash!
The sea is a snorting bull.

Gregory Shaw (Age 7)

Animal Poems

Cunning cobra
Very tall really quiet
Keeps cool

Enormous elephant
Standing tall squirts water
Keeps cool

Huge ears eats bark
Rips trees looks smart

Very noisy extremely cute
Really strong in zoos

Tremendous tiger
Has cubs eats meat
Attacks humans could retreat

Zoe Shippen (Age 9)

I Will Remember

I will remember
The first smile from my baby cousin,
My guinea pigs soft fur, rubbing against my cheek,
The spot on my puppies wet nose, like mine.
I will always remember,
My special teddy necklace that I got from my christening,
My special likeness between me and my brother,
The first sign of a summer sunray.
I will always remember,
The smell of a newly cut lawn,
My dogs smooth fur and my special toys,
The special mountains in Scotland,
I will always remember.

Camilla Sewell (Age 10)

Spyro The Dragon

Spyro the dragon has so much fun,
He went on a skateboard and broke his thumb.

He collects all the gems, that sparkle and shine,
He and his friends have an excellent time.

He does lots of tasks, to keep him busy,
When he spins around, he gets very dizzy.

Our hero takes a rest, at the end of the day,
The Sorcerers Army really had to pay.

Lee Simpson (Age 8)

Secondary Transfer

I'm scared,
I think it's great,
I think I am late,
I sprint to school,
I walk in and see,
All the big kids,
Staring at me,
I ran to find a locker
They all seem full,
I am so frustrated,
I need to call,
I need to shout,
Will it be OK,
I have my doubts!

Reece Seymour (Age 11)

Time!

Time runs by,
When you're having fun.
Time runs by,
When you're not.

Time runs by,
When you're having a laugh.
Time runs by,
When you're hot.

Time!
Time runs!
Time runs by,
When you're wandering around the mouldy old playground,
With its rusty swings.

Time runs by,
When you're out with you're mates.
Or you're out buying lots of new things.

Time!
Time runs!

Time runs by,
All the time.

Rebecca Smith (Age 11)

Ladles and Custard Pies

Ladles and custard pies
I come before you.
That's why I'm outside
To tell you something
I haven't got a clue about
On Tuesday, the day before sunday
There will be a gentleman's meeting
For animals only
Admission is free - just £25
We will give you a seat,
So please bring your own.

Daniel Spriggs (Age 11)

The Fish

I went diving in the sea
To catch a fishy for my tea
And record a recipe

The fish was hard to cook,
Because it was from the fishing book
Maybe I got it from a brook

The fish was foul,
And the dogs howled
But the wolves bowed.

Callum Stamper (Age 9)

Eyes

They stay shut up in their sockets at night,
Not seeing a thing

But in the morning they dress
With a clean pair of spectacles
And see the world in front of them

The body walks them down the stairs in to the kitchen
They pick the food for the body to eat,
That is how they are fed.

The eyes are ordered by the body to watch the television
Until the body gets bored
After they travel to the table and eat.

They leave the house
And return at 5 o'clock
The eyes make their way to the table
Eat for the last time.

They later return to bed and undress,
For then they will close and
Go to sleep.

James Stanley (Age 11)

So Much Depends Upon

So much depends upon
A very loud TV
Such clean window frames
A very busy chair
A very irritating radio

Jack Sutton (Age 10)

Sun

Sun, a gleaming ball of scorching hot fire
A marble, a football, a burning bouncy ball
A spinning sparking sphere
A round ball splintering out fire
A shimmering sphere glinting . . . . glinting at me
A shining ball of glittery fire
A sparkle, a twinkle of fire
A glimmer up in space
A sleek look of brightness
A gleam of spitting fire
A flash of fire before you
A blaze of fire shooting out
A flicker in the sky
Sun . . . a sphere of flaming, blistering,
Scorching, scalding, sizzling fire.

Rosie Spearpoint (Age 9)

Abuse

Underneath the silence I can hear . . .
The thud of a fierce fist on his blistered, bony back,
The drunken jeers of the culprit as he stumbles away,
His lonely pain, no-one to lean on, to dry his tears,
His wasted mind made up, he goes.
The raging river, under the bridge,
His failing footsteps reach the edge, he sighs.

Underneath the silence I can feel . . . .
The suffering,
The soft tears of despair as he falls to the floor,
The dark, red blood trickling out of his open wounds,
The faint cry of hopelessness as he attempts to stand upright.
The staggered panting of his final breath,
The knowing of his anguish as he reaches for the blade,
His fear of what is to come.

Jamie Stern-Weiner (Age 11)

Happiness

Happiness is to hear the birds sing
Happiness is to learn how to swing

Happiness is to laugh and have fun
Happiness is to go for a run

Happiness is something to share
Happiness is people who care

Happiness is a flower that opens every day
Happiness is forever not just for today.

Rochelle Sweeney (Age 10)

The Journey

Over the hills and through the Dales,
Behind us were fields full of bales.
Travelling on and on and on,
Through rain and hail and how bright
The sun shone.

Through towns and villages,
Across roads and streets,
Past friendly faces and people we meet.
Up north to Scotland,
Down south to the coast.
Into Wales and across to England,
That we love most.

Towards our final destination,
To tour around the entire nation.

On my way to school.

Timothy Starkie (Age 11)

Peter And The Wolf

One day I saw Peter,
Sitting in the taxi, looking at the meter.

Along came the bird flying in the sky
Flying very high and he made Peter cry.

Then came the duck
Peter said look there's my friend, the big great duck.

Along came the wolf he had a tail
And his face was red and pale.

He became Peter's friend
And that was the end.

Mohammed Subtain (Age 10)

The Rugby Match!

The players run on in multi-coloured shirts
The whistle goes
The player kicked off
The players run for the ball
And the posts are very tall
Then a player scores a try and kicks it
Over the post and it is very cold
The half time whistle goes
The players get a drink
The whistle goes again
And it starts to rain
The players keep on scoring
Then it starts pouring
Finally the whistle goes
The players are soaked
But it's all over
And we won!

Benjamin Swindell (Age 8)

Playground Journey

That horrible day.
I hated it.
All day long I moped around.

You see my best ever friend left me.
For this dreadful boy.
Now she called me names, pushed me, bullied me.

The same boring look of the fully loaded playground.
I hid in a dark, shadowed corner, out of the way.
Then suddenly she appeared,
Her face filled with unhappiness.
Her tear stained eyes stared at me for sympathy.
I walked away.

Behind me
In the distance I heard her crying.
I was alone with a free future ahead of me.

Katherine Sturman (Age 11)

Hindleap Warren 2000

One day in autumn, we climbed on the bus,
Waved "goodbye" to our parents, who made such a fuss.
We wondered if it would be cold, wet and muddy,
The bus took a long time because it was floody.

When we arrived, we jumped in a puddle,
Then collected our bags which were all in a muddle.
First thing to do was make up our beds,
So later we could rest our sleepy heads.

In archery Aaron helped load the bow,
Pull the string and then let go.
We soon realised mud didn't matter,
Our evenings were filled with fun and chatter.

In teams we had to cross a river,
Crawl under logs, it made us shiver.
We also had to climb a wall,
With harnesses so we couldn't fall.

At the end of the week we were all shattered,
And all our clothes were torn and tattered.
We'd had some fun, we'd had some laughs,
We're going home to have some baths!!!

Eleanor Swithinbank (Age 10)

Rainbow

A rainbow is pretty in the sky,
It rains in the sky,
The rainbow and rain are out,
When people dance in the rainbow,
To me the rain is very good,
When I have my Weetabix.

Tasha Siggins (Age 9)

Toffee The Hamster

I am a friendly hamster
As soft as silk
I am ginger and white
And love being stroked.
If you annoy me
I might bite as hard as a dog.
I eat nuts as crunchy as a biscuit
And dried up cabbage
As dry as an autumn leaf.
I grow as quick as the hair on your head.
My name is Toffee
And I live in a cage
As safe as a cuddle.
Upstairs in my house,
Is a tube as long as a ruler
My wheel turns as fast as a sports car
I am six weeks old.

Jolene Smith (Age 9)

Cat

Cat sleeping
Cat purring
Cat eating
Cat purring
Cat climbing
Cat purring
Cat playing
Cat purring
Cat running
Cat purring
Cat hissing
Cat purring
Cat fighting
Cat sleeping

Oliver Smyth (Age 9)

My Imaginary Friend

I sit here at my desk.
Wondering what to write,
Then she pops in front of me,
And then slips out of sight.

Long brown hair,
And shiny blue eyes,
As honest as can be,
She tells no lies.

Kicking at my legs,
Pinching at my feet,
Why doesn't she stay still,
Just so we can meet.

My legs are really tired now,
My feet start to hurt,
Why doesn't she go outside,
And play in the dirt.

I sit at my desk,
Now I know what to write,
About my imaginary friend,
Though I'm glad she is out of sight.

Katie Smaylen (Age 11)

Pizza

Pizza in my mouth
Goes down
My throat
In to my belly
It is yummy
Cheese and tomato
And pepper!
What else Mummy?

Joshua Speer (Age 6)

Frogs

I saw a little frog,
He jumped on a log.

I saw a little frog,
He bounced on a dog.

I saw a little frog,
Then he jumped on a warthog.

I saw a little frog,
It whispered a hog.

I saw a little frog
He was croaking in the fog.

I saw a little frog,
His name was tog.

Hannah Sloman (Age 9)

Flood

Floods, floods, the treacherous floods the ones that rip up trees,
I did not get how my house was gone from such a raging beast,
The glassy shine of the flood that water makes me have the frights.
The drowning clouds full of water bring back bad memories,
When the flood had stopped I was so glad the sparkling water is gone,
My friends, my family, my dog and others are all lost in the beastly shiny beast,
My friends, my family were all gone but there's nothing else to do but sob in my wet flooded room,
This is the end of my worst flood of my life.

Scott Segrue (Age 11)

The Dragon

My eyes are headlights, showing the way,
My tail is a forest of pins, poised to kill,
My body is a sleek engine, propelling itself forwards,
My legs are giant pistons, pushing me on,
My wings, acres of muscle,
I've seen men engulfed by greed,
I've heard metal men scream for mercy,
Their mounts thundering as rockets over fields and plains,
I've flown over men made of steel, their courage, like God, never ending,
They call me the Dragon of death.

James Slade (Age 13)

Haiku

I met a monkey
In the heart of the jungle
It had a long tail

Hanging in a tree
He saw me staring at him
With glowing bright eyes

Jenny Small (Age 11)

What Will Transport Be Like Fifty Years On?

What will transport be like fifty years on?
Will transport be in the air or down on the ground?
Will there be hover cars or flying cars?
Will planes travel like trains or
Trains fly like planes?

Will technology be taking over the world?
Will there be no jobs for people
Because there are robots to do it?
What will it be like fifty years on?
Yes what will it be like fifty years on?

Daniel Smith (Age 10)

Animals

Animals have stripes
Animals have spots
Some walk on four legs
And some of them hop
Animals are yellow
Some are black
Some are brown
Some animals are different
To others and some are not.

Leah Staples (Age 8)

One Small Step For Man One Giant Leap For Mankind

Blasting into outer space,
Roaming galaxies in a different place.
Wondering what will happen soon,
Smack, we land on the moon.
Excitedly I jump out of the door,
My feet don't even touch the floor.
Slowly I descend to the ground
And plant my flag without a sound.
I go floating through the atmosphere,
Tell you what,
I'm glad I'm here.

Joshua Smith (Age 11)

I'm Smarter Than You

I'm so SMART that I can do any trick,
I'm so SMART that I can lift a brick
I'm so SMART I think you're thick.

I'm so SMART I don't need school
I'm so SMART I can feed a mule
I'm so SMART I think you're a fool

I'm so SMART I can answer every question,
But when the teacher asks what is 2 + 2
I just pick my nose and make it runny
But other children think it's funny
And that is the end of that.

Amy Smith (Age 9)

The Battle

I see dead bodies rotting away in to ashes,
I see swords stabbing through people in their hearts,

I hear people shouting for some back up,
I hear swords clashing and breaking in two,

I touch my metal sword, its cold steel,
I touch my shield, its wooden and heavy,

I smell rotting blood making the grass go brown,
I smell smoke surrounding the battle field,

I taste the oozing blood from my dry mouth,
I taste the salt dripping from my mouth,

I feel my hot anger rising from my head

I think I am di . . . .uh

Charles Spence (Age 9)

War

Battle ships firing guns
People fire guns like twenty suns

Huge guns making fire
As a leader shouts out fire

Men charging fall to the ground
Others are clear from the devastating sound

Bombs hit the ground and kill enough men,
People pop up from their smelly old den

Oscar Sutcliffe (Age 8)

Tiger

Crouching deep in the grass,
Waiting for his prey.
He watches closely,
Deer running away.

His ears prick up,
With his eyes sharpened,
He stretches out his claws
And licks his lips.

Then out from the grass,
He jumps and leaps.
With his prey on the floor,
Pinned down by his claws.

Holly Stockhan (Age 11)

Our Town

Our town is fun,
Lots of things to do,
We all appreciate it.
As much as you and me.

Children like the fair.
Adults like the shops.
My best place is school.
Because our town is cool.

We all have our rules.
To keep our town tidy.
Soon it will be slidy.
Because we keep it tidy.

Jack Stevens (Age 8)

In Dreamland I See

In dreamland I see fairies dancing
Rabbits prancing in the air without a care
Bells ringing with a chime
Dance and sing its slumber time

Take a ride on the Slumberland train
Watch the golden lion shake its mane
See the sparkling river flow all night
Moon reflecting, what a sight.

So next time you get to bed
Lay down your sleepy head
The Dreamland express will take you . . .
To Slumberland.

P.S. hope you have a good time!

Louise Soothill (Age 8)

The Sea

A clash of thunder hit the sea,
The sea suddenly roared aloud.
The angry water threw itself
Against the dull rocks.

The sea rolled on the beach,
As if it was guarding the whole block of sand.
The moon shone brightly on the sea.
There wasn't a sound in the air,
Apart from the sound of the angry sea.

Alicia Socas (Age 8)

Mad Mr Mike

Mad Mr Mike got on his bike
He saw a boar
So he went on a tour of the world
In Africa he bought a pearl
In England a twirl
At last he got back to USA
After he had paid and displayed
He went inside to find that the boar
Tore the coach up
Mad Mr Mike is a commentator
Each time he turns into a tater
So I for one
Shove him up a gun
I didn't give him a bun
Because he weighs a ton
If I did
How can I get on the lid?

Samuel Staton (Age 10)

Three Men In A Muddle!

Max

There was a young man called Max,
Who didn't pay his tax,
When asked at the door,
He said, "I'm too poor",
And got a series of whacks!

Ed

There once was a fellow named Ed
Who didn't have a bed,
He's incredibly sleepy,
And also looks creepy,
Because he can't rest his head!

Fred

There once was an alien called Fred,
"I'm from Mars" he said,
He crashed his ship,
When out on a trip,
And now poor Fred is dead.

Max Sztyber (Age 10)

Snow Boarding

Swerving in and out of trees
Falling and bruising my knees
Snow all around
Ice covers the ground
I hit a bump
And do a three sixty jump
Snow boarding is something to admire
But I'm looking forward to sitting by the fire

Alfie Sutcliffe (Age 10)

What Is A . . . Giraffe?

A giraffe is a long periscope,
looking over planes,
seeing scattering ants, looking for food

A giraffe is a long ladder
of brown and yellow paint
reaching to long lost sky

A giraffe is a block of flats,
towering under the sun lit earth

A giraffe is a giant horse chestnut tree
with lots of animals on it

Becky Swallow (Age 10)

Love Is Like A Line

Love is like a line,
a rope,
starting thin at
the beginning
then, either
breaking in
the middle or
getting thicker
and lasting
forever.

Claire Stratton (Age 10)

The Trenches

Mud up to my knees
Then up to my waist

The sea of mud grows higher

The smell of dead bodies,
Arms and legs in trenches.

The only thing moving is the rats.

The ceaseless pounding of guns;
A river of blood is rising.

Why did I join the Army at all?

Shells are zooming overhead
Machine guns keep pounding.

Sometimes I wonder
What this war is all about.

Isaac Sturt (Age 10)

The Waterfall

The river flows calm and peacefully
Meandering its way towards the ocean.
Sometimes straight and sometimes bends,
But before its journey ends,
It must conquer the great waterfall!!

Flowing rapidly over the edge
It cascades with an almighty roar
On to the rocks below.
The snowy white froth soon fades away
And the river is at peace once more.

Jack Scottow (Age 9)

This Is A . . .

This is a boring poem,
Only 15 lines and 61 words,
It's no Cleirhew,
I don't think.
I could be a Tanka,
But I could be a
Kenning.
I might be a Riddle,
I could be a Rap.
I think I'm an Acrostic,
But all my friend poems
Think I'm a Haiku.
But all my enemies think I'm a
Sonnet.
But I'm a . . . .

A Free Verse

Charlotte Slater (Age 11)

A Mother's Love

I see my child,
Hurt and afraid,
My child carrying the cross,
With the crown of thorns,
My child accused of blasphemy.
But I know wherever I go
He is the Son of God .
They take him up to Golgatha hill,
To be put on the cross,
To be killed.
I stand there and see my son,
Why, why for what he's done.
He has helped not hurt,
I cry, cry, cry, for my Son,
He is the Christ and I will always believe in him,
He is the one who will never, never die.
Now I have to say goodbye to my Son.
Who has been crucified.

Emma Sage (Age 10)

Run Quickly

Run quickly,
Bombs are speeding,
Run quickly,
German's leading.
Run quickly,
To the shelter.
Run quickly,
War is always helter-skelter.
Run quickly,
Other houses smashed to pieces.
Run quickly,
The war is over time to visit our nieces.

Hayley Sheriff (Age 9)

Monkey Man

I'm a monkey man
Monkey here
And monkey there.
Monkey, monkey look over there
Mango in the morning,
Banana in the evening,
Berries for bed -
I got lots of haste
Because I love the mango taste

I'm a monkey man
Not a superman
Or a bat man.
Mango in the morning,
Banana in the evening,
Berries for bed -
I got lots of haste
Because I love the mango taste
Yeh Man

Kaan Silay (Age 10)

If My Thoughts Took Shape

If my romantic thoughts took shape
It would be like a silvery moon shining on the horizon.

If my dreadful thoughts took shape
It would be like doing a cartwheel and breaking my neck.

If my polite thoughts took shape
It would be like saying hello to a cranky old lady.

If my imaginative thoughts took shape
It would be like someone wearing pants on their head.

If my evil thoughts took shape
I wouldn't tell anyone at all.

If my empty thoughts took shape
It would be like getting stuck down a deep, dark hole.

Rebecca Sendall-King (Age 10)

The Moon

Moon a bitten biscuit,
A boomerang spinning round the galaxy
Moon an eyebrow going to freeze,
A cradle rocking a baby to sleep.

Moon a big smiling face, looking down at you,
A tasty banana.
Moon a giant frisbee,
As bright as a star at night.

Moon a football,
As round as the Millennium Wheel.

Nicola Sellman (Age 9)

I Wonder Why

Why do sweets taste so nice?
Why don't hedgehogs eat fried rice?
Why does tuna end up tinned?
Why does paper end up binned?

Why do birds fly so high?
Why does my brother always cry?
Why do bees give us stings?
Why do eagles have big wings?

Why are giraffes so very tall?
Why are snails so very small?
Why do stars twinkle so bright?
Why does mum kiss me goodnight?

Oh why, oh why, oh why I sigh,
Why do I keep wondering why?

David Sinnott (Age 10)

The Best And Worst Of Birthdays

To wake up in the scorching heat,
And pad outside, in bare feet.
To see the sunrise, scarlet with blue,
Look over the balcony a phenomenal view.
My family wake with a hearty cheer,
"Happy birthday", they cry, "Come over here".
Colourful parcels, smile up at me,
It's a wonderful sight for my eyes to see.

My brother's third birthday was an awful fright,
Sticky hands a chaotic sight.
Little children running around,
Causing havoc, shouting out loud.
Falling over, scraping knees,
Running around, climbing trees.
Overall, you may have guessed,
My brother's was worst and mine was best!

Emma Simmons (Age 11)

Smarmy

We have a part time pussy cat,
He is quite plump and rather fat.
He wants to come into our house,
And as a gift he's caught a mouse.

He has all sorts of horrible germs,
Like big black fleas and wiggly worms.
Then he likes to have a big hug,
But most of all he loves a belly rub.

At first we named him Six Dinner Sid,
But now we call him Smarmy Kid.
With human comforts plus something to play,
Smarmy the cat is here to stay.

Hannah Sabin (Age 11)

Titanic

Titanic the great ocean liner
There was no boat finer
It was hit by an iceberg
And was not heard
It went down in to the sea
I'm glad it was not me
It was smart and rich
And soon went as black as pitch
Most of the people died
Not many people survived
Titanic the great ocean liner

Tom Skinner (Age 8)

Guess Who?

He's the king of Gods
Though Roman, now now
He shared the name of a planet
Guess who?

Emily Slater (Age 9)

Oscar Our Cat

Our cat is called Oscar.
Silently he walks through the grass
Catching all before him.
Around the house he sleeps
Rolling around while he snores.

Outside he's king of his jungle.
Under every stone he knows what's there.
Round about tea time, he comes home.

Catching mice is what he likes.
Attacking unsuspecting birds
'Till he's tired out again.

Fiona Sinclair (Age 10)

Spider In The Tate

There's a spider in the Tate
Bigger than a giant
Stomping crashing crushing down houses
There's a spider in the Tate
No-one can go near it
Everyone is screaming
There's a spider in the Tate
Scary as scary can be
Knows more than any old spider
There's a spider in the Tate
Legs thicker than a classroom
Eyes staring through the glass
There's a spider in the Tate
Bigger than a giant.
Stomping crashing crushing down houses

Carl Smith (Age 8)

Woe For De Windies

Oh me god, dey've gone!
Wid no Curtly or Courtney,
Wat shall dey do now?
Wid de ball dey slaughtered de udders,
England, Australia, Pakistan and de rest,
Dey've got no chance now dey've lost de best.

Not even wid Adams and Lara
Dey can do no good.
Beaten by England, thrashed by de Aussies
Dere seems no road back.
But I never despair
While de Windies around, always beware!

Ian Sutton (Age 16)

Going Over The Top

Today showed me exactly how wrong I was,
I sat cold, cramped and drenched,

Struggling to put the camera together,
Soldiers sat silent, guns held in hand.

A loud piercing whistle blew, a face yelled from the mud,
'Stay low, we're going over the top! Going over the top? Was that as simple as it sounded?

Machine guns fired, men dropped to the ground,
Chaos began, they dropped like bowling pins.

Some fell and were silent, others cried in agony,
I still shook, soldiers fell.

Only seven men returned, the noise stopped,
Silence fell on the field, anger filled my body.

Dead bodies littered the floor, a battlefield running red with blood,
I scoured the field in hope of movement, there was no hope.

I wanted to run, did I stand a chance?
I simply sat and waited, silence homed in.

A helpless man shouted, the soldiers returned with no one.
My heart pounded, I wanted to help.

The pungent smell of rotting bodies filled the air, sickness came over me,
The mass grave became distant, I ran.

Lorna Salmon (Age 15)

Me, Myself and I

I'm a fiery marshmallow,
Boiling on the BBQ

I'm a worn out hamster,
When I'm tired.

I'm a fizzy coke,
With a slice of lemon.

I'm a windy hurricane,
When I'm high-tempered.

I'm a raging storm force ten,
From Derby's Drayton Manor.

I'm a football hooligan,
Getting beaten up.

I'm the burning yellow sand,
In the Mediterranean.

I'm a dark brown tree,
Bursting with sap.

Harry Skivington (Age 10)

Computers

What has a programme and eats chips?
What has a mouse and sits on a mat?
What types words and has keys?
What has a monitor for its jobs?
What has a screen?
A computer of course.

Kayleigh Sheppard (Age 8)

Sun

Why do you shine so much sun?
Why are you sparkling yellow?
Why do you come out in summer?

Why do you not come out in winter?
Why do you not come out in spring and autumn
Have you seen all the world sun?

How do you live without food or drink?
Do you like being in the sky?
Do you like the stars?

Laura Slack (Age 10)

Untitled

There was a young boy on a train
Who had a very small brain
Everyone laughed
At his feet in the Bath
And he never went in it again

Joseph Sheppard (Age 9)

Dolphins

Dolphins swim so gracefully,
They jump out of the water like athletes
Leaping up and down,
Their tails flap like an owl's wing
Rising and then dropping again and again,
They look as smooth as silk,
Their face is as innocent as a baby's,
Their nose is like a long tube gulping down water,
When you look them in the eyes they glisten like stars,

I gleam with happiness when I see them,
I would love to be a dolphin,
Swimming in the clear blue sea, all the time.

Lizzie Smith (Age 11)

Like A Different World

It's like a different world,
I have to be still at night,
The only one awake in the house.
The cars stop their engines,
The dogs stop barking, the wind stops howling,
It's like a different world.

It was so still,
I could hear a mouse in the kitchen,
Scurrying to the cheese in the trap.

It was so quiet,
I could hear the moon singing a song,
Shining like the sun.

It was so silent,
I could hear the sea, miles away,
In a different land.

It was so peaceful,
I could hear the sun, making fluffy white clouds,
Ready for morning.

That's why it's . . . .

. . . like a different world.

Lauren Susman (Age 8)

Bees For Tea!

Once there was a bee
Who had some friends for tea
They ate honey and jam
From a great big pan
And said could they come again please!

Maria Sweeney (Age 10)

Sammy

As I walk in the room,
He starts to purr and purr,
I cuddle him,
And feel his soft, soft fur.

He wears a black satin coat,
With a belly as white as a dove,
When he moves he seems to float,
And gives me all his love.

He loves his toy mouse,
He is always chasing it,
All around the house,
He drives my mum crazy.
Even though he is a cat,
He is a brilliant friend!

Gemma Smith (Age 11)

Magic Pencil Case?

I will put in my new pencil case,

A set of the brightest colours I can find,
And three new rubbers but now they are gone!
Where did they go?
Is this a magic pencil case?

I will put in my new new pencil case,

A brand new fountain pen made of metal,
But now it is made of bone!
Why?
Is this a magic pencil case?

I will put in my new pencil case,

A shiny small sharpener and a thin pencil,
But now they are as large as my hand!
How?
This is a magic pencil case.

I will put in my magic pencil case,

An ink bottle in exchange for a drink,
A glue stick for a book,
A ruler for a pound coin,
I like my magic pencil case.

Adam Swan (Age 11)

Haiku Poem

Laughing and playing
With my best friend Claire at school
In the fun playground

Chloe Sutton (Age 9)

Lost At Night

I once had a necklace made of pearl,
That was when I was a little girl,
When I was playing in the park,
I lost my necklace in the dark.
Which was when I heard a noise.

The noise was scary the noise was loud.
I felt it was big and going to pound.
I started to run to the park gate,
I was running at a very fast rate.
Which was when I heard a noise.

I heard a grown up shouting help,
That was when I started to yelp.
I saw a shadow it was my Mum,
I started to get butterflies in my tum.

Hayley Susan Smith (Age 10)

I Will Keep In My Heart . . .

I will keep in my heart . . .

The sound of GG's voice when I was very young,
The feel of being able to hold my sister on her first day
My first word.

I will keep in my heart . . .

My first day of school,
Learning to read,
Writing my first story.

I will keep in my heart . . .

My friends and family,
People who have left me,
My old and new pets.

I will keep in my heart . . .

The Disney Kids Awards,
Seeing The Lion King,
Being on an advertisement.

I will keep in my heart . . .

My mum's warm scent,
My dad's warm hug,
And my sister's sweet voice.

Molly Slight (Age 10)

I Am That Is

I am a blade of grass stretching towards the sun
Drinking in the life-giving light

I am a tree green and leafy
Roots stretching deep into the soil

I am a river wet and clear and flowing

I am a mountain range
Tall and grey and solemn

I am the ocean old and salty and wet

I am the world bringer of life
Warm and nurturing darkness and light

I am the sun hot and bright and shining

I am the solar system
Cold and distant orbiting around the sun

I am the galaxy
I encompass the stars and the worlds great and black

I am the universe older than time itself
And everything is part of me and I am part of you

When you hurt your world
I hurt and that hurts you

Joanna Tatum (Age 15)

Friends

I've got a friend called Olly
He's a cool big fellow
He's always a wolly
He's funny joyful and helpful
He's kind, playful and cheerful
He's my friend,
Actually, he's my best friend.

Harrison Smith (Age 9)

Winter Days

Awakening from his slumber,
Staring with his icy stare,
Freezing a passing mouse,
He points to a plant,
It spoils with white daggers,
He glides to the pool,
With a single touch it turns to ice,
Winter is aloft!

Tim Saunders (Age 9)

Monkeys Are

Monkeys are funny
Like Bugs Bunny.
Monkeys climb trees
And they have got fleas.
Monkeys swing
The monkey thing.
Monkeys eat grapes
And are like apes.

Kelly Skinner (Age 9)

The Mirror

Let no-one besmear the reflector of my image.
Do not besmirch that luminous, millpond flat, incandescent light.
Let me gaze deep, past all that others see.
Regard well all that is colourless and lacklustre.
Give the keeper all that is half-glimpsed and dark.
To be lost in the shadows behind the glimmer.
Reach out for all that bedazzles and glisters.
Dispel the darkness and illuminate within.
The solitary is imitated.
The essence of me is split.
I grasp the spectrum and the magical.
My soul dances on.

Chanah Short (Age 10)

My Sibling

I have a little brother his name is Lee
When he was a baby my dad sat him on his knee
We like to play football in the park.
Sometimes we get chased by dogs who bark.
We get on well, but sometimes fight.
Mum gets very cross and we have an early night.
Even though we argue and drive mum round the bend.
Lee I want to tell you, you are my best friend!!

Scott Simpson (Age 11)

The Door

I look beyond the door and I see . . .
A flickering flame from a distance,
Like a star shining bright.

I look beyond the door and I see . . .
The fire of a canon,
Like the eruption of world war 3.

I look beyond the door and I see . . .
The German troops firing bullets,
Like a herd of elephants running down the people.

I look beyond the door and I see . . .
People smiling brightly next to the shining city.

I look beyond the door and I see . . .
The animals running freely through the beautiful woods.

I look beyond the door and I see . . .
Bobby Moore lifting the world cup,
Like the golden silk of a cocoon.

Michael Shea (Age 10)

Bugs

Creepy crawly loads of bugs
how I like those slimy slugs
nice and juicy big and fat
sometimes they get squashed flat

Snails, spiders, ants and bees
so many for me to see
big and small, colourful too
I wonder what worms can do

The Gnats and flies
fly past my eyes
they're heading for their nest
now I'm going home
to have a little rest.

Luke Stinton (Age 9)

Strawberry

Strawberries are red,
Tasty as well.
Raspberries look like strawberries,
A strawberry is grown in a field,
Wake up and eat a strawberry from your fridge.
Be a strawberry and I will eat you!
Every day eat a strawberry because they are good for you.
Really lovely strawberries
Run away from a strawberry and you will never eat one again.
Yum yum a strawberry.

Rebecca Smith (Age 7)

Inside A Tiger

Inside a tiger's stripes, prison bars
Inside the prison bars, the tiger's fang
Inside the tiger's fang, a mountain peak
Inside the mountain's peak
Inside the tiger's claw, a bear's tear
Inside the bear's tear, the tiger's tongue

Inside the tiger's tongue, a snake's skin
Inside the snake's skin, the tiger's ear
Inside the tiger's ear, the tree's leaf
Inside the tree's leaf, the tiger's whiskers
Inside the tiger's whiskers, an antelope's tail
Inside the antelope's tail, the tiger's sharp sense of smell

Inside the tiger's smell, a hare's nose
Inside the hare's nose, the tiger's prey
Inside the tiger's prey, the tiger's glowing eyes
Inside the tiger's glowing eyes, the rabbit's fear
Inside the rabbit's fear, the tiger's fang
Inside the tiger's fang, the prison bars
Inside the prison bars, the tiger's stripes.

Kerry Louise Sadler (Age 11)

Spring

The days are getting longer
It's starting to feel warm,
The buds are bursting open
And baby lambs are born.

Daffodils and tulips
The colours are nice and bright,
The blossom on the tree tops
It's such a lovely sight.

The trees are changing colour
Blossom's starting to appear,
The rain has stopped the sun comes out
It's my favourite time of year.

Alexandra Smith (Age 8)

Ants

Ants are all different
Like human beings,
Red ants, yellow ants, brown ants,
Reddish-brown ants, flying ants.

Ants in the garden, ants in your house,
Ants in your pants, ants in your bed,
Ants living in your house
Ants living in your garden.

Ants little tiny things 2 cms long,
Some people hate ants,
Some people love 'em.

Stephen Scott (Age 10)

The Stream

The stream trundles along,
Turning and twisting like a hare frisking,
Laughing and burbling,
Writhing and climbing and twining,
Down and down it streams.

Over pebbles and rocks it dances,
Silent and beautiful it floats along.
It flows and glows in the midday sun.
How many are its bubbles?
As countless as the stars.
It roams alone underneath its pearly foam,
Until it finds comfort on the sandy sea bed.

Claire Stirling (Age 9)

When I Go To Collenswood

When I go to Collenswood
I will see at Collenswood
Ten tiring teachers
Nine horrible pieces of homework
Eight naughty new kids
Seven dirty desks
Six banging bubble gums
Five fabulous frying pans
Four chaotic corridors
Three hideously ugly head teachers
Two daring detentions
And one giant school to get lost in.

Kim Strahan (Age 11)

Living In Space

I was living in space
And I'd forgotten my brief case
I tripped over my lace
And landed in an aliens face

A rocket flew over my head
And took me back to my bed
I wanted to go back to space
So I got into my case and . . .
Off to space I went

I saw loads of aliens
And they were all Australians
They said hello and I replied back
And I landed in a sack

Corey Scott (Age 10)

The Fox

Underneath the silence I can hear . . .
Tearing through the fields
Life draining away, fighting and exhaustion
The echoes of death, louder and louder
The knowing that the end is coming
The cry as metal spiked jaws snap shut, releasing anger
A feeble beast hitting the floor

Underneath the silence I can feel . . .
Cold, heartless death approaching
Daggers of pain piercing his tortured body
The glance to see a hoard of hounds, death as their purpose
Slipping slowly into silence
His dazed eyes unfocused
The final breath of life as the bloodthirsty hounds move in . . .

Kate Stern-Weiner (Age 11)

Spring Time

As I walk through the field
I feel the cold wind blow against my rosy cheeks
But with the wind is the shining sun like a great ball of life,
Making me warm and cosy in my jacket.
I see thousands of daffodils and primroses and bluebells
Like colourful lollipops shaking in the strong wind.
I can hear the blowing grass like a sea of green
With trees like islands in the luscious green grass
But then there is a moment of silence around me
A break from all the wind blowing around
All the trees and grass are around me
Then I saw a bouncing new born lamb
Joyfully hopping along
As if it were chasing a butterfly alongside its mother.
This is what I think of if I think of Spring.

Henry Sutton (Age 10)

The Seaside

The gentle sand beneath my feet
The seagulls squawking a merry tune
The boats swaying crashing into the waves
This is what reminds me of the seaside.

The dolphins' fins skimming across the waves
The sickening sea water meeting your lips
The seagulls swooping down snatching the food from your hands
This is what reminds me of the seaside.

The shells swirling body smooth against your hand
The waves crashing into each other becoming one
The suns' rays reflecting onto you
This is what reminds me of the seaside!

Charlotte Summers-Rollingson (Age 11)

The Changes Of A Caterpillar

There was a little caterpillar, who was born upon a window siller
He was not a killer, but a very little chiller.

He would munch and crunch all day, he would never stop to play.
He would only pause to say "later I will come and play".

One day he weaved a sack, climbed in and slept just like that.
Some days later there was a loud crack, and his head shot out of the silly sack.

Try as he might he was stuck in there tight.
But he won the fight with the sack that night.

When he was out he looked to the sky.
Spread out his new wings to find he was a beautiful butterfly.

Kerhys Sterling (Age 11)

Life Poem

This used to be a blue shiny stream
Where the enormous and glittery fish
Used to swerve through the water like mini boats
Guy the fisherman used to always play with me on the squidgy green grass
I remember the slimy mud and the sparkly orange flowers
We used to all play in the trees with the fluffy green leaves
I remember the shiny clovers and we all liked playing football
This changed when the enormous factories were built and ruined everything
They made all the fish die and polluted the water
They made all the trees stop growing and us humans threw trolleys in the water
All the ducks were soon killed
The water turned brown like someone vomited in it
The whole place was covered up with smoke and dirty stuff
And there was some slime in the water to make it smell worse.

Mennar Saleh (Age 9)

School

On my school playground,
I can see daffodils smelling sweet,
The vibrant colours looking sleek,
I can hear the twittering of birds;
On they go to and fro,
I can smell fresh air,
Wiping my face as it goes.

In corridors,
I can smell school dinners,
Cooking in the school hall,
I can hear a bubbling sound,
And as I get closer I can see,
Sticky toffee pudding boiling and frothing,
And now I can't wait till dinner time.

And as the day draws to an end,
I say goodbye to family and friends,
And I walk home with imaginary
FRIENDS.

Kayleigh Sibthorpe (Age 8)

African Market

Juicy mangoes freshly grown,
Kiwi fruits whose pips are shown,
Apples, bananas and clementines,
Lemons that are full of lime.

Big fat juicy coconuts,
A noisy market lined with huts,
Sugar canes that look like twigs,
And lots of little juicy figs.

Tangerines and leaves of thyme,
Pagan fruits that make you rhyme,
Tobacco, plums and native hats,
Koala nuts and woven mats.

Poppy Shoyer (Age 9)

Spring

Hooray it's spring
The birds do sing
They've made their nests
And babies are next!

Cute bunnies come out out to play
And summer is only weeks away
The grass is growing
And now needs mowing.

The lambs are born
And love to play
The blossom is about
And catkins come out

Easter is coming
I can't wait
Chocolate eggs
And Easter cake.

Amber Shanks (Age 8)

The Monkey

I am a monkey, I swing in trees
I eat snakes and scratch my fleas.

My babies cling to my tummy
They eat their food and say it's yummy

I am a mammal
I'm as strong as enamel.

I am called Joe
And I have no foe

I'm as brown as tree bark
And as happy as a lark.

Daniel Sidders (Age 8)

Yesterday, Today, Tomorrow

Yesterday I was not in a good mood
I really lashed out at my friend
I badly hurt her feelings,
And I thought it was the end.

Today I tried to call her, but she was not in,
I saw her up town again
And tried to apologise
She said why did you fall out with me
I replied I do not really know.

Tomorrow is nearly here
I think we are going to be best friends
Because she said she is coming round to play
I'm glad we have sorted this out.
As I would not like to fall out again.

Rebecca Skitt (Age 11)

Poetic Form

Acrostic is a
Cracking and a
Rapid kind
Of poem,
Spiffing and
Terrific
In a
Clever way.

Haikus are poems,
No rhyming words, certain number
Of syllables.

It's a:
Poem that doesn't say what it is,
Just focuses on the subject,
Describes it very well,
Say what it is,
It's a
. . . .?

Katie Slater (Age 9)

My Friend

I have a friend, his name is Thor
I think you'd like him, though I'm not sure
When he speaks it's just a roar
You see, he is a dinosaur

He roams around, big and strong
If you want to find him it won't take long
Because he likes to sing a song
But he sounds just like King Kong

Joe Storey (Age 10)

Bedtime Bugs

I can wait till tomorrow
With Big Billy's gang waiting for me
Please can't I stay up late
Just for once, I'm the monster's bait.

All the horrible thoughts
Run through my mind
Is there a monster under my bed
Or is there a monstrous head.

Mum and Dad have just told me
To go to bed.
That's the moment I dread
When they tell me to go to bed.

Laura Sims (Age 11)

Star Fairy

Stars on high,
Stars on low,
A fairy flying,
Swooping low,
Swooping high
To touch the star lit sky.

A fairy on high,
A fairy on low,
Stars glittering,
Swooping low,
Swooping high around
The bright silver moon.

A fairy on a star,
A star fairy!

Emily Shepperson (Age 10)

Why Are Stars Silver

Why is the earth round?
Why do fish swim in the sea?
Why are silhouettes black ?
Why does water run?
Why does snow melt?
What makes the sun shine?
What is the green cross code?
What is the time?
Why do birds fly?
What is a question?
Where does ink come from?
What is school?
What is a liquid?
Why do scissors cut?
How do pencils write?
Why does the sun set in the west?
What is a bin for?
What materials absorb water?

Claire Stock (Age 9)

Colours

Blue is a blueberry waiting to be eaten.
Or down in the dumps.
Or summers sky.
Or a feeling when you're sad.
Red is a red burn.
Or when you are embarrassed.
Or Tomato Ketchup.
Or a red rash.
Silver is a ring.
Or the moon at midnight.
Or a shiny coin.
Or a silver watch.
Yellow is golden.
Or cheerful.
Or the shining sun in summer.
Or shimmering sunshine.
Orange is a juicy satsuma sitting in a fruit bowl.
Or the sun setting in the sky.
Or a tasty pointy carrot.
Or a halloween pumpkin glowing at midnight.

Kerri Steedman (Age 8)

Friends

A trustful - understander
A thoughtful - carer
An honest - supporter
A faithful - protector
A playful - sharer
A dedicated - helper
A generous - listener
What am I?
A friend

Claire Seagers (Age 9)

School Is Cool

In the morning I can't wait
Until I get to the school gate

I like maths
But I'd rather skip the class

English is the best
But I'd rather do the rest

Playtime is the best
It gives us time to take off our vest

The library is great
But why can't we hang round with our mates

Going home with my mates is great.

Sophie Sargent (Age 9)

When I Am Older

When I am older I might be a
Hairdresser no, no a model.
Actually a teacher no, no,
I'll just be a pet carer yes
That's better.
Oh but think of all the howling
And waste.
I'll just be someone in the kitchen
Making breakfast, lunch and tea.
Now that's what I call boring
Maybe I'll be a chef
That would keep me busy
Oh but think of all the whining
Should I be someone getting people ears pierced?
Oh my mum wouldn't agree with that
Maybe I'll be someone who lets out competitions
Oh I didn't know choosing would be so hard.

Francesca Scambler (Age 8)

School Is Great

When I'm at home I just can't wait
But I think school is great
I think English is the best
When I'm at school I'll make a mess
But I like drawing better than the rest
But I love clearing my desk
Playtime is the best
But it gives us a rest
I like the library it is great and gives us a break
But going home definitely beats the lot!

Sharnie Savage (Age 8)

The Sea

Waves

The shiny, slippery, salty waves,
The dark, scary, smelly caves
You don't want a mouthful of salt,
How disgusting, what a thought
Everybody loves the sea,
Especially me!

Creatures

Creatures of all kind,
You will have to mind,
The crabs with bright orange claws,
And sharks with white shiny jaws,
Everybody loves the sea,
Especially me!

Zoe Michelle Shellie (Age 10)

Science, Maths And Art

Maths, Science, Art
Are so smart,
They put you to the test
They're better than all the rest.

Maths is so cool
It feels like you're by a pool,
It's about signs
Sometimes.

You have to be smart
To do art,
Simply the best
It takes more brains than the rest.

Science is great
As long as you don't have a debate,
It's great
Yaaahhhhooooo!!!

Mark Scamell (Age 9)

Sealife

S ealife is great to me is it to you?
E els are small but also quite long
A n octopus has eight legs not like us!
L ife must be fun living in the sea
I like dolphins best, better than the rest.
F ish swim in groups called a shoal
E very sea animal is a great animal.

Michaela Sims (Age 8)

Horse Began

He stole the colour of a flower
He took the gleaming light of the moon
And made his glittering eyes.

He took the jagged edges off a rock
He stole the roots off a plant to build a firm foundation
Then he made his teeth.

He grabbed the grain off the farm
He took the grass off the meadows
And made his mane and tail.

He stole the shell off a tortoise
He took the ends off a tree and
Made his movement.

Jodi Stewart (Age 11)

Westlife

We are going to see Westlife.
At Wembley tonight.
I'll travel by train.
That's enough to excite.
When at the arena.
I'm two rows from the front.
That's a real delight.
The view was amazing.
The boys were just great.
I knew all the songs.
So I sang along too.
However now it's over
My throats rather sore
But it's a night I'll remember for ever more.

Emma Shirley (Age 8)

Underneath The Silence . . .

I can hear . . .

The distant call of a lonely, lost ship, sunken in the depths.
The jewels twinkle as the current crashes against them, hidden and alone.
The long lost shout of the sailors' struggle as they disappeared all those years ago.
The screech of a whistle as the panicking, passengers, crush the decks.
The screams of the children, watching their lives slowly fading, deep into the waters.
The terrible smash of the waves as they punch against the ship, swallowing it, drowning.

I can feel . . .

The bustling of the cabin crew who haven't moved for years.
The steam rising from the fiery, hot engines, now forgotten and gone
The lost, scared souls of the many wasted lives.
The fear for her infant as a mother clutches him lovingly.
The hopelessness of the captain, a silent witness.

Louise Scullion (Age 11)

What Is A Snake?

It is an oversized worm slithering through a huge garden.
Its tongue is a pointed fork waiting to stab.
Its scales are paving slabs stuck to a piece of leather.
Its skin is newly made silk, soft and smooth.
Its eyes are the red in a traffic light, red as fire.
Its body is a streamlined car speeding down a motorway.
Its nose is a deep, dark pit, damp but dry.
Its mouth is a never-ending cave waiting for another victim to wander in.

Tommy Sheldon (Age 10)

The Incredible Night

As the full moon rises, and the stars
Scatter over the nights cape, beautiful and decorative.
A shrill feeling sank into my heart
The crinkles on the moon showed up on the black cape,
And the twinkles lit up my eyes with wonder.
I feel safe in bed tonight.
His misty hands prevents bad dreams,
Which makes me happy, so I can sleep in peace.
His silk silent cloak makes me feel cozy and warm.
Every night he skims across the horizon,
A lovely sight.
And I know I've got a friend with me.
Suddenly, the sky looked behind him and sees his enemy rising.
He quickly raced down to earth to be our shadows.

Greg Satchell (Age 11)

Battle Of Bosworth Senses

I see the army coming towards me
I smell blood in the air
I want to go home to be with my loving family
I feel the ground shaking as I run
I trudge through the thick mud on the battle field
I hear the bloody cry of my best friend being stabbed

Alex Spencer (Age 9)

Dopey Dudey Dog

My Nana's magical monkey thinks he's rather funky
While dancing with a rich ravishing rat
I was feeding my pony when it ran and kicked Tony
Who fell and nearly squashed my flattering fantail fish
Are neighbours extraordinary lizard still thinks he's a wizard
But was knocked out of a magic show by a dopey dudey dog
The mayor's crazy parrot is on search for a golden carrot
With his partner my fantastic fancy finch

Michael Stedman (Age 11)

The Haunted House

There was a haunted house,
It was dark black like coal inside.
The green weeds are very long and tall,
Making the garden look like a jungle
It's all very strange and spooky!
Also very haunted!
It's very dangerous so don't go near,
You never know what will appear.

Laura Sandford (Age 9)

Dark In The Forest

Dark in the forest, in the middle of the night,
Branches snap and creatures bite.
Shadows stir and leaves sway about.
Owls shriek and creatures shout.

Dark in the forest, in the middle of the night,
The misty moon shines no light.
Brambles spike and nettles sting,
Bats fly, you see their wings.

Dark in the forest in the middle of the night,
Everything here gives you a fright.

Harriet Sharp (Age 8)

Pray For Rain

Like a fire ball
Coming this way
Like an orange cocoon
Bombing trees
Water being sucked up by the heat

Scars left in the soil
Where The water once was

Droopy sad plants
Gasping for a drink
Pray for rain

Joe Stubley (Age 8)

Mighty Dragon

Wind rushing through the trees
Rain pouring from the sky
Smoke fills the muddy ground
Monster roaring down the track
Eyes lit like blazing flames
Shiny scales coats his body
Carriages drape like a tail
Speeding past, clouds are dying
Engine sound fades away
Great monster disappears

Jack Stevens (Age 10)

Rain

Cumulus clouds gather, shutting out the light,
The air as humid as a stuffy greenhouse,
Streets are deserted as the temperature drops.

Raindrops fall, bombarding dry earth,
Lightning flashes, spitting death to everything,
Thunder crashes, rumbling, above the darkened clouds.

The skies clear, burnt trees smoulder,
Drains overflow with torrents of water ,
The storm has made its destructiveness known.

Brian Starkey (Age 11)

Darkness

D im and blind folded ravens swoop down into the mist
A ttired ghouls drift into ebony hell.
R ound and round the darkness swirls.
K ing of darkness waits for the arrival of the executioner.
N ightime falls darker still.
E xpiring darkness seals daylight in an envelope.
S nakes slither into hiding.
S creams heard from the chamber.

Sam Stafford (Age 11)

The Moon

A big silver balloon floating in the sky,
It goes away in the day time and comes back at night,
It stares down upon us,
Gleaming in its light,
When morning comes it fades away,
To a land far away,
As it fades out of the blue,
I wonder where it goes to,
As the big, bright, sun comes in,
It looks so small and weak,
In the night,
It fills the world with silver moonlight.

Katherine Stapleton (Age 10)

Thunder

I crashed through the clouds
And made people scatter like rabbits.
I made a fox stop in his tracks.
I scared a cat right out of its skin!
I boomed down onto the ground
And forced some worms to go deeper underground.
I started to sound like a bee...small and quiet, disappearing.

Adam Smith (Age 8)

Magical World Of The Morning

In the cold forest, hoofs hitting the ground,
Dust trailing behind,
The morning grass dew.
Magical world of the morning
Baby birds tweeting,
Moon disappearing from the sky,
Foxes hunting for their cubs,
Dolphins coming up to greet the morning sky.
Now the sun is in the sky,
The magical world of the morning is over once again.

Phoebe Sweeney (Age 9)

Memories

Forever gone, now you will be watching above
Body to ground, yet soul roams free
You will be forever watching over
Guiding, helping always there
Yet you'll be happy and at rest
Not a worry, nor a care.

Many thoughts left unspoken
Many feelings left always open
Memories of good and those of bad
Live on in our hearts always there
They bind us together like paper to glue
So I want you to know I'll never forget you.

Bianca Reid (Age 14)

My Special Friend

My imaginary friend is full of full of care,
When I am sad she is always there.
She is tall and has dark hair,
Best of all she is always fair.
When I am lonely she comforts me,
When I am sad she is full of glee.
When I am stuck she helps me out,
With her, hatred is never felt!

Her gleaming eyes make me laugh,
She never takes it seriously when I am harsh.
Without her, life would end,
For she is my best friend!

Rosina Smith (Age 11)

One Stormy Night

One stormy night is one fine sight.
Waves crash over the deep blue sea.
The rain lashes on to the solid rock ground like a tap has burst
Here and there are bright umbrellas soaking wet with water
The big blue velvet turns to grey.
The shimmering sun darts behind the glistening moon.
Gold lightening strikes.
Invisible thunder claps louder than ever.
Puddles get bigger and bigger until they turn to a flood.
But morning is sunny and bright.
The complete opposite to one stormy night.

Chloe Schendel-Wilson (Age 8)

Our Town!

Our town is red, black, blue and green.
We have got supermarkets and banks and swimming baths.
Sometimes our town is busy and sometimes it is not!
We have got all the emergencies like
Fire, ambulance and police.
Our town is called Redditch
Our town centre is called Kingfisher
Lots and lots of people go there to shop.
We have got cars factories and
A school like Arrowcrest.

Glenn Scott (Age 8)

The Angel

Flying so high, in the bright blue sky!
Her wings are as soft as a turtledove's.
Clouds are floating by above.
Her long golden hair,
Makes other angels stare.
Her bright blue eyes match the sky.
Her soft white hands and smiley face,
Make her look like a Barbie doll on wings.
Each day every day she sings.
Her name is Angelica.
And she floats around on her soft white wings.

Jennifer Savin (Age 8)

I Believe I Can Fly

I believe I can fly,
I touched the sky with an apple pie.
Then it splat down in me face
Then I had to get me case
Then the next time when I tried
Me mum said
Blooming heck you'll die!
And then just guess
SHE WAS REALLY RIGHT!!

James Smith (Age 9)

The Dolphin

Splish splash over the sea
Dive under the sea
Paddle splash dive again
Swim all over the sea
Swallow the fish
And drink the water
Splish splash
Dive under the sea.

Ashley Styles (Age 8)

Rocks

Upon the rocks,
I sit
And gaze
As rattling water sweeps,
Gaining strength
Caving sea
Merchants in rippling waves
Then
Thrashing, crashing
Wondrous waves hurl themselves
At the still, silent rocks . . .

Natasha Stoddart (Age 10)

Horses Wishes

I wish forever more that I was in your heart,
A place where you would keep me safe and
Warm away from everlasting danger.
A shelter full of delicious hay,
Where I would stay,
Until you would take me out to the peaceful
Green meadows,
To win lots of prizes.

All I ever wish for is for you to groom my tail,
Coat and mane tenderly

KEEP ME SAFE FOREVER MORE

Laura Say (Age 11)

Jack Frost

Frost skims the floor
Snow batters the window panes
Hail knocks against the door

"Jack Frost is here!"
"Jack Frost is here!"
Winter comes this way.

Jess Sommerlad (Age 9)

Mysteries Of The Deep

Quiver and gleam goes the sea,
The beach is sandy with some rocks,
A pavement of pearls she sees,
In the depths of the seas,
The sea beasts dive deep, deep.

The waves get stormy,
Shoréwards the salt tides come,
The waves crash against the rocks.

Spray is thrown up,
But in the depths, the mermaids,
Hide in sea caverns,
Undiscovered.

Elizabeth Smith (Age 11)

Please Save Our Rainforest

The plane came at nine
At the Machester airline
I was meeting a friend from a foreign place
Brown and green colours covered his face
He was a banana tree called Zebedee
He came from a land of trees,
With a frog called Zog in his leaves
They said they'd run away
When the hunters came yesterday
All their friends had died
So Zebedee and Zog cried
Because the hunters had cut them all down
The rainforest is dying, we should be trying
To save a tree
Just like me

Katie Smith (Age 10)

Mother's Day

Thankyou for when I needed you.
You stop me from feeling blue.
Put your feet up while I make a cup of tea.
To say thankyou for being so special to me.
HAPPY MOTHERS DAY
Lots of love from Bradley xxx

Bradley Stockwell (Age 10)

Dirty Street

The dirty street is a broken window, shattered.
The dirty street is a horrible, disgusting bomb site.
The dirty street is an old scrap yard, blown up to pieces.
The dirty street is a building site with lots of bricks.
The dirty street is a demolition derby with cars crashing about.
The dirty street is a dustcart full of smelly rubbish.

James Sparks (Age 10)

What Is?

What is thunder?
A thousand horses galloping over the sky

What is ice?
A man walking around with glitter coming off him

What is sun?
A golden sun flower held up in the sky

What is wind?
Dogs howling on top of a hill

What is fast?
Jack's diamonds scattered over the earth

What is lightning?
God's anger being released

Kirsty Smith (Age 11)

Black

Shadowy room,
Where no-one steps,
Tarmac . . . a black river.
Keep with you the dark shadow.
The darkness of silence,
The silence of darkness,
Shadows of trees bending,
Too scared to pass . . .
Out of control,
A friend lost,
A promise undone,
Out on the streets.

Andrew Summerhays (Age 10)

Happy

Happy is rosy red
It tastes like sweet chocolate
And smells like summer flowers
Happy looks like roses in my garden
And sounds like singing birds
Happy is my favourite thing

Lisa Shepherd (Age 11)

Michael Jackson

There was a young man from Matson,
Who's name was Peter Jackson.
He lived in a flat,
With his black and white cat,
Who's name was Michael Jackson.

Sean Sysum (Age 8)

The Wolf

Skimming out
Of a sleek green bush
Came the reflective shadow
Of a wolf
Glimmering in the dusty
Blank night
Watch him . . .
Watch him . . .
As he plunges for his prey
Silent . . .
Silent . . .
He has gone away.

Ashleigh Sewell (Age 10)

One, Two, Three

One, two, three, four.
I am on the shore.
Five, six, seven, eight.
Oh dear I'm late.
Nine, ten, eleven, twelve.
I have found a shell.

Ben Setterington (Age 10)

Smudge

Smudge,
Black and white,
Dwarf Dutch Rabbit,
But on the chubby Side.

Sunbathes in the summer,
Stretches her front and back legs out,
Lies on her belly with her ears up.

Hides from the rain in winter,
Cowers on top of her hutch,
Ears down, front paws tucked under,
Head down, hidden by the muff of fur around her neck.

Even though she was chubby,
A great laugh to play with,
Runs around the coffee table,
While Jade chases her.

Now she is gone,
The garden looks empty,
But always you see her,
Chasing her shadow around her run,
In the summer sun.

Amy Trood (Age 16)

Leaves

Leaves come in all shapes and sizes
Leaves come and go
Leaves come in many colours
Leaves come on trees.

Charlotte Shaw (Age 8)

Riddle

I am . . .
Jungle prowler
Deer eater
Loud growler
Four feeter
Round ears
Soft fur
Stripy rear
Quiet purr
Long tail
Silent mover
Strong but fragile
Pounce groover
What am I?

Tiger

Francesca Sunderland (Age 8)

The Tree

It's spiky
It's tall
It's brown and green
It's old
It's still
It's huge
It's gigantic
It's hard
It's woody
It's bark
It's bushy
It's rough
It's a bird's nest
It's a wasp's nest
It's a monkey's home
It's anywhere
It grows some bananas
And it grows apples and pears.

IT'S A...

Humza Salim (Age 10)

Stars

I once saw a shooting star
It floated over the lights of a car
I see them through my window sill
They shoot over the frosty hill
They shine so bright in the frosty
night.

Edward Short (Age 8)

The Girl On The Swing

(This poem is based on the murder of Sarah Payne)

She sits, alone, but not lonely,
The short blonde pigtails bob in the breeze,
The bubbling laughter fills the garden,
As the swing rocks gently to and fro.

She soars higher, not a care in the world,
The sea of colour swells beneath her,
She is the energy in an otherwise lazy garden,
She radiates light, love, warmth and happiness.

Then, quite suddenly, the dreams are jolted away,
The swing rocks once, twice, then becomes still,
The big bear's paw crushes her delicate fingers,
As he entices her into the shiny, black monster.

And now the swing remains empty and still,
The skeleton of a happiness, long ago,
The garden has been covered with a thick grey blanket.
To shroud her tears, her laughter, her life.

Lula Teunissen (Age 13)

The Dreams

Dreaming is like flapping your arms and flying
Dreaming is like dying and coming back to life.
Dreaming is like a way out for your problems.
Dreaming is like innuendo with disguise.
Dreaming is like money out of nowhere.

Justin Tosh (Age 12)

Love Is A . . .

Love is the titanic, full of hopes and dreams
Love is a rollercoaster, there's highs and lows,
Love is a speed boat in the Atlantic ocean running out of fuel.

Shane Topley (Age 12)

Grandparents

Missing my classmates, missing my best friend,
I've only got Grandma to drive me round the bend.
In the bathroom, washing my hair,
Grandad's choppers give me a scare.
Sitting down, having tea,
Faggots! Yuck! look disgusting to me.
Grandma's spoonerisms are out of control.
"Look at that 'runny babbit, it's hunning out of its role"!
Grandad's sneezes are just as bad.
Achoo! A heart attack could be had.
Whilst Grandad's snoring like a tractor in his chair,
Grandma's doing cross stitch and I'm pulling out my hair.
Although all this sounds awful, we really get on fine.

Eleanor Tilley (Age 13)

The Hunt

A streak of red dashes by
Its head down, its fear high
A cry goes up, "a fox, a fox"
The hunt pursues its prey.

Over fields and under shrub
The fox runs to escape the club
A whirl of red, a splash of white
The fox runs with all its might.

A large root protruding from the ground
The fox falls without a sound.
The hounds let out an excited yowl.
Drawing out the foxes helpless growl.

The fox was doomed from the beginning
Fifty hounds against one is always winning.
How can anyone be so cruel?
Why is this slaughter allowed by rule?

Shannon Tucker (Age 14)

Hate

Hate walked down the street,
His eyes concrete with disrespect.
Fear spread screaming,
It was pale, cold fire.

Scorching love was gone,
As fear and hate triumphed.
He turned toward me,
Making disrespectful movements.

Then I heard love whisper in my ear.
"Fight back with your heart."
I took the command,
And then hate was love.

James Thomson (Age 11)

The Moon Was Lost

I was looking through my telescope,
Late one starry night,
And I had the moon in focus,
An amazing sight.

Because the Earth was turning,
And the moon was too,
After about, five minutes,
The moon went out of view!

Oh no, the moon was lost,
But where was I to find it?
I moved my telescope round,
It was there with stars behind it.

Rebecca Trivett (Age 12)

The Dentist

Butterflies in my tummy,
As the car engine starts.
Is it really four months, since I sat in "That Chair"?

In the waiting room the clock on the wall ticks away,
The telephone rings and the receptionist smiles and chats.
How many times can I fold my appointment card 'til it's my turn?

"Charlotte, would you like to go upstairs?" the receptionist says,
No, would you? I think to myself.
The palms of my hands getting sweatier as I walk upstairs,
I wish I'd cleaned my teeth as my mum tells me every night.

Drills, needles, smells and "That Chair",
Sit down and open wide.
I can't believe it, no needles and no pain.
"Good girl," he says,
Another four months before I come back again.

Charlotte Thompson (Age 12)

Wacky Wildlife Poems

One oily original octopus went on an awful holiday
Two tough tiny tortoise talked thankfully
Three fighting funny fish floated to America
Four fat furious foxes floated away to Palestine
Five filthy fat frogs fixed the fishes car
Six sexy saucy salmon slithered sadly away
Seven stupid silly slugs stalled Steven on his way home
Eight angry elephants eat Europe
Nine naughty noxious nellons nodded to New Zealand
Ten talking tawny Tazs talked away time.

Ben Turner (Age 11)

My Poem*

This is my poem,
I wrote my poem,
I hope you like my poem,
Like I like my poem,
I think it is a good poem, as it is my poem,
Some people don't like my poem,
They say they hate my poem,
I thought when I wrote my poem,
People say I didn't write my poem,
They didn't see me write my poem,
I know I wrote my poem,
I was there when I wrote my poem,
I've forgotten what I wanted to say in my poem,
So now I have to end my poem,
I hope you like my poem.

Karl Ticehurst (Age 12)

* The full name is My Poem, which I wrote by myself
  without mentioning Robot Wars or Thermidor II

Life

You're there,
You're not,
And that's your lot,
What is this strange and bizarre plot?

They call it life,
Well that's what they say,
What does it matter what it's called anyway?

Why were we created?
Why are we here?
What is our purpose?
An experiment I hear.

The strangeness goes on,
The bizarreness remains
We have to find the key,
To unlock the chain.

Joe Thomsett (Age 13)

A True Story

As I remember that last day
All the other memories seem to fade away
I can still picture his face when we used to play
Then it all happened on my tenth birthday.

We went to visit my aunty in the A & E
The nurse went to get us a cup of tea.
Then my Grandad's face dropped
And as I looked I went hot.

The next moment he was gone
Never to see another dawn,
Forever remaining in my memory
For all eternity.

Claire Taylor (Age 12)

Pets From The Past

I had a rabbit called tootsy
He died, he died
My mum said he was sleeping
She lied, she lied
Oh why, oh why is my rabbit dead
Couldn't old age hit me instead.

I had a cat called Mitty
She died, she died
My mum said she was sleeping
She lied, she lied
Oh why, oh why is my cat dead
Couldn't the car hit me instead

James Tomlinson (Age 12)

The Charge Of The Teenagers

5 minutes, 5 minutes, 5 minutes 'til the sales,
Hooray, hooray the shops are open
In charged the teens in 100's,
A push and a squeeze, let me in!
I want those trousers and that top,
In ploughed the teens in 100's.

Everything is going so quicky,
I came here so early, what shall I get?
Dilemma, Dilemma,
Oh look at that it's so beautiful,
I want it, I want it,
Oh no, oh no that girl has got it,
Dilemma, Dilemma.

She's put it back,
Hooray, Hooray,
A push and a squeeze through the crowds,
'Excuse Me!" I'm shouting so loud,
I'm getting closer, oh it's in my hands,
Let's run to the tills, while I get the chance.
Hooray, it now is mine!

Charlotte Taylor (Age 11)

Untitled

Happy birthday to you
I didn't have a clue
I can't go to your party
Happy birthday to you.

Zoe Thorpe (Age 6)

Is this A Nightmare?

Black is the colour of the dark misty night
What shall I do?
Because it's giving me a fright.

As I look out of my window
What do I see?
A sinister black cat
Staring at me

I see in my mirror
A wicked witch's face
Holding her broomstick
Flying through space

The dangerous black wolves
Come out tonight
And will feed on anything in their sight

Will I drown in the deep black sea
Or is this a nightmare?
Can someone help me!

Shyam Thakrar (Age 12)

They Listen Not

So small I am, in a world so big,
My voice heard yet defeated,
Defeated by those of higher status,
So much to say, so little long to hear.

Like a roller Coaster, I am the car,
I follow the rusty old track,
When the track turns, so do I,
Blocking opinion and individuality.

As I turn yet another corner,
I shout, kick, and scream,
Forgetting my status Below,
Below those of higher status.

And when the ride ends,
Those people, riding me, get out,
New people jump in and laugh,
Laugh, at my minority, enjoy their superiority.

One day, the rusty old track will fall,
Break upon impact, along with me,
I hope they are riding, when all of a sudden,
Minority and Superiority collide.

Luke Taylor (Age 17)

Sun

Sun makes me feel happy
Usually I have lollies
Me and the sun are best friends
Memories of dreaming about the sea
Every day it's there
Remembering about it makes me feel happy

Frances Turner (Age 6)

Oily Puddles

Rainbows
lost souls trapped
in oily puddles
when rain falls down
the crystal drops pierce
the hard skin of the ground
exposing the colours
for all to see
I weep into those puddles
to make the colours
stronger.
sometimes I can hear them singing
mournful
beautiful
crying for their lost lives
in world with no reflections.
Fantastic blue glazed whirlpool
where souls can never fly free.

Ellie Tranter (Age 13)

Hell And Heaven

I turned and looked up,
And saw the church,

Its tower as dark as death,
The smell of Satan's breath,

Then a stroke of lightning,
Oh, its terrifying,
All the ghosts are flying.

I clamber inside, why is so light?
God's voice strikes me with fright.

Angels flying around,
Some playing harps on the ground.

Then I realise it wasn't death,
Or the smell of Satan's breath.

This was all in my head,
It was the memories of my son,
That made me feel so glum.

But now he is in heaven with the angels,
And listening to God's wise words.

Scott Thompson (Age 13)

Boil, Boil

Boil, boil eagles toes.
Fat of cow, snot of nose
Tail of rat, leg of duck
One dead rugby player from a ruck
Mane of horse, slime of toad
Make sure you add a load.

Boil, boil lizards tongue
A criminal that's been sprung
Snout of pig, a tumour of the brain
Make sure he's not insane.
Core of apple, gills of fish
Serve it up on a large round dish.

Daniel Thorogood (Age 14)

Pictures From My Mind

Life is generally kind to me,
Very satisfactory,
Sometimes good, sometimes bad,
Sometimes happy, sometimes sad.

Every day I feel blessed,
And try to do my very best,
At everything I say and do,
As God intended me to do.

Cassie Tomkins (Age 12)

Form

I'm an automatic door
(Position applied for)

I'm a tumble dryer, I'm a road junction traffic light.

I'm a health and hygiene law,
Why would I want more?

I'm an operating table, I'm a limousine in classic white.

I'm the one and only cure
(Of which illness I'm not sure),

I'm a mental affliction, the pinnacle of disillusionment.

I'm the president's address
In the event of a world war,

In hell I obey and in heaven I'm a malcontent.

To be a portable television is my main ambition
I'm a politician on the days I'm not a heart and soul.

I had a premonition
And I woke up in the feotal position.

On a dull grey Monday with nothing to do at all.

Andrew Turner (Age 17)

Parrots

Parrots are
The speed of lightning speeding across the sky.
The elegance of a model, walking down the catwalk.
The noise of a chatterbox, chatting away.
Parrots have the beautiful colours of a rainbow,
Being admired through the sky.
They fly the distance of a plane.
They're as cheerful as waves, wondering through the sea.
And have the beauty of a princess.

April Turczak (Age 12)

The Big Match

The whistle blower starts the match,
And has a big bald patch,
The sphere is kicked,
the team is picked,
In the dressing room they sat,
They didn't realise the manager was so fat,
His rumbling body part is so huge,
And he looks like Mr. Scrooge,
The match starts again,
And a news thing says the next day again! Again!
AGAIN!

Keiran Trimming (Age 10)

The Football Match

The whirl of excitement as the players enter the field.
A sea of people cheer and clap.
Tension mounts as the players wait for the whistle to blow.
The build up for the football match.

The rise and fall of the crowd in their seats.
Well known chants start from the back of each stand.
Appeals for "Off side! Hand ball! Penalty!"
The crowd excited at the football match.

The players running the length of the pitch.
Excellent tackles fly in from all directions.
As they sprint for the ball in the penalty area.
The players all fit for the football match.

Person after person stand up as the ball is passed up the pitch.
The striker gets free from his defender.
A great cross is met by his head.
GOAL! at the football match.

Helen Thompson (Age 13)

It Was So Noisy That . . .

It was so noisy that
I couldn't hear the black and white orca squeak
It was so noisy that
I couldn't hear the neigh of a baby black pinto
It was so noisy that
I couldn't hear a dog barking loudly
It was so noisy that
I couldn't hear the noisy whirring washing machine
It was so noisy that
I couldn't hear my teacher talking loudly.

Jack Tiley (Age 8)

A Weekday Diary

When I wake up from a long night sleep
I go to the bathroom and brush my teeth
After that I say my prayers
Then I say goodbye to my teddy bears.

I go downstairs and have my breakfast
It's very important so I must.
I go to school I work I play
I come home at four after a busy day

I have my dinner it's quite a meal,
Sometimes at Burger King I have a killer deal.
I go to bed at half past ten,
I wake up in the morning and do this again.

Kinza Tahir (Age 11)

Colours

Blue is the reflection of disco lights
Or blue berries on a bush
Or the summer's sky
Or not feeling well.
Red is a burning colour
Or when you are embarrassed
Or jam sitting in a pot
Or a cracker just about to be pulled
Silver is a twenty pence coin in my pocket
Or a silver key sparkling
Or a glass window smashing
Or a silver ring sparkling
Yellow is the sun glittering in the day
Or golden sunshine on a summer day
Or yellow honey on the side
Or butter sitting in the cupboard
Orange is a juicy satsuma sitting in a bowl
Or the sun setting in the sky
Or a tasty pointed carrot
Or a halloween pumpkin glowing at midnight

Craig Tunaley (Age 9)

When My Grandad Passed Away

When my grandad passed away,
It was a stormy, rainy day
I couldn't believe he'd gone so fast
Just like good times in the past

When my dad told me he'd gone
I said "he'll be back soon, won't he mum?"
"I'm afraid not", she said,
So I just cried and went to bed.

After all of the good times that we had,
Knowing he was dead made me really mad.
I miss my grandad, so much.
He had such a gentle and loving touch.

Naomi Topliss (Age 12)

Colours

Yellow is a bed of trumpeting daffodils
Or thick lumpy custard on my pie
Or long yellow hair shining in the sun

Red is a warm jumper in my wardrobe
Or a hot fire burning in my house
Or a clock ticking away
Or a field of red poppies

Blue is my favourite colour
Or the shiny sea
Or the bright sky
Or fish swimming in a pond

Charlie Tucker (Age 8)

Always Wanting, Never Giving

People always want more
More food, more drink, more fun
Always wanting never giving

Consuming up a whole area
Never sharing, always desire
Wanting more

They never think of who they're hurting
Always wanting never giving

Why are we like this?
I'll tell you why

We're like a disease
Destroying an area then moving on
Always wanting never giving

We have always been this way
Since the beginning of time
We have wanted never needed more
People are greedy
Always wanting never giving.

Mark Taylor (Age 16)

Footballer

A footballer is blue
He is the summer time
On the pitch
He is sunny
A footballer is a t-shirt
A hot bath
He is "Match of the Day"
A mix of fruit

Martin Tucker (Age 11)

School

It was my first day at school,
I was curious about one rule
I wasn't very keen on maths
But at least we didn't have baths.
I was good at the work on clocks
But I did not do well in our test on rocks.
At last it was lunch
I eat with a big crunch
Then it was playtime
I made up a rhyme
Next we had art
After that I went in a cart
Later on I went on the trim trail
I looked a bit pale
Then I went home
I talked about the Millennium Dome.

Helen Tindall (Age 8)

The Fox Hunt (From the Fox's Point Of View)

I ran faster than I'd ever ran before.
The screaming and shouting kept following,
As if it would never end.
Dogs barking.
Guns shooting.
I kept running.

I was tired.
I needed rest.
The shouting and yelling kept following,
Still not ending.
Panting and puffing.
Screaming and yelling.
I kept running.

I ran faster still
My heart pulsing like never before.
Shouting and screaming still following.
Suddenly.
Dogs barking.
Guns shooting.
Stopped.

Rachel Tutty (Age 11)

Football Crazy

I like to play football I play it every day,
I'm going to watch the cup final at the end of May
My favourite team is Newcastle
They are king of the castle
When I go training
I run ten miles
When I get home
I had a big smile

Jack Twyman (Age 9)

Birthdays

The best birthday I've ever had
Wasn't with my brother. I'm glad!
It was when, I was eleven,
And I invited Jordan and Stefan

When I was only eight,
My birthday was with the brother I hate.
We went to the Spectrum - ice skating -
But all I did was stand hesitating.

The best birthday I've ever been to
Would have to be Jenna's - at the zoo!
We saw the monkeys and the apes,
When they fed them, they gave them grapes.

Ben Thomas (Age 11)

My Friend

My friend may sound funny with orange eyes and green hair
With big long toes that touch your nose
And a really scary stare.

He is all the same to me
He is all the same to me

He lives on a planet far away
Past planets never heard of
Such as
Glip and Gloop and Glay.

Yet he is all the same to me
He is all the same to me.

His favourite foods are
Cheese, chocolate and cherries,
With a side of trout on toast.

Yet he is all the same to me
He is all the same to me

I still have not told you what my friend is yet

Well really he is an . . . . .

ALIEN!

Lewis Thomas (Age 10)

Milly The Mouse

Milly the Marvellous Muscular
Mouse soars to seize the
Freezing fridge for food
Wilma his whining wife watches
Wonderfully as he snatches the snacks!

William Toomey (Age 10)

Dreams

I wish I was anywhere but here
Somewhere hot on the beach having a nice cold drink
When I close my eyes I dream.

I wish I was anywhere but here
Somewhere where people care
Having a really good time
When I close my eyes I dream!!!

I wish I was everywhere at once
Somewhere where my life is
When I close my eyes I dream!!!

I need to look no further
Cos what I dream is here!!!!

Sophie Tuck (Age 12)

The Zoo

The birds go zoom zoom zoom,
While the elephants go boom boom boom.
The monkeys swing from tree to tree,
While watching you and me.

The seals are very clever,
And their keeper's name is Trevor.
So come to the zoo today,
And watch all the animals play.

Giraffe's necks are very long,
To keep their noses away from the pong.
So Come to the zoo today,
And watch all the animals play.

The lions ROAR is very loud
To frighten the people in the crowd.
Even though there are lots of types,
Every zebra has black and white stripes.

Penguins are extremely cold,
While the turtles are very old.
So come to the zoo today
And watch all the animals play.

Emily Turnnidge (Age 9)

Tiger

He slinks along in the grass,
The leafy trees he does pass.

The jungle floor he does prowl
Run away when he does growl.

He hears something and turns around,
Then he creeps lower to the ground.

He pounces on a big fat wren
Then he creeps back to his den

Emma Thompson (Age 9)

Get Lost!!

Shove off!!
Pick on someone
Your own size!!
You big fat boy!!
Get lost
Go away!!
Go somewhere where
I'm not playing
Don't throw stones
At me

Tom Thynne (Age 9)

Bullying

Bullying is nasty, horrible and frightening
It can end up in a fight,
Sometimes they make gangs
And do things that aren't right.

They go up to little children
And ask them for their money,
Then when they walk away
They always think it's funny.

At times there can be violence
Stealing and threatening,
When they call you rude names
It can really be embarrassing.

If they keep on and on at you
You feel sad and down,
And when you are in your class
It can often make you frown.

Bullying is nasty, horrible and frightening
It can end up in a fight.
Sometimes they make gangs
And do things that aren't right.

Ben Thould (Age 11)

Choo Choo Train

One day the choo choo train
Came to the station
It came to pick up some people.
It is time for the train go to the next station.
The train goes through the tunnel
And over cow hill and past the farm.
The choo choo train is back
At the other station

Lee Thorp (Age 10)

Bedtime

When I was two
I used to say boo to bedtime
I was scared of the dark
And the dog used to bark,
Which made me even more scared,
At bedtime.
I lived in a creepy house,
Screeching like a mouse,
And shadows on the wall,
At bedtime.
I used to have nightmares,
And nobody cared,
At bedtime.
But now I'm eleven my bed is . . .
    HEAVEN!

Jack Thomas (Age 11)

Little Eyes

Stars are aliens' torches,
Shining far away.

Stars are twinkling diamonds,
On a woman's ring.

Stars are artists' pictures,
Drawn in the sky.

Stars are a dot-to-dot,
In a child's book.

A star is an angel,
Far, far, away.

The stars are a map,
To guide a traveller home.

Stars are little eyes,
Looking at us all night.

Stars are tiny fire-flies,
Flying in the sky.

Jenny Turner (Age 12)

Mighty Mountain

Snow capped Mount Everest
People try to climb it
Dangerous and mysterious mountain

Warren Tilbury (Age 10)

My Mum

My mum's in hospital,
She doesn't like it there,
She's getting very bored now,
She wishes she wasn't there.

She's coming home tomorrow,
She's got a big stitch across her tummy,
She's very nice to me and Charlie,
She's our special mummy.

My mum's come home to rest now,
All she can do is look,
While Dad and Nan do all the work,
She sits and reads her book

She still can't life a finger,
She's getting very mad,
Dad tells her not to worry
It's really not that bad

Jessie Thomas (Age 9)

My Favourite Things

My favourite place to sit,
Is in the conservatory,
It's cosy and warm and brightly lit,
In the conservatory.

My favourite time of day,
Is at around four o'clock.
It's sunny and light and time to play
At around four o'clock.

My favourite view of hills,
Is the vast view down my road.
It's peaceful and quiet and always still,
The view down my road.

My favourite pets I have kept,
Are my dog and two black cats.
They're lively and fun and have never slept,
My dog and two black cats.

Elizabeth Thompson (Age 9)

Furniture Poem

She is a loving person,
She is a little angel,
She has light blue eyes that sparkle in the moonlight,
Her time of day is 8.00 p.m. because she gets a rest,
She is the best person in the world,
She is a little square of a chocolate bar.
She hates flowers but she likes tea,
All my friends like her,
She's a very busy bee.
Who is she?

Ellen Taylor (Age 10)

My Brother

Sneaky, sly and silent,
A plump ball of pitch black tar,
Witty, whistling and wanting,
Above us in our wisdom, a star.

Standing, stealthy and secretive,
A mysterious overlooking bat,
Whippy, wealthy and wiley
A brilliant shiney black cat.

Surprising, silky and simple
I would never swap for another
Weary, whisky and welcoming
The most brilliant . . .
Wonderful . . . . .
Brother!

Chanel Tappin-Beachey (Age 10)

The Door

Go and open the door of death.
Maybe outside there are shadows dancing behind trees
In the mystically mysterious moonlight,
Or bats waiting on the whip-like branches,
Waiting to fly down and suck every single drop of blood
From your pale body,
A bright flaring fire chasing after you,
Wrapping you in its arms of death,
Or a warty witch, waving her wand,
Casting a bad luck spell on you.

Go and open the door of wealth.
Maybe a super sized shimmering mountain
Made of 24 carat gold is right outside your doorstep.
Maybe you'll see some sparkly silver cloud
Raining solid silver coins,
Or a huge plaque encrusted with gorgeous glowing gems
Or a magic story of a magic story.

Nikita Thakrar (Age 10)

The Sea Monkeys

There were some sea monkeys which were very small
And they had nothing to do at all,
So they went on the slide which was so much fun,
So they went inside for a hot cross bun.

Caroline Thynne (Age 9)

A Dark Dream

The fear of any person walking . . .
On a silent pitch dark night
The fear of any baby
On its own that night.

The fear of any gloomy owl
On the hunt for food
The fear of any sky lark
Whistling its own tune

The fear of any tiny mouse
Lost amongst the bushes
The fear of any squirrels
Lurking in the trees

The fear of any horse
Lost amongst the misty meadow
The fear of any shadow
Lurking in the night sky

Why do I fear these things?
All alone in the night
Why, why do I fear these things?
That give me nightmares on a moon lit night

Emma Tarry (Age 11)

Untitled

Beauty!
       Beauty is gold and silver,
It smells like perfume,
It tastes like mango,
It sounds low and gentle
It feels like gold,
Beauty lives in people's spirits.

Joyfulness!
       Joyfulness is orange and yellow,
It smells like fresh air,
It tastes like birthday cake,
It sounds like pop music,
It feels like silk,
It lives in our hearts.

Boredom!
       Boredom is a dull grey,
It smells like rotten bananas,
It tastes like whisky,
It sounds like the wind,
It feels like you're watching a never ending video,
It lives in your mind.

Lisa Tuckett (Age 9)

Shadows

Spider
Last of her kind.
Scuttles underground
Safe
Prepares her nest for her young ones
But none come.

Craig Tresidder (Age 10)

If You Want To See An Alien!

If you want to see an alien,
You must...jump into a rocket,
And start it up and go up to Mars.

I know an alien who's living
Up there he's big, he's fat, he's mean.

Yes! If you want to see an alien,
You must...jump into a rocket,
And start it up and go up to Mars.

Slowly move to
His cave and
Say alien, alien
Alienenenen.
Don't stay there RUN for your life!!!

Sophie Townsend (Age 9)

Autumn Contrasted

I'm walking through the woods,
I look up I see.
Autumn leaves twisting, twirling
And crunching whooshing, whirling
All night through.
Looking hot, rusty red
Flying through the air
Swaying down
           down
           down
           down
I'm running, running, running
Through the rain
I have nowhere to go
Nowhere to hide
Suddenly there's a CRASH!
Of thunder
The leaves cascading around
Around me.
The wailing wind
Chasing behind me
Like a ferocious lion.

Jessica Timms (Age 10)

War Is Horrible

War
Scary, terrifying
Horrible, revolting, disgusting,
People very, very scared.
Worrying.

Jade Tout (Age 8)

The Haunted Park

As the clock strikes midnight
And all through the park,
I can't really see it
Though it isn't very dark.
I know it's getting closer
I run as fast as I can,
But I slip over a twig
And it touches my hand.
I scream for terror
My voice is not loud enough,
I heave it away
But it just goes "puff, puff, puff".
I kick its legs,
And it falls over,
I run for my life
And I see a clover.
I kneel down to the clover
And say a prayer,
I end up at home
With no more fear.

Michelle Tonta (Age 9)

Life

We all have feelings of a different kind
So take some time to read this rhyme

There's a time to be born and a time to die
A time to smile and a time to cry
A time to dance and a time to keep still
A time to be healthy and a to be ill
A time to be happy and a time to be sad
A time good and a time to be bad
A time to be brave and a time to bow down
A time to grin and a time to frown
A time to be calm and a time to be mad
A time to be disappointed and a time to be glad
A time to be unreasonable and a time to be fair
A time to rush and a time to take care
A time to be confident and a time to be shy
A time to miss out and a time to apply
A time to not believe and a time to have faith
A time to be dangerous and a time to be safe

Avoid the bad - Go with the good
Be happy - Not sad

Leonie Todd (Age 10)

Water

A cold freezer
A hot burner
A metal ruster
A death bringer
A cloth cleaner
A wave maker
A boat transporter
A tap runner
A fire destroyer
A soap bubbler
A bath filler
A thirst quencher
A life saver

Anthony Tugwell (Age 11)

Untitled

A wet, waggly whale
A wiggly, waggly worm
A tangled, twiggy, tree snake
I love animals.

A furry, funny fox
A flipping, funny fish
A bad, bad bear
I love animals.

A dirty, dangerous dog
A mad, male monkey
I love animals.

Jennifer Taylor (Age 7)

Haiku Poem

Glittery Blizzard
Soft, icy, snow glistening
Frosty, shiny, snow.

Sam Turrell (Age 7)

Rhinos

One grey rhino playing peek-a-boo,
Along came another and then there were two.

Two charging rhinos charged at a tree,
It broke open and then there were three.

Three puffing rhinos trying to open a door,
It opened and then there were four.

Four playful rhinos playing near a hive,
It got squashed and then there were five.

Five sleepy rhinos saw some sticks,
Out came another and then there were six.

Six up and running rhinos running to Devon,
They got there and then there were seven.

Seven charging rhinos charging at a gate,
It opened and then there were eight.

Eight little rhinos getting along fine,
They got home and then there were nine.

Nine proud rhinos watching the men,
Out came their mother and then there were ten.

Matthew Taylor (Age 7)

My Favourite Things

Holidays are such great fun,
Just relax in the heat of the sun.
I like a refreshing, cool drink,
You would too, don't you think?

A quarter past three is the best time of day.
Especially in the sun's heat in May,
Some fresh air is all I need,
Away from the school - Warren Mead.

Tom Townsend (Age 10)

Star Song

Sing a song of spaceships,
Zooming through the dark sky
Four and twenty space men
Whirling and twirling through space
Sing a song of astronauts
Upside down in the galaxy
Four and twenty rockets
Whizzing through the moonlight
Sing a song of flying comets
Exploding in the dark planet
Four and twenty flying saucers
In the starry night.

Bryn Tomes (Age 7)

Nails

Sparkly nails, glittery nails
Shining in the light, long nails
Tough nails, rough nails
It's time to have a fight.

Bright nails, colourful nails
Pink, red, and blue,
Bitten nails, wonky nails
Mine are like that too.

Long nail, pointy nails
Sharp as a knife.
Pretty nails, ugly nails,
Katie's had long nails all her life.

Sharp nails, lethal nails,
That dig into your skin.
My nails, cool nails
They make me want to GRIN!!

Georgia Thompson (Age 10)

My Little Sister

What I hate about my little sister
Is the way she scratches me
What I like about my little sister
Is when she hugs a tree.
What I hate about my little sister
Is that she will not let me in her room
And she will not share her toys.
What I like about my little sister
Is how she plays with boys.

Kelly Thorn (Age 8)

Hell Water

Whirling wonder, wicked wet,
How powerful are you?

I am powerful, I kill men,
I imprison them!

Wicked wet, whirling wonder,
Do you make men blunder?

I imprison them in hell,
Burning forever!

Whirling wonder, wicked wet,
Why do you make men struggle and sweat?

As soon as they come, they will go,
Blood flying, people dying,
That is the way I like it!

Wesley Thistlethwaite (Age 10)

A Rattlesnake

A quiet hisser,
A tail rattler
A poisonous nibbler,
A quick crawler
A non beggar
An animal stalker
A danger causer
A long user
An egg eater
A skin shedder
A child killer
A dangerous stalker

Michael Totty (Age 11)

Cats

Little looker
Bird snatcher
Tiny ducker
Mouse catcher
Dog ignorer
Large yawner

Long legger
Poor beggar
Big snorer
Noisy purrer
Sneaky lurker
Rat storer

Ben Threlfall (Age 10)

In My Pocket

I put in my pocket
A memory of my grandmother,
A roly poly down the stairs
My adult tooth.

I put in my pocket
My first scar,
My first steps,
My first word.

I put in my pocket
A picture of my grandad
My first tooth
My first smile.

I put in my pocket
My first birthday.
My first present,
My first toy.

I put in my pocket
My first look at the world,
A first breath of air,
My first bath.

Aron Tarrant (Age 11)

Snow Is . . .

Snow is a blanket of whipped cream,
Diamonds falling from the sky,
Fluffy white clouds upon roof tops,
Candy floss on the car,
Cotton wool balls on trees,
The world is covered in ice-cream.

Joanna Tebble (Age 9)

English

English, English is the best,
It beats all the rest,
You have a friend,
To tell you when to end.

English, English is the best,
It beats all the rest,
It puts you to the test,
To beat the rest.

English, English is the best,
It beats all the rest,
A lot of people think it's bad,
But the thought of it makes me sad.

English, English is the best,
It beats all the rest,
I like to read, I like to write,
Until I go to bed at night.

David Taylor (Age 10)

Alone

Turning and flying, lost in time, screaming and crying, crossed the line.
Floating around, my mind is free, quiet, not a sound, search desperately.

A world of colours, to reach out to, stuck in the darkness, what to do?
Love is untouched, as depressions disturbed, who are you, in the warp of the world?

Who am I? What do I feel? This surrounding, is not quite real.
Tears of joy, are distant to me, what is it like to laugh happily?

Give me your hand, pull me through, I'm nervous you say it, but I need you.
People stand and people stare, but I don't think they really care.

Strange dreams, not unseen, danger far, where has it been?
All my life, I've been mesmerised by this world, of pain and lies.

Space has been, holding many down, then lets up, to gasp and drown.

Kathryn Taylor (Age 12)

Racing Cars

R ooom roooom!
A ll getting ready
C rowd cheering
I nappropriate words
N oise level rising
G ranny's and Grandad's going deaf

C ar claps out
A ngry motorsport company
R ace over
S top!

Lewis Taylor (Age 10)

The Fire Lion

The fire jumps like a lion
His big fierce eyes glare
His tail flickers, hot and deadly
His sparkling mane is pretty

Richard Taylor (Age 8)

It Was So Noisy

It was so noisy that
The teacher squeaked the pen on the board
It was so noisy that
The window exploded into bits
It was so noisy that
Everybody was whining like thunder storms
It was so noisy that
The classroom was almost destroyed
It was so noisy that
The light bulbs burst from their sockets

Nicholas Taylor (Age 8)

School's Out

Coming to school on the last day of term,
In the sun's dazzling shine,
Excited faces going along,
Everything's going to be fine.

In the holiday we go swimming,
We always splash and laugh,
It's all so fun and great,
We're going to have a holiday and a half!

Then the bell goes,
We hear everyone shout,
We run out of the gate,
Because SCHOOL'S OUT!

Claire Thomson (Age 10)

The Mirror

When I walked
In a calm, silent night
And the sight was like
I was dead
I found an icy mirror in the garden
Like a rock

A little push
Then it spun around
Slow as the earth
Orbiting
While still the moonlight shines on the ground
And the silver gets lighter.

When the mirror was still spinning
The moonlight shone over my face
And the mirror disappeared...

Oliver Troward (Age 11)

Is This The Death Without A Sound?

Where have all the sheep gone?
Why have the cows all gone away?
The fields that they were upon,
Have become empty in a day.

All the farmers are so troubled,
By the sudden change.
The price of meat in the shops has doubled
But there isn't much of a range.

The countryside is banned from us,
It doesn't seem too fair.
We might never see the fresh green grass,
Which is very hard to bear.

What is the grey smoke above the clouds so high
The smell of burning all around
The fiery sparks that make my cry.
Is this the death without a sound?

Time is ticking on a lot,
Will it ever end?
I think the time has come to stop
So it can get back on the mend.

Sarah Townsend (Age 10)

The Night

The night is black.
It looks like owls flying around.
At night I feel peaceful.
I sometimes feel afraid at night.
I peep through the door,
And see my mummy and daddy.
The dark makes me think of owls and
Hedgehogs and mice.

George Tuck (Age 5)

Fog

Fog tiptoes on cats feet,
Fog glares like cats eyes,
Fog can be dangerous like cats paws,
Fog can sit and wait for hours like cats,
Fog moves slowly like cats feet.

Fog can move fast like dogs,
Fog can jump down on you like dogs,
Fog can jump up on you like dogs.

Fog is Weird

Jonathon Taylor (Age 9)

Winter Days

Stout pointy trees,
Standing in a sparkling field
Icy grounds,
Spooky trees,
Old and crooked,
I'm going to freeze,
Lonely, scary,
Arms waving,
Fingers pointing.

Robert Thompson (Age 7)

If I Had Wings

If I had wings
I would touch
The tail of a shooting star.

If I had wings
I would taste
The candyfloss floating in the blue.

If I had wings
I would listen to
The raindrops shattering on the ground.

If I had wings
I would gaze
At the scolding sun spinning like a base ball.

If I had wings
I would dream of
Turning the sky upside down and skating on it with speed.

William Turner (Age 9)

Save Me From The Fire

I'm trapped
At the bottom of the wardrobe
Can't get out
Save me

It's outside my door
Raging hot
Can't breathe at all
Save me

Nothing can save me
Can't jump out of the window
It's a worst nightmare
Help!!!

Sophie Tyler (Age 11)

My World

When I sit and wait around,
And look what there's behind me.
When the sun is shining blue,
Flowers stand and greet me.
All the animals in the woods,
Come scampering towards me.

All the buildings everywhere,
Such different shapes and sizes
So many people that I see
Unknown and questioned to me.
In this world,
There is so much yet to learn.

Jade Taylor (Age 10)

Underneath The Silence

Underneath the silence I can hear . . . the crash of waves crashing against the beach at Weymouth,
The distant cries of astronauts on the bleak moon,
The loudest roar of a lion as it catches its prey,
The rustle of giftwrap as a boy unwraps a Christmas present,
The guns shooting in war as their bullets pierce through bodies.

Underneath the silence I can feel . . . the chill biting me on a cold, snowy day,
The freezing breeze on the planet Pluto,
The ground shaking beneath me as a Boeing 747 takes off,
The trigger of a gun as it pushes against my finger,
The pain in my spine as I fall on my back.

Underneath the silence I can see . . . the streak vapour trail off the wings of a plane,
The water rushing over the edge of Niagara falls,
The rotor blades of a helicopter as it leaves for another destination,
The smoke of a Subaru burning up the track,
The children working hard in the classroom as their teacher gives them more to do.

Underneath the silence I can smell . . . the burning rubber of a dragster,
The fresh scent of shampoo as I rub it into my hair,
The tropical scent of the Caribbean as I lay back in my deck chair,
The freshly baked bread after it has been in the oven,
The cooking of egg and bacon on a Saturday morning.

John Teahan (Age 10)

Imaginary Friend

My best friend is Rose
Rose is small, Rose is pretty
She has beautiful long hair
And I take her everywhere
I tell Rose my secrets,
And she never tells.
We make each other happy
And it is good to have Rose

Gemma Taylor (Age 7)

Why?

"Teacher, why doesn't my cat eat my mouse?"
"Miss, why don't you put your e-mail in the letter box?"
"Mr, why is it you do not put your computer chips in the oven?"
"Sir, why can't I get to my Powerpoint?"
"Friend, why don't the keyboard keys open the door?"
"CAN ANYONE TELL ME WHY?"

Rosy Thorpe (Age 9)

The Great Sea

The sea is a great minotaur waiting for his victim.
The minotaur is
CLASHING
POUNDING
BASHING
AND GROWLING
The great minotaur stalks
As he is stalking
He's like blowing everyone up.
He smells like a whopping volcano.
He finds his prey.
As he eats it the sun comes down.
Now the sea is ready for his venom.
The sea is a great minotaur waiting for his victim.

Alexander Tay (Age 6)

Moods Of The Sea

The sea is a fairy godmother
Whirling her wand
Over the calm blue sea
The sea a trotting horse
Finding her friend
The sea is a ballerina dancing
Dancing on a wave
CRASH
SMASH
RIPPLE
It starts to nibble the cliffs
It slowly stops
The sea is a fairy godmother
Whirling her wand
Over the calm blue sea.

Shannon Thwaites (Age 7)

Autumn

Golden leaves glide the hushed wind
Like a surfer on crashing waves,
While the trees veer in the silent wind,
Dangerously lurching towards the soft waving grass.
The grass sways and watches the trees skim their small heads,
But still they just wave muted.
Insects in the swaying trees lull to sleep
By the sound of radiant Autumn.
Wind drives Autumn along,
Almighty and powerful.
Never to be seen.
Strikes fear into unsuspecting victim.
Watching Autumn pass is the cosy man,
Logs stacked on the fireplace,
Not affected by the transient season . . .
He says to himself will it ever end?

Michael Tilston (Age 11)

Sights And Sounds Of The Playground

People scream and shout,
While children run about.
Some people stand around,
Talk and stare at the ground.
Now and then children fall, then get up with a call.
Crisp packets scattered on the floor,
Let there be no more.
Cars whizz past,
Going very fast.
Teachers in the playground,
Walking round and round.

Florence Toch (Age 8)

Poems

P oems came after stories
O h my gosh that is some glory
E lliot was great at writing poems
M aking funny poems makes me fall on the floor
S ometimes when I'm laughing someone knocks on the door!

David Viner (Age 8)

The Monster Under My Bed

There's a monster under my bed
Who only comes out at night
I hide behind my pillow and shiver in fright.
His eyes are huge and yellow
His teeth are long and sharp
Then he nibbles at the wardrobe
And he messes up my clothes.
I often wonder what he looks like
If he's giant or he's small
And he sometimes spits venom all over the bedroom wall.
He's eaten up my mother and he gobbled up my dad
And he'll probably eat me for afters because I'm only a little lad.

Gregory Taylor (Age 10)

Latter News

Why did Jesus have to die
All he wanted was to teach, heal
He was not a killer
He never deserved to go to heaven
Or to be hung on the cross on skull hill.

Why I only got the news a few days later
Now I wish that I was not doing my chores
And I was at the crucifixion
Barabbas should have been killed.

Not Jesus he was no cheat, killer or a traitor
He should be alright alive not dead.

Matheos Tofari (Age 9)

Golf Courses

Great shot! Hole in one on hole one.
Over the hill and in the hole.
Lovely the ball lies on the soft fairway
On the way to hole two.

Chip it over the dip not easy
Oh no it's gone in the pond.
Get the umbrella it's starting to rain
Better run back to the club house or you'll get soaked.
Get something to eat, like a bacon sandwich
Or get a drink and sip it.
Go home and try again next week.

David Thomas (Age 11)

Late!

Wind is like a late man on his first date.
He races through the huge green park
Blowing away leaves as he shoots past.
Moaning and groaning trying not to be violent.
Knocking things over as he grows later and later.
His face is changing shape as he gets angrier.
Whistling along and taking over the path.
People feel a touch of cold as he rushes past.
As he approaches the bar he sighs
          PHEWWW!

Sophie Taylor (Age 10)

What I think Of the Moon

When you look up at the moon at night,
With its deep dark craters, its mysterious rocky face,
Its boulder strewn surface, its strange spooky light.
Dangling there like an invisible chained mace,
Its ball made out of pure silver.
Then, it just wanders off on its everlasting journey.

Jack Tawney (Age 10)

Allosaurus

His nickname is Big Al,
He is my pal,
He has horrible claws,
And vicious jaws,
He is the lion of the Jurrasic ,
Allosaurus is so classic,
Sometimes he eats eggs,
And he has got fast legs,
Some dinosaurs have armour,
Some are like reptiles like an Iguana,
Some have plates to show their mates.

Daniel Trevelyan (Age 6)

Statue of Liberty - New York

An incredible mass of importance
Scraping the New York skyline,
On the every morn,
The flame of liberty glows incandescently on a shimmering pool,
Sun is peering over the sleeping town,
The heart of a dormant city
Lies quiet and still,
And as the lazy sun
Cautiously creeps to the peak of day
The heart begins to beat

Molly Templeton (Age 11)

Playing In The Waves

Playing in the waves
The dolphins dive gracefully
Up and down up and down.
They dive all around.

Playing in the waves
I dive right down
With the fish

Playing in the waves
Splashing as I go.
Playing with a shark.
I DON'T THINK SO!

Jenny Taylor (Age 6)

Daydreaming

While I stare out of the classroom window all day,
Questions shot at me, teachers yelling at me,
But I don't know why I always daydream.

In P.E. everybody's doing handstands and cartwheels,
Footballs kicked at me, netballs thrown at me,
But I don't know why I always daydream.

In the playground my favourite place,
I daydream freely without getting yelled at,
Meekly I sit while thinking about what I will daydream about tomorrow!

Lauren Taylor (Age 9)

Quiz Question Poem

What is the smallest bone in your body?
Who made the world?
How did bones get in our bodies?
Why on the 11th hour of the 11th day of the 11th month do we have two minutes silence?
Why when you get married do you get a ring from your partner?
How did dinosaurs get extinct?
Who invented words and letters?
Who made a man different to a lady?
How long ago did vikings live?
Who made different religions?
Who made paint and colour?
Why do jet planes fly so fast?
Why does the earth spin round?
Who invented time?
How do we learn so fast?
Who invented flowers?
Why do french people speak differently to us?
Who invented earpiercing?

Ellen Turner (Age 9)

Fluttering

Syrupy nectar sucker,
Insect explorer.
Colourful cloud
Gentle flier.
Fluttering faster through the air.
Fluttering through the air faster and faster.

Syrupy nectar sucker,
Insect explorer.
Colourful cloud
Gentle flier.
Fluttering faster through the air.
Fluttering through the air faster and faster.

Clair Trow (Age 11)

Siberian Tigers

I adore them,
They prowl and poke on their own,
Wearing a camouflage coat, while on the hunt,
Searching for prey,
On which to gorge!

They doze and dream with their mates,
About the biggest snatch they've had that year,
They live out in the cold conditions,
Wishing o'wishing,
They had some spare meat.

Siberian tigers excite me,
The way they move so fast and sleek,
Their roar is frightening but thrilling,
Siberia's tiger rules his country with pride,
Siberia's cunning sly tiger is just the very best.

Kurt Taylor (Age 10)

Night

As the night moves swiftly on
The people of the earth, grow dreary.
He makes you scared and makes you sleepy
He knows the curse to make you weary.

He lives in the shadows
He lives in the sky
Where ever you walk he's there.
He knows the curse to find you
Because he knows you're there.

The mysterious demon walks the streets
Each and every night.
He knows the curse
To turn the planet dark instead of light.

Emma Taylor (Age 11)

Deep Blue Sea

The sea overlaps the soft silk sand,
As it falls all soggy out of my hand,
The waves get bigger as the north wind blows,
It trickles up slowly then tickles my toes,
Gently and soft I'm perched in the sand,
All mushy and wet up to my hand,
The moon shone over the whole of the sea,
Slowly but surely it left me.

As I turned my back,
I heard a whistle,
I had one last look and saw,
All the pebbles surrounding the seashore,
Shining glamorously in the starlight.

Cara Taynton (Age 11)

Underneath The Silence

Underneath the silence I can hear . . . .

The boy shouting as the brick came towards him from the building
A quiet crack of a stick as the hunter, steals through the thicket, trying to hunt his prey.
The boy's cries and screams as his parents bruise, hurt him for no reason.
Bubbles rising from beneath, swishing seas, as the plane carries on sinking.
The desperation of my friend as she gets bullied
People running away from the earthquake.
Underneath the silence I can feel . . . .
The warmth of the fire breathing onto my school.
The cold hand as it struck me again.
The bustling of the crowds as they ran away from the burning hot fire.
Pain as the hunter shoots him.
The glass shatter from the blow.
Screams of a scared frightened child.

Vicky Townsend (Age 10)

I Will Forever Remember . . . .

I will forever remember,
The flowers opening and the grass swaying in the breeze, in Spring.
I will forever remember,
The shine of the sun in the middle of summer
I will forever remember,
The leaves of the trees falling in Autumn
I will forever remember,
The snow falling as white as a newly born lamb in Winter
I will forever remember
All the seasons - breezy, hot, cool, cold - all year round
That's what I'll remember forever

James Taylor (Age 9)

Snow

Light drifting snowflakes
Landing peacefully on the ground
Crisp snow covers the field,
Not a sound
Snowmen are being made
Bushes are laid
With white drifting snow

Prudence Vertigan (Age 11)

Snake

S ilently slither across the land, looking for prey,
N ear the water he slithers by with no other animal in his way
A iming his fangs at the nearest enemy,
K illing animals as they go by
E nemies watch out or the snake will get you!

Sophie Tubbs (Age 9)

The Dead

Tears falling from the screaming widow
The pain built up like a shot from a bullet
Red roses falling from the hand to the coffin
The lowering from the surface to dead man's land
The memories of the dead striking like a sword from a knight.
The first shovel of dirt has fallen.
He's gone.

Mark Taylor (Age 14)

War!

Brave people dying,
Sharp splinters flying.

Cracking glass the biggest boom,
Spitting cobras in many rooms.

Children crying non-stop
Digging a grave for a cop.

Screaming crying screaming dying,
Screaming crying tears flying.

But then two hours after midday
Mister Hitler fades away.

Harry Tawney (Age 8)

War!!!

Fire devastating every village and town,
Guns blundering, men being shot down.

Bombs smashing every big city,
Every garden tremendously gritty.

Men's screams torturing everyone's ears,
Every child I see they are always in tears.

On the battle field it's only slaughter,
To all the women and children it' weekly torture.

Thomas Tebbatt (Age 8)

Bedtime

When I go to bed.
I go get ted.
When I go upstairs,
I juggle some pears.
When I see my bed be,
And I jump with glee.
So I climb under my quilt
And talk to my teddy Filt.
My mum comes in and gives me a kiss,
And shouts my little sis.
She goes out the door,
And my teddy counts to four.
Yipee they all say
As they party away.
Then Dan swings on the light,
And we all jump with fright.
So he swings off with might
And starts a fight.
So my mum comes in and shouts, stop that fight,
Night, Night!

Demi Thompson (Age 8)

Flowers

Flowers shine and sparkle when the rain falls
They smell as beautiful as perfume

Flowers have beautiful colours
I buy some for my mum and she's happier than ever

My garden wouldn't be beautiful without them
They are as bright as stars

Luke Usher (Age 7)

The Storm

The storm that happened on the night,
Really gave me quite a fright,
It crashed the cars,
They went to mars,
And I couldn't believe my sight!

The storm, the storm,
It's wrecking my lawn,
The flower, the weeds, the plants,
I thought they were doing a dance,
Like a prawn.

Thomas Weymouth and Nicholas Trafford (Ages 8 & 9)

Death's Happiness

When I am dead and gone
And you are left all alone
If you feel blue with no-one around
Then remember, that I am always there.

Even if you can't see me
I promise I'll always be near
To protect you from evils around
Don't think of me as gone
Imagine, I'm just in the next room.

When you speak of me don't use an awkward tone
I will always be happy as long as I still see you
Talk to me if you feel lonely
I will always listen, even if I don't reply
You will always be loved by me.

And as your days grow darker
Please don't feel afraid
Just let yourself go and don't fight
For I shall come to meet you my love
And help you to our final paradise.

Katie Vaughan (Age 14)

The Evil Dragon

The evil dragon,
Born of a myth.
Strong, powerful, beautiful.
Like a jet of flame in the sky,
Like a murderous lord of the earth.
It makes me feel terrified, but in awe,
Like a lowly subject under a cruel king.
The evil dragon
Tells us that beauty can hide horror.

Matthew Urwin (Age 10)

The Battle

I touch the blazing sword
I see blood pouring on to the grass
I see swords and shields and men scattered onto the floor
I hear cries of falling men
I hear wind blowing into me like a thousand daggers
I smell the blood rotting and bodies rotting quickly
I smell the metal of swords
I feel the fear of dying
I think we'll win I can't say

David Taylor (Age 10)

Haiku : Night

Night is drawing in
The cold breeze blows on my back
We have the whole world.

Richard Williams (Age 10)

My Love Is . . .

My love is blue
My love is deep like the blue sea
My love is strong
My love is fresh
My love is young and tender
My love is inseparable
My love is fair
My love is hot
My love can't wait
My love is true
My love is kind
My love is joy
My love is the best thing that ever happened to me.

Don't lose the love of your life whatever happens!

Roshni Thakrar (Age 11)

Animals

I saw a squirrel,
Being a spy,
I saw a squirrel,
Passing me by.

When I saw a zebra,
Eating a tree,
I saw the zebra,
Looking at me.

I saw an elephant,
Having a bath,
To see an elephant,
Walking down the path.

I saw a ferret,
Fighting in a tree,
That ferret was really,
Laughing at me.

Animals to me,
Are really quite sweet,
To see them in their habitat,
Is really hard to beat.

Rebecca Vass (Age 9)

I Hate It

I hate it
In my
Cage
I hate it
Lions roar
And lick
Their paw
Monkeys smile
And ask
For more.
I hate it
Birds cheep
Then fall
Asleep
The keeper
Comes
Sweep sweep
I hate it
I hate it
Being a
Tiger.

Steely Thatcher (Age 9)

Gran's Stay

Gran has broken her leg
It happened while getting out of a car
The leg's in plaster now
And for this reason she can't move far

She can sit at home and rest it
It's not that she's in much pain
But she's come to live with us now
To prevent any extra strain

It must be very boring
Just sitting in her chair
But we give her things to pass the time
To save her from despair!

She's only here for twelve weeks
Until her leg has mended
Then she can return home
As this has always been intended.

Katherine Winskill (Age 16)

Another Man Has Gone

A poor slave is dragged up steps,
Everyone watches like fans watching football.
The poor individual is chained down,
Priests walk out from their fanned chairs.
A shiny dagger is revealed
And is lifted above the priests head.
The glitzy knife comes crashing down,
And the stairs are stained a little more.

Carl Van Schie (Age 12)

What Is Love?

What is love, I can't explain
But I will try using my brain
When people are older they fall in love,
They think their lover fell from the skies above
When people get older and they have a love they want to share
So they get married to show they care.
When they are also older they can have a little boy or girl.
And they treat this like a diamond or pearl.
So that is love, I can explain and I don't have to use my brain

Jamie Venner (Age 13)

In The Gaza Strip

I am still thinking about the guns.
I am still hearing the noise they make.
I am still hearing the sound of people getting shot.
I see people crawling on the ground.
They are rushed to hospital.
I cry because my mum and dad are dead.
I can see cars whizzing by, killing people.
People are shouting.
They run away from the army, swearing.
How I hate war.

Antoon Van Tankeren (Age 14)

Fire

It starts with a small bright flicker,
Glistening golden, fiery red and a brilliant orange light,
The smoke twirls, dancing gracefully in the smoky air,
The wood crackles loudly and hisses sharply burning away,
Angry, leaping flames big, yellow and sparkling,
Flashing a shiny orange, brilliant sparkling red,
The fire is angry, fierce and growing bigger all the time,
The air is smoky, full of ashes being thrown by the leaping fire,
It roars and leaps higher, then falls to the ground successfully.

Bethany Turner (Age 9)

Music

M agical world, belonging entirely to yourself,
    and it is very hard not to get absorbed into it.
U biquity to everyone even though they may not know it.
S emiquavers may often be in a piece of one,
    along with a variety of other notes, and dynamics can be essential
    if you want to hear the beauty and quality in it.
I ncreases in incredibility. Each piece is individual
    by how it is played, even if the notes are the same.
C haracters can be heard throughout a piece of music.
    It is a really hard thing to describe, for it can be
    many things, though it is just one.

Alexandra Terry (Age 11)

The Party

One morning I went to a party
One morning I went to a party
And wore my best clothes
One morning I went to a party
And wore my best clothes and had some cake.
One morning I went to a party
And wore my best clothes and had some cake
And then I danced.

Temmel Vancooten (Age 8)

It Is . . .

Everybody thinks they know it, everybody starts to expect it,
Everybody overrates it, everybody underrates it.

They say seeing is believing, but we can't identify it.
Yet we support our entire lives around it.
Every emotion is influenced by it.
We cannot go for one day without it.

If we cannot physically see it, then how do we know it is there?
Is it some delusion we are expected to interpret?
Do we have to work for it?
Or does it gently descend into our lap?

Even though some people may fear it, even though others endear it.
Some could choose to neglect it, others already possess it.   Or do they?

How do they know they possess it, if they don't actually know what it is?
There are so many artificial interpretations of it.
Are there any extents to it? Is there a limit to where it has to stop?
I could ask; are there any limits to where it has to start?

Is it something we are born with? Are we fortuitous if we do get it?
Or are we fortuitous if we do not get it? How can we measure it?

There is no explanation for this mysterious force.
It is beyond our control. It cannot be helped. It is love.

Katie Vincent (Age 14)

Only Dreaming

I'm standing in the tunnel all nervous,
All my team mates trying to hide their fear,
Our manager making such a fuss,
The start of the match is just so near.

The roar of the crowd,
Makes me dizzy and excited,
Everybody is just too loud,
The ref blows his whistle, we've started.

The game is a bit of a bore,
Nothing is going to happen,
But I turn, I shoot, I score,
Then I wake up.

Sandy Veale (Age 11)

Birds

The golden eagle soaring high
The dove as white as snow
The nightingale the skillful singer,
The mighty kingfisher tall and strong.
The tiny bluetit small and weak
And the sparrow hopping about in spring.

Sam Warne (Age 10)

When My Cousins Came To Play

I played with my cousins
Taegan and Sinead

We were playing hide and seek
Then we played maid

Sinead was the maid
Taegan was the mother
And I was the horrible nasty robber

I kidnapped the maid
The mother was worried

She called the police
And I just scurried

The ending was happy
The maid was with her mother
And the horrible nasty robber went to jail

Clair Virgin (Age 9)

A Universe

There is a universe,
In that universe is a galaxy,
In that galaxy is a solar system,
In that solar system is a planet,
On that planet is a continent,
In that continent is a country,
In that country is a city,
In that city is a skyscraper,
In that skyscraper is a room,
In that room is a person,
In that person is a heart,
In that heart is blood,
In that blood are blood cells,
In those blood cells there is oxygen,
In that oxygen is atoms,
In those atoms there are protons, neutrons, nucleus and electrons.

That is what is in the UNIVERSE!!

Emerson Utracik (Age 9)

Spring Time

Spring time, spring time,
Easter holiday time,
Beginning of summer time
Spring time, spring time.
Things in my mind
Things in your mind.
Like you want to be an artist,
Or be a funny clown.
Lots of things in our minds
Beautiful things in our minds
Lots of beautiful things in our minds.
Like God and his beautiful world
Jesus, who loved us and saved us.
Oh beautiful things in our minds

Cornelia Van Den Bergh (Age 6)

Scientists

Why don't scientists ever go puff?
Why don't scientists go rat-a-tat-tat?
Why didn't scientists invent a Billy Goat Gruff?
Why don't scientists go pat-a-pat-pat?

How do scientists invent so many things?
All the scientists have big good brains?
How can scientists have so many rings?
How can people have so many veins?

I wonder how scientists invent so many things
And when I find out I'll be glad.

Stuart Unsworth (Age 9)

What Teachers Do?

Mrs Kelsey wears a wig,
Miss Davies likes to jig.

Mrs Campbell runs around,
Mrs Currie has five pound.

Mrs Westhorpe likes to wink,
Mrs Paine is the weakest link.

Mr A. acts like a muppet.
Mr Davies has a string puppet.

All our teachers are a laugh,
And some of them dress quite naff!

Sam Usher (Age 8)

Football Fate

Football is the best
it beats all the rest
every game they play
I'm up to the TV every day
they play a game

Football is great
it's better than a fete
better than an ice-cream
better than a nice dream
I love to play it

Robert Unwin (Age 8)

Frost

She's the frost princess,
As old as the world.
With eyes like the moon,
And a sharp glass nose.

Her home is a palace,
It's made of gleaming ice.
Her bed is made of frost,
She dreams of glaciers.

She moves in a pointy, spiky way,
Her teeth are sharp and severe.
Her hair is made from icicles,
Her breath is droplets of ice.

She wears a spiky, shattered-glass cloak,
She also eats freezing ice cakes.
She wants to rule the world with ice,
Her enemy is the sun.

Ella Virr (Age 10)

Children

Seven naughty children playing with sticks
One got bored and then there were six.

Six little children playing with a hive
One got stung and then there were five.

Five naughty children skidding on the floor
One broke his ankle and then there were four.

Four naughty children playing in the sea
One got washed away and then there were three.

Three little children waiting in a queue
One got tired and then there were two.

Two naughty children playing in the sun.
One got burnt and then there was one.

One little child having lots of fun
Then got called in for dinner and then there were none.

Alexandra Vece (Age 9)

Please Mr. Davidson

"Please Mr Davidson this boy Alex Way,
Keeps kicking me Sir, what shall I say?"

Say buzz off my dear, say go away,
Say leave me alone my petal, say you'll pay!

"Please Mr Davidson this boy Alex Way,
Keeps punching me, Sir what shall I say?"

Shake him all about my dear, kick him in the leg,
Knock him in the face my petal, call him smelly Meg.

"Please Mr Davidson this boy Alex Way
Keeps knocking me Sir, what shall I say?"

Knock him all about my dear, punch him in the face,
Kick him where it hurts my petal, just kick him out to space.

Kelly Venn (Age 8)

It Was So Noisy That

It was so noisy that
I couldn't hear my dad start his noisy car.
It was so noisy that
I couldn't hear the workman's wobbly dirty van go up the street.
It was so noisy that
I couldn't hear my thumping music rocking
It was so noisy that
I couldn't hear my friend speak
It was so noisy that
I couldn't hear the Welsh National Anthem

Scott Vaughan (Age 7)

Holidays

H olidays are holidays
O h holidays bring memories
L ove your holidays as you miss school
I indigo blue evening sky
D azzling stars golden and bright
A nd every day you see the light
Y et again we travel on an exhausting journey
S itting on the dusty seat at the back of our camper van

Alastair Viner (Age 8)

Underneath The Silence

Underneath the silence I can hear . . .
The silent swish of a silk sari, waving in the breeze,
A whisper of sand, twisting and turning through the midnight sky,
Forcing its way into a Sahara storm.,
Cones, being blown by the wind, disappearing into the lashing waves,
The frustration of the tossing boats, awaiting for the raging storm,
A burst of music brightening the lonely desert,
The burning, fiery, setting sun, taking the comforting warmth away on its nightly travels.

Underneath the silence I can feel . . .
The hard stones, edging from the water,
A tornado of wrappers, sweeping across the desert,
The thump of a crab's heart trembling,
A bottle of water, pouring on the stones,
The crimpled paper, swirling into my eyes.
The beach revealing its hidden glittering treasure.

Samantha Vermeulen (Age 11)

Footprints

My footprints were my future.
They wove intricate patterns in the sparkling sand.

As my knight protected his castle,
from the roaring enemy,
I, a sun-kissed child, danced in Neptune's
honour.

As his arms wrapped around,
I fell between the turquoise sheets.

The wet sand engulfed my spirit.
My mind.

As fast as it had began, it would be over,
and I would lie on the golden bed,
until I would hear Neptune beckoning me back.

To a world of carefree dreams.

I promised never to forget.

Yet, my footprints grew,
and Neptune's voice ceased to call,
while I began to forget.

My footprints melted into my memory.

Beth Wingfield (Age 16)

My Dad

My dad takes me to the cinema
We went to see a great film
He lives in Church Lench
He helps me do my reading
He takes me to Dillons to get some crisps
I really love my dad.

George Webb (Age 6)

The Storm

One night the sky darkened from grey to black
In the distance thunder crept up
The sky was happy
But then he was not
His black skin tore
He cried and the rain fell
He cried even harder and harder
It is his master, the glowing lightning
He rips and tears the sky
Suddenly the storm-wolf howled
And the wind blew
Then lightning went back to its home in the distance
The thunder stopped
Then it was peaceful.

Mia Willis (Age 7)

The View From My Bedroom Window

When I look out of my window
I see trees and fields of green
The thing I like about them most
Is when it's snowed and they glitter and gleam.

When I look out of my window
I see the flying of a kite
The thing I like about it most
Is the way it swoops and hovers in flight.

When I look out of my window
I see spring coming along
The thing I like about it most
Is the way the birds sing their song.

When I look out of my window
I see summer is nearly here
The thing I like about most
Is the way the children shout and cheer!

When I look out of my window
I see night is over head
The thing I like about it most
Is the way I can snuggle up in bed!

Jessica Waldron (Age 11)

Chocolate Cake!

Chocolate cake, chocolate
Cake you're my favourite thing to
Eat with your chocolate
Sauce in the middle and your
Sprinkles on the top. Chocolate cake
Chocolate cake you're my
Favourite thing to eat.

James Ward (Age 7)

Untitled

There are a couple of things in this world I can't stand
One of these is ~~~~~~ and everything bland

Whether a journey by car, a queue at the shops
Or perhaps a collection of milk bottle tops

The equations in maths, the way a mouse clicks
Or perhaps heated discussions on the properties of bricks

Just a few examples of things I can't stand
Examples of ~~~~~~ and everything bland.

Martyn Wildney (Age 15)

A Day In The Jungle

The kookaburra cackled
High in the canopy
As I was pestered
Pestered by a bumble bee

The ants came marching
Down a giant tree
They raided my lunch
Each with a piece bigger than a pea

I came across a swamp
It looked bigger than the sea
I saw a crocodile
SNAP! One, two, three

Along the trail still
Ouch! I've cut my knee
The branches sticking out
As though to grab me

It's time to go home
The trail I do see
That was a busy day
Time for a spot of tea.

Hannah Whitby (Age 13)

I Like Hugs

I like hugs
Because they are nice
They can cheer you up
When you are blue.
A hug can clear a child's pain
And make them happy again.
Nothing like a hug can tell people
'I love you.'
It must be why God gave us arms.
So without delay come
And give me a hug today.

Shanise Webster (Age 7)

The Storm

The fox cub cried
Like a lost little puppy
The echoing sound died

All of a sudden
A crash of drums
As thunder stomped over the land

Bang! a gun shot flew through the air
Gliding like a bird in the sky

Bam! just like that
Silence filled the air
As if there was no-one throughout the valley.

Ben Williams (Age 12)

At Home ..... Alone

I am alone in my house
I am as quiet as a mouse
I hate being alone
I'm too scarred to get the phone.

My mouth is all dry
I promise myself that I will not cry
I hear a tip-tap noise
Maybe it's just those boys.

I can't take this anymore
I have to go up to the next floor
The bathroom door. I thought I closed it
Oh, I'm losing my mind bit by bit.

I hear the noise again
He's coming to get me, but when
I'm all locked in I wish I was out
All I can do when he comes is shout and shout.

I see something through the clear glass
My body goes as cold as brass
There is probably nothing there
So why did I get such a scare?

Siobhan Walshe (Age 12)

Going To Tea With Grandma

I'm going to tea with Grandma
I wonder what there'll be?
Marshmallow dolls or strawberries
I'd better wait and see!

I'm going to tea with Grandma
I wonder what she'll cook?
Let's peep into the oven
So we can have a look!

I love going to Grandma's house.

Anna Westley (Age 6)

The Dark

I'm afraid of the dark
In the night
The
Stairs
Go
Creek
The wind blows
The tap drips
There's a funny feeling in my toes
I jump out of bed, head for the door
Race my nerves until there's light
Once more.

Patrick Wiseman (Age 11)

The Storm

Crackle of windows
Shudder of plates
People asleep as the storm awaits
At last it's here asleep from the cloud
The wind screams because the noise is so loud

The zoom of the points
The glowing of fire
The rocking of trees, ripples of grass in
The strong blazing breeze

The haunting of fear
Of objects so near the
Flashing of light gives the night a fright
The rumble of his belly gives a warning of his approach
The colour of his lines are as shiny as a brooch
As dawn is rising his belly is calm
The world is so peaceful he means no harm
He's asleep at last his visit in the past.

Ben Watson (Age 12)

On A Cold Winter's Day

On a cold winter's day
I like hot chocolate
It makes me feel warm inside
I like sitting in front of the fire
And watching the T.V.
It makes me feel cosy
All the way to the tips of my toes.

Amanda Wilkerson (Age 11)

Energy

Save your energy
'Cause it is wasted too much
Now it can't come back
Fossil fuels just burn up;
Solar is the way to go.

James Whelan (Age 11)

Autumn

Shorter days and longer nights
Can give some people quite a fright
The cold morning breeze
Can make some people freeze

Look at all the colours of the leaves
Red, brown and green
And all these colours I have seen
And how they gleam

Listen to the leaves rustle
Over the town's bustle
And listen to the conkers clash
As the children have a bash.

Shaun Winship (Age 13)

Picture From My Mind

Pictures from my mind are about
How the world should be
How I wish there was more
Peace and harmony

Too many wars
Too much strife
Too much to take
In just one life

People in the 3rd world
Whose life is one big struggle
They try very hard
Just to see it crumble

Pictures from my mind
Aren't all doom and gloom
I do think of other things
Sitting in my room.

Jodie Wakeman (Age 12)

Help Me!

They are firing at me
My friends are trying to help me
I am injured
My friends are panicking
They are scared
They might get hurt
Help!

Richard Weedon (Age 14)

The Fair

Come to the fair and you will see what
A great place it can be
With all the junk food you can eat
With all your friends that you can meet

Come to the fair and you will see what
A great place it can be
Fill your face with candyfloss and
Have a great time but don't get lost

Come to the fair and you will see
What a great place it can be
It's half past ten, it's time to go but
Don't forget to have another go.

Helen Wallace (Age 12)

Freedom

Does freedom have gates which lock it in
Built of unkindness, war and sin
Until we have strength to open them?
Does freedom have eyes which cannot see
This world of unfair poverty
Until we have courage to open them?
Does freedom have lips which cannot tell
Of people suffering through pain and hell
Until we have faith to open them?
Does freedom have pages we cannot read
Which tell of slavery, people in need
Until we have trust to open them?

And when these gates, eyes, lips and pages
Which have held us back throughout the ages
Break open and fill the world with glee
Then will we be finally free?

Lucy Walsh (Age 13)

The Earthquake

The earthquake is like thunder
I wonder will I ever get out of here?
Or can they see me? See me?
No they can't see me!
I wonder will I ever escape this?

It's dark, very, very dark
Hark hark I, I can hear people
It's scary very, very scary
I feel weary very, very weary
There is hope, hope HOPE!

Marc Waltrich (Age 13)

Sunset

As the sun shines, it watches the glistening sea,
Wave stretcher, tide turner.

As the sun goes down darkness falls,
Time the sun,
The moon just another day.

Fluffy clouds sail across the sky,
Purple, pink, orange and blue,
What a beautiful site.

The twinkling stars reflect on the sea,
Ripples make the moon look ghostly.

A sudden movement in the distance,
Nightlife has arrived,
Looking, watching your every move.

Amanda White (Age 14)

My Love

Shining brightly across the room
She's lived her life without any gloom
She lights up my life with just one smile
I've wanted her for quite a while
To ask her would take too much nerves
I've never been very good with words
But I want her oh so very much
She is so perfect, down to the last touch
How to get her one would ask
That would be the most difficult task
How will I get her to even like me
I could go up and just beg and plead
That would be so very lame
I should just go and die of shame.

Nathan Wallace (Age 13)

Love

Love is like a rollercoaster
Love is a bumpy ride
Then a heart is broken
It is like a flower
Being broke in two
Love is like a
Candle
Burning

Andie Wooltorton (Age 12)

Rats

Rats have long tails
Rats have sharp teeth
Rats have little bright eyes
Rats have sharp claws
Rats run quickly

Christopher Wells (Age 14)

What Shall I Compare Thee To?

Shall I compare thee to mud in a swirl?
Or should it be a dirty slob like toad?
Yes I shall compare thee to a toad girl,
When you came you went back on to the road.
You are worse than fiery hell itself,
Nothing like beautiful heaven on its own.
I need not any of thy richest wealth,
There is not a need to write a poem.
But now you are still an ugly toad girl,
Never thinking about the words you say.
Never ever like a beautiful pearl,
Why do you not ever go far away?
So this is the final word about you,
You are still a toad and I still hate you!

Mark Whiteley (Age 11)

Fire

The glowing fire,
The raging fire that flickers ablaze.
Oh fire that burns away.
Fire kills, fire burns, fire destroys around.
The fire burns in a fit of rage.
Fire, fire that hisses and spits, burns houses and bushes about!
To think, oh think from a spark you came.
Growing and growing ever lasting aflame
Oh raging fire, oh billowing fire, Oh fire that flickers away.
Why oh why such the torment you cause every day.

Ben Waldron (Age 12)

German Shepherds

German Shepherds are all shapes and sizes, they
Are big or small, pedigree or a mutt
That likes to play.

When out hunting he chases a fox.

He eats like a vacuum cleaner
What shall I do with him?

I throw a stick but he rather likes to
Chase the cat next door.

Jamey-Louise Wheeler (Age 12)

Cats

Fat cats
Thin cats
Lazy cats
Alive cats
Black cats
White cats
Big cats
Small cats
House cats
Street cats
I don't know how
But I've seen them all
Cats.

Andrew Wilson (Age 13)

My Tractor

I have a big tractor
With big wheels
And big feet

And it makes a noise
My digger has lights
That flash on top
I put petrol in it.

Kelvin Ward (Age 12)

Snow

Snow is in your boots
Snow on the floor
Snow on the bird table
Snow in your clothes

Snow in the house
Snow is freezing cold
Snow is crispy white
Snow is everywhere

Emma Wright (Age 9)

The Wars

I am standing in the trench, clutching my rifle, mud up to my knees, my hands caked in it
The person next to me is asleep, but standing up, his head lolling on his shoulders.

Suddenly the Captain's whistle is blown and the alarm is sounded
ATTACK, ATTACK, ATTACK
I know that if I do not, my Captain will shoot me, so I charge
Summoning up as much courage as possible
Using up the last of my strength.

Men all around me are falling to the ground
I am waiting with clenched teeth
For a bullet to pierce my skin
Shells are exploding all around me sounding like the loud bangs of fireworks
Because there are so many bullets, they look like clouds of brave bees, speeding towards their targets.

I get hit, and fall to the ground
A stretcher-bearer comes running over to me, "You are going to be fine," he said
But it was then my legs were hit by mortar fire
The stretcher-bearer and I were then dragged off the battlefield and brought back down into the trench

I am now lying in a hospital, far from the war, both my legs amputated
The stretcher-bearer on my left, my Captain on my right
Both wounded and severely shell-shocked, the war seems to be never ending
Like a nightmare that you can never wake up from.

Luke Wilson (Age 12)

Haiku - Seasons

Spring

The trees are blossoming
The grave is now deserted
Jesus is alive

Summer

The warm summer sun
Children are playing with joy
But one gets left out

Autumn

Autumn is coming
Deciduous trees are bare
Dead leaves have fallen

Winter

Coldness is coming
Snowmen are being made now
Soon a snowstorm starts.

Kathryn Waterson (Age 12)

Animals!

Animals are cute
Animals are fluffy
Animals love you
As you love them

I love animals
Hope you love them too
There are many types
BIG and small

There are wild
There are domesticated
Wild are beautiful
Domesticated are cuddly

I love BIG wild cats
Little small mice
Wild cats makes you SCREAM
Mice make you SHOUT.

Zara Weatherall (Age 13)

What Is A Poem

A poem can rhyme
A poem cannot rhyme

A poem can be long
A poem can be short

A poem can be about something
A poem can be nonsense

A poem can be funny
A poem can be sad

A poem can be written
A poem can be typed

A poem can be reality
A poem can be fantasy

A poem can be anything
As long as it makes you happy!

Carl D. Whittaker (Age 12)

Falling Leaves

Autumn leaves falling from the trees
Red hot horseshoe flying round the sun
Millions of burning yellow planets
Thousands of fireworks, orange, red and yellow
Slithering red, yellow and orange leaves

Charlie Welch (Age 6)

One Day I'd Like To Travel

When I'm older
I'd like to travel from place to place
I'd cross the channel and go to France
And over to Spain

One day I'd go to Africa
To watch the animals at play
Oryx and Springbok
Giraffe and Zebra
Under the great African Sky

I'd set off early in the morning
To see the sun rise
Over the volcanoes on Java
To see Mount Bromo smoking

When I am older
I'd like to travel from place to place
Maybe even go into space
To see the planets and stars.

Cassandra Willwohl (Age 13)

Audi T.T.

She's smooth
She's fast
She's stylish
She's top class

She's smart
She's cool
If I had her
I'd drive to school

I love you dear
Please be with me
She's cool, stylish
She's the Audi T.T.

George Wright (Age 12)

Waiting Room

The heap of glossy magazines
Sits roughly piled
Oozing gossip
Which spills
Onto the coffee table
Peppered with cigarette burns

The walls are painted
In colours scarcely recognisable
And there is the essence of Artex
(Always a mistake)

The woman
In her glass box
Stares stonily out
Chewing rhythmically
On a week old sandwich

The people sit
Staring at the floor
Stifling coughs
Trying desperately to guess
Each other's ailments.

Jen Wainwright (Age 14)

Love Unreturned

Every time I see your face a part of me dies
Because I want to be with you every minute of every day
But to know I cannot have or touch you
It tears me up inside until I want to cry
I cannot stop thinking about you; I don't want to love you but I do
And I feel so happy when you speak to me
I feel funny inside and all the hairs on my neck
Stand on end when your beautiful blue eyes meet mine
I can't sleep at night because I feel my heart beating
Thinking of stroking your hair and kissing your soft lips
When I think of you I smile but I get so nervous
I wish away every minute I am apart from you
I live to see your face and hear you call my name
I feel sick with you, but I feel sick without you
I wish one day you would wrap your arms around me
To keep me safe and protect me from everything bad there is
But you don't love me and you never will
But my heart has decided that you are the one for me
There is nothing left to do or say except
"I love you."

Katie Willan (Age 13)

Jesus My Son

They called for Barabbas
But I called and cried for Jesus
For I am his mother
As he walked to Golgatha
Some cried and some jeered and stared at my
Poor Jesus
For I am his mother
They stabbed nails into his weak hands and feet
And every time they did so, I screeched and cried
For I am his mother
I walked up to see him with Mary Magdelene
And cried and cried
John came up and put his arm round my shoulder
For I am his mother
As my Jesus' head flopped down
The sky grew dark and started to rain
They took him down and I cradled him
For I am his mother.

Hayley Woods (Age 9)

It Wasn't Me

Who smashed the window?
It wasn't me
Who lost their money on Bingo?
It wasn't me
Who messed up the bathroom floor?
It wasn't me
And left open the front door!
Oops!

Tom Wooding-Jones (Age 10)

Tanka Owl

Sharp claws to grab
Prey
Good eyesight to seek my food
A beak so pointed
You never know I am here
My prey never escapes.

Frances Wood (Age 11)

Silence

Silence is a dog asleep
Silence is a cat purring
Silence is a snake slithering
Silence is an ant walking
Silence is an elephant growing
Silence is a lion drinking
Silence is a spider making a web
Silence is a fly flying
Silence is a butterfly collecting nectar.

Joanna Wilkerson (Age 7)

Please Mrs Cheesy

Please Mrs Cheesy, can I have some cheese?
No you can't, stop calling me that please.

It is now lunchtime, go and have your lunch.
Make it quick, don't squirt your Munch Bunch.

Please Mrs Cheesy, can I have some peas?
No you can't, sit down please.

Now get your art books, and finish off your books.
But please don't do one thing, disturb the cooks.

Please Mrs Cheesy, can I have my keys?
No you can't, let me keep them please.

Put your books away, and make them very neat.
Get your reading wallets, and walk with your feet.

Hollie Woodward (Age 8)

Going To Bed

When my mum shouts go to bed
It shivers thoroughly through my head

When I start to walk up to my bedroom
The white banisters stand out

When I get into my bedroom
The floor creaks and groans

When I get into my bed
I don't dare to look under the bed

When I actually do look under the bed
I see a ghost swirling around my head

I shout for my mum
But she doesn't come!

Joseph Wolstencroft (Age 8)

The Mob

Here come the mob
Your elected
You stand there still
And feel your leg twitch.

You're in the middle
You got no plans
The mob approaches
Broken beer glass in hand

You gonna run?
Not sure you can
The mob approaches
They've found their man

Back into a wall
Ever felt your neck skin crawl?

They run straight past
You're the outcast
They've found their man
It's their friend, the one called Dan!

Richard Wood (Age 14)

Snow Poems

In the winter comes the fluffy snow,
And the freezing winds will blow.

In the snow the children play,
On a nice bright and sunny day.

The ice melts in the warming sun,
The winter day has just begun.

Nicholas Wright (Age 10)

1:00 Monday

1:00 Monday home at last
Now I can forget about the past

4:00 Tuesday I'm on my scooter
On the way I beep my hooter

5:00 Wednesday I'm having my tea
I look out of the window and see the sea

12:00 I'm in bed
In the morning I bump my head

7:00 I'm playing tig
Then I trip over a pig.

Conner Wright (Age 9)

Bob

There once was a dragon with a very long tail
He had no roar just a very loud wail
When people saw him, they just stood and stared
When they heard him cry, no one was scared

He was a handsome beast, bright green and pink
And if you were lucky he would give you a wink
His smile was wide and his teeth were blunt
And if he was happy he would give a big grunt

His favourite food was fish and chips
He also liked cherries but spat out the pips!
He lived in a cave in the south of Devon
It was near the sea, which he thought was heaven

This dragon was clever, he knew his sums
He went to school with all his chums
When he grew up he got a job
With a blacksmith who nicknamed him Bob

Bob still lives in his Devonshire cave
Now with a wife and son called Dave
He likes to have visitors so if you're in Devon
Pop into see him, but not after seven!

Meggie Wood (Age 11)

Weather

What is frost?
God's lost and precious marbles
What is a hurricane?
A devastating cycle of life
What is hail?
Glass football falling from above
What is an earthquake?
When dinosaurs ruled the earth
What is the sun?
Hell raising the temperature.

Paul Woolhouse (Age 11)

A Friend

You're just so special, do you know
My friends, my mates, my gangs
We're all so different yet so alike.

We share our lives at school each day
We sing, we play, we talk
We are best friends together
And we will always be happy with each other.

You make me laugh when we're together
When I'm sad it doesn't matter
We will always be friends forever.

Maddie Wylie (Age 10)

The Mole

Under the earth
Hiding away
From the sunlight
And the day!

Digging and eating
The night away
For he loves the dark
And worms too

For it's the dark lover
I'm talking about
The mole
Who burrows day and night

If you look at the ground
And see small mountains
You will know
My friend has come your way

Don't go and look
For him
He just wants peace
And quiet.

Joe Wibberley (Age 10)

Rain Cinquain

Raining
In the grey streets
Colourful umbrellas
Heavy raindrops fall on my face
Rainfall.

Michelle Williams (Age 9)

The Midnight Fox

The cry of the fox
Was like the cry of a puppy
Lost for food
I felt blue and down

The clumsy, dark thunder
Crashing across the sky
Boom, boom, boom, boom
The dramatic light of thunder

Uncle Fred moves
Distracted by movement
BANG!
The end

The quietness after
Just like the teacher gone mad
Missed!
"He will be back."

Stuart Watts (Age 11)

Thunder, Thunder!

Thunder, thunder
We want thunder
Thunder, thunder
It is a blunder
Thunder, thunder
It is light
Thunder, thunder
It gives you a fright.

Dale Willetts (Age 11)

Hairy Hedgehogs

Nine hairy hedgehogs trying to get bait
One fell in a hole then there were eight

Eight hairy hedgehogs looking up to heaven
One got blinded then there were seven

Seven hairy hedgehogs had a twix
One got poisoned then there were six

Six hairy hedgehogs cheering because they're alive
One sadly died then there were five

Five hairy hedgehogs went to the sea shore
One drowned then there were four

Four hairy hedgehogs climbing up a tree
One fell down then there were three

Three hairy hedgehogs playing in glue
One got stuck then there were two

Two hairy hedgehogs talking about pokemon
One lost the battle then there was one

One hairy hedgehog eating a hot cross bun
The raisins killed him then there were none.

Thomas Wilkins (Age 10)

Liam's Night Sky

The moon is an ice cream scoop sprinkled
With dust from stars, calling to chocolate
Friends Milky Way, Galaxy, Mars.

Liam Wright (Age 10)

The Elephant

The elephant stands on the African plains
He is proud of what he does
The elephant stands on the African plains
Just standing around and *EATING!*

The elephant stands on the African plains
Drinking out of a water hole
The elephant stands on the African plains
Just sitting there sucking

The elephant stands on the African plains
Defending himself from predators
The elephant stands on the African plains
Just defending himself alone

The elephant stands on the African plains
Not being lazy
The elephant stands on the African plains
HE'S NOT WORRIED AT ALL!

Steven Williams (Age 9)

Use Your Senses

Listening to the rattling telephone as they try to talk
Listening to the people rumbling about the mighty earthquake on the news
Listening to the street cars zoom fast along the road

Smelling the beautiful ice cream as the surface is so smooth
Smelling the delicious cakes in the oven, yum!
Smelling the lovely moon as it glows on you

Touching the stars as they float in the dark sky
Touching the soft bed covers of my bed
Touching the moonlight as it brightly shines on me

Tasting a cream cake as it dribbles down me
Tasting an ice cream as it is soft and cold
Tasting a great warm dinner as it has been baked in the oven.

William White (Age 7)

If

If I were a frog
I'd say
Where have you been dog?
If I were dead
I'd say
Hello Fred
If I were a truck
I'd say
Hello duck
If I were a date
I'd say
Sorry I'm late
If I were a weir
I'd say
Can I have a drink of beer?

Lawrence Williams (Age 7)

The Monkey

There was a monkey monkey
Who was funky, funky, funky
And was jumpy, jumpy
That silly old monkey monkey

MONKEY!

Becky Wiles (Age 8)

Clowns

Clowns jump
Clowns fall
Clowns juggle
With a ball
Clowns make faces
Clowns ride bikes
I like clown because
They are funny

Simon Waterfall (Age 6)

Trees

Trees are big
Trees are small
They are full of leaves
That in autumn fall
Down, down, down
To the ground

Brett Walters (Age 9)

I'll Follow You

I'll follow you through the goal net
Where the grass is all slimy

I'll follow you in the changing room
Where all the clothes stink

I'll follow you up the stand
Where all the people sit

I'll follow you when you walk, talk
And even when you run

I'll follow you when you are training
When your manager is speaking

I'll follow you everywhere!
I'll follow you in the commentator's box

I'll follow you in the football shops
I'll follow you when you are putting on your boots

I'LL FOLLOW YOU EVERY
TIME YOU BREATHE!

Jack Wilshere (Age 9)

Perfect Me

I'm Albert Einstein's brain
I'm the soft juicy satsuma
I'm the cuddly koala
I'm Michael Johnson's style
And speed
I'm the apple
From the apple juice
I'm the green and white
From the Celtic shirt
I'm the beautiful Parkhead Stadium
I'm the sandstone rock
Sparkling in the sun
I'm the space craft
That landed on Mars
I'm the sun
That gives eyes to the world
I'm Mount Everest
That reaches to the clouds
I'm Alton Towers
Giving fun to the world
I'm a leaf swaying
In the wind.

Ross Williamson (Age 10)

Autumn

Autumn is here, the summer has died,
The mist hangs motionless over the land,
Leaves are swirled in gusts of wind,
They come to rest wearily on the ground.

Jack Frost casts his spell o'er the sleeping lakes,
The trees are lonely silhouettes against the dying sun.
The animals collect berries and nuts to feed themselves in the coming winter.
A maple tree drops its last leaves;
The street stands bare.

The rippling lakes flatten to become a thin sheet of glass,
The grass is drowned by heavy shiny dew,
And the last of the birds fly south;
Empty nests show that life has started to fade.

Sunsets, red, purple and pink, dazzle you,
Only the evergreens survive the cold,
Summer has gone
But autumn is here!

Fiona Wright (Age 12)

School Dinners

S loppy semolina
C old chips
H ot ice cream
O ld cheese
O ff milk
L umpy custard

D isgusting sausages
I cky sloshy salmon
N asty mashed potatoes
N ails in your soup
E conomy fish eggs
R otten egg
S econds anybody?!!!!

Katie Wise (Age 12)

A Winter's Storm

A breeze of wind
Sweeps through the road
A cloud roars
Through the stormy sky

Puddles cover the street
Doors bang like
Loud thunder clouds
Crashing in the dark sky.

Naomi Wright (Age 8)

Story Poem

I was milking the cows,
In the garden in the shed
When I heard the wind howl,
So I put the cows to bed.

I went in the house,
To see my mum and dad,
But I saw a little mouse,
So I screamed and went mad.

The wind turned into a storm,
I hid under my covers,
Then my baby brother was born,
Now I have two brothers.

Sara Wheldon (Age 12)

It's Only A ...

It's black and silver, with a gleaming buckle
I could never have it, I say with a chuckle
For my mum can't afford it, she has no job
All because of that rich, slimy slob
He fired my mum 'cos she took a day off
On a stupid date with a spotty boff
But I really want it, what should I do
Should I get a job, make a pound or two?
It will be gone in a minute I must buy it now!
There's only one little problem. How!
Oh I give up on this short note
FOR GOD SAKE IT'S ONLY A COAT!

Thomas Worrall (Age 12)

The Beginning Of Autumn

Fiery explosions light up the sky,
Fantastic and golden and sparkling high.
Tumbling acorns and cascading leaves,
Scampering squirrels begin to flee.
All Hallow's Eve, 31st of October,
Grinning faces that scary masks cover.
Cold, pelting rain on the rooftops.
People wrap up for the winter to come.
The clocks go back, the nights draw in,
Falling leaves and Autumn begins.

Kelly Webster (Age 12)

Seven Lines

The emptiness in this room, burns through
The space we daren't occupy - for what we knew
We cannot ever not unknow,
The world we touched for want to go.
The air we breathe though mixed
And tainted with fear - holds nothing fixed
But still pulls me near.

The silence seems to tell as much to last
As the words spoken through an age-old past
We cannot speak - for deaf or dumb
The wound we've opened we try to numb
The wordless touch - the honesty
Is nothing but a false memory
That is just too much.

And the sight of it is blowing down
The paper walls we've drawn around
We cannot breathe for we breathe wrong
We cannot kiss though a kiss does belong
And though you fill me, I am not full - they diminish
For what we've started, we cannot finish ...

Beverley Willbourne (Age 17)

Meandering Through Time

I that have lived since long ago
Have watched the villages flourish and grow
I've stared at the soaring birds above
The swallows, the sparrows and the diligent doves
I am the reflection that children see
When they look down deep inside of me
All around me a town has grown
Among the banks of the seeds I've sown
My fertile silt, my fluently flow
Have built the banks of friend and foe
If I could change the damage I've done
The cars, the factories and the deeply-shallow slums
I would be so full of glee
And finally pollution would be no part of me
A lonely life is the life I lead
Withering amongst the war-torn reeds
I meekly meander to and fro
I've lost my vibrant and vagrant flow
I am now a fiendish, forgotten feature
A cowardly crawling captive creature
The past is old, the future is young
My place as a river is finally done.

Amber Wilson (Age 15)

Animals

Rabbits hopping up and down
Squirrels never ever frown
Always happy having fun
How many people like them, everyone!
All these days I've wondered how many animals there are.
I just can't count all of them, it's just all ALBASA!

Rachel Willis (Age 7)

Insufficient Redemption

Ridden with anguish
Screaming within
Such pain on the body
Pain in the mind

Nobody guesses and nobody cares

The tiny spark once left, now extinguished by
Other's glory and her own self destruction

The outer appearance is deceiving

The eyes are on others
I know they would burn into her if only they knew

But the lies that were told were hard and pressing
It was difficult to find salvation within
The person she knew she could trust the most
Was really the one she should have feared

Herself.

Nicola Warren (Age 16)

The Big Fishing Trip

There was once a man called Jon
He went fishing one day
England was where he lived

Barry, Jon's friend caught a whopper
It took ten minutes to land
Great fish said Jon

Fred, a walker by, asked how they were doing
I'm doing well said Barry, Jon's not doing so well
Shut up said Jon, I'm just getting started so ...
He punched Barry in the eye!
In the river fell Barry
Nowhere to be seen
Gareth a boat owner, stood there laughing

Trish, Barry's wife rang Jon on his cell phone
Right about ten minutes after Barry's fall
It's been a disaster said Jon
Polly, Jon's wife then shot Trish in the head!

Robert Welling (Age 15)

My Family

My family's mad
Including my dad
He's fab and bad

My family's mad
Including my mum
She shines like the sun
But weighs a ton

My family's mad
Including my bro'
He sucks his toe
He knows his foe (me).

Sarah Wilmott (Age 11)

Dolphins

D iving into the sparkling sea
O ut of the sea to take a breath
L iving next to the swaying coral reef
P eople amazed at their skills
H aving a race against each other
I nto the under water world
N icely singing together
S kimming the shiny sea

Rebecca Webb (Age 12)

A Boy In My Class Is Horrible

A boy in my class is
Horrible
He bullies me to bits -
Horrible
I have to put up with it - it's
Horrible
So I tell my teacher he's
Horrible
And she makes it -
Better
Then play time comes again and he's
Horrible again
Why me? I want to go home where
Life is not horrible.

Aimee Williams (Age 8)

Shining Star

A shining star is a big round coin shining down in the night sky
A shining star is a bright light bulb, shining brightly in the inky black sky
A shining star is a house in heaven that has left its lights on
It is a silver splodge of paint spilt in the sky
A shining star is an ear-ring in a little girl's ear, shining brightly
A shining star is a silver chain on a lady's neck glittering in the moonlight
A star is a pair of sparkling eyes
A shining star is a person watching over us

Joanna Wright (Age 11)

Eye Of The Storm

I'm lying in my bed, where I know I'm safe and snug
I was just about to doze off
When suddenly ...

The clash of lightning and the roar of thunder
The dripping of rain on the floor, as the lightning searched for prey
The thunder moaned as the wind howled!

Then. The dripping of the rain turned to hail
The roar of the thunder went on roaring
The lightning turned furious, the trees lying on the floor.

I looked out my window and the most extraordinary thing happened
...

A giant crash came down on my street, as the thunder grew louder
I fell out of my bed, it seemed as if it was a punishment!

Then the thunder faded away
The lightning disappeared
The hailstones stopped
The last clash, and the
Place looked as if
It had been
Chewed
Up!

Tamsin Wressell (Age 9)

Spring

The winter ends
The spring arrives
The leaves grow green
The grass survives
The children playing
In the sunshine
The blossom glows
With buds so fine.

Hannah Wood (Age 7)

What Am I?

Great climber
Ice slider
Good swimmer
Fish for dinner
Water mover
Ice groover
Sea Diver
Swift water glider

Robyn Wickert (Age 10)

The Lonely Sea

The soft blue sea, that laps against the shore
Glistens in the sunset, that lays upon the sky
As I walk on the shore, my head filled with dreams
I feel the warm golden sand that lies beneath my feet.

Why? I think to myself does the sea seem so lonely
Sharing its secrets only with the blowing wind above
Maybe, the wind desperate to tell them, tries to whisper them to me
But by the time they reach my ear, a muffled howl is heard.

Maybe the sea feels lonely for it feels guilty of what it has done
Taken lives of so many loved ones, who sail across its back
When its temper rises and waves grow high, drowning innocent people around
When the struggle is over, does it regret its bad evil temper.

Maybe that's why the sea seems so lonely.

Nicola Williams (Age 11)

I Am A Question Mark

I am a question mark
I come after a question
I am not a full stop
Or an exclamation mark

I am a question mark
I come after a question
And I come before asked
Or anything like that!

I am a question mark
I come after a question
I have a question for you
Do you understand?

Laura Wheatley (Age 9)

Charge Of The Grannies

Half a minute, half a minute
Half a minute it took them
Through the games room
Past the bedrooms
Piled the 30
Into the decorated room
Filled with food

Yum yum, come, come
Have some food
Pig out and stay as long as you like.

Eat the lovely treats and mince meat
Charge, charge there they go, messy as usual.

Charlotte Wheatley (Age 11)

Shuffity Shuff

Trains swaying across the line
Shuffity shuff, shuffity shuff
It's sparkling blue, it looks fine
Shuffity shuff, shuffity shuff
It's flaming like a burnt fire
Shuffity shuff, shuffity shuff
Electric coming from the wire
Shuffity shuff, shuffity shuff
First it's day, then night
Shuffity shuff, shuffity shuff
And then ......
Again it was light
Shuffity shuff
All the way to Paris
Off we get
Shuffity shuff
Off it goes again ......

Jack Woolley (Age 7)

Dolphins

DOLPHINS ARE
The noisiness of a crowd coming to watch a
Show of acrobats

THE GREATNESS
Watching the acrobats flip and twist
Into position

THE FASTNESS
Of each move they do, as they work
Together

THE BRIGHTNESS
As the lights glisten upon the main star

THE FASCINATION
As your eyes are glued to the show, and
Then you're wondering what's happening next.

Antoinette White (Age 11)

The Living Sea

The sea is a deep deep blue
A vast desert filled with life
Waves ram the ocean shore
They keep coming they never die

The ocean floor has lots to see
A jungle of seaweed full of colour
Seals diving, twisting, turning
Fish staying out of their way

The sea hits the golden beach
With shells lined up like soldiers in battle
The beach is fine for some
But I like the deep blue living sea

Some sea creatures will never be seen
Under the roaring waves
But at least we all can
Hope and dream .

Spencer Watson (Age 12)

My Upside Down Day

Got up wet the bed, ate
My weetabix and trumped on
My head, get dressed grow
The floor, got my bike out
Danced with the door
Called for Josh and
Got in his bed, played on
His computer ate his head, munched
Lunch, danced with their bread
Reached home and blew up my bed
Watched T.V. set it on fire got
Into bed climbed higher and higher.

Corin Woods (Age 11)

My Friends

All my friends live with me
They're always full of joy and glee
Creeping, crawling wherever they plea
Have you a guess who my friends could be?

They climb they run and chase
Going all over the place
Sitting by the fire at night
Prowling, growling in daylight

They sit on mats, even in hats
They're all my pet cats!

Jessica Worth (Age 10)

Thunder And Lightning

As I lay in my bed
Pictures of lightning run through my head
I could hear the sound of the roaring lightning
I must admit it was really frightening

I jumped out of my bed and looked out of the window
Lightning was darting through the sky
Then thunder came, I wonder why?

The lightning was yellow then it turned white
I saw it more clearly because it was night
I started shivering then I started to shake
The storm was tearing up the frozen lake

The lightning was flashing behind the grey clouds
And then it started making strange sounds
The storm was now starting to go
The lake was now starting to flow

Trees were lying on the floor
I don't want this storm anymore.

Chelsea Wood (Age 9)

You Know What They Say

You know what they say
Like father like son
You know what they say
Live life, have fun.

You know what they say
Like mother like daughter
You know what they say
Tall girls should be shorter.

James Lee Ward (Age 9)

Reptar

Reptar the dragon lives under my bed
My mum says that he lives inside my head
My dad thinks he is purple and sprays water from his nose
But mum and dad are wrong
I'm the only one that knows.

Reptar the dragon likes a game of hide and seek
I don't like playing it with him though
He always seems to peek!

Reptar the dragon is my bestest bestest friend
He lives underneath my bed
And we'll be friends to the end.

Ben Wride (Age 11)

Avalanche

It sets off with a tremendous roar!
And thick mass of snow starts its destructive journey
Down the mountainside, towards the unwilling town that waits below
It rips through trees with its white fists of fury
As it tumbles down the mountainside
It is a racing wall of white death
AVALANCHE ..... there is no escape
The icy avenger seeks revenge upon the spring
It smashes through nature and wildlife with no signs
Of remorse
AVALANCHE ..... the destroyer!
As the wall of snow envelopes everything in sight
It creates an icy prison from which there is no escape
But suddenly the avalanche halts
The snow settles
But the damage is done
AVALANCHE ..... THE ASSASSIN.

Christopher Webb (Age 13)

Opposites

Here is a poem of my love
And how our hearts fell from above
Twist and turn the ivy grows
Up and down the contrary hedgerows
In and out, the waves will splash
Drip and dry in one big clash
Hot and cold, the sun will shine
Then you will be a true love of mine

Hayley Williams (Age 12)

The Storm

The rough, riding winds push people over
With its black, blinding hands
The flash of lightning
Makes people take cover
The crash of thunder
Wraps round your ears with its tangling fingers.

The heavy rain beats down on the roofs
With its horse like hoofs
The bitter wind wraps around you
With its icy-cold body
The damp air clings to you with its sharp, short claws
The screaming, screeching children
Hide with their parents

The wood splintering
The ship being broken in half
By the sea's long, rough hands
The ships being tossed in the air
Whilst riding the sea's back, water pouring in
The people, being sucked out with its hands
Then it stopped as suddenly as it started.

Adam Wilson (Age 12)

Playtime

Here comes Lauren she's really clever
A good footballer that's Trevor
James Collins is the teacher's pet
He even knows how to make a net
He's really annoying and he makes me mad
Even the others think he's bad

Bethany is a really good friend
She's always there to the end
Also there's Becky she's really nice
She eats echoes and I say "Can I have a slice?"
Our playtimes are always filled with laughter
That's why we live happily ever after.

Stephanie Wong (Age 10)

The Drive

Taking the crunching steps to the car
Gripping the shining handle of the door
Occupying the relaxing leather of the seat
Holding the gleaming surface of the wheel
Seeing the curving skin of the bonnet
Pushing the dazzling metal of the pedals
Cruising the scorching surface of the tarmac
Feeling the burning heat of the sun
Turning the winding corners of the road
Blasting the purring valves of the engine
Reaching the glowing lights of the house
Closing the protecting door to the garage
And all the time
Smiling.

Joseph Worth (Age 16)

My Dream World

In my dream world I would see
A banana lake and a strawberry tree
Next of all I would meet
My mate Monkey she's a treat!
We would talk and chat all day
As I've always got alot to say
I see a desert in front of me
With a mouth watering chocolate sea
I decided to go for a chocolate swim
I can eat all I want and still stay slim
I lie on the sherbet sand
Licking my lips, then licking my hand
In my world I would see a fantastic
World for you and me.

Lauren Walbridge (Age 12)

The Old Hawk Falls

The place used to be an Inn
Laughing, joking, cheering. The men drinking the old gin.

Molly and Jack used to run the joint, it was their life
Their whole worlds point. One night they were killed with a knife.

The Inn was shut down, it was a great shame
Nothing was the same in the old town
But 'Bobbys' never placed the blame ...

The old Inn is an off-licence now, people working hard and earning wages
The spirit of Molly and Jack still lives on
The staff working there, know that there is something, but just can't place what.

Upstairs the floor boards bang, shackles scrape across the floor
Whispers fill the room like factory smoke from the old town.

Seeing black figures dart across the room
Sends shivers down anyone's spine
Looking at the CCTV, a woman with a cloak, or it appears to be
Could it be Molly Jones looking out on a new world?

The rooms are as cold as Molly's and Jack's bodies that night
Laughing and joking are embroidered in the walls
All the memories of the Old Hawk Falls.

Samantha-Jo Wild (Age 13)

Cats

One sunny day a cat sat on a mat
In a nice and a tidy flat next to a baseball bat
The cat woke up and saw a cup.
The cat broke the cup and smashed it on the floor
And there was a knock at the door!
The cat ran away and came back next day
The cat was scared in the night
The cat heard a fight
The cat went to another room it was the living room
Then the cat saw a broom in the front room
Then the fight stopped and the cat went to the shop.

Rebecca Welling (Age 9)

Chocolate

Yesterday to eat I had
Seven chocolate bars to be exact

Today I ate about four
I'm not quite sure

Tomorrow hopefully I won't eat any
But if I do, not too many.

Charlotte Wride (Age 10)

Cullompton Community College

There is a school in Cullompton, which is called its Community College.
Believe it or not it's a fact, that not one student has any knowledge.
In every MATHS lesson students chew gum,
They're not even bothered to do a sum.
In every P.E. lesson students slowly run
They wouldn't go any faster even if they were running from a gun.
In every ENGLISH lesson they don't ever write,
They are more interested in who won the latest WWF fight.
In every MUSIC lesson they sing songs by Britney Spears,
It's so bad, it bursts the drums in your ears.
So never come here, I bet you don't,
But after this I know you won't!

Charley Webb (Age 11)

Untitled

There was a young girl called Mabel
She lived her life under a table
Her nails were long
She sang a song
And spent all day watching
Cable

Stacey Wright (Age 9)

A Genie Chant

Sister lamp
Brother lamp
Mother lamp
Father lamp
Oh give me a wish
Oh home giver
Oh friendly lamp
What have you in store for a wealthy genie today?

Oh lamp give me a wish of
Love, joy, hope, wealth
And give people a home and give the sun a day to warm.

Sister lamp
Brother lamp
Mother lamp
Father lamp
Oh give me a wish
Oh home giver
Oh friendly lamp
What have you in store for a wealthy genie today?

Chloe Wookey (Age 8)

It Is Never Over

They are bigger we are smaller, I'm afraid this is over!
We are shorter they are taller, I'm afraid this is over!
We are slow, they are fast, surely this is over
They'll be first we'll be last, surely this is over
We can't jump but they leap high, I fear it may be over
Let's get together and give one last try, even if it's over
But wait, a mistake, our chance for glory?
Maybe it's not over
We've done it, we won, what a story!
It's never over!

David Wise (Age 16)

The Last Chance

Just sitting, waiting to speak that one last word
Seems eternity has gripped man's aching ears
As I gaze forward hoping to be touched by the world beyond
The fading eternal light refracts like a prism through my palm.

I have unfinished expression to speak
But no one wants to hear
My tongue feels trapped
As if in deep foliage of sound.

The pressure has hit a pause
And a burst of air with beautiful tone is revealed
Satisfaction and pleasure calms the low buzz of difference
I slowly recline to reflect on what is to be

And as the light disperses from beyond the clouds
I look back on this land and know I have made a difference.

Anna Wakefield (Age 16)

P.M.T.

Pension, Mortgage, Tax.

Bosses at work always on my back.
Always in trouble. If I get the sack,
How will I pay my ...

Pension, Mortgage, Tax.

Forty years just to get a pension;
A job I hate with too much tension,
Got to keep on working, got to pay my ...

Pension, Mortgage, Tax.

It's like a millstone round my neck,
All these statements I have to check
Keep that income steady, got to pay that ...

Pension, Mortgage, Tax.

Fill in loads of forms? No I'll send a blinking fax
My brain is one big storm, because of my ...
... Pension, Mortgage, Tax.

Karen Wilson (Age 15)

Spring's Here

Spring's coming
Everyone's running
Summer is nearly hear
Everyone's happy

Spring is in the air
And is blowing my golden hair
Babies are crying
Mummies are lying on sunbeds

I am nearly burnt
And I learnt the seasons of the year
And I hear
The birds gaily singing

I am in my spring season
Please give me a reason
Of why we have seasons
Oh lovely heavenly father

I am in my own world on one season only
To be there for everyone
Oh to be like you
Oh mighty one.

Maria Wright (Age 9)

The Bronze Door

Go and open the bronze door.
Maybe outside there's
A silver, silent tree swaying in the moonlight,
Or a giant goblin coloured airy wood,
A colourful garden with a huge golden gate,
Or a miraculous magical city which glows in the daylight.

Go and open the bronze door.
Maybe a dark, devious dog is rummaging for a bone.
Maybe you'll see a friendly face of a stranger,
Or a red eye from a Cyclops face,
Or the picture
            of a picture.

Go and open the bronze door.
If there's a deep grey fog it will clear.

Go and open the bronze door.
Even if there's only the darkness ticking in the silence,
Even if there's only the hollow wind drifting,
Even if nothing is there,
Go and open the bronze door.

At least there will be a draught.

Adam Wozniak (Age 11)

My Mum

My mum is peachy
When she is dancing
My mum sounds like the twinkle of a
Star when she lays me to bed
My mum is like a blanket when she strokes my head
My mum is like a goldfish when
She helps me to swim
My mum is like the snow when she touches my face
My mum is autumn when she looks at the sun
My mum is candy when she rubs me with fluff

Zahra Wynne (Age 7)

Space Countdown

10 is the start of the countdown to blast off into space
9 planets rotate around the scorching sun
8 thousand times hotter is the sun than the Earth's core
7 billion stars dance in the Milky Way
6 million miles is how far it seems from Earth to Mars
5 soon you'll be one with the sparkling stars
4 astronauts laying in wait for the moon
3 the world holds its breath
2 spheres give us day and night
1 billion people come to see the historical event.

O, the people scream and cheer, it's YOU
You're blasting off into space
It's true.

James Wright (Age 11)

Me

I used to be small
And now I'm really really tall.
I'm getting a puppy
Called Smutty.
I've got blue eyes
Like the sky.
When I was three I met my friend
We walked to the end of the bench.

When I was four
I ate much more.
When I was five
I started to dive.
When I was six
I picked up sticks.
Now I'm seven
I know what to do.

Katie Woolsey (Age 7)

Dexter - Dexter

Dexter - Dexter boy of wonder, Dexter- Dexter scared of thunder
Dexter - Dexter had a fish, Dexter - Dexter had it on a dish

Dexter - Dexter wanted to play, Dexter - Dexter was too gay
Dexter- Dexter had a bike, Dexter - Dexter went on a hike

Dexter - Dexter wanted an ice cream, Dexter - Dexter started to scream
Dexter - Dexter doesn't believe in the Easter Bunny, Dexter - Dexter thinks he's funny

Dexter - Dexter watches Noddy, Dexter - Dexter hates Mr Blobby
Dexter - Dexter went to the beach, Dexter - Dexter had a peach

Dexter - Dexter had a smack, Dexter - Dexter had it on his back
Dexter - Dexter didn't know the time, Dexter - Dexter wanted to rhyme

Dexter - Dexter ran over his cat, Dexter - Dexter said, "That's that."

Simon Wood (Age 9)

Walking Through The Jungle

Walking through the jungle
What did I see?
A big round hippo, lumbering after me.

Walking through the jungle
What did I see?
A quick and shy gazelle, running away from me.

Walking through the jungle
What did I see?
A fat and funny ostrich, flapping wings at me.

Walking through the jungle
What did I see?
A big and stripy tiger, growling at me.

Walking through the jungle
What did I see?
A big hairy gorilla, swinging towards me.

Natalie West (Age 10)

Butterfly

B is for beautiful
U is for unique
T is for tremendous wings
T is for twice flying at a wall
E is for enormous colourful wings
R is for red spotted wings
F is for flying over tree tops
L is for flying over tree tops
Y is for yellow as the sun

Jemma White (Age 10)

Our Town

Our town has houses
Our town has mouses
Our school has drains
Our school has canes

Our shops has bananas
Our shops has pyjamas
Our fields has skies
Our fields has flies

Daniel Williams (Age 8)

Colours

C olours bright colours, dark colours shining on the top
O n the hill tops shining really hot
L ogs dark when creatures come and pop out
O h how lovely is tonight
U nless it's bright when we are about
R ed makes you go in and out
S leeping time is the end of the day where you sleep all the night.

Michelle Wong (Age 7)

The Alien's Spaceship

5, 4, 3, mission count 2, 1, we have ignition
Aliens fly from far away lands
Launch pad break into two
Get some weapons to protect and guard
Enemies stopping and shooting

As aliens eat rust metal
The humans put on the kettle
Booby traps fall from ceiling and floor
As there's a war in space
There could be an earth boy tying his lace
The floor and ceiling smell really bad
I wish I could be up there
But instead I'm down here
Oh no we speak on the radio
We're getting attacked
As we fight and win
I saw this paper and chucked it in the bin
As everything goes silent
And then all of a sudden

KA BOOM!

Matthew Webster (Age 9)

Spring Days

Spring days time for the buds to open
Spring days the birds have spoken
Spring days the sun shines strong
Spring days nothing will go wrong
Spring days the butterflies have come to play
Spring days everyone will always love today.

Sarah White (Age 8)

Stars

S parkling white spots in the black sky
T errific light to make the night bright
A quarius is a star sign in February
R eally good to look at through a telescope
S aturn is a star with rings.

Susan Wright (Age 7)

Purple

What is purple?
Purple is
A purple
Bobble in my hair
Purple car
Purple cup
Purple crayon
Purple lollipop
Purple book.

Lauren Woods (Age 5)

Africa

Africa is a sunny place with animals everywhere,
Spots and tusks and stripes you're sure to find them there.
Some animals are nocturnal like the aardvark or antbear.

Some live in trees all day and night,
This wide variety of animals also include the big five,
These animals are elephant, rhino, lion, leopard and buffalo.
So when you see sleet or snow Africa's the place to go.

Sarah Williams (Age 11)

Screaming

Babies are whinny and whingy
Babies cry alot and scream
Wherever they go you don't know what they want
They're not even like a wizard
They're not even a bit wizardry
But they can get up to mischief
They like chewing the carpet or bullying the pet
Maybe it's a good one that never cries at all
Maybe it needs a nappy change or a bottle or is feeling sick.

Chloe Winchester (Age 6)

It Was So Noisy ...

It was so noisy that I
Couldn't hear my dad drilling a hole in the wall
It was so noisy that I
Couldn't hear my dad snoring in the chair
It was so noisy that I
Couldn't hear the glass breaking on the floor
It was so noisy that I
Couldn't hear my sister screaming her head off
It was so noisy that I
Couldn't hear my mum calling for my dinner
It was so noisy!

Jessica Warren (Age 8)

Fire

It starts with a little yellow spark
Sparkly golden, shining yellow and bright orange light
The grey smoke starts to grow dancing with the wind
The burning wood starts to crackle and hiss as it meets its fiery doom
Little leaping flames growing higher and bigger
Flashing sparkling growing colours, red, orange and yellow
The fire is angry snapping the wood, burning everything in its path
The air is smoky and full of leaping bits of wood trying to get away
It starts to rain, the fire squeaks as it dies down into nothing but hot ash.

Amy Williams (Age 10)

My Special Tree

My special tree was planted when I was born
It was planted by the corn
I called it Toad
Like the one on the road

It swishes and sways
It shuffles and plays
It's a special tree you know
But some day I've got to let it go.

Jordan Williams (Age 10)

A Lady From Morilla

There was an old lady
From Morilla
When she went out
She rode a gorilla
She took it outside
People laughed til they cried
What a silly old lady
Of Morilla.

Sarah Winch (Age 10)

I Am A Lion

Many people are afraid of me
They say I am fierce and scary
But one little girl said to me
MUM! he's not scary
He's like my bear at home
You're not the one that's scared.
I am all alone no one to talk to
Just sit in my cage
One little boy said he's like my cat
One man called Chris the caretaker
Kept poking me to get me to do something
I am scared! I am scared! I am scared!
Of you!

Stephen Whitaker (Age 10)

Cats

Outside lover
Dives for cover
Dog teaser
Mouse seizer
Heavy sleeper
Night creeper
Sharp scratcher
Rat catcher
Sock stealer
Fish peeler

Hannah Willman (Age 10)

The Moon

When will you orbit the Earth, oh moon?
Soon, unlike Neptune.

Will you ever orbit Venus, oh moon?
Maybe soon.

Moon, will you ever go round Mars?
I don't know, but maybe in the future.

Will you ever see Saturn?
I'll maybe see it in a pattern.

Will you ever hide in the daylight?
Yes, because I only come out at night.

Moon, do you ever stay up late?
No, because I may evaporate.

Will you ever see Mercury?
No because she's too soft furry.

Are any of stars friendly, oh moon
Yes, and I'd like to go back to them soon.

Do you ever give people a fright, oh moon?
Yes, because of my silvery light!

Kayleigh Walsh (Age 11)

Snow

Light drifting snowflakes
Landing peacefully on the ground
Footsteps don't make
A sound
Light drifting snowflakes
Landing peacefully on the ground
Not a trace of footprints
Are found

Ruth Warnes (Age 10)

Football, Football, Football

Football, football, football
It's in my head all day
Owen, Beckham, Fowler
How brilliant they all play

Goalies, strikers, defenders
Scattered over the pitch
Headers, crosses and volleys
Sometimes cuts that need a stitch

A cheer goes up from the crowd
As Owen blasts one in
The team shout and celebrate
What a brilliant win!

Jorge Wadman (Age 10)

The Finding Week

On Monday, as I walked down a lonely street
I found a leaf skeleton
Flittering, fluttering away from me.

On Tuesday, as I walked across a crumbling bridge
I found a glittering glass bottle
With a curious map inside.

On Wednesday, as I waded through a babbling brook
I found a shining stone
That was a perfect sphere.

On Thursday, as I skipped through golden, wavy corn
I found a fiery blanket
Of scarlet poppy flowers.

On Friday, as I splodged through a sea of slippery mud
I found a glowing crystal
To treasure forever.

On Saturday
I found an apple
Rolling in the hedge's tangled feet.

On Sunday I found in the soil's earthy caves an ancient bronze box.
Into its icy chamber I placed
All the finding week's findlings.

Hannah Walker (Age 9)

My Teacher

Her hair is as rich as a Queen's diamond in its box
She is as white as a white dove in the morning sky
She is kinder than Daniel Wagstaff in a mood
Her eyes are bluer than the sea at night
Who do you think it is?

Emma-Louise Wagstaff (Age 9)

The Door

Open the door of day
See tractors ploughing through the dark soil
Farmer's crops growing in the ground
Straw bales scattered in fields
And maybe some pigs are walking in the farmyard.

Open the door of day
Maybe you'll see a stray dog walking through the crowded streets of a city
Maybe people are calling for taxis or going to pubs
Maybe children are racing out of school on a hot day
Or traffic lights turning red and people honking at them.

Carl Walters (Age 10)

The Things

Don't wait for it to get here
Pack your bags and just leave
If you can't, help yourself to a weapon
Defend as best you can
But soon it'll get you
'Cause they always do
So my advice is to run
Just don't wait for them to come
They'll destroy, they will sting
'Cause they love to watch burning
They'll be here, they'll be here
IT'S THE THINGS!
Their leader is hideous, it's got 20 legs
It'll smash down your walls in one blow
A description of it is too horrid to live
It's the things, it's the things, IT'S THE THINGS!

Simon Whiteway (Age 8)

Holiday

I got in my boat
I sailed quickly
I cast my rod
Caught a fish
And then I went home again

Shaun Williams (Age 9)

The Rat In The Hat

I have a rat in a hat
It has red deadly eyes
Some people say they have a rat in a hat
But I know they haven't
I was going to get it out
But the rat was too quick - like lightning
I still have the rat in the hat
It's under my bed, in the hat
... OR IS IT?

Tristan Whitehead (Age 9)

Spring Has Come Again

Spring has come again
My favourite time of the year
I am going to play in the sun and warmth
Of this new year.

Spring has come again
The brightest months of the year
The birds are building their nest
Flowers are blooming, spring has come again.

Anthony White (Age 10)

My Hamster

My hamster is a kind male
He has a very short, small tail
His name is Smokey, he is always on the run
Smokey eats anything in the world but his favourite
Is a bun
I'm a child, he's a hamster
Smokey is like a fluffy panda
Smokey is the best and runs quick
I'm slow, he gets ill, I get sick
I always have to feed him
His girlfriend hasn't got time to breed
Smokey has a kind loving heart
But instead he would have a jam tart
When I have roasted chicken pie
He sulks until he says "Oh my"
Then he will get his pie
His food is always crushed as mould
But by now I think he should be sold.

Charlotte White (Age 8)

Pogo Power

I met an old man
His name was Mick
He jumped around
On a pogo stick

One day he was jumping
He was jumping so high
That he bounced in the kitchen
And landed in a pie

He jumped into the bathroom
And bounced into the shower
He turned it on and with gurgle
Shouted "Pogo Power!"

Jade Wall (Age 10)

Our Millennium

At the beginning of the first millennium
At the time of Jesus' birth
There were lots of flowers and running streams
We were blessed with this wonderful earth

At the beginning of the second millennium
As it is said in the doomsday book
There were forests, fields and villages
Where the Saxons would live and cook

Now it's the third millennium
The trees and the rivers are dying
We've polluted the world in so many ways
It's really time for crying

Jack Wadey (Age 8)

Please Mr Davidson

Please Mr Davidson this boy Alex Way
Keeps kicking me, sir, what shall I say?
Say he's sad, love, say he'll pay
Say he's fat, dear, say away.

Please Mr Davidson, this boy Alex Way
Keeps talking to me, sir, what shall I say?
Say you'll hit him, dear, say you'll push him in the hay
Say get lost, say it's a horrible day

Please Mr Davidson, this boy Alex Way
Keeps pulling my hair, what shall I say?
Do the same, lamb, say he won't have a birthday in May
Say leave me alone, but don't ask me I am going away!

Francesca Wickett (Age 8)

It Was So Noisy

It was so noisy that
The windows exploded with a massive bang!

It was so noisy that
The carpet split in half with a crack!

It was so noisy that
The glasses smashed into millions of pieces!

It was so noisy that
My trousers fell straight down!

It was so noisy that
The children trembled with fear!

Samuel Ware (Age 8)

The Inventor's Workshop

In an old workshop
There is a very important inventor,
He sits at his ideas desk
Thinking ...thinking... thinking all the time,
In a big room as big as a warehouse
That stinks of petrol, oil, plus smoke,
In the corner it is cold and draughty
Where the inventor sits.

Toby Weedon (Age 8)

A Kenning

An athletic - sweater
A pulse - racer
A track - burner
A fast - runner
A trophy - winner
A finish line - skidder
A healthy - eater

What am I?

Jack White (Age 11)

My Bean Bag

I love my bean bag
It's comfy and it's cosy
I love my bean bag
Where I sink and sink and sink!

I love playing on it
When I sink I'm in a pit
As dark as dark can be!
I love my bean bag

I love my bean bag
On evenings it's the best
Of all I own, it's better than the rest
I love my bean bag

On my bean bag
I sometimes read a book
And when I'm sinking, I get scared
But I love my bean bag!

Leon Walsh (Age 9)

Stealing

Everybody sit down
Nobody steal anything from the room
You do think you are a clown
I shall send you to the moon

Never ever do it again
When you are not told
To play with that stupid train
I know you're freezing cold

You'll get a detention
I'll keep you in at play
Probably not today
Now you've got your message never do it again

Because I'll be so hard
I doubt you'll give me a birthday card
So I suggest you never do it again.

Lewis Walker (Age 9)

My Friend Jesus

I could not believe anything.
My heart was full of sorrow.
No not him, the one they called CHRIST,
Not him. Why not Barrabas?
Jesus was not a criminal, a murderer or a thief.
I held his mother as I saw him die.
Jesus will rise again.
Jesus, Jesus, JESUS!

Matthew Walker (Age 10)

My Grandad

Here is my grandad sitting in his chair
Here is my grampa without his hair
Fatter than a hog with just no care
Slow as a sloth but can stand up to a bear

He can only stuff his face with a pie
He can only eat, sleep and lie
And he tells us stories by the by
So this is my grandad from his grandson
Guy

Guy Wallis (Age 10)

Peace Poem

There is a word, a good word, a joyful word,
A word with a meaning great and wonderful,
That meaning is quiet, tranquillity and calm.
It is a word that spreads through noise and arguments
And at its arrival the quarrels stop.
That word brings smiles and tears of joy,
When wars stop that word is at large
In churches, in houses.
That word is peace.

There is a cruel word, an evil word,
A word with a meaning, devastating and terrible,
That meaning is silence, sadness and terror.
It is a word that cuts through happiness, through joy
And when it gets there the peace stops.
That word brings pain and tears of unhappiness,
When peace halts that word rules
On battle fields and playgrounds.
That word is war.

Anna Watts (Age 9)

Numbers

1 is for microphone standing on the stage
2 is for a hook hanging from the wall
3 is for cartoon eyes coming from the side
4 is for elevators on the move
5 is for a playground ready for the children
6 is for a rocking chair rocking away
7 is for half a blue tent really, really dry
8 is for glasses for reading within a book
9 is for a tractor with one wet wheel
10 is for a wheel and one old tool.

Megan Watson (Age 9)

10 Shiny Sharks

Ten shiny sharks waiting hidden in line
One saw food then there was nine
Nine shiny sharks getting ready to mate
One was left out then there was eight
Eight shiny sharks looking up to heaven
One died then there was seven
Seven shiny sharks picking up sticks
One got stuck in a net then there was six
Six shiny sharks trying to stay alive
One didn't make it then there was five
Five shiny sharks beginning to get sore
One swam away then there was four
Four shiny sharks eating dead bees
One got stung then there was three
Three shiny sharks all on the loo
One fell off then there was two
Two shiny sharks looking after their son
The son bit his dad then there was one
One shiny shark going insane
After that she was never seen again!

Matty Watson (Age 10)

The Devil

The devil
He who rests in the soul of hell
The one who patrols the entrance
And sees any sign of happiness and sucks it out of you
As you enter ...

The devil
He who sees through all the protection
And knows when a dirty deed is done
He pulls you through all the protection the moment you die
Few people have seen this terrible creature
The ones who have
Can't tell anyone anyway ...

Ashley Waters (Age 11)

Spiritual Ghost

Knock, knock, knock.
As I opened the door, it felt as though
It didn't want to open.
As soon as I let go of the handle,
The door slammed behind me.
As I walked up the cobbley, stone steps,
I stopped and looked around.
I'm sure I heard whispers.
I felt something icy go through my body.
All the hairs on the back of my neck prickled up.
As I looked around the lonely corridor, I saw a door as black as the night.
It was an inch open and blinding light came out of it.
I walked over to the door, I counted three, two, one then pushed the door open.
There was a blinding light coming out of the door.
I saw white faces zooming towards me!
Then I blacked out ... When I woke up I was lying outside.
Was it a dream or not?
As I got up, I thought to myself.
Then I walked to the door,
Knocked and went in ...

Alistair Watson (Age 9)

Cricket

Cricket, cricket it's the best
Sometimes you play different tests

The fielders are ready to catch the ball
They have to be pretty tall

Umpire, umpire you are crazy, your decisions are unbelievable
I don't know how you can cope with all the shouting and standing up

You swing your bat up and down hitting sixes
The crowd shout and bawl because I had my Weetabixes.

What sport do you like?

James Walton (Age 9)

A Storm

Snow lashes down to earth
Forming a white blanket
Covering houses, shops and buildings
Slowly dark clouds move over
Many rumbling noises beat across the land
The snow switches off and is replaced
By thunder and hailstones
Slowly darkness dies down and morning is here
Rain is hurtling down and many
People stay inside their warm houses.

Miriam Wilson (Age 9)

Cat

There lived a cat so fair and red
She swung her tail
And shook her head
She sat at home on her owner's lap
She saw something move
But was taking a nap.

Rebecca Wing (Age 8)

There Is ...

There is a fast horse inside me
That runs with the wind
There is a vicious tiger inside me
Whose eyes show the inner strength
There is a slithery snake inside me
With no sharper teeth
There is a tiny rat inside me
That's always up to something
There is a mole inside me
It can always smell food and hunger.

Patty Wai (Age 10)

The God

The God is good
The God is cool
The God is everywhere
God doesn't send my bill
And even though he has to blow
He still has time to make the river flow

The God is really nice
The God is really big
The God made us
And if we didn't have a God
Bad would break us

Juan Williams (Age 7)

Engineers

Dials ticking quite quickly
Chains rattling, very noisy
Pipes clattering, hitting each other
Gears clinking, turning quickly
Machines whistling blowing smoke
Wheels spinning very very quickly
Wires twisting very stretched
Tanks puffing very very fast
Buttons being pushed quite fast
Valves opening and shutting very fast.

Alexander Walton (Age 7)

My Death

Jesus
Lord is here, Lord is there, Lord is everywhere
Lord gave me my life today
Lord care for me like a son even though I'm his only one
The world is like an oyster and I am its pearl
Some people die and go to heaven even if they live in Devon
Lord takes lives away, I care for them and heal them
My disciples are calm and clothes are made out of yarn
I was born in a barn, I made new friends, I cared for them, I laughed with them
I helped them love their life, I helped them love each other
I was caught and whipped and given a crown of thorns and a black coloured robe
My life is slowly but sadly going away
I'm forced to carry part of my cross.

Then I am left there to die hanging above the crowd
What did I do it wasn't a lie
But I had to die for Barabbas the cold blooded killer and thief
My life is now the cross.

Samuel Williams (Age 9)

It Was So Noisy

It was so noisy that the windows
Cracked with a crash
It was so noisy that my tights
Fell down very quickly
It was so noisy that the children
Covered their small ears
It was so noisy that
The floor was shaking
It was so noisy that you could
Not hear my nana snoring
Like a dinosaur
It was was so noisy that I couldn't hear
The Simpsons!
It was so noisy that
The leaves fell off the trees
IT WAS SO NOISY!

Bethan Williams (Age 7)

My Silly Dog

My silly dog is so stupid
That the next door neighbour
Rings up and goes "SHUT UP!"

My silly dog is so stupid
That she even killed my fish
Just dashing around!

Sammy-Jo Wilcock (Age 9)

Computers

C omputers are fun
O n and off
M ouse moves everywhere
P rinter prints all your work
U se the computer
T alk to people on line
E-mail your friends
R ead your e-mail
S o much fun!

Samantha Whitham (Age 7)

What Are Materials?

Glass bottles lots of juice
If you smash it, it's no good use

Rubber rubbers rubby, rubby
Scruffy work grubby, grubby

Woolly socks to warm your feet
Needed always for the heat
Wooden tables just to work on
Work getting harder day by day.

Anica Whitmore (Age 7)

My Sense Poem

Touching my sister's blonde long hair, touching my old dog's muddy fur
Touching the silver moon as it glows in the dark, touching the night sky as it grows from evening to morning.

Listening to my sister's beautiful flute, listening to my quiet songs
Listening to Miss Neill scratching on the black board, listening to Mr Landowski play on the piano, bing!

Smelling my dad's lovely casseroles, smelling my mum's lovely penne pasta
Smelling my nan's sugary doughnuts, smelling my aunty's smooth custard.

Looking at the late night darkness with stars of gold and silver, looking at Rebecca being funny, ha ha!
Looking at the star light as I remember, looking up in my car

Tasting the fresh cold breeze, tasting my mum's lovely penne pasta
Tasting my dad's lovely casseroles, tasting the cold night air.

Wishing for my mum to come home, wishing for my dog Alfie to come home
Wishing for my mum and dad to come everywhere I go, wishing for a cheetah to be my cat.

Megan Wells (Age 7)

Birthdays

Birthdays and parties are celebrations
Families and friends come for your special occasion
You might have a party with a sporty theme
Or go to a movie which your friends might have seen.
Whatever your party, it is specially for you
So spend your birthday in the way you want to.

I remember my mum's when she was 40 years old
It was outside in winter and she said she was cold
There were a hundred people at our house that night
And I think they all partied 'til dark turned to light!
Mum that party was specially for you
Next time on your birthday you can choose what to do!

I suppose you think birthdays are just fun and cake
But remember the people who set up and bake
Imagine your party was a a total disaster
And all your friends came before or worse, after!
Have a great time whose birthday might be today
And make sure you don't mess the house up ... OK!

Eleanor Weatherseed (Age 11)

Good Things And Bad Things

I love school
But home time is better
I hate getting wet
I love surfing the net
I hate writing
Unless it's exciting
When I use a tool
People call me a fool
I love school
Because it's cool

Freya Wark (Age 9)

Please Mr Davidson

Please Mr Davidson, this boy Tom Drew
Keeps sharpening his pencil, sir what shall I do?

Go and sit in the library dear, go and sit in the sink
Take your pencil on the roof my love, do whatever you think.

Please Mr Davidson, this boy Tom Drew
Keeps taking my pencil sir, what shall I do?

Keep it in your hand dear, hide it up your sleeve
Swallow it if you like my love, do whatever you please

Please Mr Davidson, this boy Tom Drew
Keeps calling me names sir, what shall I do?

Lock yourself in the toilet, run away to the city
Do whatever you like, but don't ask me!

Rebecca Williams (Age 9)

Sharks

Sharks are mean, nasty and vicious,
And the fish they eat are very delicious.

If they bite you, they'll give you a scare,
Because it would hurt absolutely everywhere;

The shark's teeth, scrape along the coral reef,
The sharks swim along, doing nothing wrong;

The people shout and run away,
The sharks swim near the beach all day.

The sharks are swept into the bay,
The little children run away.

Michael Wilcox (Age 10)

Black

The deteriorating body of a murderer's victim
A dagger stained with blood
The cave degenerates
The body never to be found
The victim never to be seen again.

Sam Ward (Age 10)

My Doughnut

Sweet and sugary, round and glittery
Soft and squidgy, full of jam
Mouthwatering
Tempting
Delicious in every way
Eaten quickly .....
Gone!
My doughnut.

Edward Weetman (Age 9)

What Is Christmas?

Elves working every day
While children do their play

Decorate the tree with glowing lights
While the fairy gives you your delights

Mistletoe hung upon the door
While presents scattered on the floor

Snow falls in the night
While some people get frostbite

Santa comes every year
While our presents are very near

So MERRY CHRISTMAS
And a Happy New Year!

Emma Williams (Age 10)

The Goon Of The Lagoon

The bloodthirsty monster that lives in the murky lagoon
Awaiting his next juicy victim for his lunch
His bloodshot claws, ready to rip and tear
His demonic face screwed up and filled with anger
Pale green skin mutilated and wrinkly
Hair like seaweed dangling down from his steel-like head.

Crouched down ready to pounce on his warm-blooded prey
His long, immaculate fins help glide him through the water
He flies out the water and grabs his prey with his sharpened claws
And he rips out his guts with his teeth that are sharp as a butcher's knife
He chews aggressively on this piece of tough meat

The Goon of the lagoon strikes back
Yet another poor, innocent creature abducted
And ripped into segregated, minuscule pieces of anatomy
Will he be stopped?

Chris Wickham (Age 11)

Our Town

The cafes are as clean as sky
With tables that are shiny and dry
I hope you love the great big shops
Especially children doing hops.

I think the pubs are really good
Especially if they have a fire with real wood
The roads are marked white and grey
With donkies trotting eating hay.

Rachel Wearing (Age 8)

Sharks

S licing teeth and calm
H acking through the water waiting for the alarm
A ttacking seals fast and slow
R acing fin so low
K illing smile in the dark
S o shark, shark, shark

Toby Webb (Age 9)

Loneliness

In an isolated space in the playground
I sit on a bench watching people playing football
I am invisible to the naked eye
No attention, no one listens to me
I hide in the shadows of the castellated wall
The whistle blows, we line up
I am jeered at and shoved for no reason
My happiness is fading slowly from my heart
My world is disappearing day by day
I need a miracle to make me happy
I am drowning in a pool of tears.

Anthony Welch (Age 9)

The Thar Desert

Thar Desert
As hot as the sun's surface
The heat makes you collapse
You dehydrate
Energy drained by the temperature
Hallucinating
Sand dunes all around
Wind rode waves
Thar desert

Thar Desert
Camels the ships of the desert
Blinding sandstorms
Perceived haziness
Extremely tired
Makes you thirsty
Shivering
Shiny sand
Thar desert.

Matthew Wenham (Age 10)

Esme Westgate

Esme Westgate
Blue eyes
Brown hair
Loves pies

Big eyebrow
So hairy
Get close
She's scary!

Very tall
Quite plump
Really strong
Hard thump

Pretty clever
Big mind
Plays instruments
Not kind.

Esme Westgate (Age 9)

Hit By A Car

Eyes glimmering like stars at night
Silently she stares at her past.

A beautiful tabby kitten
With furry face and pointed ear
But what was she now?

Her past flickered suddenly
Breathlessly her eyes dim
As she falls into unawakened sleep.

Rachel Whitwood (Age 9)

When I Was ...

When I was young and had no sense, I used to lie in my crib,
I used to cry for hours and hours and dribble on my bib.
When I was a toddler, I ate spare ribs,
And many more things like this.

When I was a toddler for years and years,
I had loads of fears.
When I was six I used to dream,
I would fix many things and be in a football team.

When I was eight,
Everyone complained of me being late,
I used to say my dog was ill,
But no he wasn't, poor old Bill.

When I was ten,
I got a new dog called Ben,
But she didn't agree
Because she thought the dog couldn't see.

And now I'm eleven
I think my mum sees my point,
That I have a pet,
And there's nothing else I want to get.

Leanne Wells (Age 11)

The Aliens

The aliens landed on the grass
And they chased after me
And I got in the spaceship
And I took off in to the
Sky and it was dark and I
Liked it in the sky and I
Played on the computer and you get
To play and games.

Martin Wiggins (Age 7)

Seashore

The furious horses jump and crash
As they ride the waves
Fishes scurry round in a flash
Birds fly to their nests

The wind throws a tantrum
And starts to make a fuss
The clouds cover the sun
As the sky darkens

The beach is deserted all alone
No children laughing and playing around
No ringing of a mobile phone
Another day end and soon another will start.

Leanne Whelan (Age 10)

What Is Pink?

What is pink? A pig is pink
In its muddy rink.

What is red? Strawberries are red
Painted on my bed.

What is blue? The sea is blue
What a glorious view.

What is white? A ghost is white
Haunting you at night.

What is yellow? A banana is yellow
Rich and ripe and mellow.

What is green? A leaf is green
Hanging in between.

What is gold? A crown is gold
Shining from the old.

What is orange? Why an orange
Just an orange!

Alice White (Age 9)

What Are Materials?

Plastic spoons are rock hard
Never break at all
Rubberband really bouncy
Can be really painful
Woollen socks keep you warm
Especially when it's morning dawn
Glass bottles do always break
But some of them are in a state
That's what materials are.

Jamie Whittaker (Age 7)

The Dapple Grey Pony

The pony trotted down the lane
She was going to the city to win her fame
She was travelling, very far
All she wanted, was to be a star.
But then it struck her, what would she do
What would happen if she caught the flu?
Or what if, she lost her way
And nobody could hear her neigh?
So she turned around and went straight back
To see the sight of her lovely tack
A terrible feeling, came inside
She fled to the stables, knowing someone had died
Her owner had, she was heartbroken
It was too late, death had spoken.

Becky Ware (Age 10)

Pictures From My Mind

Pictures from my mind I think of years ago
From dinosaurs to dragons
I think of a dragon
From being as fiery
As a flame
I think of a dinosaur
As being green as grass

Pictures from my mind
I think when I'm older
About 53
I think I might be fashionable
As can be
I will wear mini skirts
Wear high heels
And all fashionable things
But I guess I'll stick
To being a child with
PICTURES FROM MY MIND

Amy Whitehurst (Age 11)

I'll Follow You

I'll follow you through your T.V. set
Through the twisting wires
Where the electricity comes from the pylons
When click the T.V. flicks on

Wherever you go I'll be there
Through the Simpsons, Neighbours the Nine O'Clock news
Through ghostbusters where all the slime oozes
I'll follow you through wrestling
And pow the rock bottom on you and me
I'll follow you stalking you all the way.

Harry White (Age 9)

Cheetah

The blood red eyes
Pierce the sun's rays through the trees
Charcoal coloured spots mark
The sun's season
The predators prance
At the skinned antelope
Running for its life, over the burnt canopy
The savager sleeps looking forward to a new blood thirsty day

It rises gallant and crystalized
From its beauty sleep
A new day of hunting will attract his mate
Confused, but attracted the female
Gives an eye
He raises his chest and stands upon high
Complaining and sighing does he
Trying to impress he licks his lips.

Robert Weldon (Age 11)

A Bolt Falling

A bolt falling
A name calling

A huge crash
A long dash

A big flash
A tall clash

A big bang
A great clang

A loud band
A helping hand

A list to make
Me a
Storm

Jasmine Ward (Age 9)

The Snake

I saw a snake
Eating a cake
When I went to the woods
I ran away
And it said hey
So why don't you come and play

We started playing chase
Then we had a race
I like meat
So turn up the heat
Because you're my dinner
So don't get thinner

Get on my plate
Because you're ready to be ate
I think you're yummy
So get in my tummy
You weren't my bud
So give me your blood
All in a flood.

Oliver Webb (Age 11)

The Gale

What a tempestuous night!
The wind howled and wailed
It tore slates from the roof
Threw them down in anger
Whirls of wind weaved around in the branches.
As the moon peeped
The clouds raced
The wind moaned and roared
As if it were in pain.

Kimberley White (Age 11)

Jess

One day Jess was thinking
About everything he could do
Maybe win a race
Or sit by the fire too
He ran around the pond
And jumped upon the wall
When suddenly he fell off
His mother heard him call
She got up off her cushion
And ran up to her son
She picked him up and carried him in
Until her job was done
Tears sprang in his eyes
Jess wanted to say ow
But instead he gave a loud
MEOW!

Charlotte Wheatcroft (Age 10)

Love

Love
What is love?
Is it an object? Or a person?
Nobody knows.

Love is a thing you feel when you look at something or someone
It isn't a solid, liquid or gas
For you it may be that it's a thing that lives in you or your loved one
For others it may be a thing that when it's taken away it's impossible to survive.

But what we do know is that no feeling or emotion can hurt as
Much as a broken heart
If they leave you keep holding on
With that eternal flame of love burning inside you.

Kirsty Willson (Age 11)

Wondering About Weather

What is hail?
Little people kicking and thumping at your skin.

What is snow?
A white fur animal sleeping across the earth.

What's a hurricane?
God opening a can of coke and sucking everyone up.

What's a heatwave?
5,000 suns melting across your forehead.

What's air?
The biggest human with the biggest breath.

Nina Wilkinson (Age 11)

Chocolate

Chocolate is a heavenly sensation
All its creamy textures are divine
Fuse, Chocolate Buttons, Twix and Time-Out
All of the varieties are fine

Chocolate is a beautiful, creamy, dreamy way to live
Even though it makes me feel sick
I love to eat it in a deep hot bath
With the gentle light of a flickering candle wick

Chocolate makes me feel calm and relaxed
When it is melted I love to lick
If I could have all the chocolate in the world
Like a fox I'd steal it still and slick

Chocolate is the best thing in the world
Its colour, taste and best of all its scent
It's a shame really I'd eat loads, if I could
But I'm giving up eating it for Lent!

Natasha Walker-Shaw (Age 11)

The Burning Beach

The fiery sun
Is burning the sand
The leaves crinkle as
You stand on them

The sea strokes the sand
As your feet sink in the sea
And tickles between the toes

The sun fires at you
As you walk closer.

Joshua Walker (Age 9)

My Pets

I have a rabbit
With a naughty habit
When I let her out to eat
She digs the lawn up with her feet

Barney is my guinea pig
He's brown and white and very big
My other guinea's very small
He's brown and has no white at all

I have an old cat called Patter
When she was young she was a very good ratter
Now she's old she sleeps all day
And doesn't often want to play.

Alice West (Age 9)

Anger

Anger
Anger is red
Anger smells like smoke
Anger tastes terrible
Anger sounds like something about to explode
Anger feels hard and sharp
Anger lives in your spirits.

Beauty
Beauty is the colour of the rainbow
Beauty smells like roses
Beauty tastes so nice
Beauty sounds sweet and cheerful
Beauty feels like silk
Beauty lives in your heart.

Charlotte Welham (Age 9)

Hostage - The Voyage Out

Swimming in a sea of screaming memories, he lies quiet on a deck-chair,

Watching, wondering what will come next, in this fairytale land

Of black despair. Around a corner, reality returns,

And again, he's alone

In his cell,

The

Whispering silence

Ripping at his ears, chorusing

Horrified rhymes, which tell of lost battles,

In the back of a mind, that are forgot or never talked of,

Like the one he is fighting now on this voyage out of madness.

Dot Wales (Age 10)

The Silver Night

Slowly, silently, now the moon
Walks the night in her silver shoon
The silver stars
Shine near Mars

Up in the night time sky I see a silver shadow
As I'm looking through my bedroom window
Now on the rough log
Lays a silver hearted dog
His silver eyes stare at me alone
How I wish I could give him a home.

Kirsty Wasylyczyn (Age 10)

Loneliness

Left alone friendless on a bench
Not popular like the other girls
Getting bullied, kept out of secrets
And getting pushed and jostled

Sat there in a world of her own
Dreaming of being popular
But afraid of asking other girls
To be her friend

Looking around the playground
At groups of children laughing
And shouting to each other
Not seeing the loneliness she feels

She spotted a girl on a bench like hers
On her own, looking sad
There and then she found the courage
To go over and end the loneliness

Lucy Walsh (Age 9)

What Is It?

Pick it from the ground
Put it to your ear
Listen to the wavy sound
Is this what you hear?

I hear the wind
I hear the sea
I hear the great, long ships
But what can you see?

I see some steps
I see some ridges
I see a sharp end
But what could it be?

Is it a rock?
Is it a bell?
Is it a pebble?
No, it's a sea-shell!

Paul Wateridge (Age 9)

Night Time

In the night
We have a fright
We have bad dreams
Everybody screams
We open our eyes
And say bye bye
And say to yourself
It's over now.

Heather Walrond (Age 8)

The Tale Of Steven Clark

This boy Steven Clark really is a pain
He keeps taking the train
He bought a goat
Instead of a boat
He went to the car
To find a jam jar
This little lad
Really is quite bad
He bought a drum
To sell to his chum
He found a beehive
So he went for a dive
In a swimming pool
People think he's cool (not!)
Oh this boy Steven Clark
He comes in the dark.

Alexander Way (Age 8)

What I Imagine ...

Take your mind inside a life what does it tell you?
What do you see? Come there with me ...

I imagine the bright blue sea, fraying the waves from you to me
Riding into the sea on horseback, the waves slashing our legs with a crash
Stroking the cat until it purrs with a smile, just as if it had laid there all the while
Looking through your imaginative eyes, skimming through the moonlight skies
Swimming in a pool of dolphins waving a fin, in the waters wild gloom and din
Our wildest dreams take wind and come to life, escaping danger from a life of strife
Being left in a frenzy of a fiery room, the flames curling and licking awaiting your doom
The day passes being still and quiet, then there would be no almighty riot
Imagine love without a heart. How would it begin? How would it start?
Imagine sleeping without any dreams, what would it feel like, how would it seem?

Naomi Webb (Age 10)

Dogs

Dogs are cute and funny
When they're silly they start running
Some catch foxes, rats, cats or a bunny
And some really like it when it's sunny
Some help farmers with their cows and sheep
Some are lazy they just sleep
Most stay from work and just play
People play with them every day
Most are kind
Some have a big mind
Some have big feet
Some dogs love to eat lots of food
But most dogs love to be rude
But I like them all
I wish I had many dogs in one hall.

Tasha Willett (Age 8)

Why, Why, Why

Why is the sky blue
Why are some things not true
Why do we have to work hard
Why do we sometimes buy a card
Why is my mum different to any other mums
Why do we have to do lots of sums?

Why do my friends like different things, like going to a friend's house?
Why are people scared of a mouse
Why is my pen running out of ink
Why is gravity not in some things
Why do we make a wish?

Milli Walker (Age 9)

Spring

Go away rain, Spring is here again.

We do not need snow and ice,
Spring can be very nice.

The smell of the grass being mowed,
Means it's time to get those seeds sowed.

The leaves come out green,
And the flower buds can be seen.

Oh yes, Spring is very exciting,
Whoops! Mind that bee does not sting!

Luke Weingart (Age 8)

Summer

Summer is very hot,
Us playing in the paddling pool
Mum sunbathing in the garden enjoying herself.
Mummy being silly,
Eagles flying about,
Rabbits put their sun glasses on.

June Yan (Age 6)

It Was So Noisy

It was so noisy that I couldn't
Hear the traffic storming down the road
It was so noisy that I couldn't
Hear my dog barking in the garden
It was so noisy that I couldn't
Hear my mum shouting to my sister down stairs
It was so noisy that I couldn't
Hear my mum hoovering in the living room
It was so noisy that I couldn't
Hear my sister's CD player playing very loud
IT WAS SO NOISY!

Wendy Watkins (Age 8)

Autumn

Early morning, misty, damp
Leaves, colourful,
Spiralling madly down from the swaying trees,
Silver diamond drops shine in the hedgerows,
White mist swirling lazily,
Orange, red, yellow leaves dance gracefully with
The playful wind,
A carpet of clothes getting larger and larger,
As trees let go their summer wear.

Ryan Wiles (Age 8)

A Poem In The Style Of Tennyson

He clasps the crag with crooked hands
Close to the sun in lonely lands
Ring'd with the azure world, he stands;

The wrinkled sea beneath him crawls
He watches from his mountain walls
And like a thunderbolt he falls,

He shoots up to the cliff's shoulder
His creased feet sat on a boulder
He's off, wings like a closed folder.

Lucy Whitfield (Age 10)

The Waterfall

Rushing faster, faster it goes
Coming up and tickling my toes
Smashing through the rock, quick, quick, quick
Then it splashes on again, flick, flick, flick
Rushing through incoming streams
It's the ride of your dreams
Hurry up, hurry up, gotta keep going
Howling, howling the wind is blowing
Then as it approaches the tumbling fall
It seems that it is not moving at all
Then it falls, down, down, down
Can you hear their tremendous sound?

Alistair Watkins (Age 9)

The Green Grass Grows

In winter when the green grass grows
The daffodils pop up and the church bells ring
And the birds begin to sing
And the post man comes round the corner and starts delivering

As the children walk to school their fingers like ice and their noses all cold and red.
They get into class and moan to the teacher, turn on the heating please.

Olivia White (Age 7)

The Jungle

Twirling whirling vines and trees
Look at all the things to see

Squiggling worms on the ground
Down comes a bird without a sound

A young buffalo lost in the heat
Lions looking for something to eat

Sharks are swimming in the heat
Looking for some kind of meat to beat

Crabs crawling across the beach
Looking for a fish to eat.

Matthew Whitchurch (Age 8)

Silence

Silence is somebody painting
Silence is a baby dreaming in its cot
Silence is fire burning around
Silence is night, very dark and gentle
Silence is a bird gliding through the air
Silence is being in a church on your own
Silence is the hills of Scotland and in deserts
Silence is in a cave
Silence is the tombs in a graveyard.

Maddison Whiffin (Age 6)

Storm At Sea

Once lake Galilee was calm.
Then a storm came.
Jesus' disciples were scared.
WAKE UP WAKE UP the disciples said.
What's the matter, God is looking after you.
The boat stopped tossing.
The wind stopped howling.
And the lightning stopped flashing.
The rain stopped lashing.
And the thunder stopped crashing.

Francis Zieleniewski (Age 6)

Playing The Game

Football is a wonderful game,
No two matches are ever the same,
You win you lose sometimes a draw,
But playing is never a bore.

Matches go on in wind and rain,
But they keep on playing despite the pain,
In the slush in the mud,
They kick the ball with a mighty thud.

The fans keep cheering,
It's a wonderful sound,
You can hear their voices around the ground.

At the end of the game,
Win or lose there is no shame,
Everyone can hold their head high,
Shaking hands and saying goodbye.

Alex Young (Age 9)

I am An Ant

I am an ant,
I am stuck in a gutter,
I used to crawl in peoples houses,
And other peoples drawers,
But I am still stuck in a gutter.

Along I crawl through the watery sewers,
As I try to get up but the sides are too slippery,
But I am still stuck in a gutter.

As I try and try to get up the slippery ditch,
But I got up the gutter
And I was released!!!

Zena Young (Age 10)

Warm Winter Fire

W arm winter fire burning bright.
A rmchair rocking, through the night.
R osy cheeks glowing bright,
M uddy boots stand upright.

W ind howling outside the door.
I nside drafts creep along the floor.
N oisily sleet hits the pane,
T urning to ice the lashing rain.
E ven the stars abandon their glow,
R aging clouds soar black and low.

F lames flicker, flail and then die,
I ncense-like smoke begins to rise,
R eturning home wet and cold,
E ntering warmth as the night grows old.

Katy Yearsley (Age 11)

My Best Friend

Lauren is her name,
and netball is her game,
She runs around like crazy,
And no-one calls her lazy.

In school she likes to tell me jokes,
And in the gym she is good on the ropes.

Her hair is brown,
And so are her eyes,
I know that she would never tell lies.

All in all she is my best friend,
Always there with an ear to lend,
Always there to show the way,
Always there with something to say.

It is sad to say that when we go,
We will be in different schools, this I know,
But I am sure we will stay in touch
And I wish Lauren the best of luck.

Leonie Yerrell (Age 11)

Dolphins

Dolphins swim in graceful ways,
Across the salty peaceful bay
The people watched the lovely sight
Across the ocean clear and bright.

The dolphins swim in playful ways
In and out of the lovely bay
The sight was lovely to watch them play
I wish I could swim with them today

Now it's time to swim away
I hope we meet again some day
Now it's time to say goodbye
The sun is setting in the sky.

Holly Young (Age 10)

A Widow

I look outside my window
In the bright blue sky.
And thinking I'm a widow
It really makes me cry.

My husband died last week,
It made me cry and cry,
And in the chest he left behind
A dead owl stands by.

Sarah Yellowley (Age 9)

War

When I was 19 I was in the war
I had never handled a weapon before.
I killed lots of soldiers and stopped people dying,
There were lots of people sadly crying.
There were quite a few traps while everyone fought.
One day I got caught.
I went unconscious after a fall,
When I woke up my ankle was chained to a ball.
Some Germans took me to their camp,
I had to sleep without a lamp.
One day I got tortured and I felt bad.
I thought my family would feel sad.
Then some English men set everyone caught free,
I was hidden in the camp but I was glad they found me.
When it was over I went home, saw my family and went to a bar,
When I came out I got ran over by a car.

Robert Young (Age 12)

Night

The stars come out and shine very bright,
They look so wonderful, what a beautiful sight.
The moon is like an alarm, telling us its night,
It goes dark by the slightest might.
The moon is like a burglar stealing the light,
That's what gives us a feel of night.
Whilst people are snoring,
The sky is black and boring.
People are having dreams,
While some turn out to be screams,
Some people are having bad dreams.

Carly Zyla (Age 11)

Sea Shell Sea Shell

Sea shell, sea shell,
Spiral shaped,
When people see it
They are amazed.

Sea shell, sea shell,
Sounds like waves,
Slow calm drones
Throughout the days.

Sea shell, sea shell,
Quivering slow,
Sea shell, sea shell
Down below.

Sea shell, sea shell,
Free for all
Sea shell, sea shell
Jewells galore!

James Young (Age 9)

Mars

If you go to Mars,
You won't have cars,
Or you might get put behind bars,
But you can still see the stars

You can take cats
But you have to fight bats,
Only using hats,
If you don't, you've to eat rats.

You have to write in tens,
Without using pens,
Or you have to eat hens,
Right from their dens.

Nazneen Zaman (Age 10)

A Model Kenning

A funky female
A stylish slim-line,
A gorgeous girl
A dancing queen
A groovy chick
A wonderful figure,
A tight slim dress she wears
A happening babe
A millions maker

Becky Young (Age 11)

School Poem

Matths is great fractions isn't
English can be boring and some times fun,
P.E. is cool but sometimes rubbish,
Georgraphy feels very long.

Jamie Young (Age 10)

Dinner Time

When it's dinner time people throw
Food at children and teachers
The teachers tell them off
But they don't listen.
When they get their dinner
They don't say thank you
They just throw sweet wrappers
At the dinner ladies
They get their water
And splash it on children
The dinner ladies
And the teachers get cross
The children
Say sorry.

Samah Zaheer (Age 9)

The Battle

I see Richard digging his heels into his horse
I see Henry calling one of his nurses into the scene
I look up and see Richard charging towards me.
I see my sword and I use it.

I hear Richard scream as I cut a deep wound in his arm
I hear Henry saying I had done a good job.
I hear my boot squelching in the mud.
I hear the shout of my father as he falls to the ground.

I smell hot, musty air
I smell smoke from flaming arrows
I smell danger lurking around the corner
I smell my damp salty sweat.

I touch my sword and I feel bad.
I touch my soaking wet armour
I clench my shield and dodge an arrow
I touch my sweaty forehead.

I taste anger at the back of my mouth
I taste my blood as I lick my lips
I taste my salty sweat I taste the smoky air.

I feel very faint I feel very lonely though there are people all around me.

Nicola Quiggin (Age 9)

Rockets

Rockets blast through outer space
At one hundred miles per hour or more,
Watch them, see them, blast into the atmosphere
The Americans won the race of space,
On the moon there is no air.

In space there is a sun which burns every day,
Rockets, small rockets, big oil burning,
Earth below, space up high,
I wish I could be an astronaut.

Michael Young (Age 7)

Colours

Red is as red as blood
Green is as green as the dew on the silk grass
Brown is the colour of leaves falling at autumn
Think of all the colours in the rainbow sparkling
In the rain. Colours.

Amy Walters (Age 8)

The 13th Day

Dying like flies.
Getting hit with the gas.
It hangs round the trench.
Like mist and fog.
Killing the men
Every second of the day.

Brett Young (Age 14)

Leaves

Leaves are falling to the ground
As they turn a golden brown
They make a crisp and crunching sound

Look at the tall trees
As the leaves float in the breeze
Red and amber leaves

Hannah Walsh (Age 9)

My Kenning

They can come in all shapes and all sizes,
They have three hands but no legs,
They have a face with no expression
Some can go in water, some can't,
You can stop them and start them
They can run on quartz and are like many others,
They even come in different types,
Nearly every household has one.

Paul Yellowley (Age 11)

The Door

Go and open the door of fear
Maybe outside there's a powerful army invading a city,
Or an angry volcano's erupting and hot lava flowing fast from it,
An earthquake destroying thousands of homes,
Or a world where no-one cares about your dreams.

Go and open the door of fear
Maybe a comet's heading towards planet earth,
Or a world where there's no daylight,
Or your property suddenly belongs to someone else,
Or the world coming to an end.

Khant Zaw (Age 10)

BIOGRAPHIES
OF
POETS

ABBOTT, JONATHAN: [b] 15/05/90 Redditch; [home] Stoke Prior, Worcs; [p] Philip & Ann; [school] Aston Fields Middle; [fav sub] Art; [hobbies] Collecting Warhammer 40,000; [ambition] To study at University;

ABBOTT, TAMISHA: [b] 15/2/89 Norwich; [home] Norwich, Norfolk; [p] Robert & Rafeah; [brother] Taquila; [school] South Hartford Middle; [fav sub] Art, Reading & Writing; [hobbies] Cooking & Singing; [pets] 2 Cats; [ambition] To become a Model and a Singer;

ACKROYD, JADE MELODY: [b] 25/10/89 Bradford; [home] Bradford, W. Yorks; [p] Lynda; [school] Buttershaw Primary; [fav sub] English; [hobbies] Dance & Music; [ambition] To work abroad as a Haven Mate;

ADAMS, DAVID ANDREW: [b] 24/12/92 Burnley; [home] Rawtenstall, Lancs; [p] Neil & Margaret; [sister] Jennifer; [school] Constable Lee CE St Pauls; [fav sub] Maths; [hobbies] Swimming & Snooker; [pets] Goldfish; [ambition] To be an RAF Pilot;

ALISON, NATASHA GEORGIA ROSE: [b] 13/12/92 London; [home] Chiswick, London; [p] Sebastian & Sasha; [sister] Sophia; [school] Belmont Primary; [fav sub] Science; [hobbies] Drama, Piano, Brownies & Swimming; [pets] Rabbit (Honey) & Dog (Lucky); [ambition] To travel around the world and have a dog of my own;

ALLCOCK, LIZZIE: [b] 18/4/88 Nottingham; [home] Nottingham, Notts; [p] David & Krysia; [school] Loughborough High; [fav sub] Mathematics; [hobbies] Riding, Cycling & Reading; [pets] A pony called Gemstone; [ambition] To work in Accountancy or Law;

ALDRIDGE, MATTHEW: [b] 20/3/86 Cheltenham; [home] Cheltenham, Glos; [p] Alison & Alan; [sister] Jenny; [school] Winchcombe; [fav sub] Geography & Sport; [hobbies] Life saving, Sport & Air Training Corp; [ambition] To play Rugby at Premiership level;

ALLEN, SARAH: [b] 19/7/90 Watford; [home] Hemel Hempsted, Herts; [p] Brian & Sharon; [sister] Katy; [school] Two Waters; [fav sub] Art; [hobbies] Dancing & Art; [ambition] To be a TV News Presenter or Poet;

ALLEYNE, SERETSE: [b] 24/8/90;

[home] Thornton Heath, Surrey; [p] Shelly-Ann & Tyrone; [brother] Marcus; [sister] Afeisha; [school] St James The Great Primary; [fav sub] Maths; [hobbies] Model Construction & Stamp Collecting; [ambition] To become a Judge;

ALLMAND, FELICITY: [b]12/1/91 Welwyn Garden City; [home] Aylesbury, Bucks; [p] David & Barbara; [brother] Henry; [school] Turnfurlong Junior; [fav sub] History; [hobbies] Sport, Swimming & Writing Stories; [pets] Guide dog puppy; [ambition] To do things that help people;

ALPS, MATTHEW: [b] 17/1/92 Gloucester; [home] Quedgeley, Glos; [p] Joe & Julie; [sister] Lauren; [school] Fieldcourt Junior; [fav sub] P.E.; [hobbies] Football; [pets] Cat; [ambition] To play football for Leeds United;

AMOR, MADDIE: [b] 6/2/91 Devizes; [home] Market Lavington, Wilts; [p] Alison; [sister] Sophie Louise; [school] Dauntsey Aided Primary; [fav sub] Art; [hobbies] Animal Keeping; [pets] 4 Cats, 1 Hamster, Fish & Sea Monkeys; [ambition] To be a Vet;

ANDERSON, CHARLOTTE: [b] 2/6/93 Derby; [home] Swadlincote, Derbyshire; [p] Nigel & Dawn; [brother] Rory; [school] Belmont Primary; [fav sub] Maths [hobbies] Gymnastics, Swimming & Reading; [pets] A Lop Eared Rabbitt (Blossom Strawberry); [ambition] To be a Marine Biologist or a Vet and a Poet in my spare time!;

ANDERSON, DEAN: [b] 27/4/90 Cheshunt; [home] Waltham X, Herts; [p] Patrick & Julie; [brother] Jake; [school] Bonneygrove Primary; [fav sub] Art; [hobbies] Football; [pets] Dog & Cat; [ambition] To be a Footballer;

ANDERSON, JAMES: [b] 18/7/90 Chertsey; [home] Chertsey, Surrey; [p] May & Hugo; [brother] David; [sister] Libby; [school] St Anne's RC Primary; [fav sub] English & P.E.; [hobbies] Skateboarding & Rollerblading; [pets] 3 Stick Insects, 1 Rabbit, 1 Guinea Pig, 3 Canaries & 11 Goldfish; [ambition] To be an Author of Action Thrillers;

ANDREWS, EMILY: [b] 27/6/94 Guildford; [home] Chilworth, Surrey; [p] John & Iris; [sister] Samantha; [school] Chilworth C of E Infants; [fav sub] Maths; [hobbies] Horse Riding & Swimming; [pets]

Rabbit (Jill); [ambition] To become a Horse Riding Teacher;

ANDREWS, RICHARD HENRY: [b] 12/7/88 Chester; [home] Chester, Cheshire; [p] William & Gillian; [brother] Thomas; [sister] Kathryn; [school] Upton High; [fav sub] Computers & Sports; [pets] Golden Labrador (Bonnie); [ambition] To be successful;

ARNOLD, EMMA: [b] 30/6/90 [home] Brandon, Suffolk; [p] Mark Arnold & Clare Biggs; [brother] Gareth Oxborough; [school] Breckland Middle; [fav sub] Drama; [hobbies] Horse Riding & Swimming; [pets] Esta, Jake, Spud & Tiny; [ambition] To be a Solicitor or Social Worker;

ARNOLD-HARMAN, BEVERLEY: [b] 6/3/90 Bexhill; [home] Ninfield, E. Sussex; [p] Paul & Mandy; [brothers] Max, Charlie, Eddy; [sisters] Ellie, Laura, Demi & Sad; [school] Ninfield C.E.; [fav sub] PE & Poetry; [hobbies] PE & Baton Twirling; [pets] Fish & Hamster; [ambition] To work with children;

ARSCOTT, KELLY: [b] 22/7/89 Canterbury; [home] Canterbury, Kent; [p] Barry & Janet; [sister] Zoë; [school] St Anselms Catholic School; [fav sub] English & Drama; [hobbies] Dancing at Dance School; [pets] Labrador (Millie); [ambition] To be a Famous Dancer;

ASHENDEN, LOUISE MICHELLE: [b] 4/9/91 Hastings; [home] Hastings, E. Sussex; [p] Darren & Michelle; [brother] Steven; [sister] Samantha; [school] Hollington Primary; [fav sub] Art; [hobbies] Collecting Dinosaur Toys; [pets] Misty, Mog; [ambition] To work in Tescos;

ASHTON, SOPHIE: [b] 18/7/91 Romford; [home] Rayleigh, Essex; [p] Malcolm & Donna; [sisters] Cheryl & Lucy; [school] Down Hall Primary; [fav sub] English; [hobbies] Swimming & Dancing; [pets] Cat (Sparky); [ambition] To be a Vet;

ASTLES, SOPHIE: [b] 15/1/94 Frimley; [home] Fleet, Hants; [p] David & Judith; [brother] James; [school] Fleet Infant; [fav sub] English; [hobbies] Reading, Swimming & Piano; [pets] Goldfish (Bobby & Mercedes; [ambition] To swim with Dolphins and to be a Poet;

ATHERTON, CHYNALOUISE: [b] 19/10/89 Cleveleys; [home] Cleveleys,

Lancs; [p] Dean & Shelley; [brother] Ben Clifford; [sisters] Natalya & Natasya; [school] Manor Beach CP; [fav sub] Art; [hobbies] Netball & Guides; [pets] Rabbit, Hamster, Budgie & Guinea Pig; [ambition] To be a Vet;

ATKINS, JODIE: [b] 11/6/92 London; [home] Birch, Essex; [p] Natalie & Steven; [brothers] Billy & Freddie; [sister] Georgina; [school] Birch C of E Primary; [fav sub] Art; [hobbies] Drawing & Making Books; [pets] 1 Cat & 2 Hamsters; [ambition] To visit Egypt and see the Pyramids;

ATKINSON, DANIEL: [b] 20/4/87 Burnley; [home] Burnley, Lancs; [p] Tracy & David; [sister] Tiffany-Rae; [school] Gawthorpe High; [fav sub] Maths; [hobbies] Supporting Burnley FC; [pets] 2 Dogs (Sophie & Olivia); [ambition] To own my own Business;

ATKINSON, NICHOLAS: [b] 9/7/93 Macclesfield; [home] Bollington, Cheshire; [p] Pauline & Harry; [brothers] David & Robert; [sisters] Vicky, Debbie & Joanna; [school] Dean Valley Primary; [fav sub] History; [hobbies] Lego building, Karate & Reading; [pets] Cats (Oscar & Jess) Hamster (Whizzy) & Fish (Tom); [ambition] To be a Lego Model Designer & Builder;

ATTACK, JODIE: [b] 8/3/92 Bradford; [home] Clayton, W. Yorks; [p] Julie & Michael; [sister] Lydia; [school] Clayton Village; [fav sub] Art; [hobbies] Swimming; [pets] Dog (Masher); [ambition] To swim with Dolphins;

AUBREY, JAKE: [b] Basingstoke; [home] Basingstoke, Hants; [p] Louise Dewey & Steven Aubrey; [sister] Beth; [school] Merton Junior; [fav sub] Maths & P.E.; [hobbies] Kickboxing;

AVERY, JOE: [b] 5/10/91 London; [home] Beaconsfield, Bucks; [p] Shaun & Belinda; [brother] Daniel; [sister] Isabel; [school] Davenies School; [fav sub] Art; [hobbies] Swimming; [pets] Goldfish; [ambition] To be an Olympic Swimmer;

BAILEY, ABIGAIL: [b] 8/8/92 Cambridge; [home] Thame, Oxon; [p] Annette & David; [brother] Jacob; [sister] Harriet; [school] John Hampden Primary; [fav sub] English, Reading; [hobbies] Drawing, Piano, Rollerblading, Pets & Cycling; [pets] Dog (Millie) & Guinea Pig (Twinkle); [ambition] To play the piano as well as Mummy;

BAILEY, JONATHAN: [b] 4/5/92 Preston; [home] Euxton, Lancs; [p] Jeanette & Stuart; [brother] Christopher; [school] Euxton C.E. Primary; [fav sub] Art/Dinosaurs; [hobbies] Making Lego Models; [pets] Dog (Tess); [ambition] To be a Policeman, to try Paragliding & to play the

keyboard proficiently;

BAILEY, LAURAN: [b] 15/11/90 Cheltenham; [home] Evesham, Worcs; [p] James & Eliza; [brother] Joe; [school] Swan Lane First; [fav sub] Music & History; [hobbies] Drama, Singing, Flute, Netball & Swimming; [pets] 2 Rabbits & 2 Fish; [ambition] To write & be good at music;

BAKER, JOSHUA: [b] 24/3/92 Croydon; [home] Ivybridge, Devon; [p] Janet & Mac; [sister] Annie; [school] Stowford Primary; [fav sub] Maths; [hobbies] Horse Riding, Football & Swimming; [pets] Cat (Millie); [ambition] To become a Vet;

BAKER, MARTIN: [b] 18/10/85 Sheerness; [home] Sittingbourne, Kent; [p] Mark & Carolyn; [sisters] Nicola, Beverley & Lindsay; [school] Borden Grammar; [fav sub] All; [hobbies] Football, Tennis, Snooker & Golf; [pets] Dog (Boz); [ambition] To be rich and famous;

BALL, ADRIAN CONRAD BLANCHET: [b] 26/3/93 London; [home] Beckenham, Kent; [p] John Ball & Lisette Blanchet-Ball; [school] St Mary's R.C. Primary; [fav sub] Maths; [hobbies] All Sports, Cello & Singing; [ambition] To be a Comedian;

BALL, STEPHANIE: [b] 15/4/87 Burnley; [home] Burnley, Lancs; [p] Jane & Glynn; [brothers] Jonathan & Sam; [school] Gawthorpe High; [fav sub] Geography; [hobbies] Riding; [pets] Horse (Beau); [ambition] To be a Show Jumper;

BANKS, CALLI CHRISTINE: [b] 30/7/92 Gloucester; [home] Gloucester, Glos; [p] Joanne & Steven; [brothers] Aaron & Brandon; [school] Fieldcourt Junior; [fav sub] Maths; [hobbies] Swimming; [ambition] To be a Teacher or a Nurse;

BARBER, DANIELLE: [b] 1/8/91 Welwyn Garden City; [home] Blackmore End, Herts; [p] Tim & Wendy; [brother] Luke; [school] St Nicholas CE VA Primary; [fav sub] English; [hobbies] Dancing, Swimming & Skating; [ambition] To be an Author or Actress and believer in God;

BARDELL, FREYA S.I.: [b] 6/11/91 Wycombe; [home] Little Chalfont, Bucks; [p] Lesley Bardell & Brian Street; [brother] Lucas (12); [sister] Sappho (6); [school] Little Chalfont; [fav sub] Drama; [hobbies] Drama/Theatre; [pets] Guinea Pigs, Budgies, Lizard, Dog, Fish, Rabbits & Quails; [ambition] To be a famous and successful Actress;

BARIMANI, BARDIA: [b] 15/7/90 Aaruhus, Denmark; [p] Afson Ferdosmakan & Manouchehr Barimani; [brother] Rozbeh; [school] Great Chart Primary; [fav sub] Mathematics; [hobbies] Books & Football; [ambition] To be a Computer Programmer;

BARKER, MITCHELL, GEORGE: [b] 26/4/91 Basingstoke; [home] Basingstoke, Hants; [p] David & Lesley; [brothers] Dennis, Craig, Michael & Jack; [school] Merton Junior; [fav sub] D.T. & Art; [hobbies] Computers & Games; [pets] 3 Cats; [ambition] To work with Computers;

BARMBY, GEMMA: [b] 1/4/91 Rintlen, Germany; [home] Tidworth, Wilts; [p] Karen & John; [school] Zouch Primary; [fav sub] Maths; [hobbies] Karate (Brownbelt) Reading, Basketball, Football, Swimming & Computers; [pets] Guinea Pig (Monty); [ambition] To be a Cartoonist or an RSPCA Inspector;

BARNES, RICHARD JAMES: [b] 24/7/92 Rawtenstall; [home] Rawtenstall, Lancs; [p] David & Margaret; [brother] Steven; [school] Constable Lee St Pauls; [fav sub] Art; [hobbies] Cycling, Cub Scouts; [pets] Cat (Print) & 2 Fish; [ambition] To get as many cub badges as possible and to be a short story writer;

BARNETT, MARCUS: [b] Preston; [home] Chorley, Lancs; [p] Ann & Steve; [school] Euxton C of E; [fav sub] History; [hobbies] Playing Out; [pets] 2 Cats (Virago & Bart); [ambition] To get one of my Band's songs on the Radio;

BARRY, GEMMA: [b] 13/5/90 London; [home] Norbury, London; [p] Peter & Teresa; [brother] Shaun; [sister] Sinéad; [school] St James the Great; [fav sub] Maths; [hobbies] Netball & Football; [ambition] To travel around the world;

BARTLETT, ABIGAIL: [b] 3/11/89 Salisbury; [home] Salisbury, Wilts; [p] Sarah & Chris Page; [brother] William Page; [school] Sarum St Pauls; [fav sub] Maths; [hobbies] Horse Riding; [pets] Guinea Pigs & Fish; [ambition] To meet Robbie Williams;

BARTON, MICHAEL: [b] 14/1/92 Gloucester; [home] Gloucester, Glos; [p] Elizabeth & Clive; [brothers] David & Richard; [school] Field Court Junior; [fav sub] D.T., Science & English; [hobbies] Inline Skating & Hockey; [pets] 2 Cats & Fish; [ambition] To work for one of the Emergency Services;

BATCHELOR, TOM: [b] 18/11/89 Hillingdon; [home] Bournemouth, Dorset; [p] Tina & Martin; [brothers] David & Sam; [school] St Michael's Middle; [fav sub] IT; [hobbies] Windsurfing, Cycling & Swimming; [pets] 3 Guinea Pigs; [ambition] To become a Doctor;

BEALES, FELICITY: [b] 12/12/88 Norwich; [home] Hethersett, Norfolk; [p] Vanessa Loughlin & Nicholas Beales; [sisters] Isobel, Ellie & Sophie; [school] South Hartford Middle; [fav sub] Art; [hobbies] Horse Riding; [pets] Horse (Kira) & Rabbit (Freckles);

BEARD, JACK: [b] 24/8/94 London; [home] Penn, Bucks; [p] Jeremy & Emer; [brothers] Charlie & Danny; [school] Davenies; [fav sub] Sport; [hobbies] Football; [ambition] To become a professional Sportsman or Sports Commentator;

BEDDOE, KEREN LOUISE:[b] 2/3/91 Ronkswood; [home] Bewdley, Worcs; [p] Louise & Michael; [brother] Sean; [school] St Annes Middle; [fav sub] French; [hobbies] Reading, Swimming & Brownies; [pets] Cat, Guinea Pig & Fish; [ambition] To become an Author of childrens books;

BEDDOW, KERRY: [b] 3/12/91 Southampton; [home] New Milton, Hants; [p] Debra & Lee; [brothers] Matthew & Lewis; [sister] Laura; [school] New Milton Junior; [fav sub] Maths, Literacy & PE; [hobbies] Swimming, Riding my bicycle & scooter; [ambition] To be a Vet;

BELLERBY, EMMA: [b] 19/5/93 [home] Seapalling, Norfolk; [p] Lesley & Eddie; [brother] Samuel; [school] Hickling VC First; [fav sub] English & Maths; [hobbies] Reading & Swimming; [ambition] To become a Teacher;

BELLRINGER, EMMA LOUISE: [b] 28/11/89 Taunton; [home] Taunton, Somerset; [p] Jacqueline; [school] Halcon Community Primary; [fav sub] English & Science; [hobbies] Netball; [pets] Cockatiel; [ambition] To become a Writer;

BELSEY, ANNA: [b] 10/3/91 Margate; [home] Broadstairs, Kent; [p] Mary Ann; [sister] Jenny; [school] Bromstone Primary; [fav sub] English & Art; [hobbies] Clarinet, Church Choir & Swimming; [pets] Budgie (Pete); [ambition] To visit Australia and to drive a Mercedes;

BENJAMIN, TUI: [b] 25/4/91 Sheffield; [home] Hartford, Cheshire; [p] Dorothy & Philip; [sister] Elin; [school] Hartford Primary; [fav sub] English; [hobbies] Swimming & Writing Poetry; [ambition] To become a famous Poet;

BERRY, CHRISTOPHER: [b] 15/11/85 Farnborough; [home] Cove, Hants; [p] Paul & Sandy; [sister] Katie; [school] All Hallows RC; [fav sub] English & History; [hobbies] Poetry, Fiction Writing & Music; [pets] 2 Rough Collies; [ambition] To work in Law and be a part time Writer;

BERRY, JADE: [b] 16/3/91 Poole; [home] Evercreech, Somerset; [p] Dee & Phillip; [brothers] Nathan & Kieren; [sisters] Xenia & Savannah; [school] Upton Noble C of E VC Primary; [fav sub] Maths; [hobbies] Ballet, Violin, Dancing, Acting; [ambition] To be a Musician, a Ballet Dancer or an Actor;

BERRY, JASON: [b] 21/11/88 Banbury; [home] Banbury, Oxon; [p] Simon & Jackie;

[sister] Abigail; [school] Blessed George Napier; [fav sub] History; [hobbies] Football & Sport; [pets] Dogs & Cats;

BERRYMAN, LIAM: [b] 27/5/93 Worcester; [home] Evesham, Worcs; [p] Ian & Alison; [sister] Charlotte; [school] Swan Lane First; [fav sub] Maths; [hobbies] Football & Swimming; [pets] Dog (Copper); [ambition] To play football for West Brom;

BEVAN, ZOE REBECCA: [b] 2/7/87 Cheltenham; [home] Alderton, Glos; [p] Julian & Shelly; [brother] Toby (10); [school] Winchcombe; [fav sub] Drama; [hobbies] Horse Riding & Cycling; [pets] Cat (Charlie), Tortoise (Sam) & Rabbit (Bunny); [ambition] To be a Show Jumper and to work with horses;

BHATT, ASHIKA: [b] 10/1/94 Wembley; [home] Hemel Hempstead, Herts; [p] Sanjay & Priti; [brother] Vishal; [sister] Shalini; [school] Aycliffe Drive JMI; [fav sub] Science; [hobbies] Swimming, Reading & Skipping; [ambition] To be a Teacher;

BICKERSTAFF, SAM: [b] 17/12/89 Stevenage; [home] Stevenage, Herts; [p] Tom & Nicole; [brother] Alex; [school] Peartree Spring Junior; [fav sub] P.E.; [hobbies] Football, Swimming & Golf; [pets] 2 Dogs & 1 Cat; [ambition] To be a famous Footballer;

BINNEE, LAURA: [b] 27/7/92 High Wycombe; [home] Thame, Oxon; [p] Martin & Mandy; [brother] Ryan; [school] John Hampden Primary; [fav sub] Maths; [hobbies] Roller Blading & Trampolining; [pets] My Brother!; [ambition] To become a Model;

BINNINGTON BARRETT, VICTORIA MORGAN: [b] 3/9/89 Ipswich; [home] Ipswich, Suffolk; [p] Sharon Elizabeth & Kevin Raymond Barrett; [school] Downing Primary; [fav sub] English, Maths & Art; [hobbies] Violin, Swimming & Sports; [pets] Rabbit & Goldfish; [ambition] To be a Popstar, Violinist or Artist;

BLACKER, AMY: [b] 10/10/93 Bath; [home] Melksham, Wilts; [p] Glen & Kerry; [brother] Samuel; [school] Forest & Sandridge; [fav sub] English & PE; [hobbies] Gymnastics & Reading; [pets] 2 Rabbits (Button & April) & 2 Cats (Squiggles & Norman); [ambition] To be a Nursery School Teacher or Dolphin Trainer;

BLACKMORE, ELLIE: [b] 3/6/91 Taunton; [home] Taunton, Somerset; [p] Beverley & Ross; [brothers] Sean & Callum; [sisters] Carly, Georgia & Daisy; [school] Thurlbear V.A. Primary; [fav sub] Music; [hobbies] Dancing; [ambition] To be a Vet;

BLANKLEY, ELISSA: [b] 22/5/93 Farnham; [p] Ken & Sadie; [brothers] Ben & Richard; [school] St Peters; [fav sub]

Geography & History; [hobbies] Reading & Brownies; [pets] Cat (Cocoa); [ambition] To be a Vet or run a Cattery;

BLAYER, JOE: [b] 2/2/89 Ashford; [home] Staines, Middx; [p] Jane & Howard; [brother] Sam; [school] The Magna Carta School; [hobbies] Skateboarding & Keyboard; [ambition] To be a professional Musician;

BLITZ, JAMIE: [b] 18/7/89 London; [home] Blandford Forum, Dorset; [p] John & Gill; [sister] Maddy; [school] Milldown Middle; [fav sub] IT; [hobbies] Trampoline, Archery & Computers; [pets] Cat (Clyde) Guinea Pigs (Blizzard & Pepper); [ambition] To work in ICT;

BOGOOD, ISI: [b] 22/4/94 London; [home] London; [brother] Dylan; [sister] Daisy; [school] Belmont Primary; [hobbies] Reading, Swimming & Writing;

BOLTON, DANIEL ALAN JOHN: [b] 5/10/90 Poole; [home] Wimborne, Dorset; [p] Ken & Jan; [brothers] Will & Matt; [sisters] Emma & Lauren; [school] St Michaels Middle; [fav sub] Maths; [hobbies] Football & Rugby; [pets] Dog (Scamp) & Fish; [ambition] To be a professional Footballer;

BOLTON, MADISON JANE: [b] 15/12/90 Rayleigh; [home] Rayleigh, Essex; [p] Mark & Debby; [sister] Paige; [school] Down Hall Primary; [fav sub] Science; [hobbies] Takes an active role in Whale & Dolphin Conservation; [pets] Dog (Millie) & Rabbit (Ben); [ambition] To be a Marine Biologist;

BOLTON, OLLIE: [b] 18/5/91 High Wycombe; [home] Amersham, Bucks; [p] Joanne & Gareth; [sister] Emma; [school] Little Chalfont Combined; [fav sub] Art & Maths; [hobbies] Tennis, Football, Snooker & Playstation; [pets] Dog (Drum) & Cat (Meg); [ambition] To travel round the world;

BOND, EMILY VICTORIA: [b] 29/6/90 Birmingham; [home] Bromsgrove, Worcs; [p] Jane & Michael; [sister] Laura; [school] Aston Fields Middle; [fav sub] English; [hobbies] Swimming, Reading & Writing; [pets] Tropical Fish; [ambition] To become a Vet or a Barrister;

BOND, JOSEPH: [b] 22/8/90 Pembury; [home] Hever, Kent; [p] Stephen & Deborah; [sister] Rachel; [school] Chiddingstone CE; [fav sub] Science; [hobbies] Cricket, WW11 & Riding; [pets] 3 Dogs, Cat & 2 Hamsters; [ambition] To become an RAF Pilot;

BOOTH, NATHAN [b] 10/12/92 Welwyn Garden City; [home] Ware, Herts; [p] Tom & Gill; [sisters] Charlotte (4) & Molly (1½); [school] Christ Church; [fav sub] Maths; [hobbies] Bionicles, Lego & Playstation; [pets] Cat (Mattie); [ambition] To be an Astronaut;

BOUD, YAZZY: [b] 30/11/89 Fareham;

[home] Stubbington, Hants; [p] Debbie & Gary; [brothers] Jordan & Wayne; [school] Crofton Hammond; [fav sub] Singing; [hobbies] Playing Keyboard &Trombone; [pets] 7 Cats & 1 Dog; [ambition] To act in Eastenders & write more poems;

BOULTON, ALEX: [b] 21/9/88 Nr. Chippenham; [home] Thickwood Colerne, Wilts; [p] Cathrine & Jeremy; [brothers] Michael & Edward; [school] Corsham; [fav sub] English; [hobbies] Basketball & Horse Riding; [pets] Dog (Bramwell), Cat (Polish) & 2 Fish; [ambition] To become a Primary School Teacher or an English Teacher;

BOWERS, RICKY: [b] 17/12/87 Colchester; [home] Thetford, Norfolk; [p] Mark & Michell; [brother] Luke; [sister] Samantha; [school] Breckland Middle; [fav sub] P.E.; [hobbies] Fishing & Football; [ambition] To become a Footballer;

BOWTLE, TERRY: [b] 1/4/89 Chelmsford; [home] Chelmsford, Essex; [p] Mr & Mrs Bowtle; [brother] Desmond; [sister] Heather; [school] Hayward; [fav sub] Art & Woodwork; [hobbies] Football & Riding; [pets] Birds & Fish; [ambition] To write poetry;

BOYLE, ELEANOR: [b] 7/10/92 London; [home] Sydenham, London; [p] Joe & Geraldine; [brother] James; [school] St Mary's R.C.; [fav sub] English; [hobbies] Swimming, Drawing & Reading; [pets] Cat (Paddy); [ambition] To become a Vet;

BRADLEY, HOLLIE: [b] 7/10/88 Bromsgrove; [home] Bromsgrove, Worcs; [p] Teresa; [school] Aston Fields Middle; [fav sub] P.E. [hobbies] Swimming, Writing Poems; [pets] Gerbils (Salt & Pepper); [ambition] To be a Teacher, Writer, or a Spy!

BRADLEY, LAURA: [b] 24/12/92 Worcester; [home] Aylesbury, Bucks; [p] Paula & Jerry; [brother] Matthew; [school] William Harding Combined; [fav sub] Numeracy; [hobbies] Bowling, Biking, Drawing, Computers & playing with friends; [pets] Dog (Molly), Guinea Pigs (Silver Star & Rodney); [ambition] To go to College and learn about Art or Animals;

BRANCH, JULIA: [b] 3/9/87 Cambridge; [home] Haslingfield, Cambs; [p] Bob & Christine; [brother] Edward; [sister] Maria; [school] St Bede's Cambridge; [fav sub] History; [hobbies] Music, Reading, Travel, Singing, Guides & Birds; [pets] Hamster; [ambition] To travel, Act or become an Astronaut or Nurse;

BRECKON, KAYLEIGH JAYNE: [b] 15/9/89 Southampton; [home] New Milton, Hants; [p] Caroline & Leslie; [school] New Milton Junior; [fav sub] Physical Education; [hobbies] Dancing (Ballet) & Gymnastics; [pets] Cat (Pip); [ambition] To be an Actor or Dancer;

BREWSTER, STEPHEN: [b] 14/1/88 Tooting; [home] Mitcham, Surrey; [p] John Brewster & Phyllis Welford; [sister] Sasha; [school] Bishopsford Community; [fav sub] ICT & PE; [hobbies] Ice Skating & Computers; [pets] 2 Cats & 1 Rabbit; [ambition] To become a computer expert;

BRIERLEY, KATIE ELIZABETH LOUISE: [b] 15/4/92 Gloucester; [home] Quedgeley, Glos; [p] Michelle & Stewart; [brothers] Robert & Carl; [school] Fieldcourt Junior; [fav sub] Science; [hobbies] Singing, Drawing & Running; [pets] Hamster, Cat & Fish;[ambition] To be an Archaeologist and own a German Shepherd;

BRIGGS, JAMES: [b] 20/7/89 Chester; [home] Mickle Trafford, Cheshire; [p] Joanne & Gary; [brothers] Tom & Luke; [school] Upton-by-Chester; [fav sub] Design Technology; [hobbies] Ski-ing; [pets] Cat (Mitzi); [ambition] To be an Airline Pilot;

BROAD, FREDDIE JAMES: [b] 5/12/90 Bough Beech; [home] Bough Beech, Kent; [p] Maggie & John; [brother] Lewis; [sisters] Katie, Gemma, Megan + cousin Sophia; [school] Chiddingstone C.E.V.C. Primary; [fav sub] Science; [hobbies] Catching snakes & lizards + playing the trombone; [pets] Horse, Chinchilla & Cat; [ambition] To be a famous Rugby Player;

BROCK, RACHEL VICTORIA: [b] 16/1/89 Sint Niklaas, Belgium; [home] Alsager, Staffs; [p] Melanie & Michael; [sister] Megan; [school] Alsager School; [fav sub] English; [hobbies] Reading & Painting; [pets] Cat (Atkinson), Hamster (Squeaky); [ambition] To work with animals;

BROCKLESBY, JOSHUA PETER: [b] 11/10/89 High Wycombe; [home] Little Chalfont, Bucks; [p] Ian & Anna-Kay; [brothers] Benjamin, Matthew & Nathan; [school] Little Chalfont Combined; [fav sub] History; [hobbies] Sports, Reading; [pets] Cats (Aui, Marco & Ziggy); [ambition] To go into Politics;

BROCKLESBY-MILLARD, LENNY: [b] 25/8/90 Ashford, Middx; [home] Sunbury, Middx; [p] Sharon & David; [brother] Jake; [school] Springfield Primary; [fav sub] Sport; [hobbies] Football, Computers & Music; [ambition[To be a Football Manager;

BROOKER, SAMANTHA: [b] 20/12/91 Plymouth; [home] Reading, Berks; [p] Prudence & Nicholas; [sisters] Perdita, Catherine & Diana; [school] Bearwood; [fav sub] Maths; [hobbies] Swimming; [pets] Cats; [ambition] Haven't decided;

BROUGH, JAMES WALLACE: [b] 13/11/89 Barking; [home] Theydon Bois, Essex; [p] Trevor & Suzanne; [brother] Joseph; [sister] Louise; [school] Theydon Bois Primary; [fav sub] English & PE; [hob-

bies] Football, Tennis, Golf, Swimming & Piano; [pets] Cat (Puddikins); [ambition] To play football for Manchester United FC;

BROWN, ANDREW DAVID: [b] 30/1/90 Blackpool; [home] Thornton, Lancs; [p] Yvonne & Don; [brother] Christopher; [school] Manor Beach Primary; [fav sub] Mathematics & English; [hobbies] Football & Cricket; [ambition] To obtain a place at Oxford University;

BROWN, DANIEL: [b] 19/8/92 Colchester; [home] Tollesbury, Essex; [p] Lorraine & Paul; [sister] Abigail; [school] Birch C of E Primary; [fav sub] Maths; [hobbies] Swimming; [pets] Rabbit (Misty); [ambition] To become a Fireman or a Pilot;

BROWN, HARRY ROBERT: [b] 5/5/90 Stevenage; [home] Stevenage, Herts; [p] Mark & Lynda; [sister] Rebecca; [school] Peartree Spring Junior; [fav sub] Maths; [hobbies] Computers & Football; [pets] Cat, Dog & 2 Fish; [ambition] To be an Author;

BROWN, HENRY JOHN: [b] 1/6/91 London; [home] Chiswick, London; [p] Catherine & John; [brother] Guy Alexander; [sister] Isobel; [school] Belmont; [fav sub] Maths; [hobbies] Football & Drawing; [ambition] To be a Footballer;

BROWN, NEIL: [b] 18/1/91 Upton; [home] Little Chalfont, Bucks; [brother] Craig; [school] Little Chalfont County Combined; [fav sub] Maths & DT; [hobbies] Drawing Cartoons; [ambition] To be a cartoonist;

BROWN, SARAH BRYONY: [b] 26/8/90 London; [home] Radlett, Herts; [p] Ruth & Neil; [sisters] Alice & Clare; [school] Newberries Primary; [fav sub] Design Technology; [hobbies] Horse Riding, Ballet, Piano; [pets] None, but I would like a Pony; [ambition] To own a horse, to learn to use a Potters Wheel and to live and work with Horses;

BROWN, SIÂN: [b] 15/12/93 Eastbourne; [home] Eastbourne, East Sussex; [p] Alison & Colin; [brother] Zack; [fav sub] English; [hobbies] Pokémon & Reading; [ambition] To be successful;

BROWNING, LAURA AMY: [b] 12/5/92 Canterbury; [home] Whitstable, Kent; [p] David & Alison; [sisters] Hayley & Sarah; [school] Joy Lane Junior; [fav sub] Maths & PE; [hobbies] Dancing; [pets] Dog, 2 Guinea Pigs & Budgies; [ambition] To become a Vet;

BRUNSDON,CRAIG: [b]17/10/89 Quedgeley; [home] Gloucetser, Glos; [p] Lloyd & Jackie; [brother] Thomas; [sister] Hayley; [school] Field Court Junior SCI; [fav sub] Maths & P.E. [hobbies] Football; [pets] Cat (Jiggy); [ambition] To be a Footballer, Author or Accountant;

BRYAN, DANIEL: [b] 30/8/91 Epping; [home] Theydon Bois, Essex; [p] Anne-Marie & Christopher; [brother] Stephen; [school] Theydon Bois; [fav sub] Maths; [hobbies] Football; [pets] Dog; [ambition] To be great Footballer;

BRYANT, ADAM: [b] 21/6/92 Oxford; [home] Thame, Oxon; [p] Eileen & Andy; [brother] Sean; [school] John Hampden CP; [fav sub] History; [hobbies] Model Railways, Battles with Knights & Bowmen; [pets] Guinea Pig (Biscuit), Budgie (Cheekie) & Goldfish; [ambition] To own a Steam Train;

BUCK, MICHAEL PHILIP: [b] 7/10/93 Chesterfield; [home] Hollingwood, Derbyshire; [p] Stephen & Judy; [brother] Robert; [sister] Michelle; [school] Hollingwood Primary; [fav sub] History; [hobbies] Cricket & Pokemon Cards; [pets] Cat, Rabbit & Guinea Pig; [ambition] To join the Army;

BUCKINGHAM, GEORGE: [b] 20/1/89 Chertsey; [home] Staines, Middx; [p] Steve & Jill; [sister] Chelsea; [school] Magna Carta; [fav sub] I.T.; [hobbies] Computers & Golf; [pets] Cats; [ambition] To design Computer Games;

BULL, SAM: [b] 1/10/91 London; [home] Hampton, Middx; [p] Sally & Stuart; [brothers] James, Nick & Adam; [school] Bishop Perrin C of E; [fav sub] Geography; [hobbies] Football & Cricket; [pets] 1 Dog & 3 Cats; [ambition] To live until I'm 100!

BULLARD, RIA: [b] 29/12/84 Essex; [home] Shirrell Heath, Hants; [p] Andrew & Maggie; [brother] Ross; [school] Swanmore Secondary; [fav sub] Drama; [hobbies] Singing; [pets] 2 Dogs & a Rabbit; [ambition] To make it to Hollywood!!

BULLOCK, ANDREW: [b] 15/7/90 Gloucester; [home] Quedgeley, Glos; [p] Michael & Donna; [brother] Stuart; [school] Field Court Junior; [hobbies] Football; [pets] Cats (Meowth & Maisy);

BULLOCK, GEMMA: [b] 30/9/88 Gloucester; [home] Bromsgrove, Worcs; [p] Ruth & Andy Bullock + Step Dad John Walker; [brother] Jordan (6); [school] Aston Fields Middle; [fav sub] Sports; [hobbies] Guides; [pets] Dog, Hamster, Fish, Frogs & Chickens; [ambition] To become a Children's Nurse;

BUNDOCK, DANIEL: [b] 8/3/88 Canterbury; [home] Bridge, Kent; [p] Malcolm & Jan; [brother] Jonathan; [sister] Emma; [school] St. Anselm's School;

BUNN, MARTIN: [b] 17/3/89 Wordsley; [home] Bromsgrove, Worcs; [p] Stephen & Jo; [brother] Paul; [school] Aston Fields Middle; [fav sub] English & Games; [hobbies] Rugby, Cricket & Reading; [pets] Black Dog called Jet; [ambition] To become a professional Sportsman & run my own Business;

BURCH, AIMÈE ROSE: [b] 25/8/92 Aylesbury; [home] Aylesbury, Bucks; [p] Aliosn & Adrian; [brother] Jamie; [school] William Harding Combined; [fav sub] Literacy; [hobbies] Reading & Swimming; [pets] Rabbit (Charcoal); [ambition] To become a Teacher;

BURGE, CHRISTOPHER: [b] 8/10/90 Watford; [home] Watford, Herts; [p] Stephen & Susan; [brother] Jason; [school] Kingsway Junior; [fav sub] I.C.T.; [hobbies] Sailing, Football & Tennis; [pets] Rabbit (Basil); [ambition] To join the Navy;

BURGESS, CLAIRE: [b] 26/12/90 Wantage; [home] Grove, Oxon; [p] Joanne; [brother] Ryan; [sister] Nicola; [school] Millbrook Primary; [fav sub] Art & Maths; [hobbies] Reading & Swimming; [ambition] To be a Dancer or Singer;

BURR, DANIEL: [b] 20/9/89 Redhill; [home] Merstham, Surrey; [p] Beverley & Martin; [brothers] Nick, Russ & Christopher; [school] Merstham Primary; [fav sub] Drama & English; [hobbies] Acting, Dancing, Singing & Trampolining; [pets] Cat (Trixie) & Tropical Fish; [ambition] To be a famous Actor;

BURROWS, PATRICK: [b] 23/1/92 Southampton; [home] New Milton, Hants; [p] Beverley & Steve; [brother] Tom; [school] New Milton Junior; [fav sub] Science; [hobbies] Football & Bikes; [pets] 6 Guinea Pigs and a Rabbit; [ambition] To be really good at Football and to own a Motorbike;

BURT, DUSTIN: [b] 12/12/91 Bulawayo, Zimbabwe; [home] Hardwicke, Glos; [p] Brian & Marcelle; [brother] Jason; [school] Field Court Junior; [fav sub] Science; [hobbies] Football & Art; [pets] 2 Dogs; [ambition] To become an Artist or Pilot;

BYRNE STEVENS, HELENA: [b] 18/11/92 Oxford; [home] Bledlow Ridge, Bucks; [p] Liz & Richard; [sister] Annie (10); [school] John Hampden Primary; [fav sub] Games; [hobbies] Horse Riding & Swimming; [pets] Black Labrador (Luna); 2 Guinea Pigs, Cat (Twinkle); [ambition] To be a Pop Singer, Teacher or an Actress;

CACHIA, ALEX: [b] 20/12/89 Enfield; [home] Cheshunt, Herts; [p] Linda & John; [sister] Sophie; [school] Bonneygrove CP; [fav sub] Maths, PE, Poetry; [hobbies] Football, Gameboy & Running; [pets] Dog, Hamster, Budgie; [ambition] To be a Footballer;

CALLAGHAN, EMILY: [b] 14/11/91; Southampton; [home] New Milton, Southampton; [p] Tom & Sharon; [brother] Thomas; [school] New Milton Junior; [fav sub] Art & Maths; [hobbies] Swimming & Cycling; [pets] Rabbit (Flopsy); [ambition] To work in a Bank;

CAMERON, GEORGINA: [b] 28/9/89 Harpenden; [home] Harpenden, Herts; [p] Jocelin & Colin; [brother] Stuart; [sister] Louise; [school] St Nicholas; [fav sub] P.E.; [hobbies] Dance, Drama & Flute; [pets] Cats (Tom & Lizzie) & Hamster (Hanky); [ambition] To become a professional Dancer;

CAMERON, ROSS: [b] 19/1/92 Dover; [home] Canterbury, Kent; [p] Ron & Wendy; [brother] Dominic; [school] St Thomas's R.C.; [fav sub] Science; [hobbies] Acting & Singing; [ambition] To be a Singer or Actor;

CAMPBELL, CHRIS: [b] 12/9/91 Bristol; [home] New Milton, Hants; [p] Paul & Mel; [brother] Nick; [sister] Issy; [school] New Milton Junior; [fav sub] Maths; [hobbies] Rugby, Football & Swimming; [ambition] To become a famous Sportsman;

CANNELL, OLIVER: [b] 9/9/89 King's Lynn; [home] South Wootton, Norfolk; [p] David & Lorraine; [school] South Wootton Junior; [fav sub] English; [hobbies] Speedway & Cricket; [pets] Cocker Spaniel (Barney) & Siamese Cat (Sassy); [ambition] To be a Journalist or BBC Correspondent;

CARNEY, JAKE ALAN: [b] 30/3/89 Tiverton; [home] Tiverton, Devon; [p] Ena & Laurence; [brother] Jason; [sister] Kirsty; [school] Cullompton Community College; [fav sub] I.C.T; [hobbies] Football, Tennis, Music & Snooker; [ambition] To be successful in whatever I do;

CARPANINI, STEPHANIE LOUISE: [b] 7/5/90 Burnley; [home] Burnley, Lancs; [p] Mr & Mrs S.J. Carpanini; [sister] Joanne Marie; [school] St Hilda's RC Girls High; [fav sub] English & Geography; [hobbies] Reading, Drama & Swimming; [pets] Hamster; [ambition] To be a Vet or a Journalist;

CARPENTER, EMMA: [b] 1/7/91 Queensland, Australia; [home] Ramsgate, Kent; [p] Michael & Lorna; [school] Bromstone CP; [fav sub] English & Art; [hobbies] Writing & Artwork; [pets] Spice the Rozella; [ambition] To join the Police Force or become an Art Teacher;

CARTER, JOSEPHINE MARIE: [b] 17/9/92 Salisbury; [home] Tilshead, Wilts; [p] Pat & Becky; [brother] Alex; [sisters] Tess & Mimi; [school] St Thomas à Becket; [fav sub] Art; [hobbies] Drawing & Piano; [pets] Rabbit, Dog, Cat & Gerbil; [ambition] To become a Writer or a Poet;

CARTER, RICHARD: [b] 12/7/91 Chertsey; [home] Poringland, Norfolk; [p] Trevor & Sarah; [sister] Emily; [school] Poringland CP; [fav sub] Literacy; [hobbies] BMX, Football, Grass Cutting; [pets] Rabbit, Hamster & Fish; [ambition] To become the BMX Freestyle Champion and a famous Electric Guitarist;

CARTER, SARA: [b] 31/12/84 Winchester; [home] Bishops Waltham, Hants; [p] Robert & Monica; [brothers] Sean & Joseph; [sister] Anna; [school] Swanmore Secondary; [fav sub] Drama; [hobbies] Dancing;

CATNACH, VICKY: [b] 17/8/90 Peterborough; [home] March, Cambs; [p] Debbie & Jim; [brother] David; [school] All Saints Primary; [fav sub] Art; [hobbies] Drawing; [pets] Dogs, Fish & 2 Cats; [ambition] To be a Primary Teacher, teaching Year 1;

CATT, STACEY: [b] 27/3/90 Frimley; [home] Farnham, Surrey; [p] Stephen & Lynn; [sister] Keely; [school] Pilgrims Way; [fav sub] Maths & English; [hobbies] Dancing & Singing; [ambition] To enjoy anything I turn my hand to;

CAUFIELD, ROBYN: [b] 28/5/90 Oxford; [home] Wroxton, Oxon; [p] C. Ansell & P. Caufield; [brother] Benjamin Ansell; [sister] Charley Caufield; [school] Wroxton CP; [fav sub] Art; [hobbies] Reading & Swimming; [pets] Dog; [ambition] To be an Artist or Poet, or Author;

CAULKETT, JOSEPHINE: [b] 2/8/90 Cambridge; [home] Cambs; [school] All Saints Inter-Church; [fav sub]; Art; [hobbies] Drawing, Swimming & Music; [petes] Rabbit (Jolly); [ambition] To be a famous Graphic Designer;

CAULTON, LAURENCE: [b] 11/5/90 St Albans; [home] Radlett, Herts; [p] Jeremy & Tammy; [brother] Maxwell; [school] Newberries; [fav sub] Art; [hobbies] Computer Games & Skate Boarding; [pets] Dog & Cat; [ambition] To live in America and be a professional Skate Boarder;

CAWLEY, LAURA JANE: [b] 19/6/90 Blacksod, Co. Mayo; [home] Thornton Heath, Surrey; [p] Shannon & Gerald; [brother] Niall; [sister] Erin; [school] St James The Great; [fav sub] ICT & Maths; [hobbies] Dancing, Drama & Rounders; [pets] Dog (Sandy); [ambition] To become a Policewoman and to dance more;

CHAÏR, IRWIN-MALEK: [b] 30/3/89 High Wycombe;[home] Seer Green, Bucks; [p] Rosemary & Nabil; [school] Davenies; [fav sub] English & Maths; [hobbies] Travel & Writing Stories; [pets] I used to have a Spaniel called Sacha, but she died when she was 11 years old; [ambition] To go back to live in Rome, where I lived for 3 years;

CHAMBERLIN, NIAMH: [b] 25/7/92 London; [home] Haworth, W. Yorks; [p] Sarah & John; [school] Haworth Primary; [fav sub] English; [hobbies] Ballet, Tap, Drama & Music; [ambition] To be a Teacher and have lots of pets (animals!);

CHAMBERS, JEMMA: [b] 15/11/84 Tooting; [home] Mitcham, Surrey; [p] John & Jackie; [sisters] Donna (25) & Nikki (21); [school] Bishopsford Community; [fav sub] Drama & English; [hobbies] Singing, Dancing, Reading & Ice Hockey; [pets] Black & White Rabbit (Tipsy); [ambition] To be a Theatre Actress, or work within an area of Media and to be happy!;

CHAMBERS, MELI'SA: [b] 9/8/88 Newmarket; [home] Brandon, Suffolk; [p] Nicholas Chambers & Sandra Henry; [sister] Jasmin; [school] Breckland Middle; [fav sub] English & Music; [hobbies] Swimming & Cycling; [pets] Dog (Sherry); [ambition] To be a Singer;

CHANDLER, KATE: [b] 24/9/91 Bath; [home] Stoney Stratton, Somerset; [p] Sally & Gerry; [brothers] Jack & William; [sister] Lucy; [school] Upton Noble Primary; [fav sub] English; [hobbies] Crafts & Writing; [pets] 2 Rabbits & 2 Guinea Pigs; [ambition] To become an Author;

CHANTLER, ADAM: [b] 28/4/90 Enfield; [home] Cheshunt, Herts; [p] John & Jane; [brother] Steven; [sister] Victoria; [school] Bonneygrove CP; [fav sub] Science; [hobbies] Rugby; [pets] Gerbils; [ambition] To be a Policeman;

CHARLTON, GEMMA: [b] 28/7/85 Oxford; [home] Hazlemere, Bucks; [p] Mark & Janet; [brother] James; [school] The Arts Educational School, Tring; [Fav Sub] Drama [hobbies] Writing stories and poems; [pets] Loves Cats & Dogs; [ambition] To be an Actress, mainly in films;

CHARTERIS-BLACK, SARAH: [b] 14/5/91 Bandar Seri Begawan, Brunei; [home] Guildford, Surrey; [p] Jonathan Charteris-Black & Fadila Sqalli (Moroccan); [sister] Tanya; [school] Sandfield Primary; [fav sub] English; [hobbies] Writing & Piano; [ambition] To become an Author of childrens' books;

CHATFIELD, HARRIET: [b] 17/11/95 High Wycombe; [home] Thame, Oxon; [p] Andrew & Denise; [sister] Charlotte; [school] John Hampden Primary; [fav sub] Drawing & Counting; [hobbies] Ballet & Swimming; [ambition] To become a Dentist!

CHESSMAN, PAUL: [b] 3/10/89 King's Lynn; [home] Wisbech, Cambs; [p] Doreen & Martin; [sister] Alice; [school] The Gordon Fendick School; [fav sub] Maths; [hobbies] Stock Car Racing; [ambition] To be a Stock Car Racing Champion;

CHESTER, EMILY JAYNE: [b] 23/4/90 Worcester; [home] Offenham, Worcs; [p] Dilan & Julie; [sister] Jenny Louise; [school] Blackminster Middle; [fav sub] Art; [hobbies] Piano, Sports & Dancing; [pets] Budgies & Goldfish; [ambition] To swim with Dolphins;

CHESTERS, KELLY ROSE: [b] 2/6/88 London; [home] Belton, Norfolk; [p] Jacqueline & Terry; [brothers] Lee, Paul & Dean; [school] Lynn Grove High; [fav sub] English & Art; [hobbies] Drawing; [pets] Dog (Sophie); [ambition] To be a Designer;

CHEUNG, ROSALIE: [b] 31/10/92 Yeovil; [home] The Lizard, Cornwall; [p] Marianne & Colin; [sister] Chloe-Anne; [school] Landewednack CP; [fav sub] History; [hobbies] Ballet Dancing & Music; [pets] Budgies & Tropical Fish; [ambition] To become an Actress;

CHOWDHURY, SAKHAWATUL: [b] 24/7/90 Farnham; [home] Farnham, Surrey; [p] Fazlul & Shahanara; [brother] Sarwar; [sisters] Shakila & Uroosa; [school] The Pilgrims Way; [fav sub] Maths; [hobbies] Football & Computer Games; [pets] Fish; [ambition] To be a Footballer;

CHOWNS, DANNY GEORGE: [b] 1/10/92 Oxford; [home] Thame, Oxon; [p] Brett & Karina; [school] John Hampden Primary; [fav sub] English; [hobbies] Making things & Swimming; [pets] Rabbit (Flopsy); [ambition] To become an Author or Footballer;

CHRISTIAN, JESSICA BETH: [b] 10/6/92 Lymington; [home] New Milton, Hants; [p] Debbie Christian & Paul Rogers; [sister] Jennie; [school] New Milton Junior; [fav sub] Science; [hobbies] Swimming, Singing & Piano; [pets] Dog (Ollie); [ambition] To become a Veterinary Surgeon;

CHRUMKA, NICHOLAS: [b] 17/9/94 Farnborough, Kent; [home] Beckenham, Kent; [brother] Dominic; [school] St Mary's Catholic Primary; [fav sub] Art; [hobbies] Digging the garden & Football; [ambition] To be a Baker;

CHURCH, SAMUEL JAMES: [b] 21/12/91 Sutton; [home] Ivybridge, Devon; [p] Peter & Pauline; [brother] Mason Anthony; [school] Stowford Primary; [fav sub] I.T.; [hobbies] Football & Rugby; [pets] African Grey Parrot (Stumpy); [ambition] To be a Footballer or a Policeman;

CIRILLO, LOUISA: [b] 30/11/91 Aylesbury; [home] Aylesbury, Bucks; [p] Tracy & Luigi; brother] Luca; [school] William Harding Combined; [fav sub] English (Poetry); [hobbies] Football; [pets] Dog (Barney) & Cockatoo (Bella); [ambition] To be a Pop Star, or Policewoman, or Private Investigator;

CLANFORD, LUCY MAY: [b] 9/9/89 Shoreham-by-Sea, W. Sussex; [home] Sunbury-onn-Thames, Middx; [p] Gaynor & Calvin; [brother] Jared; [school] Springfield; [fav sub] Maths & Science; [hobbies] Karate, Pop Music & Swimming; [pets] Dog, 2 Fish & 4 Hamsters; [ambtion] To be a Vet and to write poetry for childrens books;

CLARK, ADAM: [b] 12/11/89 Rochford; [home] Rayleigh, Essex; [p] Chris & Jennie; [brother] Sam; [sister] Hayley; [school] Downhall Primary; [fav sub] English; [hobbies] Break Dancing & Football; [pets] Cat (Tabitha); [ambition] To write my own book of poems;

CLARK, ALEX: [b] 26/4/94 Perth, Australia; [home] Goffs Oak, Herts; [p] Susan & Chris; [school] Bonneygrove; [fav sub] Art; [hobbies] Drawing & making things; [ambition] To become a Vet;

CLARK, CHARLIE JON: [b] 27/01/92 Bexley; [home] Home; [p] Lynda & Wayne; [brother] Whyatt & Kieron; [school] Royston Primary; [fav sub] English, P.E. & Art; [hobbies] Judo, Sports & Doing Puzzles; [pets] 2 Dogs & Fish; [ambition] To be a Policeman or a Racing Driver;

CLARKE, AMY: [b] 11/9/91 Worcester; [home] Quedgeley, Glos; [p] Stephen & Kyla; [sisters] Becky & Katie; [school] Field Court Junior; [fav sub] Design & Technology; [hobbies] Brownies, Dancing & Swimming; [ambition] To go to College and become a Teacher;

CLARKE, CAMILLA H.R.: [b] 14/04/92 Swindon; [home] Pewsey, Wilts; [p] Elaine; [school] Oare C of E Primary; [fav sub] Art; [pets] Horses, Dogs, Cats, Rabbits & Fish;

CLAYTON, MICHAEL EDWARD: [b] 8/8/91 Harpenden; [home] Harpenden, Herts; Joanna & Ian; Maudsley; [sisters] Jennifer & Julia Clayton; [school] Crabtree Junior; [fav sub] Maths; [hobbies] Cycling, Football, & Reading; [pets] Hamster (Nibbles), Rabbits (Snowy & Bobbin); [ambition] To be a Policeman;

COHEN, SEAN: [b] 18/8/92 Reading; [home] Reading, Berks; [p] Ann & Steve; [sister] Stephanie; [school] Micklands Primary; [fav sub] Art; [hobbies] Sports; [pets] Rabbit (Jumpy); [ambition] To be a Sportsman;

COKER GORDON, NICOLA: [b] 2/3/91 London; [home] Berkhamsted, Herts; [p] Christina Coker & Stafford Gordon; [sister] Lauren; [school] Bridgewater Middle; [fav sub] Computers & Technology; [hobbies] Cello, Diving, Dancing, Singing, Swimming, Piano & Making things; [ambition] To work at a Sports Resort, be a Musician & an Artist;

COLE, ELIZABETH: [b] 26/1/90; [home] Middle Littleton, Worcs; [p] Gill & Ken; [school] Blackminster Middle; [fav sub] Art; [hobbies] Guides, Clarinet, Star Gazing; [pets] Hamster (Tiny); [ambition] To be an Interior Designer;

COLLINS, JESSAMINE "POPPY": [b] 26/7/93 King's Lynn; [home] Snettisham, Norfolk; [brother] Joshua; [school] Hunstanton First; [[fav sub] English; [hob-

bies] Reading, Gymnastics, Kung Fu, Writing & Art; [pets] None, but would love a Rabbit; [ambition] To become an Author, Vet, Artist or Teacher and to travel!

COLLINSON, MARK: [b] 3/4/90 Bury St Edmunds; [home] Santon Downham, Suffolk; [p] Carol & Martin; [sister] Louise; [school] Breckland Middle; [fav sub] PE; [hobbies] Play Station; [ambition] To do well at School;

COLLOP, ROSY: [b]26/5/91 Ponta Delgada; [home] Wadebridge, Cornwall; [p] Leaf & Steve; [brother] Jack, [sisters] Beatriz & Nina; [school] Wadebridge CP; [fav sub] Art & Creative Writing; [hobbies] Riding & Roller Skating; [pets] Dog (Jessie); [ambition] To become a Lawyer;

CONNELLY-WEBSTER, ROBYN: [b] 21/9/94 Bromley; [p] Beckenham, Kent; [p] Jim & Maureen; [brother] Max; [school] St Mary's R.C.; [fav sub] English & Music; [hobbies] Swimming, Scootering & Writing; [ambition] To be an Author;

CONNOLLY, ELISHA JO: [b] 24/8/91 Tiverton; [home] Witheridge, Devon; [p] Mic & Lynne; [brother] Liam; [school] East Worlington Primary; [fav sub] Maths; [hobbies] Cycling, Riding & my Pets; [pets] 5 Fish, Dog (Dulcie) & 4 Mice (Vodka, Houdini, Bracken & Nettle); [ambition] To be a Vet or animal rescue worker;

CONNOLLY, JACK: [b] 26/11/90 Redditch; [home] Bromsgrove, Worcs; [p] Tracey & Shaun; [sister] Holly; [school] Aston Fields Middle; [fav sub] History & Sports; [hobbies] Football; [pets] Bessie, Nanny's dog, 14 and a babe; [ambition] To play football for England and be a famous Actor;

COOKE, ESTHER: [b] 16/9/88 Redditch; [home] Cullompton, Devon; [sister] Rose; [school] Cullompton Community College; [hobbies] Playing Keyboard & Sport; [ambition] To be a Zoologist & live in a Mansion;

COOKE, THOMAS: [b] 6/3/90 Oxford; [home] Aston Rowant, Oxon; [p] Brian & Jean; [brother] Matthew; [sister] Jemma; [school] Aston Rowant CE Primary; [fav sub] English; [hobbies] Football & Running; [pets] Airdale Dog (Max); [ambition] To play for Manchester United;

COOMES, MICHAEL: [b] 26/6/90 Chertsey; [home] Walton-on-Thames, Surrey; [p] Chris & Gordon; [brothers] Paul & Simon; [school] Ambleside Junior; [fav sub] Maths; [hobbies] Reading & Drawing; [pets] 3 Cats (Amber, Button & Minnie); [ambition] To be an Artist;

COOPER, EMMA: [b] 1989 Peterborough; [home] March, Cambs; [p] Vicky Cooper & Ian; [brother] Daniel; [sister] Sarah; [school] All Saints; [fav sub] English; [hobbies] Dancing, Drama & TV; [pets] Dog (Sox) &

Fish; [ambition] To be an Actress/Dancer on TV & Stage;

CORBY, JADE ASHLEIGH: [b] 15/7/92 Canterbury; [home] Beltinge, Kent; [p] Elisabeth & Tim; [brother] Joe; [sister] Chloe; [school] Herne Juniors; [fav sub] Art; [hobbies] Swimming; [ambition] To be a Pop Star;

CORDELL, EMMA: [b] 26/8/94 Holmbury St Mary; [home] Shamley Green, Surrey; [p] Chris & Jacky; [brother] Nick; [school] Chilworth Infants; [fav sub] Writing; [hobbies] Cricket & Swimming; [pets] Gerbil; [ambition] To help animals and to be an Artist;

COTTLE, DORIAN: [b] 24/5/91 Bath; [home] Potterne, Wilts; [p] Karen & Andrew; [sister] Kalisha; [school] D.A.P.S.; [fav sub] Art, Technology & PE; [hobbies] Archery, Swimming & Football; [pets] Horse, 2 Dogs, Rats, Guinea Pigs & Rabbit; [ambition] To become a skilled Archer;

COTTRELL, BENJAMIN DIETER: [b] 15/2/93 High Wycombe; [home] Amersham, Bucks; [p] Virginia & Dieter; [brother] Thomas William; [school] Little Chalfont County Combined; [fav sub] Maths; [hobbies] Piano & Football; [pets] Dogs (Tansi & Ruby); [ambition] To be a Racing Driver;

COULTER, CHRISTINE: [b] 22/9/91 St Albans; [home] Hemel Hempstead, Herts; [brothers] Luke & Dominic; [school] Aycliff Drive; [fav sub] History & English; [hobbies] Reading, Animals & Brownies; [pets] Bubbles the Fish; [ambition] To become a Vet and to keep Dalmations;

COUPE, HELEN: [b] 3/7/91 Preston; [home] Goosnargh, Lancs; [p] Anthony & Shirley; [brother] Tony; [sisters] Jenny, Sam, Joanne & Megan; [school] St Francis; [fav sub] PE & Art; [hobbies] Netball & Swimming; [pets] Dog (Liz); [ambition] I would like to be a Pop Star;

COVENEY, HANNAH RUTH: [b] 31/1/92 Truro, Cornwall; [home] Whaddon, Wilts; [p] Craig & Teresa; [brother] James; [school] Alderbury & West Grimstead; [fav sub]; Literacy; [hobbies] Reading, Writing & Playing Violin; [pets] 3 Cats & 2 Dogs; [ambition] To be a Forensic Scientist or Vet;

COWAN, HANNAH: [b] 11/8/88 Hullbridge; [home] Hullbridge, Essex; [p] Caroline & Barry; [brother] Daniel; [school] The Sweyne Park; [fav sub] Drama & English; [hobbies] Dancing, Singing & Drama; [ambition] To be an Actress, Dancer, Singer, or Author;

COWAN, JAMIE: [b] 7/1/89; Great Yarmouth; [home] Chelmsford, Essex; [p] Christine & Bob; [brother] Bobby; [school] Rainsford High; [fav sub] Geography & PE; [hobbies] Athletics; [pets] Dog (Toffee) &

Cat (Felix); [ambition] DJ? I don't know yet;

COWLES, RACHEL: [b] 4/4/90 Chertsey; [home] Shepperton, Surrey; [p] Diana & John; [brother] Timothy; [school] Springfield; [fav sub] Music; [hobbies] Swimming; [pets] Rabbit; [ambition] To Sing or Teach;

COWLEY, RICHARD: [b] 24/2/93 Sheffield; [home] Weir, Lancs; [sister] Kat; [school] Constable Lee St Pauls; [fav sub] Art & Design; [hobbies] Cycling & bugging my sister!; [pets] 2 Cats (Shoe & Dexie); [ambition] To be a games tester for Playstation;

COXALL, CHANTELLE CHERYL SUSAN: [b] 13/2/94 Sutton, Cambs; [home] Hickling, Norfolk; [p] Richard & Michelle; [brother] Dominic; [school] Hickling V.C. First; [fav sub] Science; [hobbies] Brownies & Reading; [pets] 2 Rabbits, 2 Hamsters, Cockatiel, Budgie & Dog; [ambition] To be a Vet, Hairdresser or Beautician;

COZINS, TIMOTHY: [b] 27/3/92 Welwyn Garden City; [home] Ware, Herts; [p] Debbie & Chris; [sister] Madeleine; [school] Christ Church; [fav sub] P.E. & I.C.T.; [hobbies] Football; [pets] Dog, Fish, Gekos & Newt; [ambition] Don't know yet;

CRAIG, JONATHAN DAVID: [b] 1/11/90 Hertfordshire; [home] Ware, Herts; [p] Alastair & Jo; [brother] Ben; [sister] Hannah; [school] Christ Church; [fav sub] English & Maths; [hobbies] Writing Poems, playing Saxophone & Piano; [ambition] To design and build a Theme Park;

CRANDON, KATY: [b] 26/1/93 Newport; [home] Risca, Wales; [p] Emma & Paul; [sisters] Bethan (14), Victoria (13), Molly (4) & Lilly (2½); [school] Risca Primary; [fav sub] Art & D.T.; [hobbies] Playing in the Park; [pets] West Highland Terrier;

CRIPPS, JADE: [b] 2/12/92 London; [home] Chiswick, London; [p] Mrs J & Mr C Cripps; [brother] Jake; [school] Belmont Primary; [fav sub] Art & Maths; [hobbies] Swimming & Brownies; [pets] Hamster (Charlie Brown); [ambition] To be a Beauty Stylist;

CRISP, DANIEL: [b] 7/10/91; [home] Herne, Kent; [p] Kevin & Nikki; [brother] Jonathan; [school] Herne C of E Juniors; [fav sub] Design & Technology; [hobbies] Swimming; [pets] Dog & Parrot; [ambition] To be a Pilot & visit Florida;

CRISP, JAMES ROBERT: [b] 9/7/92 Gloucester; [home] Tuffley, Glos; [p] Rachel & Nicky; [sister] Georgia; [school] Fieldcourt Junior; [fav sub] Art; [hobbies] Art, Motorbikes, Football; [pets] Budgie (Robbie Williams), Goldfish (Black Paul & Orange Paul); [ambition] Art - Illustrating books;

CRONIN, HANNAH: [b] 8/11/88 Surrey;

[home] Beckenham, Kent; [p] Sheila & Paul; [brother] Francis; [sister] Megan; [school] Langley Park School for Girls; [fav sub] History; [hobbies] Music, Films; [ambition] To be a Writer;

CROOK, GEORGE: [b] 13/10/88 Bromsgrove; [home] Bromsgrove, Worcs. [p] Sarah & Simon; [brother] Thomas; [school] Aston Fields Middle; [fav sub] Games; [hobbies] Skate Boarding & Rugby; [ambition] Professional Rugby Player;

CROPPER, CHARLOTTE: [b] 6/12/94 Bromley; [home] Beckenham, Kent; [p] Elizabeth & Andrew; [sister] Abigail; [school] St Mary's Primary School; [fav sub] English; [hobbies] Dancing; [ambition] To be a Writer;

CROSS, MICHAEL: [b] 18/7/90 Middx; [home] Walton-on-Thames, Surrey; [p] John & Christine; [brother] Matthew; [sister] Katie; [school] Ambleside Junior School; [fav sub] P.E. [hobbies] Football, Swimming; [pets] Budgie (Taz); [ambition] Professional Footballer or Policeman;

CROUCH, HOLLY: [b] 6/12/89 Epsom; [home] Epsom, Surrey; [p] Christine & Ron; [brothers] Toby & Darren; [sisters] Tamsin & Melissa; [school] Warren Mead; [fav sub] Art; [hobbies] Netball and Football; [pets] 4 Cats, 1 Dog, 1 Terrapin; [ambition] To be Famous;

CROUCH, NAOMI: [b] 13/5/91 Enfield; [home] Broxbourne, Herts; [p] Eve & John; [brother] Laurie; [school] Broxbourne C of E Primary; [fav sub] Art; [hobbies] Drama, Brownies, Learning to play Double Bass, Art work, Writing Poetry & Stories; [pets] Goldfish & Stick Insects; [ambition] to be a Vet, Writer, Actress & Singer;

CROUCHER, WAYNE: [b] 30/8/90 Chertsey; [home] Walton-on-Thames, Surrey; [p] Sharon & Terry; [sisters] Kylie & Kelly; [school] Ambleside Junior School; [hobbies] Gardening & Scouts; [pets] Cat, Guinea Pigs & Rat;

CUMMINGS, PHILLIP: [b] 2/3/92 Plymouth; [home] Sparkwell, Devon; [p] Frank & Lynne; [brother] Darryl; [school] Stowford Primary; [fav sub] Science; [hobbies] Cycling & Football; [pets] Dog (Cali);

CURLAND, MICHAEL: [b] 3/10/91 London; [home] Herne, Kent; [p] Joseph & Wendy [brother] Daniel; [sister] Zoe; [school] Herne C of E School; [fav sub] Art; [hobbies] Football, Drums & Music;

CURTIS, MAXWELL M.: [b] 29/6/89 Watford; [home] Chorley Wood, Herts; [p] Max & Carolynn; [brothers] Felix, Eden & Austin; [school] Northwood Prep; [fav sub] Geography & Latin; [hobbies] Swimming & Trampoline; [pets] Cat (Jade); [ambition] Medical Research, Cure Cancer;

CUSENS, EMILY: [b] 10/3/92 Gloucester; [home] Quedgeley, Glos.; [p] Alison & Jeremy; [sister] Nicola; [school] Field Court Junior School; [fav sub] Art & D.T. [hobbies] Swimming, Sewing & Drawing; [pets] Cats (Willow & Hetty), Rat (Harry), Hamster (Fatty Patty); [ambition]To be a Designer;

DABROWSKI, SARAH: [b]11/7/89 Sutton, Surrey; [home] Andover, Hants; [p] Kris & Sue; [brother] Ross (10); [school] Winton School; [fav sub] English & History; [hobbies] Writing, Crafts & Horse Riding; [pets] Hans the Rabbit, died last year, subject of my poem; [ambition] To become an Author;

DALGADO, MARTIN S.: [b]15/11/89, Thornton Heath; [home] Thornton Heath, Surrey; [p] Ginny & Desmond; [brothers] Michael & Timothy; [school] St James The Great; [fav sub] Maths; [hobbies] Football & Cricket; [ambition] Not sure;

DAUWALDER, KATE: [b] 9/3/90 Salisbury; [home] Salisbury, Wilts; [p] Steve & Alison; [brothers] Michael & Phillip; [school] Sarum St Pauls; [fav sub] English; [hobbies] Music & Dancing; [pets] Goldfish; [ambition] To be an Actress & Entertainer;

DAVEY, JENINE: [b] 27/4/89 Clacton-on-Sea; [home] Clacton-on-Sea, Essex; [p] Debra & David; [school] Tendring Technology & Sixth Form College; [fav sub] Drama; [hobbies] Girl Guides & Animals; [pets] Dog, Cat, Rabbit, Guinea Pig & Rosella; [ambition] To become a Vet or work with animals;

DAVI, TÉTÉVI: [b] 29/12/89 London; [home] Thornton Heath, Surrey; [p] Pierre & Heather; [brother] Chukwuma; [sister] Dédé; [school] St James The Great; [fav sub] Art; [hobbies] Karate & Football; [pets] Guinea Pigs; [ambition] To attend University & study Law, then be a Lawyer;

DAVIES, AARON SIMON: [b] 21/7/84 Sheerness; [home] Halfway, Kent; [p] Susan & Graham; [school] Borden Grammar; [fav sub] Music; [hobbies] Acting, Reading & Music; [pets] 2 Persian Cats; [ambition] To become an Actor or Concert Pianist;

DAVIES, KAYLEIGH: [b] 8/8/92 Farnborough; [home] Penge, London; [p] Tracey & Keith; [sister] Courtney; [school] Royston Primary; [fav sub] Maths; [hobbies] Swimming & going to the woods; [pets] " Cats & 3 Kittens; [ambition] To be the worlds greatest Pop Singer;

DAVIES, PETER: [b] 28/8/90 Eastbourne; [home] Ninfield, E. Sussex; [p] Peter & Louise; [brothers] Harry & Jonathan; [sister] Cathy; [school] Ninfield CE; [fav sub] Maths; [hobbies] Football; [pets] Cats (Benny & Blinky) & Guinea Pigs; [ambition] To be a Wrestler or play for Manchester United;

DAVIES, REBECCA JAYNE: [b] 4/1/93 Aylesbury; [home] Aylesbury, Bucks; [p] Kim & Jeremy; [sister] Sarah Louise; [school] William Harding Combined; [fav sub] Literacy; [hobbies] Horse Riding & Ballet; [pets] Cat (Norman); [ambition] To work with animals;

DAVIES, SAM: [b] 13/2/90 Oswestry; [home] Trefonen, Shropshire; [p] Lee & Christine; [brother] Callum; [school] Trefonen C.E.; [fav sub] Art; [hobbies] Drawing & Cycling; [pets] Cat (Sooty), Gerbils (Erica & Whitey); [ambition] To become a famous Artist or a Stuntman;

DAVIES, THOMAS: [b] 10/2/93 Epsom; [home] Purley, Surrey; [p] Simon & Allison; [brother] Dominic; [sister] Cora; [school] St Annes; [fav sub] Maths; [hobbies] Football & Gameboy; [ambition] To be a Footballer and play for Liverpool;

DAVIES, WAYNE: [b] 5/2/87 Clacton; [home] Little Clacton, Essex; [p] Mike & Jean; [sisters] Tracey & Jemma; [school] Tendring Technology College; [fav sub] Geography & P.E.; [hobbies] Badminton, Rugby & Volleyball; [pets] 3 Dogs, Cockatil & Pony; [ambition] To become a Royal Marine;

DAVIS, CHRISTINA: [b] 22/9/89 Lyons, France; [home] Banstead, Surrey; [p] Jim & Petra; [brother] Jonathan; [school] Warren Mead Junior; [fav sub] Art; [hobbies] Dancing, Swimming, Cycling & Theme Parks!; [ambition] To be famous Actor, Chef, or Teacher;

DAVIS, DAVID: [home] Wadebridge, Cornwall; [brother] Jack; [school] Wadebridge CP; [hobbies] Playing with Lego;

DAVIS, LAUREN (LOLLY) REBECCA: [b] 27/6/92 Harlow; [home] Marston Bigot, Somerset; [p] Glenn & Jackie; [brother] Robert; [sister] Ruth; [school] Upton Noble Primary; [fav sub] English; [hobbies] Netball; [pets] Dog & Rabbit; [ambition] To be a Zoo Keeper;

DAVIS, TAMSIN: [b] 3/2/93 London; [home] Beckenham, Kent; [p] Alison & Mark; [sister] Isobel; [school] St Mary's RC; [fav sub] English; [hobbies] Tennis, Swimming & Talking; [pets] Cats (Phil & Dill) & Fish (Prince & Patrick); [ambition] To be a Vet, or work with animals;

DAWSON, HANNAH, LOUISE: [b] 17/3/93 Cornwall; [home] Aylesbury, Bucks; [p] Nicola & Peter; [brother] William; [school] William Harding Junior; [fav sub] Literacy; [hobbies] Dance & Drama;

DAWSON, LAURA: [b] 17/9/87 Croydon; [home] West Wickham , Kent; [p] Ellen & Martin; [brother] Robert; [school] Baston; [fav sub] PE & Art; [hobbies] Horse Riding, Shopping, Running & Sports; [pets] Dog (Sam)

& Guinea Pigs (Toffie & Tickles); [ambition] To be a Vet Assistant; I dedicate this book to all my family who are special to me;

DAWSON, OLIVER H.L.: [b] 26/10/92 London; [home] Pewsey, Wilts; [p] Mark & Rebecca; [brothers] Joshua & Samuel; [school] Oare C of E Primary; [fav sub] Maths; [hobbies] Football, Swimming & Tennis; [pets] 2 Cats, 2 Gekoes & 1 Corn Snake; [ambition] To become a Palaeontologist;

DAY, ALISON ESTELLE: [b] 13/8/90 London; [home] South Wootton, Norfolk; [p] John & Colleen; [brother] Stephen; [sister] Nicola; [school] South Wootton Junior; [hobbies] Tennis, Netball & Computer; [ambition] To be a Writer;

DEACON, ADAM BENJAMIN: [b] 6/7/90 Salisbury; [home] Alderbury, Wilts; [p] Fiona Spring & Tim Spring (Stepdad); [brothers] Paul & Christopher Deacon & Frederick Spring; [sister] Phoebe Spring; [school] Alderbury & West Grimstead; [fav sub] Art; [hobbies] Football & Basketball; [pets] 3 Goldfish; [ambition] To become a Policeman;

DEAM, ALEXANDER: [b] 9/11/89 Redditch; [p] Kate Deam & Richard James; [school] Aston Fields Middle; [fav sub] Maths; [hobbies] Football & Cricket; [pets] 2 Cats & 2 Rabbits;

DEAN, HENRY: [b] 30/9/93 Derby; [home] Beaconsfield, Bucks; [p] Micky & Micky; [sister] Georgina; [school] Davenies; [fav sub] Games; [hobbies] Football & Art; [ambition] To be a Pop Star;

DEAN, JORDAN THOMAS: [b] 5/7/90 Glos; [home] Whitminster, Glos; [p] Michael; [brother] Jamie; [sister] Laura; [school] Whitminster; [fav sub] PE; [hobbies] Football; [ambition] To be a Footballer;

DESMOND, HANNAH: [b] 14/2/86 Grimsby; [home] Cheddar, Som; [p] Shaun & Linda; [brother] Daniel; [school] Kings & Wessex; [fav sub] Drama; [hobbies] Spider-Man & Drumming; [pets] Dog (Sam); [ambition] To marry Spider-Man! & drive a Steam Roller;

DHANAK, RAVI: [b] 6/3/88 London; [home] Pinner, Middx; [p] Umed & Rama; [brother] Anuj; [sisters] Ashika, Chanonz & Radha; [school] Northwood Preparatory; [fav sub] I.T & D.T.; [hobbies] Football & Cricket; [ambition] To travel the world and achieve my goal of becoming an Accountant;

DICK, GARY: [b] 17/2/91 St Austell; [home] Wadebridge, Cornwall; [p] Susan & David; [brother] Steven; [school] Wadebridge Community Primary; [fav sub] Numeracy; [hobbies] Football; [pets] Cat (Darby); [ambition] To be a Footballer;

DICKINSON, JAMES: [b] 7/7/90 Leytonstone; [home] Widford, Herts; [p] Scott & Linda;

[sister] Astrid; [school] Bishop's Stortford College; [fav sub] English; [hobbies] Rugby, Hockey, Cricket, Reading & Writing; [pets] Burmese Cats (Rum & Raisin); [ambition] To play Rugby for England and to be a Poet;

DICKSON, HELEN: [b] 31/1/85 Cambridge; [home] Cambridge, Cambs; [p] Caroline & John; [brothers] Matthew & John; [school] St Bede's Inter-Church; [fav sub] Art; [hobbies] Drawing & walking the dog; [pets] Dog (Poppy); [ambition] To be an Artist or Writer;

DITCHFIELD, EMMA-JAYNE: [b] 8/8/92 Welwyn Garden City; [home] Ware, Herts; [p] Angela & Paul; [brother] Samuel; [school] Christ Church CE Primary; [fav sub] Art; [hobbies] Swimming & Gymnastics; [pets] Hamster (Cutey) & Cockatiel (Tutti Fruiti); [ambition] To become a Vet;

DOBSON, GRANT: [b] 14/8/90 Gravesend; [home] Frindsbury, Kent; [p] Mark & Lisa; [brother] Liam (2); [sister] Zoë (8); [school] Cliffe Woods; [fav sub] Science; [hobbies] Football & Horse Riding; [pets] Dwarf Rabbit (Blue Eyes); [ambition] To work in my Parents Company (Office Cleaning). Maybe chemical distribution for science interest;

DOBSON, JESSICA: [b] 22/6/92 Trowbridge; [home] Melksham, Wilts; [p] Mark & June; [sister] Lucy; [school] Forest & Sandridge CE Primary; [fav sub] English; [hobbies] Singing, Dancing & Acting; [ambition] To be a well known Singer or Actor;

DODD, HARRY: [b] 5/2/93 Hemel Hempstead; [home] Hemel Hempstead, Herts; [p] Michael & Alison; [brother] Jonathan; [sister] Joanna; [school] Aycliffe Drive Primary; [fav sub] Maths; [hobbies] Computing, Computer Games, Sports, Arts & Crafts; [pets] Dog (Nina), Kittens (Britney & Bradley), Snake (Jake) & Hamster (Haydn); [ambition] To be a famous Artist;

DODSON, MARK: [b] 17/5/90 King's Lynn; [home] Wisbech, Cambs; [p] Susan & Martin; [sister] Samantha; [school] Gordon Fendick Junior; [fav sub] Maths; [hobbies] Collecting Pokemon & Digimon cards; [pets] Dog (Sheba), Cats (Tiger & Shadow) & Rabbits (Snowy, Scamps, Flopsy & Jo-Jo); [ambition] To go to University and then become a Cartoonist;

DOHERTY, HANNAH E.: [b] 10/6/89 Farnborough; [home] West Wickham, Kent; [p] Ann & James; [sister] Anita Cook; [school] Langley Park School for Girls; [fav sub] Drama; [hobbies] Trampoline, Music & Drama; [pets] African Land Snail, Cat & Rabbit; [ambition] To be an Actress;

DOLOR, PATRICE: [b] 27/4/90 London; [home] Thornton Heath, Surrey; [p] Marcia & Peter; [brothers] Andrew, David & Samuel; [sister] Deanna; [school] St James The Great; [fav sub] Maths; [hobbies] Roller Blading; [ambition] To be a Singer or Dancer;

DONALD, HANNAH: [b] 20/12/90 RAF Halton; [home] Berkhamsted, Herts; [p] Rogan & Karen; [brother] Joshua; [sister] Beth; [school] Bridgewater School; [fav sub] Technology; [hobbies] Dancing, Singing & Drama; [pets] 3 Gerbils; [ambition] To bcome a Pop Star or a Vet;

DONNELLY, ANNE MARIE: [b] 9/6/88 Burnley; [home] Todmorden, W Yorks; [p] Michael & Brenda; [brother] Peter; [sisters] Gillian, Lisa & Michelle; [school] St Hildas RC Girls High; [fav sub] English; [hobbies] Writing, Reading & Gymnastics; [pets] Dog & Rabbit; [ambition] To own a Farm and to look after abandoned animals;

DONOVAN, LUKE SAM: [b] 25/8/90 Isleworth; [home] Sunbury, Middx; [p] Kelly & Jeremy; [brother] Joshua; [school] Springfield Primary; [fav sub] Maths; [hobbies] Football & Music; [ambition] To be a professional Pianist;

DOUGLAS, ADAM GEOFFREY: [b] 28/6/92 Plymouth; [home] Ivybridge, Devon; [p] Sophie & Neil; [brother] Harry Richard; [sister] Melody Jade; [school] Stowford Primary; [fav sub] Maths & Computers; [hobbies] Computers; [pets] Guinea Pigs (Gerry & Gus);

DOUGLAS, JENNY: [b] 24/9/87 Macclesfield; [home] Macclesfield, Cheshire; [p] Wendy & Sholto; [sister] Sheena; [school] All Hallows; [fav sub] English; [hobbies] Horse Riding; [pets] Dog, Cat, Gerbil & 2 Terrapins; [ambition] To teach Drama;

DOWDING, RACHAEL: [b] 26/12/89 Chelmsford; [home] King's Lynn, Norfolk; [p] Steve & Sue; [sister] Rebecca; [school] South Wootton Junior; [fav sub] Maths; [hobbies] Swimming & Music; [pets] Cat (Sophie) & Dog (Pippa); [ambition] To be a Maths Teacher;

DRAPER, JESSICA: [b] 17/11/90 Burton upon Trent; [home] Swadlincote, Derbys; [p] Giulia & Andrew; [brothers] Tom & Sam; [school] Belmont Primary; [fav sub] History; [hobbies] Dancing; [pets] 3 Cats, 2 Hamsters, 2 Goldfish & a Dog; [ambition] To be famous and to travel;

DU BOULAY, MICHAEL: [b] 10/4/93 Welwyn Garden City; [home] Ware, Herts; [p] Gill & Andrew; [brother] Chris; [school] Christchurch School; [fav sub] Maths; [hobbies] Basketball & Swimming; [pets] Goldfish (Fireball & Streaker); [ambition] To run the London Marathon;

DUDLEY, SHANNON: [b] 22/6/91 Eastbourne; [home] Ninfield, East Sussex; [p] Kerry & Carl; [sister] Maddison; [school] Ninfield CE; [hobbies] Dancing, Singing & Drama; [pets] Dog (Lucky) & Guinea Pig (Ginger); [ambition] To be a Dancer, Singer and Actress;

DUFFY, RICHARD PATRICK: [b] 23/3/92 Preston; [home] Euxton, Lancs; [p] Sandra & Shaun; [brother] Matthew (half brother) [sisters] Rachel & Leah; [school] Euxton EC Primary; [fav sub] Art; [hobbies] Playstation; [pets] Cat, Rabbit & 1 goldfish; [ambition] Would like to go down and see the wreck of the Titanic;

DUNNE, KATIE: [b] 1/2/92 Gloucester; [home] Quedgeley, Glos; [p] Greg & Sue; [sisters] Rachel & Ellie; [school] Field Court Junior; [fav sub] Maths & Art; [hobbies] Cycling & Skating; [ambition] To be a Hair Stylist;

DURODIE, MARC THOMAS: [b] 6/8/92 Redhill; [home] Redhill, Surrey; [p] Elisabeth & Jerome; [brother] Benjamin; [school] St John's Primary; [fav sub] Maths; [hobbies] Football, Swimming & Lego; [ambition] To visit Africa's National Parks and to be a Footballer;

DYER, GEMMA:[b] 7/4/86 Hammersmith; [home] Cheshunt, Herts; [p] Janice & Alan; [brother] Mark; [sister] Natalie; [school] Goffs; [fav sub] PE; [hobbies] Sport, Art & watching TV; [ambition] To become a PE Teacher;

EARLL, ASHLEY: [b] 14/10/89 [home] Kent; [p] Kevin & Joanne; [brother] Matthew; [school] Cliffewoods Primary; [fav sub] Maths, Geography & English (Literacy); [hobbies] Football, Ice Hockey, Basketball & Baseball; [pets] Dog (Rosie) & Kitten (Kip); [ambition] To become a professional in any of my hobbies or become a Policeman;

EARNSHAW, SAMMI-MARIE: [b] 17/6/92 Bromley; [home] Broomfield, Kent; [p] Sherrie & Paul; [brother] Callum; [school] Herne C of E Junior; [fav sub] Art; [hobbies] Dancing; [ambition] To become a Dance Teacher;

EASTERBROOK, LEREESA ESTELLE: [b] 6/10/91 Aylesbury; [home] Aylesbury, Bucks; [p] Dean & Donna; [brother] Arlen; [school] Turnfurlong Junior; [fav sub] Literacy; [hobbies] Tennis & Basketball; [pets] Goldfish; [ambition] To go to University and to be a top Tennis Player;

ECCLESTON, LUCINDA CHLOE: [b] Burnley; [home] Cliviger, Lancs; [p] Caroline; [brother] Kyle (my twin); [sister] Francesca; [school] St Hilda's; [fav sub] English; [hobbies] Dancing & Theatres; [pets] Dalmation (Lucky) & Jack Russell (Muffin);

EDENS, LISA: [b] 11/3/91 Salisbury; [home] Tilshead, Wilts; [p] Wendy & Dany; [brother] Darren; [sister] Dionne; [school] St Thomas a 'Becket CE (Aided) Primary; [fav sub] English & Sport; [hobbies] Sports;

[pets] Dog (Sadie) & 3 Gerbils; [ambition] To become a Volcanologist;

EHRMANN, GEORGIA: [b] 5/12/92 London; [home] Little Chalfont, Bucks; [p] Liz & Philip; [sister] Natasha; [school] Little Chalfont Combined; [fav sub] Art; [hobbies] Exercising; [pets] Kitten & 2 Fish; [ambition] To be a Train Driver;

ELLIOTT, DEVON JAMES ANDRÉ: [b] 11/10/90 Barking; [home] Wormley, Herts; [p] Karen Elliott & Julian Halls; [sister] Rave; [school] Broxbourne CE Primary; [fav sub] English; [hobbies] Hockey; [pets] Goldfish; [ambition] To play Hockey at the Olympic Games;

ELLIOTT, NICHOLAS: [b] 18/9/90 High Wycombe; [home] Chalfont St Giles, Bucks; [p] Sandra & James; [school] Robertswood Combined; [fav sub] Maths; [hobbies] Football & Tennis; [pets] Dog (Sabre); [ambition] To become famous;

ELLIOTT, ROSANNA: [b] 30/9/94 Ipswich; [home] Gt Massingham, Norfolk; [p] Roy & Lisa; [brother] Tom; [school] Great Massingham VC Primary; [fav sub] Literacy & Art; [hobbies] Gymnastics & Reading; [pets] Dog (Dylan); [ambition] To be a Teacher and to be happy;

ELLIOTT, TOM: [b] 3/12/89 Gloucester; [home] Painswick, Glos; [p] David & Michelle; [sister] Rebecca; [school] Fieldcourt Junior; [fav sub] Music; [hobbies] Brass Bands & Football; [pets] Rufus; [ambition] To play in an Orchestra and to be a DJ;

ELLISON, RUKAYA: [b] 19/12/91 Penge; [home] Penge, London; [p] Anthony & Sonia; [brother] Emmanuel; [school] Royston Primary; [fav sub] English; [hobbies] Art, Running & Cooking; [pets] Puppies; [ambition] To be a Surgeon or Doctor;

ELVIDGE, NATASHA: [b] 1/10/91 Plymouth; [home] Ivybridge, Devon; [p] Tony & Angela; [sister] Kirstie; [school] Stowford Primary; [fav sub] Maths; [hobbies] Reading, Art & Karate; [pets] Cat [ambition] To go diving with Dolphins;

ENKEL, CASEY: [b] 2/5/90 Orset; [home] Kelvedon Hatch, Essex; [p] Alison & Adrian; [brother] Tyler; [school] Kelvedon Hatch CP; [fav sub] Maths; [hobbies] Cycling, Dog walking, Netball, Swimming & Harry Potter books; [pets] Dogs (Coco & Misty), Parrot (Polly), Hamster (Whiz), 64 Tropical Fish & a Big Spider; [ambition] To do Parachuting, become an Actress and be a Millionaire;

ESSALMI, YASMIN: [b] 20/10/91 Southampton; [home] New Milton, Hants; [p] Sara & Abdellah; [sister] Amina; [school] New Milton Junior; [fav sub] Art; [hobbies] Swimming, Tennis, Piano,

Taekwondo & Basketball; [pets] Cat (Lana); [ambition] To be a famous Athlete, Presenter or Poet;

ETERE, MICA A.: [b] 20/6/90 Stevenage; [home] Stevenage, Herts; [p] Miss S.P. Cooke; [school] Peartree Junior; [fav sub] English & Maths; [hobbies] Music, Dancing & Netball; [pets] 3 Cats; [ambition] To become a professional Dancer;

ETHERINGTON, DANIELLE: [b] 3/9/90 Gravesend; [home] Swanley, Kent; [p] Tony & Kim; [sister] Holly; [school] Crockenhall Primary; [fav sub] Science; [hobbies] Football & Swimming; [pets] Hamster (Millie); [ambition] To be a Doctor and play in a Ladies Football Team;

EYRE, STEPHEN: [b] 25/1/91 Buxton; [home] Buxton, Derbys; [p] Raymond & Sheila; [brother] Matthew; [school] Buxton Junior; [fav sub] Art & Technology; [hobbies] Sports & Computers; [pets] Cat; [ambition] To be a TV Presenter or Footballer;

FIELDHOUSE, KATY: [b] 12/10/88 Bromley; [home] Bromley, Kent; [p] Linda & Stuart; [brother] Thomas; [sister] Grace; [school] Babington House; [fav sub] English, Maths & PE; [hobbies] Gymnastics; [pets] Cats (Pepys, Wills, Seth & Porthia) & Goldfish (Finn & Noodles); [ambition] To be a Policewoman;

FINCKEN, LARA: [b] 28/6/91 Aylesbury; [p] Trudi & Paul; [sister] Jenna; [fav sub] History; [hobbies] Flute, Piano & Singing; [pets] Cat (Pepsi); [ambition] To be in a Film;

FITCH, SIMON: [b] 5/11/88 Ascot; [home] Wimborne, Dorset; [p] Gary & Elisabeth; [brother] Antony; [school] St Michaels; [fav sub] Football & Science; [hobbies] Football; [ambition] To become a professional Footballer;

FLACK, THEO: [b] 18/7/92 Redhill; [home] Redhill, Surrey; [p] Caroline & Simon; [school] St John's Primary; [fav sub] PE; [hobbies] Football & Tennis; [pets] Fish & Cat; [ambition] To become a Pilot, or Footballer, or Tennis Player;

FLANDERS, STEPHANIE: [b] 12/12/90 Truro; [home] Wadebridge, Cornwall; [p] Bill & Janet; [sister] Melissa; [school] Wadebridge CP; [fav sub] Art; [hobbies] Barbie Doll & playing with and walking my dogs; [pets] Bassett Hound (Gem), 2 Japanese Chins (Hana & Jenna) 2 Cats (Graeme & Spike) & 2 Goldfish; [ambition] To be a Veterinary Nurse or work with animals;

FLANNERY, SINEÁD: [b] 22/2/90 London; [home] Norbury, London; [p] Frank & Agnes; [brother] Owen; [school] St James The Great; [fav sub] Maths & Science; [hobbies] Netball & Football; [pets] Fish; [ambition] To be happy with who I am;

FLAXMAN, CATHERINE: [b] 28/11/93 Norwich; [home] Sea Palling, Norfolk; [p] Ian & Maxine; [brother] Luke; [school] Hickling First; [fav sub] Science; [hobbies] Swimming & Cycling; [pets] Goldfish; [ambition] To be a Vet or work with animals;

FLETCHER, SALLY: [b]8/1/91 Epsom; [home] Epsom, Surrey; [p] Mr & Mrs M.J. Fletcher; [brother] Peter; [sisters] Michelle & Lucy; [school] Warren Mead Junior; [fav sub] English; [hobbies] Guides & Dance;

FLINT, JOE: [b] 3/1/91 Basildon; [home] Margate, Kent; [p] Robert & Jennie; [brother] Danny; [sister] Carly; [school] Bromstone; [fav sub] Art; [hobbies] Collecting Beano Comics & Football; [pets] Cat (Tiggy) & Guinea Pig (Bubbles); [ambition] To hold the F.A. Cup and become a Rally Driver;

FORD, CHARLOTTE: [b] 12/6/90 Portsmouth; [home] Lee-on-Solent, Hants; [p] Janice & Greg; [brothers] Jack & James; [hobbies] Neopets; [ambition] To be a Vet;

FORREST, PERRY: [b] 16/7/92 Southampton; [home] New Milton, Hants; [p] Theresa; [brother] Brandon Leigh; [school] New Milton Juniors; [fav sub] Music; [hobbies] Swimming & Taekwondo; [pets] Hamster & Cat; [ambtion] To become a Policeman or a Musician;

FOSTER, ALICE: [b] 14/8/90 Sutton; [home] Whaddon, Salisbury, Wilts; [school] Alderbury & West Grimstead C of E (Aided) Primary; [fav sub] Maths; [hobbies] Music & Ballroom Dancing; [pets] 4 Mice; [ambition] To be a Veterinary Surgeon;

FRAIS, SIMON: [b] 19/1/88 London; [home] Pinner, Middx; [brother] Benjamin; [school] Northwood Preparatory; [fav sub] Music; [hobbies] Music & Scouts; [ambition] To be a Hotel Manager or professional Musician;

FRANCIS, DAVINA: [b] 6/6/86 Colchester; [home] Kirby Cross, Essex; [p] Brian & Christine; [brother] Gavin; [school] Tendring Technology College; [fav sub] Drama; [hobbies] Dancing & Football; [pets] Budgie (Thunder); [ambition] To be Happy and aim for World Peace;

FROMENT, SAMUEL: [b] 30/6/92 Aylesbury; [home] Aylesbury, Bucks; [p] Mark & Julia; [brother] Joshua; [sister] Louise; [school] William Harding Combined; [fav sub] History; [hobbies] Football & Drama; [pets] Rabbit (Barny); [ambition] To become an Actor;

FROST, RICHARD: [b] 24/9/85 Ipswich; [home] Ipswich, Suffolk; [p] Roy & Debbie; [brother] Simon; [sister] Lauren; [school] Beacon Hill; [fav sub] Science; [hobbies] Snooker & Cycling; [ambition] To be happy in life;

FROUD, CHARLOTTE: [b] 28/9/91 Plymouth; [home] Ivybridge, Devon; [p] Karen & John; [brothers] Alexander & Joshua; [school] Stowford Primary; [fav sub] Art; [hobbies] Ballet, Tap & Modern Dancing, Brownies & playing the Piano; [ambition] To teach Dance;

FULLER, VERITY JANE: [b] 18/3/92 Crockenhill; [home] Crockenhill, Kent; [p] Gary & Karen; [brother] William; [sister] Fredrika; [school] Crockenhill Primary; [fav sub] Art; [hobbies] Athletics, Art & Writing; [pets] Hamster (Harry) & Dog (Nelson); [ambition] To illustrate children's books;

GANGAIDZO, ARNOLD: [b] 29/10/91 Triangle, Zimbabwe; [home] Aylesbury, Bucks; [p] Roben & Sarah; [brothers] Tapiwa & Roben (Jnr); [school] William Harding Combined; [fav sub] Literacy; [hobbies] Playstation, Gameboy & Pokemon; [ambition] To become a Doctor;

GARDNER, GRACE: [b] 15/6/88 Beckenham; [home] Beckenham, Kent; [p] Simon & Kathryn; [brothers] George & Henry; [school] Baston; [fav sub] PE; [hobbies] Piano, Singing, Dancing, Acting & all Sports; [pets] Dog (Tasha) & Hamster (Speedy); [ambition] To be a Singer and perform in Musical Productions. I would also like to dedicate my poem to my Grandma, Daphne Finney who I love very much;

GATLEY, HOLLI: [b] 8/8/88 Tooting; [home] Morden, Surrey; [p] Karen; [sister] Casey; [fav sub] Maths; [hobbies] Listening to music; [pets] Cat & Hamster; [ambition] To become a Model;

GENT, NAOMI MARGARET: [b] 4/3/94 Preston; [home] Adlington, Lancs; [p] Shirley & Mark; [brother] Nathan; [school] Adlington; [fav sub] Spellings; [hobbies] Drawing, Reading & Cross Stitch; [pets] Hamster, Tortoise & 2 Cats; [ambition] To be a Vet;

GHAZANFAR, TAYYAB: [b] 27/7/92 Bradford; [p] Ghanzafar & Mahmood; [sisters] Sanah Mehnaz, Mehuish Mehnaz, Aisha Batool & Sehrish Batool; [school] Undercliffe Primary; [fav sub] Maths; [hobbies] Karate; [pets] Puppy; [ambition] To be a Footballer;

GIBBON, RHYS: [b] 24/9/92 Sutton Coldfield; [home] Aylesbury, Bucks; [p] Guy & Kerry; [brother] Daniel; [school] William Harding Combined; [fav sub] Art; [hobbies] Football & Reading Poetry; [pets] Cat (Maddie) [ambition] To be an Artist and to visit my cousins in New Zealand;

GIBBONS, CHLOE: [b] 15/1/94 Greywell; [home] Greywell, Hants; [p] Nick & Pam; [brother] Sam; [school] Bury Fields Infant; [fav sub] English; [hobbies] Swimming, Recorder & Brownies; [pets] Hamster (Fudge); [ambition] To be a Writer & Illustrator;

GIBBONS, GRACE: [b] 16/4/91 Wycombe; [home] Bourne End, Bucks; [p] Lucy & David; [brothers] George & Charles; [school] Claytons Combined; [fav sub] English & French; [hobbies] Karate & Football;

GIBBS, AMY LOUISE: [b] 4/11/87 Frimley; [home] Fleet, Hants; [p] Raymond & Anita; [brother] Christopher; [school] Courtmoor; [fav sub] History, Geography & PE; [hobbies] Socialising; [pets] 2 Dogs & 1 Rabbit; [ambition] To be a vet;

GIBBS, MOLLY: [b] 18/2/91 Hounslow; [home] Drimpton, Dorset; [p] Shirley; [brother] Tom; [sisters] Amy & Emily; [school] Parrett & Axe CE Primary; [fav sub] Design & Technology; [hobbies] Horse Riding & Youth Club; [pets] Hamster; [ambition] To be a Model, a Pop Star, or an Actress and a Jockey;

GIDDINS, JASON: [b] 21/12/89 Gloucester; [home] Hardwicke, Glos; [p] Tracey & Derek Oram; [brothers] Scott, Adam & Jack Oram; [sister] Amy Oram; [school] Field Court Junior;

GILBERT, JESSICA CLAIRE: [b] 19/9/90 King's Lynn; [home] South Wootton, Norfolk; [p] Tim & Amanda; [brother] Charlie; [sister] Lucy; [school] South Wootton Junior; [fav sub] Art, English & Music; [hobbies] Brownies, Drawing, Reading & playing the Cornet; [pets] Cats (Daisy & Bagheera) Dog (Ben); [ambition] To be a Vet, or Archaeologist, or work with young children;

GILL, DOUGIE: [b] 31/5/91; [home] Salisbury, Wilts; [p] Derek & Julie; [brother] Max; [school] Alderbury & West Grimstead Primary; [fav sub] Maths; [hobbies] Swimming & Racket Games; [pets] Cat (Fergus) & Fish; [ambition] To attend University and become an Aircraft Design Engineer;

GILLETT, JAMIE: [b] 5/9/89 Bournemouth; [home] Barton-on-Sea, Hants; [p] Guy & Hazel; [brothers] Matt & Luke; [sister] Heidi; [school] New Milton Juniors; [fav sub] Maths; [hobbies] Football, Tennis & Dancing; [pets] 7 Dogs, 2 Gerbils & Dwarf Hamster; [ambition] To be a professional Footballer or Cricketer;

GLASS, ANTONY: [b] 17/12/87 Chatham; [home] Sittingbourne, Kent; [p] Clair & Garry; [sisters] Andrea & Kimberley; [school] Borden Grammar; [fav sub] Spanish; [hobbies] Cricket & Computer Games; [pets] Dog, Rabbit & Fish; [ambition] To play Cricket for England and to be an Accountant;

GODDARD, JOHN MICHAEL: [b] 7/1/89 Poole; [home] Colehill, Dorset; [p] Sharon & Michael; [sister] Jessica; [school] St Michaels Middle; [fav sub] English; [hob-
bies] Football, Karate, Composer & DJ; [pets] Cat (Pussa); [ambition] To be a DJ, a Designer or a Cartoonist;

GODDEN, AILSA: [b] 27/5/89 Macclesfield; [home] Macclesfield, Cheshire; [p] Mark & Louise; [sister] Esme; [school] All Hallows; [fav sub] English; [hobbies] Trampoline, Hockey & Badminton; [pets] Guinea Pig (Joey); [ambition] To be a Writer or TV Presenter;

GOLDUP, NATASHA: [b] 22/11/85 Ashford; [home] Ashford, Kent; [p] Stephen & Evelyn; [brother] Matthew (my twin); [sister] Melissa; [school] The North School; [fav sub] English; [hobbies] Drama, Singing, Dancing & Writing Poetry; [ambition] To become a Musical Actress;

GOODAY, LISA: [b] 12/12/88 [home] Chelmsford, Essex; [p] Wendy & Brian; [brothers] Steven & Mark; [school] Rainsford High; [fav sub] PE & Dance; [hobbies] Gymnastics & Dancing; [pets] Rabbits, Birds & Tropical Fish; [ambition] To look after animals;

GOODYEAR, DAVID: [b] 6/5/89 Slough; [home] Beaconsfield, Bucks; [p] Adrian & Elizabeth; [school] Davenies; [fav sub] Science; [hobbies] Golf & Snooker; [pets] Cat, Rabbit & Fish; [ambition] To become a Pilot and Technical Drawer;

GOSS, CHLOE: [b] 25/5/90 Aylesbury; [home] Aylesbury, Bucks; [p] Sue & Brian; [brothers] Ben & Sam; [school] William Harding Combined; [fav sub] English; [hobbies] Swimming, Dancing & listening to Music; [pets] Cats (Sasha, & Buster) & Dog (Bess); [ambition] To be a Fashion Designer;

GOULD, ELEANOR: [b] 15/6/93 Worcester; [home] Evesham, Worcs; [p] Keith & Sheila; [school] Swan Lane First; [fav sub] History; [hobbies] Reading, Tennis & Swimming; [ambition] To teach at a school like mine!

GRAINGER, BETHANY: [b] 7/3/85 Cambridge; [home] Cambridge, Cambs; [p] June & Paul; [brother] Sam; [school] St Bede's; [fav sub] English; [hobbies] Skater Hockey;

GRANGE, JAMES: [b] 26/7/88 Harrogate; [home] Ramsgate, Kent; [p] Carole; [brothers] Andrew & Richard; [school] King Ethelbert; [fav sub] English; [hobbies] Skate Boarding & Music; [ambition] To be successful in all that I do;

GRANT, ELLIOTT: [b] 15/12/89 Welwyn Garden City; [home] Cheshunt, Herts; [p] Kelvin & Georgina; [brother] Oliver; [sister] Courtney; [school] Bonneygrove CP; [fav sub] English; [hobbies] Scouts & Football; [pets] 3 Goldfish; [ambition] To be a Zoo Keeper;

GRANTHAM, SANGEETA: [b] 7/2/92
Harrow; [home] Garston, Herts; [p] Kevin & Davinder; [brother] Sahil; [school] Kingsway Junior; [fav sub] English & Maths; [hobbies] Swimming & Cycling; [ambition] To become an Author;

GREEN, DANIEL: [b] 29/12/91 Barnstaple; [home] Ivybridge, Devon; [p] Rick & Jen; [brother] Bradley; [school] Stowford Primary; [fav sub] History; [hobbies] Swimming, Bike, Scooter & Blades; [pets] Guinea Pigs (Spot & Patch); [ambition] To become a Vet;

GREEN, MATT: [b] 28/2/90 Reading; [home] Reading, Berks; [p] Geoff & Val; [brother] Jonathan; [sister] Laura & Jenny; [school] Micklands; [fav sub] Literacy; [hobbies] Computing, Martial Arts & Magic; [pets] Cat (Bonnie); [ambition] To be Famous;

GREENHALGH, REBECCA (BECKY): [b] 16/10/90 Worcester; [home] Malvern, Worcs; [p] David & Carol; [brother] Tim & Matt; [sister] Clare; [school] Wyche CE Primary; [fav sub] Science & English; [hobbies] Horse Riding; [ambition] To be a Vet;

GREENWOOD, LIAM: [b] 30/3/87 Chatham; [home] Margate, Kent; [p] Ann & Damian; [brother] Callum; [school] King Ethelberts; [fav sub] PE; [hobbies] Hockey & Football; [pets] House Rabbit; [ambition] To own my own Haulage Firm;

GREGORY, LAUREN: [b] 29/4/92 Aylesbury; [p] Joanne & David; [brother] Jack; [school] William Harding Combined; [fav sub] English; [hobbies] Writing, Reading & Singing; [pets] Cocker Spaniel (Molly); [ambition] To be a Nurse and help people;

GRIFFIN, LAURA: [b] 30/3/90 Redditch; [home] Bromsgrove, Worcs; [p] Karan & David; [brother] Brett; [school] Aston Fileds Middle; [fav sub] Maths & D.T.; [hobbies] Reading, Swimming & Cinema; [pets] Dog & 4 Cats; [ambition] To help animals and work for a Vet;

GRIFFITHS, KIERAN: [b] 23/9/91 Hythe; [home] Ivybridge, Devon; [p] Chris & Jenny; [brother] William; [sister] Caitlin; [school] Stowford Primary; [fav sub] Maths; [hobbies] Cycling & Skateboarding; [pets] Fish; [ambition] To be a famous Skateboarder;

GRIMES, HANNAH: [b] 5/11/89 London; [home] Cheam, Surrey; [p] Patrick & Patricia Gleeson; [brother] Harry Grimes; [sister] Nancy Grimes; [school] Morden Farm; [fav sub] Art & PE; [pets] Cat & Guinea Pigs; [ambition] To be an Author, Actress or Archeologist;

GRIMSHAW, LUKE: [b] 21/12/90 Iver; [home] Chalfont St Peter, Bucks; [p] Michael & Sheila; [sister] Joanna; [school] Robertswood Combined; [fav sub] Maths; [hobbies] Trumpet

& Judo; [pets] Rabbits & Chickens; [ambition] To be a Musician and Actor;

GROVES, DAVID: [b] 23/5/91 Danbury; [home] Danbury, Essex; [p] Robert & Cherie; [brother] Raymond; [school] The Hayward; [fav sub] Art & Technology; [hobbies] Cycling; [pets] Rabbit (Toffee); [ambition] To learn to drive;

GROVES, PAUL MICHAEL: [b] 26/8/89 Chelmsford; [home] Chelmsford, Essex; [p] David & Patricia; [sister] Amy; [school] Rainsford High; [fav sub] PE; [hobbies] Cycling, Football, Basketball, Rugby; [pets] Goldfish & Cat; [ambition] To be open minded;

GRUNDY, KATIE: [b] 20/7/91 Buxton; [home] Buxton, Derbys; [p] Jim & Julie; [brother] Marc; [school] Buxton Junior; [fav sub] Art; [hobbies] Swimming & Tennis; [pets] Hamster & 4 Fish; [ambition] To be a Vet;

GUILLE, PAUL: [b] 19/4/89 Colchester; [home] Clacton on Sea, Essex; [p] John & Julia; [brothers] Alex (15) & Mattew (10); [sisters] Sarah, Jo, Bethany (10); [school] Tendring Technology College; [fav sub] History, German, English; [hobbies] Basketball & Scouts; [pets] Dogs (Suki & Fern), Cat (Dizzy) & Hamster (Shearer); [ambition] To help in Church Youth Group and become a Teacher of English in Germany;

GULBRANDSON, ERIKA: [b] 23/7/89 London; [home] Staines, Middx; [p] Thomas & Suzanne; [sister] Katrina; [school] Magna Carta; [fav sub] Maths; [hobbies] Swimming & Piano; [pets] Cat (Sabrina); [ambition] To be a Lawyer;

GUY, NATHAN: [b] 25/3/92 Aylesbury; [home] Aylesbury, Bucks; [p] Kim & Richard; [brother] Lee; [school] William Harding Combined; [fav sub] Maths; [hobbies] Radio Controlled Cars; [ambition] To become a Policeman;

HADJIPOUROU, MICHAEL: [b] 25/6/94; [home] Harpenden, Herts; [p] Wendy & John; [brothers] Alexis & Nicholas; [sister] Katherine; [school] St Nicholas; [fav sub] Maths; [hobbies] Football, Golf & Tennis; [pets] Dog (Billy); [ambition] To become a builder;

HALE, MICHAEL: [b] 22/4/93 Farnham; [home] Farnham, Surrey; [p] Andy & Diane; [sister] Lauren; [school] St Peters; [fav sub] Art & Science; [hobbies] Art & Judo; [pets] 2 Dogs (Bracken & Megan) Cat (Smudge) & Fish; [ambition] To run a Hotel and a School;

HALL, REBECCA: [b]19/4/88 Burnley; [home] Cliviger, Lancs; [p] Rod & Lyn; [school] St Hildas RC Girls; [fav sub] German & Cookery; [hobbies] Horse Riding, Reading & Cooking; [pets] Dogs (Tom & Geri) & Ponies (Flirt & Lulu); [ambition] Something to do with animals;

HAMPTON, SAMANTHA: [b] 15/4/91 Colchester; [home] Colchester, Essex; [p] Michael & Carolyn; [sisters] Charlotte & Allison; [school] Gosbecks Primary; [fav sub] Maths; [hobbies] Swimming & Dancing; [pets] Cats (Dennis & Tigger);

HAMSON, GEORGE: [b] 4/12/91 Salisbury; [home] Salisbury, Wilts; [p] Amanda & Stephen; [brother] Harry; [school] Alderbury & West Grimstead; [fav sub] Maths; [hobbies] Golf, Cubs & Swimming; [ambition] To be a F1 Driver;

HANCOCK, JOSHUA ADAM: [b] 5/6/92 Bury; [home] Rawtenstall, Lancs; [p] Lynn & John; [sister] Elli; [school] Constable Lee St Pauls Primary; [fav sub] Poetry & Art; [hobbies] Ski-ing & Rugby; [pets] Dog (Suzy); [ambition] To be a WWF Wrestler;

HARALAMBOUS, KATIE: [b] 20/7/92 Reading; [home] Caversham, Berks; [p] Nicholas & Tracey; [brother] Christopher; [school] Micklands Primary; [fav sub] Art; [hobbies] Swimming & Computer Games; [pets] Cat (Sooty) & Fish (Alice);

HARDAKER, NICHOLAS: [b] 2/2/91 Bradford; [home] Eccleshill, W. Yorks; [p] Helen; [sister] Jenna; [school] St Francis Primary; [fav sub] Maths; [hobbies] Football & Cricket; [ambition] To be a professional Footballer;

HARDING, MARK: [b] 17/10/87 Carshalton; [home] Mitcham, Surrey; [p] Miss H Johnson; [sister] Rachael Harding; [school] Bishopsford High; [fav sub] History & Science; [hobbies] Football & Computers; [ambition] To be a professional Footballer;

HARDING, SIMON: [b] 25/9/89 Gravesend; [home] Rochester, Kent; [p] Helen Gransden; [brother] George; [sister] Sian & Sara; [school] Cliffwoods Primary; [fav sub] Maths; [hobbies] Football; [pets] Dog (Sandie); [ambition] To run a Marathon;

HARDY, ALEX: [b] 18/12/91 London; [home] Beaconsfield, Bucks; [p] Tessa & Warren; [brother] Max; [sister] Paige; [school] Davenies; [fav sub] Maths; [hobbies] Cricket & Rugby; [pets] Dogs (Pebbles & Lettice) Cats (Jose & Frank); [ambition] To be a famous Actor or Sportsman;

HARPER, REBECCA: [b] 10/6/92 Gloucester; [home] Quedgeley, Glos; [p] Sara Vale & Adrian Harper; [brother] Lincoln Harper; [sister] Amy Vale; [school] Field Court Junior; [fav sub] English; [hobbies] Horse Riding, Swimming, Reading & Cycling; [pets] Cat (Joey) & Fish (Misty); [ambition] To become a Vet;

HARRAGAN, EMMA LOUISE: [b] 11/1/89 Chelmsford; [home] Chelmsford, Essex; [p] Heather & Andrew; [brother] Tyler Andrew Louis; [sister] Sophie Ashton;

[school] Rainsford High; [fav sub] Geography; [hobbies] Reading, Horse Riding, Writing & Cadets; [pets] Dog (Snowy); [ambition] To be a Vet or Doctor;

HARRIS, LUKE A.: [b] 10/4/89 Chatham; [home] Rainham, Kent; [p] Mark & Mia; [brother] Karl; [school] Rainham Mark Grammar; [fav sub] History & Games; [hobbies] Football & Reading; [pets] 2 Dogs, Cat, Bird, Shetland Pony, Rat, Hamster, Guinea Pig & Rabbit; [ambition] To be an Archaeologist;

HARRIS, SAM ANTHONY: [b] 22/2/92 Watford; [home] Watford, Herts; [p] Claire & Geoff; [brother] Lee; [school] Kingsway Junior; [fav sub] Maths; [hobbies] Football & Sketching; [pets] Puppy, 2 Hamsters & Goldfish; [ambition] To be a Cartoonist;

HART, CHLOÉ EMMA: [b] 30/8/90 Chatham; [home] Cliffe Woods, Kent; [p] Debra & Robert; [brother] Matthew; [school] Cliffe Woods CP; [fav sub] Literacy; [hobbies] Dancing & Beanie Babies; [pets] Rabbit (Truffle); [ambition] To swim with Dolphins;

HARWIN, SAMUEL: [b] 2/5/90 Ely; [home] March, Cambs; [p] Philip & Hazel; [brothers] Robert, Thomas & Joseph; [sister] Rachael; [school] All Saints Inter-Church Primary; [fav sub] Art; [hobbies] Skateboarding; [pets] Cats (Polly & Jack);

HASLAM, EMILY: [b] 24/6/88 Worcester; [home] Kidderminster, Worcs; [p] Alison & William; [sisters] Rebecca & Jessica; [school] Sladen CE Middle; [fav sub] Maths & English; [hobbies] Reading; [pets] Parrot, Dog & 3 Cats; [ambition] To be a Reporter or Critic;

HAVERS, CATHERINE: [b] 16/8/90 Shropshire; [home] Shropshire; [brother] Freddie; [fav sub] Art; [hobbies] Tennis, Cycling & Shopping; [pets] Cat (Tigger); [ambition] To be a Tennis Player;

HAWKINS, EMMA: [b] 12/7/95 London; [home] Alderbury, Wilts; [brother] Thomas (twin); [school] Alderbury & West Grimstead Primary; [fav sub] Reading & Colouring; [hobbies] Ballet & Swimming; [pets] 2 Cats & Rabbit; [ambition] To be a Teacher or a Vet;

HAWKINS, ROBERT J: [b] 2/9/90 Reading; [home] Caversham, Berks; [p] Ian & Janet; [brother] Edward G.; [school] Micklands Primary; [fav sub] Art & English; [hobbies] Football; [pets] Hamster, Dog & Fish; [ambition] To be a famous Builder;

HAYES, LUCY: [b] 1989 Redditch; [home] Bromsgrove, Worcs; [p] Denise & Tony; [sister] Rosie; [school] Aston Fields; [hobbies] Games & PE; [hobbies] Playing Piano; [pets] Rabbit & Guinea Pig; [ambition] To be an Actress;

HAYES, SOPHIE: [b] 4/8/92 Southampton; [home] New Milton, Hants; [p] Susan; [brothers] Christian & Edward; [school] New Milton Junior; [fav sub] Numeracy; [hobbies] Trampolining, Singing & Writing; [pets] Rabbits (Abi & Ginger); [ambition] I would like to be a Mummy and look after animals;

HAYTER, BRETT: [b] 26/11/93 Yeovil; [home] Yeovil, Somerset; [p] Alan & Lorraine; [brothers] Darren & Liam; [school] Pen Mill; [fav sub] English; [hobbies] WWF Wrestling; [ambition] To visit America;

HEARN, BRYONY CLAIRE: [b] 14/2/93 Oxford; [home] Thame, Oxon; [p] Kevin & Kerry; [brother] William; [sister] Lucy; [school] John Hampden Primary; [fav sub] Writing; [hobbies] Horse Riding, Brownies & Swimming; [pets] Rabbit & Goldfish; [ambition] To be a Singer;

HEBDITCH, MAX: [b] 8/9/90 Morden; [home] Morden, Surrey; [p] Gary & Tracy; [brother] Jacob; [sister] Ella; [school] Morden Farm Middle; [fav sub] Poetry; [hobbies] Karate, Reading & Painting; [pets] Cat (Pepe), Dog (Tango), Hamster (Nibbles) & Fish; [ambition] To become a Junior Black Belt and to write more poetry;

HEDGES, CLAIRE: [b] 11/9/92 Aylesbury; [home] Aylesbury, Bucks; [p] Gary & Diane; [sister] Holly; [school] William Harding Combined; [fav sub] Art & Maths; [hobbies] Reading, Swimming & Cubs; [pets] Cats (Thomas & Muffin);

HEELS, NATHAN: [b] 29/8/93 [p] Sheena & Michael; [school] William Harding; [fav sub] Maths; [hobbies] Gardening; [pets] Parrot (Sebastian); [ambition] To be a Racing Driver;

HEINZ, NADINE: [b] 8/5/90 Bromsgrove; [home] Bromsgrove, Worcs; [p] Peter & Simone; [brother] Christian; [school] Aston Fields Middle; [fav sub] History; [pets] Cats (Eric & Bon Bon;); [ambition] To be an Author or History Teacher;

HELM, CAROLINE: [b] 26/1/90; [home] Cleveleys, Lancs; [p] Jill & Vic; [school] Manor Beach Primary; [fav sub] Art & Maths; [hobbies] Playing the Keyboard & Art; [pets] Dogs (Tootsie (12), Lucy (9) & Lily (4); [ambition] To be a successful Racehorse Trainer;

HEMMING, JESSICA: [b] 6/4/92; [home] Stoke Mandeville, Bucks; [p] Angela & Neil; [sister] Samantha; [school] William Harding Combined; [fav sub] Art; [hobbies] Karate, Writing Poems & Drawing; [ambition] To get a black belt in Karate and to be a Dress Designer;

HERD, ANDREW G.: [b] 24/2/90 Bromley; [home] Rayleigh, Essex; [p] David & Linda; [sister] Claire; [school] Downhall

Primary; [fav sub] Design Technology; [hobbies] Railway Modelling; [ambition] To be a Cameraman;

HEWETT, VICTORIA: [b] 31/3/89 High Wycombe; [home] Brandon, Suffolk; [p] Peter & Sandra; [sister] Kylie; [school] Breckland Middle; [fav sub] French & English; [hobbies] Swimming; [pets] Dog (Missy) & Hamster (Toffee); [ambition] To become an Air Hostess;

HEWISH, ELLIE: [b] 6/3/97 London; [home] Croydon, Surrey; [p] Mark & Annette; [brother] Jack (7); [sister] Bethany (3); [school] Tunstall Nursery; [fav sub] Playing with bricks; [hobbies] Playing with Barbie; [ambition] I would like to be a Princess when I grow up;

HILL, JADE: [b] 16/11/88 Taunton; [home] Wellington Somerset; [p] Helen & Martin; [school] Wellesley Park Primary; [fav sub] English & Art; [hobbies] Dancing, Singing & Writing poems; [pets] Dog (Hamish) [ambition] To become a successful Teacher of English;

HINKS, EMILY: [b] 17/2/92 Nottingham; [home] Gayton, Norfolk; [p] Deborah & William; [brother] Thomas; [sister] Ellen; [school] South Wootton Junior; [fav sub] History; [hobbies] Dancing, Drama, Gymnastics & Swimming; [pets] Cat (Nedd) & Guinea Pig (Daisy); [ambition] To be an Archaeologist, an Author and an Actress;

HIRST, SARAH ELIZABETH AVRIL: [b] 15/9/95 Torquay; [home] Crowmarsh Gifford, Oxon; [p] Tim & Kathryn; [sisters] Georgia & Madeleine; [school] Watlington Primary; [fav sub] Art & Craft; [hobbies] Drawing, Writing & Cycling with friends; [ambition] To be an Artist & Writer;

HOARE, GEORGE: [b] 24/8/84 Reading; [home] Reading, Berks; [p] Tony & Louisa; [brother] Harry; [school] Reading School; [fav sub] English; [hobbies] Football & Music; [pets] Cats (Spike & Dusty; [ambition] To study English at University and become a Journalist or Writer;

HOLDEN, ELIZABETH: [b] 26/7/88 Guildford; [home] Grayshott, Hants; [p] Ruth & John; [sister] Catherine; [school] Bohunt; [fav sub] French; [hobbies] Netball, Dancing & Music; [pets] 4 Goldfish; [ambition] To get a Poetry book published;

HOLDEN, JACK: [b] 11/5/89 Bath; [home] Corsham, Wilts; [p] Jude & Ian; [brothers] Robert & Tom; [school] Corsham; [fav sub] PE; [hobbies] Computer Games, Rugby, Cinema, Seeing Friends; [pets] Guinea Pig, Rabbit, 2 Hamsters, 2 Goldfish & 2 Mice;

HOLLEY, JESSICA: [b] 19/10/90; [home] Evesham, Worcs; [p] Mr & Mrs S. Holley;

[brother] Blake; [school] Swan Lane First; [fav sub] Art; [hobbies] Shopping & Music; [ambition] To get my A-Levels & to swim with Dolphins;

HOLMES, ALISTAIR: [b] 6/3/92 Redhill; [home] Redhill, Surrey; [p] Annette & Meyrick; [sisters] Gemma, Stephanie & Jessica; [school] St John's CP; [fav sub] Literacy (Reading & Writing); [hobbies] Football, Squash & Swimming; [ambition] To be a professional Sportsman & Author;

HOLMES, SARAH: [b] 1/11/92 Chertsey; [home] Walton-on-Thames, Surrey; [p] Steve & Sue; [brother] Stephen; [school] Ambleside Junior; [fav sub] Art; [hobbies] Ballet & Stagecoach (Performing Arts), Swimming & Reading; [ambition] To become a Vet or a Nurse;

HOLNESS, ADEM: [b] 26/12/89 London; [home] Stevenage, Herts; [p] Ingie & Neville; [brothers] Joseph & Theo; [sister] Nevin; [school] Peartree Spring Junior; [fav sub] Art & PE; [hobbies] Swimming, Basketball & Playstation; [ambition] To be a Lawyer;

HOLROYD, EMMA: [b] 27/4/90 Bexhill on Sea; [home] Bexhill, E. Sussex; [p] Juliette Shapiro & Chris Holroyd; [brothers] Michael & Cameron; [sister] Zoe; [school] Ninfield CofE; [fav sub] I can't decide!; [hobbies] Piano & Horses; [pets] Labrador Puppy; [ambition] To own my own Pony;

HOLT, LAUREN MELISSA: [b] 9/4/92 Watford; [home] Watford, Herts; [p] Ray & Kerry; [brother] Nathan; [school] Kingsway Junior; [fav sub] Art & English; [hobbies] Tap, Ballet & Swimming; [pets] 2 German Shepherds (Rosie & Sasha); [ambition] To swim with a Dolphin;

HONEYMAN, LISE: [b] 25/4/91 Oslo, Norway; [home] Tetsworth, Oxon; [p] Janice & Tony; [brother] James; [sister] Kirsten; [school] Aston Rowant; [fav sub] Poetry; [hobbies] Horse Riding; [pets] 5 Goldfish, 2 Dogs, 2 Ponies & 2 Horses, special pony is Charlie.com (found on the Internet); [ambition] To become a Vet;

HOOK, JAMES: [b] 7/9/91 Southampton; [home] New Milton, Hants; [p] Virginia; [brothers] John & Jay; [sisters] Vicki & Louise; [school] New Milton Junior; [fav sub] Games; [hobbies] Computer Games; [pets] Dog; [ambition] To be a Policeman;

HOOK, SARAH: [b] 28/4/90 Redditch; [home] Bromsgrove, Worcs; [p] Barbara & Geoff; [brother] Chris; [school] Aston Fields Middle; [fav sub] Design & Technology; [hobbies] Music: Flute & Keyboard; [ambition] To always do my best;

HOPES, CAITLIN ROSANNA: [b] 8/5/88 Greenwich; [home] Clacton-on-Sea, Essex; [p] Lorraine; [school] Tendring Technology

College; [fav sub] English & Art; [hobbies] Singing & Dancing; [pets] Cat (Tigger); [ambition] To be a Poet or an Author;

HOPLEY, DANIELLE: 12/9/91 Chester; [home] Blacon, Cheshire; [p] Helen & Andrew; [school] Thomas Wedge; [fav sub] English; [hobbies] Drama; [pets] Dog (Zoe); [ambition] To be famous;

HORNBY, CATHERINE: [b] 29/7/86 Colchester; [home] Clacton, Essex; [p] Philip & Sally; [sisters] Sarah & Elizabeth; [school] Tendring Technology College; [fav sub] Art; [hobbies] Drawing & Writing; [pets] Dog; [ambition] To be an Artist or Author;

HOUSTON, JAMIE NEIL: [b] 7/11/97 Chester; [home] Chester, Cheshire; [p] Derek & Kim; [sister] Kelly; [school] Upton-by-Chester High; [fav sub] PE & Sport; [hobbies] Tae Kwon Do; [pets] 4 Cats, Dog; [ambition] To be a famous Martial Artist;

HOWELL, SAM: [b] 24/4/93 Salisbury; [home] Guildford, Surrey; [p] Karen & Richard; [brother] Joe; [school] Sandfield CP; [fav sub] Sewing & Design Technology; [hobbies] Rollerblading; [pets] 4 Guinea Pigs; [ambition] To work in a Shop & visit Disneyland in Florida;

HOYT, RYON: [b] 20/2/88 Chelmsford; [home] Chelmsford, Essex; [p] Deborah & Jeff; [sister] Tayla; [school] The Hayward; [fav sub] PE; [hobbies] Football & Kung Fu; [pets] Dogs (Max & Storm); [ambition] To do my best;

HUGHES, JASON: [b] 8/1/88 Mitcham; [home] Mitcham, Surrey; [p] Ian; [brothers] Daniel & Chris; [sister] Jodie; [school] Bishopsford; [fav sub] Drama; [hobbies] Football & Singing; [pets] Bird & Fish; [ambition] To play football for Chelsea or get a No.1 Hit;

HUMM, EMMA LOUISE: [b] 3/3/93 Colchester; [home] Salcott, Essex; [p] Barry Humm & Julie Henderson; [brother] Conor; [school] Birch CofE Primary; [fav sub] PE; [hobbies] Reading, Poetry & Singing; [pets] Cat (Arthur); [ambition] To be a Pop Star;

HUMPHREYS, JOSHUA: [b] 3/1/90 Bangor; [home] Trefonen, Shropshire; [p] Marie & Russell; [brother] Ben; [sisters] Jessica & Ellie; [school] Trefonen; [fav sub] Art; [hobbies] Athletics & Cycling; [pets] Rabbit; [ambition] To be a famous Athlete;

HUNDLEY, ZOE LOUISE: [b] 12/9/89 Worcester; [home] South Littleton, Worcs; [p] Jonathan & Carol; [brother] Liam John; [school] Blackminster Middle; [fav sub] Art; [hobbies] Stamps & Beanie Collecting; [pets] 2 Dogs, 11 Guinea Pigs & 1 Snail; [ambition] To be a Vet;

HUSSEY, REBECCA: [b] 11/10/92

Oxford; [home] Tracy & David; [sister] Natasha; [school] John Hampden Primary; [fav sub] Maths; [hobbies] Swimming & Tennis; [pets] Hamster (Smokey); [ambition] To be a Farmer;

HYAM, GISELLE: [b] 2/10/88 Ashford; [home] Kennington, Kent; [p] Michelle & Russell; [brother] Fernand; [school] St Anselms; [fav sub] PE; [hobbies] Athletics; [pets] Hamster (Chewy); [ambition] To be an Interior Designer or a Vet;

IBRAHIM, LEYLA: [b] 20/6/86 Maidstone; [home] Bromley, Kent; [p] Hüseyin & Claire; [brother] Kaan; [sister] Sûreya & Antalya; [school] Baston; [fav sub] PE; [hobbies] All Sports; [ambition] To become a great Athlete;

IBRAHIM, LIBAN: [b] 15/10/91 Penge; [home] Beckenham; [p] Mohamed Ibrahim; [brother] Iman; [sister] Ladan; [school] Royston Primary;

INNES, MARK: [b] 14/12/88 Hackney; [home] Chingford, Essex; [p] John & Susan; [brothers] Iain & David; [school] Hayward; [fav sub] Technology; [hobbies] Cars; [pets] Dog, 3 Cats & Giant African Snails; [ambition] To become a Mechanic;

ISMAY, HAYLEY SIAN: [b] 15/3/90 Wokingham; [home] Winnersh, Berks; [p] Fran & Mike; [sister] Nicole; [school] Bearwood Primary; [fav sub] Literacy & Art; [hobbies] Dancing; [pets] Cats (Tom & Harry); [ambition] To be a professional Dancer or a Graphic Designer;

IVES, RAE FRANCESCA: [b] 28/7/88 Farnborough; [home] West Wickham, Kent; [p] Raymond & Jackie; [brother] Nico; [school] Baston; [fav sub] Art, English & PE; [hobbies] Singing Dancing & Drama; [pets] Dog (Flora) & Cat (Katie); [ambition] To become a Vet;

JACKSON, BONNIE: [b] 10/9/88 Sidcup; [home] Shooters Hill, London; [p] Miss Bernice Jackson; [school] Babbington House; [fav sub] English; [hobbies] Running & Writing; [pets] Goldfish & Dogs; [ambition] To travel the world;

JACKSON, LAURA: [b] 19/9/89 Redhill; [home] Merstham, Surrey; [p] Graham & Dytha; [brother] Philip; [school] Merstham Primary; [fav sub] Maths & Science; [hobbies] Horse Riding; [pets] Cats, Birds, Rabbits & Hamster; [ambition] To be a Biologist;

JACKSON, SOPHIE: [b] 22/12/92 London; [home] Farnham, Surrey; [p] Eileen & Doug; [brother] Sam; [school] St Peters; [fav sub] PE; [hobbies] Swimming; [pets] Dog, 2 Cats, Gerbil & Fish; [ambition] To become a Veterinary Nurse;

JACQUES, KELLIE LOUISE: [b]

21/9/91 Minster; [home] Minster Sheppey, Kent; [p] Kevin & Cimanda; [brother] Arran; [school] Halfway Houses Primary; [fav sub] Art & English; [hobbies] Dancing, Writing & Reading; [pets] Cat (Lacey); [ambition] To become an Author;

JAEGER, NATANYA: [b] 31/5/90 Luton; [home] Hemel Hempstead, Herts; [p] Sandra & Martin; [sister] Natasha; [school] Two Waters; [fav sub] English; [hobbies] Dancing & Singing; [ambition] To be a Singer and write my own music;

JAMES, ELEANOR: [b] 18/5/89 Guildford; [home] Liphook, Hants; [p] Richard & Jane; [sister] Natasha; [school] Bohunt; [fav sub] PE; [hobbies] Dancing & Swimming; [pets] Hamster (Buffy) belongs to my sister; [ambition] To be a TV Make Up Artist;

JAMES, KATY VICTORIA: [b] 26/4/91 Oxford; [home] Grove, Oxon; [p] Cheryl & Ray; [brother] Matthew; [school] Millbrook Primary; [fav sub] Art; [hobbies] Dancing & Reading; [pets] Cat, Hamster & Fish; [ambition] To work with animals;

JAMES, MARCUS: [b] 30/5/93 Guildford; [home] Guildford, Surrey; [p] Lance & Nicola; [school] Sandfield CP; [fav sub] Drama; [hobbies] Liverpool F.C.; [pets] Rabbit, Guinea Pig & Hamster; [ambition] To be a famous Actor or Pop Star;

JAMES, SIENNA: [b] 11/10/90 London; [home] Amersham, Bucks; [p] Ariane & Ray; [sisters] Electra & Ria; [school] Little Chalfont County Combined; [fav sub] PE, Science, PHSE; [hobbies] Swimming, Gymnastics, Singing & Drama; [ambition] To become a Lawyer or Actress;

JAVED, ADNAAN: [b] 2/5/90 Bradford; [home] Bradford, W. Yorks; [p] Nasreen & Mohammed; [brother] Zeeshan; [sisters] Zebun & Mehrun; [school] St Phillips Primary; [fav sub] Science; [hobbies] Football & Reading; [pets]Would love an Eagle; [ambition] To be a Doctor and save lives;

JEFFERY, RHIAN: [b] 27/6/89 London; [home] Rayleigh, Essex; [p] Paul & Glynis; [brothers] Craig (19) & Sean (14); [school] The Arts Educational; [fav sub] Ballet, Modern & Science; [hobbies] Dancing; [ambition] To appear in 'Cats' & other West End Stage Productions. (Musical Theatre);

JENKIN, SOPHIE: [b] 19/5/94 Yeovil; [home] Yeovil, Somerset; [p] Douglas & Charmaine; [sister] Katie; [school] Pen Mill; [fav sub] PE; [pets] Cat (Sooty);

JENNER, JASON: [b] 7/5/91 King's Lynn; [home] King's Lynn, Norfolk; [p] Mandy & Dvid; [brothers] Steven & Chris; [school] South Wooton Junior; [fav sub] History & Art; [hobbies] BMX Riding; [ambition] To be an Actor & win Dirt Bike Races;

JEWSBURY, SOPHIE: [b] 2/6/94 Harrow, Middx; [home] Little Chalfont, Bucks; [p] Alison & Robin; [brothers] Alex (5) & David (2); [school] Little Chalfont County Combined; [fav sub] English; [hobbies] Swimming, Skipping & Disco Dancing; [ambition] To be a Ballerina or Poet;

JOHANSEN, DAVID: [b] 5/6/90 Stevenage; [home] Stevenage, Herts; [p] Tracey; [brother] Richard; [sister] Anne-Marie; [school] Peartree Junior; [fav sub] Maths; [hobbies] Playing Games & watching TV; [pets] 4 Cats, 2 Dogs & Goldfish; [ambition] To be a really good Vet;

JONES, CLAIRE: [b] 13/10/86 Hampstead; [home] Chelmsford, Essex; [p] Debbie & Terry; [sisters] Srebecca & Natalie; [school] Rainsford High; [fav sub] PE & Art; [hobbies] Netball & Drawing; [ambition] To be a PE Teacher & help save animals kept in cruel conditions;

JONES, DARREN: [b] 5/1/88 Gillingham; [home] Wigmore, Kent; [p] Bev & Carol; [brother] Andrew; [sister] Kellyanne; [school] Rainham Mark Grammar; [fav sub] French; [hobbies] Reading; [pets] Cat (Billy); [ambition] To be a Writer;

JONES, ELLEN: [b] 7/6/94 London; [home] Surbiton, Surrey; [p] Justin & Barbara; [sister] Georgia; [school] Tolworth Infants; [fav sub] English; [hobbies] Drama & Dancing; [pets] Cats; [ambition] To be a Ballet Dancer;

JONES, MEGAN KATIE: [b] 7/9/93 Adlington; [home] Adlington, Lancs; [p] Gill & Glyn; [brother] Ryan Cantona; [school] Adlington CP; [fav sub] Reading; [hobbies] Horse Riding & Art; [pets] Horse & 2 Parrots; [ambition] To become a Vet;

JONES, RACHEL: [b] 25/8/90 Rochford; [home] Rayleigh, Essex; [p] Thomas & Dorothy; [brother] Matthew; [school] Downhall CP; [fav sub] Science & English; [hobbies] Football & Karate; [pets] 2 Japanese Spitz Dogs; [ambition] To be an Actress in a Soap;

JONES, RHIANNON LOUISE: [b] 25/10/92 Chester; [home] Chester, Cheshire; [p] Deren & Colin; [brothers] Thomas & Gareth; [school] Thomas Wedge; [fav sub] Art; [hobbies] Swimming; [ambition] To swim in the Olympics;

JONES, SHELBY: [b] 3/5/92 Stafford; [home] Bicester, Oxon; [p] Amanda & Andrew; [sister] Shannon; [school] Glory Farm Primary; [fav sub] Art; [hobbies] Ballet, Tap & Pop Music; [pets] German Shepherd (Marcus); [ambition] To be an Artist or Illustrator;

JORDAN, CHLOE: [b] 18/1/88 London; [home] Wimbledon, London; [p] Mary & Lionel; [sister] Emma; [school] St Catherines; [fav sub] English; [hobbies] Piano; [ambition] To be a Writer;

JURY, PHILIP IAN LUMBSDEN: [b] 18/11/91 Southampton; [home] New Milton, Hants; [p] Jeffrey & Barbara; [sister] Sarah; [school] New Milton Junior; [fav sub] Design Technology; [hobbies] Stamp Collecting & Football; [pets] Cats (Tom & Poppy); [ambition] To fly in a spaceship to Pluto & become the world's best Footballer;

KASSAM, IMRAN: [b] 5/12/88 London; [p] Dr & Mrs S.G. Kassam; [sister] Aziza; [school] Northwood Preparatory; [fav sub] Maths & Art; [hobbies] Badminton, Drums & Piano; [pets] Goldfish (Pepsi & Coke); [ambition] To be a successful Banker;

KAYE, NIGEL: [b] 12/10/87 Wordsley; [home] Kidderminster, Worcs; [p] Wendy & Murray; [sister] Chelsey; [school] Sladen Middle; [fav sub] English & Maths; [hobbies] Skateboarding; [pets] Hamster (Nelson); [ambition] To win a 'Nobel' Prize award;

KEENLYSIDE, HARLEY NICOLE: [b] 14/3/94 Enfield; [home] Waltham X, Herts; [p] Michelle; [brother] William Jo; [school] Bonneygrove Primary; [fav sub] Writing Stories; [hobbies] Football; [pets] Mice; [ambition] To be a Horse Rider;

KELLY, CHARLOTTE: [b] 15/4/93 Gt. Yarmouth; [home] Gorleston, Norfolk; [p] Stephen & Denise; [brother] Daniel; [sister] Emma; [school] Cliff Park First; [fav sub] Maths & Art; [hobbies] All Sports; [pets] Cats; [ambition] To be a Princess or a Hairdresser;

KEMP, LAURA FENOLA: [b] 15/10/89 Canterbury; [home] Whitstable, Kent; [p] Thérèsa & Paul; [sisters] Twins-Hannah & Megan (9) & Katie (3); [school] Joy Lane County Junior; [fav sub] History; [hobbies] Reading, Writing, Playing Violin & Roller Skating; [pets] Bearded Collie (Charlie) & Cats (Pepper & Jazz); [ambition] To be a Vet:

KEMP, MEGAN BETHANY: [b] 7/7/91 Canterbury; [home] Whitstable, Kent; [p] Thérèsa & Paul; [sisters] Laura (11) & Twin-Hannah (9) & Katie (3); [school] Joy Lane County Junior; [fav sub] English; [hobbies] Swimming, Reading, Playing Keyboard & Roller Skating; [pets] Bearded Collie (Charlie) & Cats (Pepper & Jazz); [ambition] To work with animals;

KEMP, REBECCA: [b] 18/7/90 Maidstone; [home] E.Malling, Kent; [p] Andrew & Jill; [sister] Sophie; [school] Offham CP; [fav sub] Art; [hobbies] Netball & Rounders; [pets] 2 Cats & Guinea Pig; [ambition] To do well at School and to be happy;

KENDALL, LOUISE: [b] 21/8/90 Essex; [home] Theydon Bois, Essex; [p] Brian & Karen; [brother] Paul; [school] Theydon Bois Primary; [fav sub] English; [hobbies] Swimming, Netball & Reading; [pets] Cats (Misty & Foggy); Hamster (Smokey); [ambition] To become a famous Writer or be in the Olympic Swimming Team;

KENNY, NICHOLAS JAMES: [b] 11/2/90 Chertsey; [home] Walton-on-Thames, Surrey; [p] Valerie & Anthony; [sister] Victoria; [school] Ambleside Junior; [fav sub] English; [hobbies] Football, Tennis & Swimming; [pets] Budgie, Hamster, Rabbit & Guinea Pig; [ambition] To be rich and successful;

KEOHANE, ABBY ELIZABETH: [b] 3/6/92 Gloucester; [home] Quedgeley, Glos; [p] Andy & Sharon; [brother] Richard; [school] Field Court Junior; [fav sub] Information/Communication Technology; [hobbies] Horse Riding, Arts & Crafts, Drawing & Board Games; [pets] Parrot (Sophie), Rabbit (Magic) & Guinea Pig (Monty); [ambition] To be an Air Stewardess;

KERR, ALASTAIR: [b] 17/4/91 Chesham; [home] Chesham, Bucks; [p] Fiona; [brother] Alan; [school] Little Chalfont County Combined; [fav sub] Art; [hobbies] Judo & Cubs; [pets] Hamster; [ambition] To do Extreme Sports;

KETT, CHRISSY: [b] 8/10/89 Watford; [home] Borehamwood, Herts; [p] Roger & Gillian; [sister] Laura; [school] Newberries Primary; [fav sub] English; [hobbies] Drama, Dance, Reading; [pets] Rabbits (Lucky & Mischief); [ambition] To do something creative like performing or designing;

KING, REBEKAH: [b] 16/4/90 London; [home] Beckenham, Kent; [p] Suzanne & Stephen; [brother] Antony; [sister] Francesca; [school] St Mary's RC Primary; [fav sub] Art; [hobbies] Dance, Creative Writing, Swimming & Girl Guides; [pets] Rat, Cat & Tropical Fish; [ambition] To work with animals and visit all the Greek Islands;

KING, ROSIE: [b] 13/5; [home] Aylesbury, Bucks; [p] Jennifer; [brother] Rory; [school] William Harding; [fav sub] Maths; [hobbies] Trampoline, Swimming & Ballet; [pets] Dog (Lucy); [ambition] Anything to do with the Trampoline;

KINGSHOTT, DANIEL JASON: [b] 24/10/93 Guildford; [home] Chilworth, Surrey; [p] Andrew & Nina; [brother] Joshua Andrew; [school] Chilworth C of E Infant;

KIRK, LOUISA HICKLING: [b] 22/10/86 Derby; [home] Stanton-on-the-Wolds, Notts; [p] I live with my mother & stepfather Carole & Kenneth Kirk. My father lives on a narrowboat and I see him quite often; [sisters] Victoria & Samantha; [school] Loughborough High; [fav sub] History, German & ICT; [hobbies] Swimming, Horse Riding, Shopping & Fencing; [pets] Cats (Eve & Melody) & Dogs (Jack & Elsa); [ambition]

To become a Lawyer, do a lot of Drama & write my own films;

KNEEBONE, LAURA: [b] 6/2/90 Chalfont St Giles; [home] Chalfont St Giles, Bucks; [p] Alicia & Stephen; [brother] Christopher; [school] Little Chalfont Combined; [fav sub] Maths; [hobbies] Netball & Badminton; [pets] Fish;

KNIGHT, ZOË ROBYN ALICE: [b] 14/5/92 Wendover; [home] Aylesbury, Bucks; [p] Richard & Kaye; [brothers] Calam & Adam; [school] William Harding Combined; [fav sub] Maths; [hobbies] Dancing; [pets] Dog (Odin) & Cat (Sophie);

KNOWLES, ANNA: [b] 25/9/90 St Albans; [home] Harpenden, Herts; [p] Jane & John; [brother] Simon; [sisters] Helen & Alison; [school] Crabtree Junior; [fav sub] History; [hobbies] Horse Riding, Swimming & Tennis; [pets] Dog, Cat, 3 Guinea Pigs, Rabbit & 2 Fish; [ambition] To work with animals;

LADKIN, KATE: [b] 15/8/88 Sidcup; [home] Bexley, Kent; [p] Caroline & Alen; [sister] Emma; [school] Babington House; [fav sub] Art & Textiles; [hobbies] Singing, Gymnastics & Ballet; [pets] Cat (Scampi) & Guinea Pig (Tilly); [ambition] To be a Teacher;

LAMB, MICHAEL: [b] 14/5/88 Eastcote, Middx; [home] Pinner, Middx; [p] Stephen & Nicola; [brother] David; [school] Northwood Prep'; [fav sub] English & Maths; [hobbies] Reading, Cycling, Sport & Animals; [pets] Cat (Vickers) & Goldfish (Squeak); [ambition] To play Rugby, become a Vet and travel the Galaxy!;

LAMBERT, TORIA: [b] 6/2/88 Aldershot; [home] Fleet, Hants; [p] Bron & Richard; [brother] Bill; [sister] Alexandra; [school] Court Moor; [fav sub] English; [hobbies] Majorettes, Reading & Drama; [pets] Rabbit, 2 Hamsters & 3 guinea Pigs; [ambition] To become a Journalist;

LAMBETH, CHRISTOPHER: [b] 4/5/93 Farnborough, Kent; [home] Beckenham, Kent; [p] Mary & Richard; [sister] Katherine; [school] St Mary's Catholic Primary; [fav sub] Maths; [hobbies] Football, Chess & playing the Cello; [ambition] To be a professional Footballer;

LAM-MOORES, CHLOÈ: [b] 12/3/92 Rawtenstall; [home] Rossendale, Lancs; [p] Pui Wan Lam & David Moores; [brother] Joseph Moores; [sister] Holly Lam-Moores; [school] Constable Lee St Pauls; [fav sub] Poetry; [hobbies] Horse Riding; [pets] Rabbit; [ambition] To become a Vet;

LANDER, CHARLOTTE: [b] 28/12/90 Farnborough; [home] Swanley, Kent; [p] Susan & Keith; [sister] Emma; [school] Crockenhill CP; [fav sub] English, Art & History; [hobbies] Swimming & Reading;

[pets] Cat (Sparky) & Rabbit (Hoppy); [ambition] To be an Author or Dancer;

LANDS, SARA: [b] 19/7/90 Croydon; [home] Thornton Heath, Surrey; [p] David & Linda; [sister] Ellen; [school] St James The Great; [fav sub] English & Art; [hobbies] Reading & Guides; [pets] Goldfish (Ellie & Slippery); [ambition] To be an Author and Illustrator;

LANGFORD, BILLY: [b] 5/3/90 Enfield, Middx; [home] Cheshunt, Herts; [p] Steve & Michelle; [brother] Charlie; [sister] Nikki; [school] Bonneygrove Primary; [fav sub] Science; [hobbies] Rugby; [pets] Hamster (Nibbles); [ambition] To own my own Company;

LAWLESS, RICKY: [b] 30/10/89 Thornton Heath; [home] Thornton Heath, Surrey; [p] Debbie & Trevor; [brother] Ben; [sister] Terri; [school] St James The Great; [fav sub] Art; [hobbies] Football; [ambition] To be an Actor;

LAWRENCE, MADELEINE EMMA: [b] 27/11/90 Gravesend; [home] South Fleet, Kent; [p] Deborah & Patrick; [sisters] Farrah & Natasha; [school] Sedleys CE Primary; [fav sub] English; [hobbies] Dancing, Piano, Guitar, Swimming & Football; [pets] Cat; [ambition] To become a Doctor;

LEE, MATTHEW: [b] 8/1/90 Reading; [home] Reading, Berks; [p] Simon & Nikki; [brothers] Thomas & Ryan; [school] Micklands Primary; [fav sub] Art & English; [hobbies] Football; [ambition] To be an Artist or something to with Art;

LEE, REBECCA LOUISE: [b] 6/7/92 Preston; [home] Adlington, Lancs; [p] Phillip & Susan; [sisters] Vicky; [school] Adlington Primary; [fav sub] English; [hobbies] Reading & Swimming; [pets] Guinea Pigs (William & Peter); [ambition] To become a Vet;

LEHANE, TARA ELIZABETH: [b] 19/11/89 Croydon; [home] Norbury, London; [p] Kevin & Sheila; [brothers] Thomas & Nicholas; [school] St James The Great RC; [fav sub] English; [hobbies] Dancing, Acting & Swimming; [pets] Rabbit (Pickles) & Budgie (Harriet); [ambition] To be a Poet or a Vet;

LEIGH, RACHEL: [b] 23/7/90 Wexham Park; [home] Denham, Bucks; [p] Shaun & Debbie; [brother] Adam; [school] Tilehouse; [fav sub] Art; [hobbies] Drama; [pets] Cat; [ambition] To become an Actress;

LENNON, CONOR: [b] 6/3/93 Carshalton; [home] Beckenham, Kent; [p] Kevin & Gill; [brother] Ciaran; [school] St Mary's RC; [fav sub] English; [hobbies] Karate & Swimming; [ambition] To be a Wrestler;

LEVENE, RACHEL: [b] 9/7/88 [home] Leicestershire; [school] Loughborough High School;

LEVETT, JESSICA: [b] 8/6/91 Kings Lynn; [home] Kings Lynn, Norfolk; [p] Penny & Paul; [school] South Wootton Junior; [fav sub] Art & Technology; [hobbies] Playing the Keyboard & Choir; [pets] Bearded Collie (Dylan); [ambition] To work with animals or teach people the Keyboard;

LEWIS, BLISS: [b] 31/5/92 Whitstable; [home] Whitstable, Kent; [p] Robert & Julie; [sister] Holly; [school] The Endowed; [fav sub] PE; [hobbies] Gymnastics & Swimming; [pets] 2 Cats & 2 Fish; [ambition] To become a Teacher;

LEYLAND, WILLIAM: [b] 4/7/94 Salisbury; [home] Salisbury, Wilts; [p] Pete & Paula; [brothers] Sam & Alex; [school] Highbury First; [fav sub] Reading; [hobbies] Cycling; [ambition] To be a Policeman;

LILBURN, ALEX [b] 5/12/89 Macclesfield; [home] New Milton, Hants; [p] Mal & Julie; [brothers] James & Cerith; [sister] Rebecca; [school] New Milton Junior; [fav sub] Maths; [hobbies] Football, Swimming & Tennis; [pets] Golden Retriever (Dougal); [ambition] To play professional Football;

LILLEY, HEATHER: [b] 27/3/90 Aylesbury; [home] Aylesbury, Bucks; [p] A & K Lilley; [brother] David; [sister] Michelle; [school] Turnfurlong Junior; [fav sub] Design & Technology; [hobbies] Keyboard, Drums & Animals; [pets] Dog & Hamster; [ambition] To be a Writer or Teacher, have a Flat and adopt a child;

LILLEY, JAMES J.: [b] 18/8/87 Keighley; [home] Keighley, W. Yorks; [p] Lynne & Stephen; [school] Oakbank; [fav sub] Biology; [hobbies] Swimming & Piano; [pets] Cat (Katy); [ambition] To be a Zoologist;

LILLINGTON, DANIELLE: [b] 8/2/88 Birmingham; [home] Bromsgrove, Worcs; [p] Steve & Lynn; [brother] Ashley; [sister] Stephanie; [school] Aston Fields Middle; [fav sub] Science; [hobbies] Netball, Basketball, Ski-ing, Music & Tag-Rugby; [ambition] To have a happy life, become a Doctor and make a parachute jump;

LIM, WILLIAM: [b] 29/5/88 Chelmsford; [home] Great Waltham, Essex; [p] Toni; [sister] Constance; [school] Hayward; [fav sub] Maths; [hobbies] Swimming; [pets] Guinea Pig; [ambition] To become an Actor;

LIMBRICK, RUBY: [b] 23/1/91; [home] Thames Ditton, Surrey; [p] Julie & Martin; [sister] Isabelle; [school] Thames Ditton Juniors;]fav sub] Music; [hobbies] Clarinet & Sailing; [pets] Hamster (Lady Penelope);

LINFORD, EMMA JAYNE: [b] 7/7/89 Burnley; [home] Briarfield, Lancs; [p] John & Elaine; [sister] Rebecca; [school] St Hilda's RC Girls; [fav sub] Art; [hobbies] Horse Riding, Swimming & Music; [pets] Fish; [ambition] Nursing;

LINSELL, CATHERINE: [b] 8/2/91 Chichester; [home] Chorley, Lancs; [p] Judith & David; [sister] Abigail & Rose; [school] Euxton C of E; [fav sub] History; [hobbies] Horse Riding & Trumpet; [pets] Cat (Rambo);

LIPTROT, ZOE EMILY: [b] 30/6/92 Leyland; [home] Preston, Lancs; [p] Kathleen Howson; [brother] Charlie Howson; [sister] Stephanie Liptrot; [school] St James CE; [fav sub] Art; [pets] Horse, Chipmonks, Dog, Cat & Ferrets; [ambition] To be a Zoo Keeper;

LITTLE, CHARLOTTE: [b] 8/1/92 Salisbury; [home] Salisbury, Wilts; [p] George & Sara; [brother] Jack; [school] Highbury First; [fav sub] Maths; [hobbies] Craft Work & Paper Making; [pets] 1 Goldfish; [ambition] To visit Australia and have an interesting and enjoyable job;

LOADER, AMY: [b] 15/7/92 Southampton; [home] New Milton, Hants; [p] John & Julie; [brother] Shane; [school] New Milton Junior; [fav sub] Writing; [hobbies] Singing, Dancing & Horse Riding; [pets] Rabbit (Thumper); [ambition] To do well at School;

LONG, SAMUEL: [b] 22/7/91 Manchester; [home] Harpenden, Herts; [p] Colleen Williamson & Robert Long; [brother] Jake; [school] Crabtree Juniors; [fav sub] History; [hobbies] Football, Reading, Cycling & Music; [ambition] To be a Singer, Musician and Computer Games Designer;

LONGLEY, JAMES ANDREW: [b] 16/4/92 Gravesend; [home] Swanley, Kent; [p] Derek & Teresa; [sister] Rebecca Alice (4½); [school] Crocken Hill CP; [fav sub] Maths & Geography; [hobbies] Football & Reading Reference Books; [pets] Cats (Ash & Charlie); [ambition] To visit Australia and swim with Dolphins;

LOUDEN, VICTORIA (VICKI): [b] 28/2/88 Maldon; [home] Althorne, Essex; [p] Martin & Debbie; [sister] Laura; [school] Hayward; [fav sub] Art; [hobbies] Swimming, Dancing & Horse Riding; [pets] Dog (Suzi); [ambition] To be a good Hairdresser;

LOVELL, IAIN: [b] 17/4/90 Redhill; [home] Merstham, Surrey; [p] Martin & Mary Ann; [sister] Naomi; [school] Merstham Primary; [fav sub] Science; [hobbies] Stamps, Sea Cadets & Bluebell Railway; [ambition] To join the Navy;

LOWE, AMY JENNY: [b] 6/11/93 Chigwell; [home] Waltham Abbey, Essex;

[p] John & Susie; [sister] Lisa & Vicky; [school] Waltham Holy Cross Infants; [fav sub] Literacy (at school), Scooby Doo (not at school); [hobbies] Swimming, Ballet & Brownies; [pets] Cat (Smudge); [ambition] To become a Vet;

LOZINSKI, ALEXANDER: [b] 23/1/93 Colchester; [home] Brightlingsea, Essex; [p] Richard & Pam; [brother] Julian; [school] Birch C of E Primary; [fav sub] English & Art; [hobbies] Drawing, Computer Games & Model Railways; [ambition] To be an Artist and Designer;

LUCAS, ELLIE: [b] 5/1/91 Oxford; [home] Grove, Oxon; [p] Steve & Alyson; [brother] Stuart; [sister] Hayley; [school] Millbrook; [fav sub] PE; [hobbies] Drama, Violin & Running; [pets] Guinea Pigs & a Puppy; [ambition] To be a Vet, Footballer, Singer & Actress;

LYNCH, LUCY: [b] 2/3/93 London; [home] Watford, Herts; [p] Sue & Adrian; [brother] Jamie; [school] Kingsway Junior; [fav sub] Maths; [hobbies] Roller Skating & Swimming; [pets] Hamster (Bubbles);

LYNES, ZOE LOUISE: [b] 3/5/91 Banbury; [home] Horley, Oxon; [p] Ian & June; [brother] Christopher; [school] Wroxton CE Primary; [fav sub] Maths, History & Art; [hobbies] Brownies & Skipping; [pets] Cat; [ambition] To be a Cook & Food Critic;

MACE, RYAN: [b] 20/6/90 [home] Brentwood, Essex; [p] Ann & Keith; [brother] Kevin; [sister] Natasha; [school] Kelvedon Hatch; [fav sub] Maths; [hobbies] Football; [pets] Cat & Rabbit; [ambition] To be a Footballer;

MACKIE, SAFFRON: [b] 20/6/92 Keighley; [home] Haworth, W. Yorks; [p] John & Vanessa; [sister] Jade; [school] Haworth Primary; [fav sub] Art, English & History; [hobbies] Athletics, Gymnastics, Drawing & Football; [pets] Persian Cat (Simba); [ambition] To be a Cartoonist, Illustrator or Scientist;

MACKLIN, MAXINE: [b] 23/9/89 Kingston on Thames; [home] Shepperton, Middx; [p] Debbie & Mark; [brother] Jack; [sisters] Alisha & Ellie; [school] Springfield; [fav sub] Art; [hobbies] Drawing & Sports; [pets] 2 Cats; [ambition] To be a Marine Biologist;

MAHMOOD, ZEENAT: [b] 21/5/90 Bradford; [home] Bradford, W. Yorks; [p] Mr & Mrs Shah; [brother] Qasim Ali; [sister] Zahra Naqvi; [school] Lapage Primary; [fav sub] Art & English; [hobbies] Writing Poetry, Art & Reading; [ambition] To be a G.P., Author of poetry or a Teacher;

MAHONEY, JADE: [b] 5/9/91 Bradford;

[home] Shelf, W. Yorks; [p] Karen Mahoney & Carl Bridgewater; [brothers] Jamie & Timothy Mahoney & Paul Bridgewater; [sisters] Teresa Mahoney & Laura Bridgewater; [school] Buttershaw Primary; [fav sub] Maths; [hobbies] Horse Riding, Football, Baking, Recorder, Rollerblading, Music & Cycling; [pets] Cat; [ambition] To be a Vet & own my own Horse;

MAKIN, LAUREN BETHANY: [b] 22/11/90 Northallerton, N. Yorks; [home] Wroxton, Oxon; [p] Richard & Diane; [brother] Stuart Adam; [school] Wroxton CP; [fav sub] Literacy & Writing; [hobbies] Ballet, Karate, Scouts & Royal British Legion Youth Band; [pets] Greyhounds (Tammy & Joey) & Hamster (Houdini); [ambition] To own and run a small animal farm with my friend Leah;

MANNING, CONNOR: [b] 17/3/92 London; [home] Norfolk; [brother] Philip; [sister] Scarlett; [school] Mileham Primary; [fav sub] Sports, English & Science; [hobbies] Football, Judo & Tennis;

MANNION, NATHALIE C.: [b] 17/12/91 Bradford; [home] Bradford, W.Yorks; [p] Paul Mannion & Julie Spence; [brother] Louis, James; [school] St Francis RC Primary; [fav sub] Maths; [hobbies] Dancing, Swimming, Drawing, & Playing; [ambition] To be a Teacher or Solicitor;

MARCHESELLI, MAX: [b] 11/9/89 London; [home] Kelvedon Hatch, Essex; [p] Karin & Gian; [sister] Franziska; [school] Kelvedon Hatch CP; [fav sub] Science; [hobbies] Tennis & Football; [ambition] To play Tennis or become an Athlete;

MARKS, OLIVER JAMES: [b] 18/5/90 Rochford; [home] Rayleigh, Essex; [p] Robin & Lesley; [sisters] Megan & Jemma; [school] Down Hall Primary; [fav sub] Art; [hobbies] Golf; [pets] Dog & Cat; [ambition] To become a racing car Designer;

MARSHALL, JOSHUA: [b] 25/8/92 Reading; [home] Caversham, Berks; [p] Pauline & Kevin; [brother] Chris; [sister] Kate; [school] Micklands; [fab sub] Poetry; [hobbies] Football; [pets] Hamster, 2 Cats & 2 Fish; [ambition] To be a Policeman;

MARSHALL, THOMAS: [b] 27/11/91 Grimsby; [home] Quedgeley, Glos; [p] Donna; [brothers] Oliver & Daniel; [school] Fieldcourt Junior; [fav sub] Science; [hobbies] WWF, Playstation & Cycling; [pets] Cat (Bobby); [ambition] To design and create new games and videos;

MARTAYN, LAURA RACHEL: [b] 1/12/92 Chester; [home] Chester, Cheshire; [p] Vince & Helena; [brother] Jordan; [school] Thomas Wedge Junior; [fav sub] Art; [hobbies] Dancing-Tap, Ballet & Modern, Reading & Brownies; [ambition] To be a Dancer;

MARTIN, ABBEY ANN: [b] 6/9/92 Gorleston; [home] Hopton, Norfolk; [p] Simon & Julie; [sister] Esme Niamh; [school] Cliff Park First; [fav sub] Art & English; [hobbies] Karate & Horse Riding; [pets] Bulldog (Bertie), Cats (Boots & Bumble); [ambition] To be a Policewoman or a Singer;

MARTIN, HOLLY: [b] 26/9/91 Ware; [home] Ware, Herts; [p] Michelle & Barry; [brother] Danny; [sister] Sophie; [school] Christchurch JMI; [fav sub] Art; [hobbies] Drawing & Writing; [pets] None, but would like a Cat & a Hamster!; [ambition] To be a Vet, Writer or Illustrator;

MASKELL, DANIELLE: [b] 15/6/93 Newport; [home] Risca, Gwent; [p] Richard & Rachel; [school] Risca Primary; [fav sub] Music; [hobbies] Horse Riding & Swimming; [pets] Rabbit & Hamster; [ambition] To work with Horses;

MASON, JOSHUA: [b] 30/10/91 Chester; [home] Saughall, Cheshire; [p] Will & Tracey; [brother] David; [sister] Katie & Hollie; [school] Thomas Wedge; [fav sub] Literacy; [hobbies] To be with my Dogs; [pets] 2 Dogs & 4 Fish; [ambition] To work with animals;

MASSEY, JAIDE MAY: [b] 1/4/92 Oxford; [home] Thame, Oxon; [p] Dawn & David; [brother] Adam; [sister] Brogan; [school] John Hampden Primary; [fav sub] English & Sciences; [hobbies] Reading;

MASTERS, ALEX: [b] 27/6/90 Swindon; [home] Wilcot, Wilts; [p] Tony & Heather; [½ brother] Jamie; [½ sister] Ruth; [school] Oare CE Primary; [fav sub] Maths; [hobbies] Skateboarding; [pets] 2 Cats & Fish; [ambition] To be a Skateboarder;

MASTERS, JORDAN: [b] 13/4/91 Chertsey; [home] Poringland, Norfolk; [p] Mark & Sue; [brother] Jake; [school] Poringland Primary; [fav sub] Art & Music; [hobbies] Horse Riding & Gymnastics; [ambition] To own my own horse;

MATTHEWS, EMMA: [b] 3/5/93 Welwyn Garden City; [home] Ware, Herts; [p] Christine & Paul; [brother] Thomas; [school] Christ Church CEVA Primary & Nursery; [fav sub] Art; [hobbies] Collecting Beanie Babies TY; [pets] Fish; [ambition] To be a Story Writer & a Vet;

MATTHEWS, KIZZY: [b] 22/4/91 Cheltenham; [home] Whitminster, Glos; [p] Rosemary; [school] Whitminster Endowed CofE; [fav sub] Art & History; [hobbies] Swimming & Painting; [pets] Guinea Pig (Fidget); [ambition] To be a Writer, Pop Star or Policewoman;

MAXWELL, JAMES: [b] 29/1/90 Yeovil; [home] March, Cambs; [brothers] Ben, Joe & Thomas; [school] All Saints Primary; [fav sub] Art; [hobbies] Hokey Pokemon; [pets] Cats (Bubble, Squeak & Joy); [ambition] To be a Police Firearms Officer;

MAYNARD, DIONNE: [b] 7/4/88 Bracknell; [home] Bracknell, Berks; [p] Erol & Caroline; [brothers] Gary & Reese; [sister] Leanne; [school] Garth Hill; [fav sub] Music & English; [hobbies] Ice Skating; [pets] Dog (Lexus); [ambition] To become a Singer and Child Minder;

McCALL, ROSIE: [b] 27/1/93 Chapel Hill, USA; [home] London; [p] James & Caitlin; [sisters] Alice & Imogen; [school] Belmont Primary; [fav sub] Art; [hobbies] Art, Cycling & Piano; [pets] Cat (Daisy); [ambition] To be a Scientist & travel the world;

McCALMONT, NATALIE: [b] 20/12/88 Omagh; [home] Chester, Cheshire; [p] Karen & Cedric; [brother] Oliver; [school] Upton High; [fav sub] Drama & PE; [hobbies] Ballet, Tap, Jazz & Modern; [pets] Dog (Ranger) & Cat (Thumer); [ambition] To be a Dancer; I dance with the Roberts Morgan School of Dance;

McCARTHY, CARLA: [b] 31/7/95 Cheltenham; [home] Yeovil, Somerset; [p] Dean & Cher; [school] Pen Mill Infants; [fav sub] Maths; [hobbies] Drawing; [pets] Rabbit (Doodles) & Rat (Bella);

McCARTHY, CLAIRE: [b] 11/6/84 Winchester, Hants; [home] Corsham, Wilts; [p] Val & Dennis; [school] The Corsham School; [fav sub] History; [hobbies] Horse Riding & Hockey; [pets] Horse, Cat & Guinea Pig; [ambition] To finish my A-levels, go to University to do Nursing;

McCARTHY, JAMES: [b] 26/1/91 London; [home] Hooe, E. Sussex; [p] Sandy & Jeff; [brothers] Thomas & Ben; [sister] Samantha; [school] Ninfield; [fav sub] Art; [hobbies] Drawing, Writing & Dancing; [pets] Pointer (Fielder); [ambition] To be an Artist or Architect and to live in New Zealand with my cousins, aunties, uncles & grandparents;

McCLUSKEY, ALEXANDRA EVE: [b] 6/5/93 Stockport; [home] Bollington, Cheshire; [p] Anthony & Pauline; [sister] Lydia Jane; [school] Dean Valley CP; [fav sub] Poetry; [hobbies] Swimming & Sports; [pets] West Highland White Terrier (Murphy); [ambition] To be a Vet or Dolphin Trainer;

McCAULLY, HANNAH: [b] 6/1/90 W-0-T; [home] Walton on Thames, Surrey; [p] Mildred; [sister] Deenagh; [school] Ambleside Junior; [fav sub] Art, PE & History; [hobbies] Football, Tennis & Drama; [ambition] To be famous;

McERLEAN, REBECCA JAYNE: [b] 3/5/92 Manchester; [home] Rawtenstall, Lancs; [p] Jason & Karen; [sister] Maria Jayne (13 mths); [school] Constable Lee St Paul's; [fav sub] Art, English & History; [hobbies] Reading, Swimming, Art & Drama; [pets] Fish (Survivor); [ambition] To be a Doctor;

McKEAN, WILLIAM: [b] 19/5/89 Canterbury; [home] Sittingbourne, Kent; [p] Antony & Cheryl; [brother] Oliver; [school] Bordern Grammar; [fav sub] French; [hobbies] Reading & Football; [ambition] To go to University;

McKENNER, CLAIRE: [b] 1/10/93 Kingston upon Thames; [home] Tolworth, Surrey; [p] David & Karen; [sister] Louise (Twin); [school] Tolworth Infants; [fav sub] Art; [hobbies] Drawing & Swimming; [pets] Rabbit (Hamish); [ambition] To be a Vet;

McKENNER, LOUISE: [b] 1/10/93 Kingston upon Thames; [home] Tolworth, Surrey; [p] David & Karen; [sister] Claire (Twin); [school] Tolworth Infants; [fav sub] English; [hobbies] Swimming & listening to CD's; [pets] Rabbit (Hamish); [ambition] To own a Pet Shop & a Florist Shop;

McLEAN, JACK: [b] 17/9/90 Cambridge; [home] King's Lynn, Norfolk; [p] Jan & Bob; [brother] Daniel; [school] South Wootton Junior; [fav sub] English; [hobbies] Warhammer & Music; [pets] 2 Dogs & 2 Cats; [ambition] To become an Archeologist;

McLEAN-ASH, KIRA: [b] 9/12/92 Maidstone, Kent; [home] Swadlincote, Derbys; [p] Karen & Stacey; [brother] Trent; [sister] Charlie; [school] Belmont Primary; [fav sub] Art & Writing; [hobbies] Colouring, Helping, & playing the Clarinet; [pets] Cats (Max, Holly, Hugsy & Bam Bam) & Snake (Cal); [ambition] To be a Teacher & eventually a Head Teacher;

McMENEMY, LIANNE: [b] 14/9/88 Dublin; [home] Cheltenham, Glos; [p] Pamela & Ron; [brother] Robert; [school] Bishops Cleeve; [fav sub] Music; [hobbies] Swimming, Piano & Horse Riding; [pets] Dog (Tara) & Hamster (Nico); [ambition] To be the worlds most successful Lawyer!;

McNERNEY, JOSEPH: [b] 24/1/90 Chertsey; [home] Addlestone, Surrey; [p] John & Bianca; [brother] Edward; [sister] Molly; [school] St Anne's RC Primary; [fav sub] English; [hobbies] Football & Rollerblading; [ambition] To be a Footballer;

McWILLIAMS, KITTY: [home] Beckenham, Kent; [sisters] Jemima, Mary & Eliza; [fav sub] English; [hobbies] Irish Dancing & Swimming; [pets] 2 Cats, Hamster;

MEAD, CHARLOTTE ELIZABETH: [b] 13/2/94 Abbots Langley; [home] Hemel Hempstead, Herts; [p] Geraldine & John; [brothers] Paul & Mark; [sister] Anna; [school] Aycliffe Drive; [fav sub] Science;

[hobbies] Gameboy, Reading & Swimming; [pets] Cat (Squirrel); [ambition] To be a Teacher or Shopkeeper;

MEEK, CATHERINE JANE: [b] 10/1/91 Malvern; [home] Malvern, Worcs; [p] Chris & Debbie; [sister] Charlotte Rose; [school] The Wyche CE Primary; [fav sub] Art & Maths; [hobbies] Art, Swimming & Horse Riding; [pets] Cat & Goldfish; [ambition] To learn something new every day!;

MEHMET, KIM: [b] 26/1/89 Banbury; [home] Banbury, Oxon; [p] Karen & Ahmet; [brother] Lee; [sister] Clare; [school] Blessed George Napier; [fav sub] Maths; [hobbies] Music & Dancing; [pets] Cats (Kitty, Sandy & Bella), Hamster (Gracie); [ambition] To be an Air Hostess for Virgin;

MEIKLE, ROBBIE: [b] 29/11/90 Exmouth; [home] Meshaw, Devon; [p] Sally & Andrew; [sister] Cathy; [school] East Worlington Primary; [fav sub] Maths; [hobbies] Football & Athletics; [pets] Dog & Cat; [ambition] To be a computer games Tester or a Footballer;

MELDRAM, JONATHAN: [b] 17/1/91 Kingston, Surrey; [home] Thames Ditton, Surrey; [p] Debbie & David; [brother] Nicholas; [sister] Lauren; [school] Thames Ditton Junior; [fav sub] Maths; [hobbies] Sport, especially Football & Tennis;

MELLER, CLAUDIA: [b] 13/12/90 Exeter; [home] Black Dog, Devon; [p] Jane Schofield & Hugh Meller; [school] East Worlington CP; [fav sub] Art, Music & Writing; [hobbies] Horse Riding, Dogs & Drawing; [pets] Dogs, Ponies, Cat, Guinea Pig, Sheep & Ducks; [ambition] To make Rocking Horses;

MEREDITH, ROBYN ELIZABETH: [b] 24/4/92 Newport; [home] Newport, Gwent; [p] Steve & Gerry; [brothers] Ben, Justin & Gerald; [school] St Julian's Juniors; [fav sub] Art, History & PE; [hobbies] Singing, Gymnastics & Sports; [pets] Dog & Hamster; [ambition] To be a Singer, Vet, famous Gymnast or Dance Teacher;

METSON, KEELEY: [b] 21/2/89; [home] Chelmsford, Essex; [p] Martin & Nicola; [brother] Gavin; [school] Rainsford High; [hobbies] Reading & Cross Stitch; [pets] Hamster (Honey); [ambition] To be a Veterinary Nurse and do the best in everything I do;

MEYER, SARAH: [b] 11/5/91 Huntingdon, Cambs; [home] Bourne End, Bucks; [p] Erika & Chris; [brother] James (11); [sister] Sophie (3); [school] Claytons Combined; [fav sub] English & Art; [hobbies] Swimming, Brownies, Trampolining & Reading; [ambition] To be a TV Presenter, Newsreader or Actress;

MEYNELL, REBECCA L.: [b] 8/8/88 Northampton; [home] Chester, Cheshire; [p]

Michael & Heather; [sister] Sarah; [school] Upton-by-Chester County High; [fav sub] French; [hobbies] Reading & Jig-Saw Puzzles;

MIDDLETON, LEIGH: [b] 22/5/91 Stockport; [home] Buxton, Derbys; [p] Jane & Andrew; [brother] Scott; [school] Buxton Junior; [fav sub] English; [hobbies] Swimming & Rollerblading; [pets] 2 Boxer Dogs; [ambition] To be a Teacher;

MILLS, FIONA: [b] 10/7/93 Aylesbury; [home] Aylesbury, Bucks; [p] Kristi (mum) & Haj (Mum's partner); [school] William Harding Combined; [fav sub] Art; [hobbies] Sport, Writing & Computers; [pets] Dog (Sala); [ambition] To be a Vet;

MILLS, JAMES: [b] 17/12/90 Tunbridge Wells; [home] Hever, Kent; [p] Robert & Rosemary; [brother] Thomas; [school] Chiddingstone CEVC Primary; [fav sub] Art; [hobbies] Rugby, Football, Cricket, Swimming, Basketball & Rounders; [pets] Dog (Roger); [ambition] To play Rugby for England;

MONTAGUE, JAMES DANIEL: [b] 5/8/93 Watford; [home] Hemel Hempstead, Herts; [p] Julie & Dale; [brother] Lewis; [school] Aycliffe Drive Primary; [fav sub] Geography; [hobbies] Playing Keyboard & Computers; [pets] Greyhound (Linford);

MOORE, CRAIG: [b] 10/2/87 Carshalton; [home] Morden, Surrey; [p] Larraine-Anne & James; [brothers] Duncan & Bruce; [sister] Caragh-Anne in memory; [school] Bishopford Community; [fav sub] Science & Art; [hobbies] Music; [ambition] To work with Special Needs Children;

MOORE, SAMANTHA: [b] 23/3/88 Sidcup; [home] Welling, Kent; [p] Karen & Derek; [sister] Nicola; [school] Babington House; [fav sub] Drama & English; [hobbies] Roller Blading & Shopping; [pets] Cat (Smudge); [ambition] To become an Actress and always be happy;

MORAN, KATHRYN: [b] 4/5/90 Crewe; [home] Wokingham, Berks; [sister] Ceri; [school] Bearwood Primary; [fav sub] English; [hobbies] Dancing & Piano; [pets] Dog (Tom); [ambition] To be a Teacher or Dancer;

MORGAN, HARA: [b] 23/8/89 Bromsgrove; [home] Bromsgrove, Worcs; [p] Dave & Trish; [sister] Samantha; [school] Aston Fields Middle; [fav sub] Science; [hobbies] Keyboard & Music; [pets] Dog (Jake); [ambition] To finish grades in Keyboard;

MORGAN, JENNY: [b] 10/10/87 Manchester; [home] Woodhouse, Leics; [school] Loughborough High; [fav sub] Science; [hobbies] Athletics, Hockey & Riding; [pets] 4 Horses, 3 Dogs & a Cat; [ambition] To be a Vet and travel the world;

MORRIS, CATHERINE: [b] 20/5/92

Gloucester; [home] Quedgeley, Glos; [p] Peter & Janice; [sister] Rachel; [school] Fieldcourt Juniors; [fav sub] Art; [hobbies] Swimming; [pets] 2 Cats, Guinea Pig & Tropical Fish; [ambition] To be an Artist;

MORRIS, CLARE: [b] 10/11/89; [home] Bromsgrove, Worcs; [p] Jenny & Jamie; [brother] Alex; [school] Aston Fields Middle; [fav sub] Design & English; [hobbies] Piano, Guides & Drawing; [pets] Cat, Hamster & 2 Rabbits; [ambition] To be a Fashion Designer;

MORRIS, HANNAH EVE: [b] 29/7/91 Wimbledon; [home] Esher, Surrey; [p] John & Nadia; [brothers] Christopher & Richard; [school] Thames Ditton Juniors; [fav sub] History; [hobbies] Flute, Brownies, Choir, Orchestra & Cycling; [pets] Guinea Pig (Dinkey); [ambition] To be a Vet;

MORRIS, RACHEL: [b] 10/5/91 Oxford; [home] Grove, Oxon; [p] Stephen & Gillian; [sisters] Hazel, Claire & Bethan; [school] Millbrook; [fav sub] Art; [hobbies] Swimming & Music; [pets] Cat, Dog, Hamster; [ambition] To be an Actress;

MORTELLARO, MIRELLA LINA BRUNA: [b] 17/9/89 Chertsey; [home] Addlestone, Surrey; [p] Luigi & Gina; [brother] Luca; [school] St Annes RC; [fav sub] English; [hobbies] Reading, Singing & Guitar; [ambition] To be an Historian or Make Up Artist;

MORTON, MAXWELL: [b] 31/7/91 Harlow; [home] Broxbourne, Herts; [p] Pat & Allen; [school] Broxbourne CE Primary; [fav sub] English; [hobbies] Football & Reading; [pets] Cat, would like a Dog; [ambition] To be an Author or a Footballer;

MULVANNY, SARA ROSE: [b] 28/9/87 Basingstoke; [home] Basingstoke, Hants; [sister] Bernice; [school] Courtmoor; [fav sub] ICT; [hobbies] Taekwondo & Riding; [pets] Horse (Magic) & Cat (Tigger); [ambition] To travel the world;

MUMFORD, RICHARD ANDREW: [b] 9/12/90 Luton; [home] Harpenden, Herts; [p] Gail & Andrew; [sister] Alice; [school] Crabtree Junior; [fav sub] ICT (Computer Studies); [hobbies] Cycling & Motor Racing; [pets] Tortoise (Freddie & Bertha); [ambition] To be a Rally Driver;

MURALI, MADHUMATHI: [b] 28/12/90 London; [home] Little Chalfont, Bucks; [p] Krishnaswamy & Manhala; [brother] Mayor; [school] Little Chalfont Combined; [fav sub] Maths & PE; [hobbies] Sports, Indian Classical Dance, Reading & TV; [ambition] To become a good Scientist and perform Indian Classical Dance in the UK;

MURPHY, LEWIS: [b] 23/7/91 Hillingdon; [home] Chalfont St Peter, Bucks; [p] Sallyann & Alan; [brother]

Matthew; [school] Robertswood Combined & Nursery;

MVUBU, SINDIWE: [b] 19/7/91 Ealing; [home] Sunbury, Middx; [p] Mispah (dad) & Bongi (mum); [brothers] Mluleki & Mthabisi; [school] Springfield; [fav sub] PE & Maths; [hobbies] Swimming, Drama & Singing; [ambition] To be a Singer, Actress or Pop Star;

MYLES, LIVVY: [b] 18/10/90 Devizes; [home] Worton, Wilts; [p] Alison & Paul; [brother] Nick; [school] Dauntsey's Aided Primary; [fav sub] Art; [hobbies] Plying the Cello; [pets] Hamster, Dog & Rabbit; [ambition] To be an Author;

NANCE, MIGUEL: [b] 7/2/89 Lima, Peru; [p] Michael & Cristina; [sister] Lima; [school] St Anselm Catholic; [fav sub] English & Science; [hobbies] Fossil Collecting; [ambition] To be an Astronomer;

NAPIER, KELLY: [b] 27/3/90 Yeovil; [home] Stoke-Sub-Hamdon, Som; [p] Jacki & Graham; [sister] Zoe (12); [school] Castle Primary; [fav sub] Art, Maths, Reading, Art & Crafts; [hobbies] Disco Dancing, Music & Gymnastics; [pets] 2 Guinea Pigs & 2 Cats; [ambition] To go in a Hot Air Balloon, make a Parachute jump and go to the top of the Statue of Liberty in New York;

NARDELLI, MARTY: [b] 10/7/88 Watford; [home] Northwood, Middx; [p] Dennis & Suzanne; [brother] Leigh; [sister] Beverley; [school] Northwood Prep; [fav sub] English; [hobbies] Tennis, Ski-ing & Football; [pets] Dog, Snake & Mouse; [ambition] To travel the world;

NEDD, ARON: [b] 7/8/90 Croydon; [home] Norbury, Surrey; [p] Jacqueline Munroe-Nedd & Roydon Nedd; [brother] Rohan; [school] St James The Great; [fav sub] Creative Writing; [hobbies] Table Tennis & Swimming; [ambition] To become a Swimmer and Poet;

NEWBY, LEE TOWNEND: [b] 24/7/92 Chatham; [home] Chinnor, Oxon; [p] Wendy & Mark; [school] John Hampden Primary; [fav sub] Literacy; [hobbies] Aeroplane & Playstation; [pets] Dog (Asti) & Cat (Kimmy); [ambition] To be an RAF Pilot;

NEWMAN, MARK: [b] 28/4/85 Winchester; [home] Bishops Waltham, Hants; [p] Jane & David; [brother] Alexander; [sister] Elizabeth; [school] Swanmore Secondary; [fav sub] Biology; [hobbies] Horse Riding & Swimming; [pets] Cats (Hebe & Billy); [ambition] To become a Veterinary Surgeon in the RAVC;

NEWMAN, SUSIE: [b] 20/3/90 Guildford; [home] Worplesdon, Surrey; [p] Peter & Sharon; [sister] Claire; [school] Worplesdon Primary; [fav sub] English; [hobbies]

Reading & collecting furniture for my Dolls House; [pets] Cat (Millie); [ambition] To work with animals;

NEWTON, LISA: [b] 10/1/90 Reading; [home] Reading, Berks; [p] Moira & Michael; [brothers] Scott, Kirk & Mitchell; [sister] Kelly; [school] Micklands Primary; [fav sub] Art; [hobbies] Reading, Writing & Music; [pets] Cat & 4 Budgies; [ambition] To be a Pop Star or an Author;

NICHOLL, DAVID: [b] 8/2/91 Stockport; [home] Buxton, Derbys; [brother] Adam; [school] Buxton Junior; [fav sub] Maths & English; [hobbies] Cricket & Football;

NIGHTINGALE, JAMES: [b] 5/6/91 Truro; [home] St Breock, Cornwall; [p] Jonathan & Tina; [brothers] Rowan, Ben & Daniel; [school] Wadebridge CP; [fav sub] Maths & Art; [hobbies] Climbing, Rugby, K'nex & Farming; [pets] 2 Dogs, 2 Cats, 9 Hens & lots of Cows; [ambition] To become an Inventor;

NOLAN, KIRSTY: [b] 15/7/89 Enfield; [home] Frinton-on-Sea, Essex; [p] David & Julia; [school] Tendring Technology College; [fav sub] English, Art & Drama; [hobbies] Art, Drama & Tennis; [ambition] To be a Teacher;

NORMAN, CHARLOTTE: [b] 25/10/90 Norwich; [home] Norfolk; [sister] Helena; [hobbies] Cross Country, Tennis & Reading; [ambition[To be a Fashion Designer;

NORTON, LOUISE RACHAEL: [b] 27/1/94 Harlow; [home] Waltham Abbey, Essex; [p] Angela & Colin; [school] Waltham Holy Cross Infants; [fav sub] Science; [hobbies] Collecting Beanie Babies; [pets] Rough Collie Dog (BJ) & Goldfish; [ambition] To become a Teacher or Library Assistant;

OATEN, KATIE: [b] 10/8/91 Taunton; [home] Thurlbear, Som; [p] Donna & Andy; [sisters] Lucie & Sophie; [school] Thurlbear; [fav sub] English; [hobbies] Karate; [pets] 19 various; [ambition] To be a Poet and a Policewoman;

OATEN, LUCIE: [b] 10/8/91 Taunton; [home] Thurlbear, Som; [p] Donna & Andy; [sisters] Katie & Sophie; [school] Thurlbear; [fav sub] Maths; [hobbies] Karate; [pets] Cats, Chickens, Dog, Horses & Fish; [ambition] To be a Policewoman or Air Force Pilot;

OATHAM, DAISY: [b] 24/5/95 Leytonstone; [home] Waltham Abbey, Essex; [p] Angela & Jamie; [sister] Molly; [school] Holy Cross Infants; [fav sub] Reading; [hobbies] Cycling; [pets] Dogs (Bally & Penny), Rats (Basil & Sybil); [ambition] To be a Hairdresser;

O'BRIEN, MORWENNA: [b] 8/4/90 Croydon; [home] Norbury, London; [p] Denis & Yvonne; [brother] Ross; [school] St James the Great; [fav sub] Maths; [hobbies] Swimming, Ice Skating & Football; [pets] Cat, Gerbil & Fish; [ambition] To be a Vet;

O'CALLAGHAN, CRAIG: [b] 12/4/91 Kettering; [home] Colchester, Essex; [p] Mark & Joanne; [brothers] Kyle & Ben; [school] Gosbecks Primary; [fav sub] Maths & English; [hobbies] Football & Reading; [ambition] To be an Author, Journalist or Footballer;

O'CONNOR, ANNA LOUISE: [b] 24/6/92 Chelmsford; [home] Chelmsford, Essex; [p] Claire Louise; [brother] Jack Paul; [school] The Hayward; [fav sub] French; [hobbies] Swimming; [pets] Cat (Jessie); [ambition] To be an Artist on television. I dedicate this to Ben;

OGLEY, CHARLOTTE: [b] 30/3/93 Gorleston; [home] Gt. Yarmouth, Norfolk; [p] Zoë & Steven; [brother] James; [sister] Alexandra; [school] Cliff Park First; [fav sub] English & Art; [hobbies] Dancing & Reading; [pets] Cat & 2 Rabbits; [ambition] To be famous;

O'GORMAN, AIMEÉ: [b] 28/11/91 Welwyn Garden City; [home] Ware, Herts; [p] Peter & Diane; [brother] Scott; [school] Christchurch; [fav sub] English; [hobbies] Computers & Music; [pets] Cat (Lewis); [ambition] To be a Vet;

O'GORMAN, HEATHER: [b] 17/11/89 Morden; [home] Morden, Surrey; [p] Sharon & Tony; [sister] Hannah; [school] Morden Farm Middle; [fav sub] English & Maths; [hobbies] Collecting polished stones; [pets] Rabbit (Lopsi); [ambition] To become a Vet;

OLANG, YVONNE: [b] 27/3/90 Kenya; [home] Bromley, Kent; [p] Lettetia & Robert; [brother] Joe Bradley; [sister] Belinda Diana; [school] St Mary's RC; [fav sub] Science; [hobbies] Dancing & Sports; [ambition] To be an Author, Doctor or Scientist;

O'REILLY, MEG: [b] 18/2/91 Wadebridge; [home] Wadebridge, Cornwall; [p] Sandra & Don; [brother] Dane; [school] Wadebridge CP; [fav sub] English & Art; [hobbies] Amateur Dramatics & Horse Riding; [pets] 4 Cats; [ambition] Not really sure yet. Interested in lots of things;

ORME, DANIELLE: [b] 1/9/89 Bromley; [home] Bromley, Kent; [p] Lisa & David; [sisters] Rebecca & Lauren; [school] Baston; [fav sub] PE; [hobbies] Watching TV, Swimming & PE; [pets] Hamster (Ice-Cream); [ambition] To be a PE Teacher;

OWEN, JAMES RUSSELL: [b] 20/9/90 Truro; [home] Wadebridge, Cornwall; [p] David & Elizabeth; [sister] Jenna Elizabeth; [school] Wadebridge CP; [fav sub] PE; [hobbies] Football & Shooting; [pets] Dog

(Dylan) & Cat (Ginger); [ambition] To become a Fighter Pilot;

OWEN, WILL: [b] 19/5/90 Durban R.S.A; [home] Harpenden, Herts; [p] Helen & David; [brother] Richard; [sisters] Jessie & Vicky - all born 19/5/90 - Quads; [school] Crabtree Junior; [fav sub] Maths; [hobbies] Rugby, Cricket, Tennis & Golf; [ambition] To play Rugby for Wales;

PADGETT, SARAH: [b] 14/10/90 Wrose; [home] Bradford, W.Yorks; [p] John & Kathy; [brothers] James & Matthew; [sister] Abbie; [school] St Francis Primary; [fav sub] English; [hobbies] Disco Dancing; [pets] Rabbit (Toffee); [ambition] To be a Writer;

PAGE, REBECCA JANE: [b] 22/10/90 Banbury; [home] Banbury, Oxon; [p] Myra & Stephen; [brothers] James & Cameron; [school] Wroxton CE Primary; [fav sub] Literacy (English); [hobbies] Rounders & Badminton; [pets] Dog & 8 Fish; [ambition] To be an Air Hostess or Pop Star;

PAHANG, FARRAH LEIGH: [b] 13/6/86 Margate; [home] Broadstairs, Kent; [p] Donna & Ghasem; [sister] Tara; [school] King Ethelbert; [fav sub] Music & Science; [hobbies] Singing; [pets] 2 Cats & Fish; [ambition] To be an RAF Officer;

PALMER, BETHANY: [b] 21/12/92 Welwyn Garden City; [home] Ware, Herts; [p] Wendy & Gary; [sister] Evie; [school] Christ Church CE Primary; [fav sub] Literacy; [hobbies] Drawing & Animals; [pets] Cat (Twinkle); [ambition] To be an Artist;

PALMER, CAROLYNE: [b] 18/4/87 Ascot; [home] Bracknell, Berks; [p] Trevor & Shirley; [brother] Christopher; [sister] Jacqueline; [school] Garth Hill; [fav sub] Information Technology; [hobbies] Shopping & Swimming; [pets] Rabbit (Thumper); [ambition] To travel the world;

PALMER-YOUNG, TAMMI: [b] 8/4/88 Kidderminster; [home] Kidderminster, Worcs; [p] Mick & Kim; [brother] Sam; [sisters] Stacie & Toni; [school] Sladen CE Middle; [fav sub] English; [hobbies] Scouts; [pets] 2 Cats & Hamster; [ambition] To climb a famous mountain;

PARKER, CAITLIN LUCY: [b] 12/11/90 Brighton; [p] Siobhan & Philip; [brother] Joseph; [fav sub] PE & Art; [hobbies] Netball & Ice Skating; [ambition] To be an Author, Artist and to swim with Dolphins;

PARKER, EMILY: [b] 20/12/92 Epsom; [home] Banstead, Surrey; [p] Mary & Graham; [brother] Henry; [sister] Alicia; [school] St Ann's; [fav sub] History; [hobbies] Skipping & Swimming; [ambition] To be a Pop Star!;

PARNHAM, LINDSAY: [b] 8/1/90

Bradford; [home] Bradford, W. Yorks; [p] Sean & Janet; [brother] Andrew; [school] St Francis RC; [fav sub] Design & Technology; [hobbies] Swimming, Dancing & Singing; [ambition] To be a Pop Star, Solicitor or Dance Instructor;

PARSONS, GEMMA LOUISE: [b] 18/5/90 Canterbury; [home] Ashford, Kent; [p] Glenn & Lindsey; [sisters] Lauren & Danielle; [school] Great Chart Primary; [hobbies] Reading; [pets] Cat (Sasha);

PARSONS, HELLEN PHILLIPPA: [b] 11/7/90 Bradford; [home] Buttershaw, W. Yorks; [p] Hayley & Bill; [brother] Ashley; [sister] Lorna; [school] Buttershaw Primary; [fav sub] Maths; [hobbies] Art & Craft, Reading; [pets] 2 Dogs & 3 Cats; [ambition] To be a Nurse looking after old people;

PATON, MARC: [b] 19/2/90 Medway; [home] Cliffe Woods, Kent; [p] Marina & Bob; [sister] Amy; [school] Cliffe Woods Primary; [fav sub] Science & English; [hobbies] Music (playing & listening), Sports & VW Beatles; [pets] Rabbit & Guinea Pig; [ambition] To own a Beetle;

PATTERSON, LAUREN: [b] 1989 London; [home] Hayes, Kent; [p] Alison & Stuart; [brother] David; [sister] Georgia; [school] Babington House; [fav sub] Drama & English; [hobbies] Singing, Acting & Dancing; [pets] Guinea Pig (Owen) & Cats (Sooty, Sidney & Stefan); [ambition] To be a Singer, or to perform on TV and Stage;

PAXFORD, LAURA: [b] 27/8/92 Keighley; [home] Haworth, W. Yorks; [p] Martin & Joanne; [sister] Amy; [school] Haworth Primary; [fav sub] Ballet, Tap & Jazz; [pets] Goldfish & Guinea Pig;

PAYNE, KYLE SPENCER: [b] 15/2/88 Misawa USAF Base; [home] Witchford, Cambs; [p] Matthew & Elizabeth; [brothers] Joshua & Zachary; [sister] Shannon; [school] St Bede's Church School; [fav sub] Maths; [hobbies] Biking, Model Building, Fishing & Sports; [ambition] To write a novel, own a business and raise a family;

PEARCE, AIMEE: [b] 5/10/91 Norway; [home] Ivybridge, Devon; [p] Antony & Toni; [brother] Sam; [school] Stowford Primary; [fav sub] Art; [hobbies] Karate, Swimming & Football; [pets] Rabbit & Cockatiel (Wallace & Grommit); [ambition] To swim with Dolphins;

PEARCE, THOMAS GEORGE WILLIAM: [b] 25/3/88; [b] Latchingdon, Essex; [p] Allan & Alethea; [brother] Brian Allan Peter; [sisters] Tracey & Victoria; [school] The Hayward; [fav sub] Maths; [hobbies] Looking at Tractors; [pets] Dog, Cat & Horse; [ambition] To drive a Tractor;

PEARSON, AMANDA LOUSIE; [b]

7/12/88 Redditch; [home] Bromsgrove, Worcs; [p] Gillian Brown; [sister] Kelly Jane Pearson; [school] Aston Fields Middle; [fav sub] English; [hobbies] Reading; [pets] Dogs, Parrot & Fish; [ambition] To be a Poet;

PEARSON, CHRISTOPHER: [b] 27/2/90 King's Lynn; [home] Heighton, Lincs; [p] Kevin & Gillian; [sister] Samantha; [school] Millfield CP; [fav sub] Maths; [hobbies] Judo; [pets] Cats (Bat & Splodge); [ambition] To own a Silver Tabby;

PEARSON, JACK HENRY: [b] 29/10/93 Welwyn Garden City; [home] Cheshunt, Herts; [p] David & Gillian; [brother] Samuel Joseph; [sister] Gemma Louise; [school] Bonneygrove Primary; [fav sub] Maths; [hobbies] Playing & collecting animals; [pets] 2 Fish, Cat & soon a Duck; [ambition] To be a Zoo Keeper and own the Zoo;

PEARSON, MATTHEW: [b] 5/9/90 Pembury, Kent; [home] Chiddingstone Hoath, Kent; [p] Sally & Gary; [sister] Rachel; [school] Chiddingstone Primary; [fav sub] Maths; [hobbies] Playstation, Playing the Recorder & Writing Stories;

PEGG, SARAH: [b] 10/4/92 Hitchin; [home] Hitchin, Herts; [p] Steven & Sandra; [brother] Michael; [school] Whitehill Junior; [fav sub] English & Handwriting; [hobbies] Reading & playing with friends; [pets] Gerbils & Goldfish; [ambition] To be a Vet:

PEGG-SMITH, ASTON: [b] 4/1/91 Margate; [home] Ramsgate, Kent; [p] Tracie & Matthew Pegg (step dad) & Jarrett Smith (dad); [brothers] Josh & Kane Pegg-Smith & Chester Pegg; [sisters] Maddison Pegg & Josie Archer-Smith; [school] Bromstone CP; [fav sub] PE; [hobbies] Football & Cricket; [ambition] To be a professional Footballer;

PENDLEBURY, CARL: [b] 26/12/87 Stevenage; [home] Stevenage, Herts; [p] Yvonne & Russell; [brother] Scott; [sister] Thea; [school] Marriotts; [fav sub] Drama; [hobbies] Cycling & Football; [pets] Cat (Tinker) & Rabbit (Betty); [ambition] To be an Actor;

PENNINGTON, JAMES: [b] 13/2/87 Guildford; [home] Hindhead, Surrey; [p] Richard & Sheila; [school] Bohunt; [fav sub] Drama & Maths; [hobbies] Acting & Scuba Diving; [ambition] To be an Actor;

PERKINS, JOSHUA: [b] 6/5/89 Chatham; [home] Sittingbourne, Kent; [p] Jayne; [brothers] Joseph (twin) & James; [school] Borden Grammar; [fav sub] P.E., English & I.T.; [hobbies] Football & Poetry; [ambition] To be a professional footballer or computer wizard;

PERRY, JESSICA: [b] 10/2/91 Taunton; [home] Stoke St Mary, Som; [p] Hannah; [school] Thurlbear; [fav sub] Poetry & Art; [hobbies] Horse Riding; [pets] Cats, Dog &

Horse; [ambition] To be a Vet or a Teacher;

PERRY, SAM: [b] 8/3/90 Godalming; [home] Barton-on-Sea, Hants; [p] Karen & John; [brother] Joe; [sisters] Hannah Catherine; [school] New Milton Junior; [fav sub] PE; [hobbies] Cycling, Cooking, Guitar & Violin; [pets] Hamster & 2 Guinea Pigs; [ambition] To release the worlds first Commercial Solar Powered Car;

PHELAN, TOBIE: [b] 8/4/90 Redhill; [home] Merstham, Surrey; [p] Barbara & Sean; [brother] Craig; [sister] Tammy; [school] Merstham Primary; [fav sub] PE; [hobbies] Football; [pets] 3 Cats, 2 Budgies, Rabbit, Gerbil, Hamster, 3 Goldfish & Tropical Fish; [ambition] To be a Footballer;

PHILLIPS, ANTHONY R.W.: [b] 27/10/89 Stevenage; [home] Stevenage, Herts; [p] Beverley & Richard; [brother] James; [sister] Emily; [school] Peartree Spring Junior; [fav sub] Maths; [hobbies] Swimming, Cycling & Pokemon; [pets] Horse, Dog, Rabbit, Budgie & Goldfish;

PHILLIPS, LAURA ELIZABETH: [b] 4/8/92 Gloucetser; [p] William & Helen; [school] Field Court Junior; [fav sub] Design & Technology; [hobbies] Listening to Music; [ambition] To be a Doctor;

PHILLIPS, NICOL LOUISE: [b] 23/3/89 Exeter; [home] Bradninch, Devon; [p] John & Janice; [brother] Lee & James; [school] Cullompton Community College; [fav sub] Drama & English; [hobbies] Swimming, Piano & Poetry; [pets] Hamster (Patch); [ambition] To be an Actress;

PILLEY, RACHEL: [b] 20/6/91 Poole; [home] Upton, Dorset; [p] Caroline & Kevin; [brother] James; [school] Upton Junior; [fav sub] Art; [hobbies] Dancing & Music

PLUMMER, VICTORIA: [b] 6/8/89 Bury; [home] Haslingden, Lancs; [p] Caroline & Greg; [brothers] Matthew & Andrew; [school] St Hilda's RC Girls High; [fav sub] Art; [hobbies] Swimming, & Street dancing; [pets] Rabbit & 2 Fish; [ambition] To be a Reception Class Teacher;

PLUMRIDGE, IMOGEN VICTORIA: [b] 30/9/90 Oxford; [home] Wroxton, Oxon; [p] Nigel & Carol; [brother] Arron; [sister] Meghan; [school] Wroxton CE Primary; [fav sub] D.T.; [hobbies] Horse Riding & Swimming; [pets] 2 Fish; [ambition] To be a Vet;

POOLE, ANDREA: [b] 2/5/88 Rochford; [home] Hullbridge, Essex; [p] Derek & Irene; [brother] Nick; [sisters] Sam & Katie; [school] Sweyne Park; [fav sub] Art; [hobbies] Dancing & Animals; [pets] Cat (Singe), Rabbit (Molly), Fish (Ripples & Bubbles); [ambition] To hang-glide and to be a Vet and own my own Practise;

PORTER, BENJAMIN: [b] 12/2/91 Chesham, Bucks; [home] Crockenhill, Kent; [p] Garry & Fiona; [sister] Hannah-Rose; [school] Crockenhill Primary; [fav sub] History; [hobbies] Watching Gillingham F.C., Cricket, Art, Writing Poetry & playing Flute; [pets] Dog (Scallywag), Cat (Winston); [ambition] To be an Archeologist;

PORTSMOUTH, ADAM: [b] 18/10/89 Wexham; [home] Bourne End, Bucks; [p] Andy & Sue; [sister] Laura; [school] Claytons Combined; [fav sub] English; [hobbies] Reading, Computer Games & Cycling; [pets] Dog (Cassie) & Mice (Bubble & Squeek); [ambition] To see the world and be a millionaire;

POTTER, JAKE MARCUS: [b] 31/10/90 Buxton; [home] Buxton, Derbys; [p] Lorraine & Gareth; [sisters] Emma, Bethany & Jazlin; [school] Buxton Juniors; [fav sub] PE & Art; [hobbies] Computers, Swimming, Football & Snooker; [pets] Poodle (Chelsea); [ambition] To own my own business and build my own house;

POTTER, JOSEPH: [b] 15/8/93 London; [home] Chiswick, London; [p] Simon & Tamara; [brothers] Rory & Matthew; [school] Belmont Primary; [fav sub] English; [hobbies] Football & Running; [pets] Cat (Woody) & 4 Stick Insects; [ambition] To be a Footballer;

POTTER, KATHERINE: [b] 11/7/89 Chertsey; [home] Englefield Green, Surrey; [p] Virginia & Rob; [school] The Magna Carta; [fav sub] Drama; [hobbies] Fashion; [pets] Cats (Penrose & Daisy); [ambition] To become a Drama Teacher;

POTTER, LISA JANE: [b] 29/5/89 Rochford; [home] Hullbridge, Essex; [p] Pamela & Stanley; [sister] Maria; [school] Riverside Junior; [fav sub] French; [hobbies] Scouts & Horse Riding; [pets] Dog (Chloe) & Horse (Jake); [ambition] To become a Teacher;

POULTER, GEORGINA: [b] 23/5/90 Chertsey; [home] Lyne, Surrey; [p] Sarah & Alan; [brother] Jack; [school] St Anne's Catholic Primary; [fav sub] Maths & PE; [hobbies] Riding, Dog Training & Swimming; [pets] 3 Dogs, 2 Cats & 1 Rat; [ambition] To be an Animal Behaviourist to train an Agility/Show Champion to compete at Olympia;

POULTON, DAVID: [b] 4/10/93 London; [home] Beaconsfield, Bucks; [p] Simon & Gill; [brother] Tom; [school] Davenies; [fav sub] Art, Science, Topic Work; [hobbies] Sport, Piano & Art; [ambition] To have fun;

POWELL, CRAIG: [b] 13/2/92 Gloucester; [home] Quedgeley, Glos; [p] Martin & Amanda; [sister] Kirsty; [school] Field Court Junior; [fav sub] Music; [hobbies] Computer; [pets] Dog;

POWELL, KARLINA: [b] 3/2/88 Bromsgrove; [home] Finstall, Worcs; [p] Anita & Roger; [sister] Lydia Scarlett; [school] Aston Fields Middle; [fav sub] English & Music; [hobbies] Drama & Music; [pets] In memory of my Cavalier, Jayne; [ambition] To be an Actress;

POWELL, STEVEN: [b] 19/7/88 Chester; [home] Hoole, Cheshire; [p] Trudi & Phil; [brother] Jack; [school] Upton-by-Chester High; [fav sub] English; [hobbies] Cycling & Computer Games; [pets] Dog (Dodge) & 2 Fish; [ambition] To be an Air Steward;

PREEDY, ALEXANDRA: [b] 12/3/93; [home] Little Chalfont, Bucks; [p] Alison & Barry; [brothers] Adam, James, Robert & Christian; [school] Little Chalfont; [fav sub] Maths, Art & DT; [hobbies] Brownies, Drama & Having friends over; [pets] Dog (Tilly); [ambition] To become a Vet;

PRICE, JOSHUA: [b] 10/2/92 Ashford, Middx; [home] Shepperton, Middx; [p] Terry & Sharon; [sister] Rhiannon; [school] Saxon; [fav sub] Science & PE; [hobbies] Tennis, Swimming, Supporting Arsenal & Collecting model cars; [ambition] To be an Arsenal Home Mascot and when I grow up to be a Police Officer or Firearms Officer;

PROVIS-EVANS, TALFRYN: [b] 23/10/90 St Albans; [home] Harpenden, Herts; [p] Sally & Nefyn; [brothers] Cei & Ceri; [school] Crabtree Junior; [fav sub] Science; [hobbies] Badminton, Football & Swimming; [ambition] To be an Airline Pilot or a Cartoonist;

PRUITT, ASTRID VICTORIA: [b] 27/8/91 Napoli, Italy; [home] Little Chalfont, Bucks; [p] Lowe & Dorte; [brother] Aleksander; [school] Little Chalfont Combined; [hobbies] Playing the fruit, Competitive Disco Dancing & Swimming; [pets] 2 Goldfish; [ambition] To be a Pop Star, a Nurse, a Doctor or professional Dancer;

PRYKE, JACOB HENRY: [b] 15/3/90 Peterborough; [home] March, Cambs; [p] Sarah; [brothers] Levi & Nathan; [school] All Saints; [fav sub] Maths; [hobbies] Talking; [pets] Dog (Mouie); [ambition] To be an Actor;

PUGH, REBECCA: [b] 12/5/91 Kingston; [home] Thames Ditton, Surrey; [p] Mary & David; [brothers] Ben & Jonathan; [school] Thames Ditton Junior; [fav sub] Art; [hobbies] Ballet, Tennis & Pop Music; [pets] Cat, Fish & Snake; [ambition] To be an Actress;

PURTILL, SARAH: [b] 7/6/89; [home] Blacko, Lancs; [p] Stephen & Trisha; [sisters] Emma, Rebecca, Lorna & Olivia; [school] St Hilda's RC Girls High; [hobbies] Dancing, Music & Sport; [pets] Cats (Sally & Pop); [ambition] To be a Vet;

RANCE, ZOE ELIZABETH: [b] 29/1/90 Aylesbury; [home] Aylesbury, Bucks; [p]

Trudy; [sisters] Shannon & Sophie; [school] William Harding Combined; [fav sub] History; [hobbies] Swimming & Cycling; [ambition] To be a Dancer;

RANKIN, KATHRYN: [b] 17/1/88 Rochford; [home] Hullbridge, Essex; [p] Trevor & Susan; [brothers] Jason & James; [school] Sweyne Park; [fav sub] English; [hobbies] Playing Piano; [pets] 2 Cats & 2 Birds; [ambition] To be rich and famous;

RATCLIFFE, ALISON: [b] 18/12/93 Sydenham, London; [home] Evesham, Worcs; [p] Nick & Lynn; [brother] Michael; [school] Swan Lane First; [fav sub] Art; [hobbies] Brownies, Swimming, Dancing & Pogo Stick; [pets] Cat (Fluffy) & Rabbit (Skipper); [ambition] To become a Teacher;

RATHBONE, LEANNA: [b] 9/8/90 Bourne End; [home] Bourne End, Bucks; [p] Allen & Helen; [sister] Bethany; [school] Claytons Combined; [fav sub] Maths; [hobbies] Singing, Netball & playing the Babitone; [pets] Hamsters (Molly, Milly & Louis); [ambition] To be a famous Musician or Singer;

READ, RUTH AMY: [b] 7/9/87 Chester; [home] Saughall, Cheshire; [p] Alec & Susan; [brother] Alec; [school] Upton By Chester High; [fav sub] Physical Education; [hobbies] Hockey, Tennis & Dance; [pets] Cat; [ambition] To have happiness and success;

REDGRAVE, JAMES: [b] 21/7/90 St Albans; [home] Bromsgrove, Worcs; [p] Mick & Angie; [school] Aston Fields Middle; [fav sub] History; [hobbies] Computer Games & Wrestling; [pets] Cavalier King Charles Spaniels (Paddy & Max); [ambition] To be a professional Wrestler, or a Games Software Designer;

REED, HEATHER: [b] 19/12/90 Berkhamsted; [home] Little Gaddesden, Herts; [p] Paulette; [½ brother] Matthew; [½ sister] Alexa; [school] Bridgewater; [fav sub] English & Maths; [hobbies] Reading, Writing, Acting, Singing & Dancing; [pets] Dog (Woody); [ambition] To be a Writer, a Poet, a Teacher, an Actress or Singer;

REYNOLDS, POPPY: [b] 28/9/93 Basingstoke; [home] Odiham, Hants; [p] Hugh & Jane; [sister] Flo; [school] Buryfields Infant; [fav sub] Science & Art; [hobbies] Rollerblading & Making things; [pets] Hamster (Silky); [ambition] Don't know yet!;

REYNOLDS, RACHEL LOUISE: [b] 27/5/90 London (Mayday); [home] Norbury, London; [p] Sue & Marcus; [sister] Lisa; [school] St James the Great; [fav sub] Art & PE; [hobbies] Football, Netball & Dancing; [pets] Hamster (Lucky), Cat (Bruno) & Fish (Goldie Silver); [ambition] To be a great Dancer;

RHODES, CATHERINE: [b] 23/11/94

London; [home] Beckenham, Kent; [p] Richard & Anne; [brother] James; [school] St Mary's Catholic Primary; [fav sub] English; [hobbies] Looking after animals and riding Horses; [pets] Cockatiel (Denis), Hamster (Millie) R.I.P. & lots of Sea Monkeys; [ambition] To own a Dog and to become a Vet;

RICE, RHIANNON: [b] 8/10/93 Salisbury; [home] Salisbury, Wilts; [p] Sean & Lesley; [brother] Conor; [sister] Sophie; [school] Highbury First; [fav sub] History; [hobbies] Reading & Singing; [ambition] To become an Author or Actress;

RICHARDSON, IAN: [b] 13/4/94 High Wycombe; [home] Little Chalfont, Bucks; [p] Mark & Angela; [brother] Karl; [sister] Chloe; [school] Little Chalfont County Combined; [fav sub] Maths & English; [hobbies] Football & Cricket; [pets] 2 Dogs, Rabbit, Hamsters & 5 Fish; [ambition] To play football for West Ham United or be a F1 Racing Driver;

RICHARDSON, KELLY: [b] 31/1/91 Canterbury; [home] Broadstairs, Kent; [p] Paul & Tracey; [brother] Adam; [school] Bromstone Primary; [fav sub] English; [hobbies] Brownies, Swimming & Music; [ambition] To be an Air Hostess;

RIDDLE, JEMMA DAISY: [b] 10/3/92 Ware; [home] Ware, Herts [p] David & Gillian; [brothers] Stephen & Matthew; [sister] Victoria; [school] Christchurch; [fav sub] Art; [hobbies] Karate & Basketball; [pets] Cat (Jinx);

RILEY, STACEY SUE: [b] 1/7/90 Brandon; [home] Brandon, Suffolk; [p] Sue & Andy; [school] Breckland Middle; [fav sub] Music; [hobbies] Swimming & Guides; [pets] Cats (Zippy & Georgie); [ambition] To become a Vet;

RIX, AMY: [b] 8/2/91 Bury-St-Edmunds; [home] Framingham Earl, Norfolk; [p] Annette; [school] Poringland CP; [fav sub] Art; [hobbies] Horse Riding & Swimming; [pets] Hamsters (Salt & Pepper); [ambition] To work with animals;

RIZA, ERSIN SAMI: [b] 9/11/91 Romford; [home] Bradwell-on-Sea, Essex; [p] Sevil; [school] The Hayward; [fav sub] Whale, Dolphins & Marine Life; [hobbies] Pokemon & Digimon; [pets] Dog (Patch) & Cat (Tigger); [ambition] To be a Marine Biologist;

ROBERSON, MICHAEL ALAN: [b] 25/12/87 Bury St Edmunds; [home] Brandon, Suffolk; [p] Patricia & Alan; [brother] Matthew; [sisters] Esther & Jenna; [school] Breckland Middle; [fav sub] PE; [hobbies] Football & Cricket; [pets] Springer Spaniel (Jasper); [ambition] A career in Sport or to work for my Fathers business;

ROBERTS, ASHLEY: [b] 8/10/83 Minster; [home] Sittingbourne, Kent; [p] Michael & Debbie; [sister] Melissa; [school] Borden Grammar; [fav sub] Theatre Studies; [hobbies] Amateur Dramatics, Cinema, Piano & Reading; [pets] Hamster (Gorden); [ambition] To become a Writer or Critic;

ROBINS, ALASTAIR: [b] 10/2/90 Bridgwater; [home] Catcott, Som; [p] Brian & Dee; [school] Catcott; [fav sub] Maths; [hobbies] Football & Sea Cadets; [p] Dog & Bird; [ambition] To be a DJ or an Accountant;

ROBINSON, BENJAMIN: [b] 19/3/92 Gloucester; [home] Quedgeley, Glos; [p] Martin & Martina; [brothers] Thomas & Daniel; [school] Field Court Junior; [fav sub] Games & Art; [hobbies] Rugby; [pets] Rabbit (Hop); [ambition] To become a Policeman or join the Army;

ROBINSON, SALLY: [b] 9/4/90 Caversham; [home] Reading, Berks; [p] Isobel & Dave; [sister] Julia; [school] Micklands Primary; [fav sub] Art & PE; [hobbies] Football & Guitar; [pets] Goldfish (Bubbles & Speedy); [ambition] To work in Design and be a good Footballer;

ROCKALL, ALEX: [b] 5/12/93 Edmonton; [home] Cheshunt, Herts; [p] Elaine & Brett; [sisters] Laura & Chloe; [school] Bonneygrove Primary; [fav sub] Maths; [hobbies] Football; [pets] Cat; [ambition] To be a great Footballer;

ROGERS, EMMA: [b] 14/6/93 High Wycombe; [home] Little Chalfont, Bucks; [p] Paul & Clare; [brother] Jonathan; [school] Little Chalfont Combined; [fav sub] Art; [hobbies] Dancing, Climbing & Swimming; [pets] Cats (Max & Murdoch); [ambition] To be a Teacher;

ROGERS, FREDERICK: [b] 22/7/92 Bath; [home] Melksham, Wilts; [p] Allison & Gary; [school] Forest & Sandridge; [fav sub] Football; [hobbies] Football; [pets] Cats (Henery & Marmaduke) & Rabbit (Buster); [ambition] To be a Footballer;

ROGERS, NATALIE: [b] 29/10/91 Lincoln; [home] Quedgeley, Glos; [p] Neil & Val; [sister] Abigail; [school] Field Court Junior; [fav sub] Art & History; [hobbies] Dancing, Swimming & Football; [pets] Cat, Rabbit, Guinea Pig & 2 Love Birds; [ambition] To become a Policewoman;

ROLPH, LEE: [b] 7/6/87 Harold Wood; [home] Gt Leighs, Essex; [p] Stephen & Deborah; [brothers] Sam & Marc; [school] Hayward; [fav sub] English; [hobbies] Music & Television; [ambition] To get married;

ROPER, JAMIE: [b] 9/3/92 Preston; [home] Euxton, Lancs; [p] Debbie & David; [brothers] William & Todd; [school] Euxton CE Primary; [fav sub] Art; [hobbies]

Football & Swimming; [ambition] To become a professional Footballer;

ROWE, REBECCA: [b] 12/10/91 Kings Lynn; [home] Reffley Estate, Norfolk; [p] Paul & Julie; [sister] Annabelle; [school] South Wootton Junior; [fav sub] Art; [hobbies] Brownies & Animals; [pets] Rabbit, Fish & Bird; [ambition] To be a Vet;

RUDDOCK, DARCY: [b] 22/6/91 Colchester; [home] Colchester, Essex; [p] Adrian & Jackie; [brother] Max; [school] Gosbecks CP; [fav sub] Art & D.T.; [hobbies] Brownies & Swimming; [pets] Ferrets, Dogs, Cats & Fish; [ambition] To write my own book of Poetry;

RULE, HENRY: [b] 14/12/89 Southampton; [home] Salisbury, Wilts; [p] Debbie & Ben; [school] Alderbury & West Grimstead CofE; [fav sub] Geography; [hobbies] Rugby, Football & Surfing; [pets] Kitten (Puff); [ambition] To be a professional Footballer or Prime Minister;

RUSSELL, LEE: [b] 1/2/89 Harlow; [home] Brandon, Suffolk; [p] Paul & Wendy; [brother] Glenn; [school] Breckland Middle; [fav sub] PE, Maths & I.T.; [hobbies] Computers & Wrestling; [pets] Cats (Lucy, Jet & Rory); [ambition] To be a Mechanic, Air Steward or Policeman;

RUSSELL, SUSANNAH JANE: [b] 5/8/92 Welwyn Garden City; [home] Harpenden, Herts; [p] Peter & Gill; [brothers] James & Nicholas; [school] St Nicholas Cof E [fav sub] Art; [hobbies] Writing, Dance, Singing, Acting & Piano; [pets] Rabbit, [ambition] To be famous;

RYAN, CHRISTIE LEIGH: [b] 29/8/89 Barking; [home] Chelmsford, Essex; [p] Natalie Jenkins; [sisters] Rianne & Toni; [school] Rainsford High; [fav sub] Maths; [hobbies] Horse Riding; [pets] Horse, Dog, Cat, Fish & Hamster; [ambition] To be a Vet:

SACH, GEORGIA: [b] 13/11/91 St Albans; [home] Harpenden, Herts; [p] Claire & John; [brothers] Alex, Hugo & James; [school] St Nicholas; [fav sub] Art; [hobbies] Dancing-Tap & Modern; [pets] Dog; [ambition] To travel the world and become a famous Dancer;

SALEH, MENNAR: [b] 19/8/91 London; [home] Brentford, Middx; [p] Wajdi & Iman; [brothers] Majdi & Jihad; [school] Belmont; [fav sub] Maths; [hobbies] Football; [pets] Fish; [ambition] To be a Doctor & Footballer;

SAMPLES, MARK: [b] 6/9/89 Edgeware; [home] Harpenden, Herts; [p] David & Janice (Stepmum); [brothers] Jason & Liam; [sister] Janet; [school] Crabtree Junior; [fav sub] Science & English; [hobbies] Reading, Chess & Football; [pets] Greyhounds (Gypsy

& Champ; [ambition] To be a Scientist;

SAUNDERS LOUISA: [b] 22/4/85 High Wycombe; [home] Hedge End, Hants; [p] Andrew & Elizabeth; [sister] Victoria; [school] Swanmore Secondary; [fav sub] Drama; [hobbies] Singing & Reading; [ambition] To be a Singer and continue writing poetry;

SAUNDERS, TIM: [b] 4/11/91 Malvern; [home] Malvern, Worcs; [p] Hazel & Nick; [brother] Robin; [school] Wyche CE Primary; [fav sub] Art & Poetry; [hobbies] Keyboards, Cubs, Orienteering, Chess & Art Club; [pets] Gerbils (Eric & Ernie, the demolition crew!); [ambition] To be a Pop Star or Stunt Man;

SAVAGE, SHARNIE: [b] 12/5/92 Plymouth; [home] Ivybridge, Devon; [p] Wayne & Susie; [brother] Macauley; [school] Stowford Primary; [fav sub] Art & Writing; [hobbies] Swimming & staying with my Nan & Grandad; [pets] Cat & 2 Rabbits;

SAVILE, KELLY ELIZABETH: [b] 12/12/82 Mitcham; [home] Mitcham, Surrey; [p] Rosemary & Johnnie; [brothers] Tommy & Steven; [sister] Emma; [school] Bishopsford Community High; [fav sub] Drama; [hobbies] Going out with friends & watching football; [pets] Cat; [ambition] To be a Nursery Nurse and run a Marathon in 2003;

SAVIN, JENNIFER LOUISE: [b]17/7/92 Oxford; [home] Colchester, Essex; [p] Nick & Heather; [school] Gosbecks Primary; [fav sub] Everything except Maths!; [hobbies] Reading, Music, Computing & Art; [pets] Cat (Jethro) & 2 Goldfish; [ambition] To be a singing & writing Actress;

SAY, LAURA: [b] 7/3/90 West Drayton; [home] West Drayton, Middx; [p] Jon & Julie; [sister] Emma; [school] Cherry Lane Primary; [fav sub] English; [hobbies] Horse Riding & Ten Pin Bowling; [ambition] To be a Hairdresser or Veterinary Nurse;

SCAMBLER, FRANCESCA JANE: [b] 11/5/92 Oxford; [home] Postcombe, Oxon; [p] John & Dorothy; [brother] William George; [sister] Victoria Louise; [school] John Hampden Primary; [fav sub] Design & Technology; [hobbies] Gymnastics, Acting & Swimming; [pets] Cat; [ambition] To be 10, I'm still waiting until I'm older!;

SCOTT, COREY: [b] 9/9/90 Hastings; [home] Ninfield, Sussex; [p] Clive & Lynda; [brother] Jake; [sister] Holly & Fallon; [school] Ninfield CE; [fav sub] English; [hobbies] Football; [ambition] To be a professional Footballer;

SCOTT, GEMMA LOUISE: [b] 9/1/89 Canterbury; [home] Canterbury, Kent; [p] Debbie & Warren; [sister] Megan; [school] St Anselms; [fav sub] Art; [hobbies]

Swimming, Gym & Drama; [ambition] To become a Primary School Teacher;

SCOTT, MEGAN: [b] 9/6/94; [home] Cheshunt, Herts; [p] Karen & David; [school] [school] Bonneygrove Primary; [fav sub] Maths; [hobbies] Art & Crafts; [ambition] To be Happy;

SENDALL-KING, REBECCA: [b] 20/3/90 Ashford; [home] Ashford, Kent; [p] John & Cynthia; [brothers] Matthew & Daniel; [school] Great Chart Primary; [fav sub] English; [hobbies] Reading & Collecting Beanies;

SETTERINGTON, BEN: [b] 10/1/91 Chelmsford; [home] Witham, Essex; [p] Paula & Dave; [sister] Jemma; [school] Haywood; [fav sub] Computers; [hobbies] Computers & Pets; [pets] 9 Cats, 1 Dog & 2 Rabbits; [ambition] To be the best I can;

SHAH, NISHI: [b] 5/6/85 Leicester; [home] Thurmaston, Leics; [p] Sailesh & Nina; [brother] Sunny; [school] Loughborough High; [fav sub] French & English; [ambition] To be the best at what I do and to be happy doing it. Also to keep smiling because "What sunshine is to flowers; smiles are to humanity!";

SHANMUGAM, BEN: [b] 19/2/89 London; [home] Sittingbourne, Kent; [p] Thana & Danni; [brother] Joshua; [sister] Natasha; [school] Borden Grammar; [fav sub] Maths; [hobbies] Football, Swimming & Crystal Collection; [ambition] To travel to foreign Countries and speak another language fluently;

SHEARS, KRISTY: [b] 23/6/93 Watford; [home] Watford, Herts; [p] Martin & Kathy; [sister] Melanie; [school] Kingsway Junior; [fav sub] History & English; [hobbies] Dancing, Swimming & Ice Skating;

SHEFFIELD, ABBEY: [b] 6/7/94 Welwyn Garden City; [home] Waltham Abbey, Essex; [p] Victoria & Douglas; [brother] Jake; [school] Waltham Holy Cross Infants; [fav sub] PE; [hobbies] Swimming & Dancing; [ambition] To be a Nurse;

SHELDON, TOMMY: [b] 13/6/90 Aylesbury; [home] Aylesbury, Bucks; [p] Richard & Sheena; [brother] Sammy; [sister] Cassie; [school] Stone Cof E Combined; [fac sub] I.C.T.; [hobbies] Cycling; [pets] Budgie & Rabbit; [ambition] To make a Robot;

SHERE, CLAIRE LOUISE: [b] 27/8/85 Exeter; [home] Plymtree, Devon; [p] Roger & Sue; [sister] Jayne Marie; [school] Cullompton Community College; [fav sub] Food Technology; [hobbies] Cooking; [ambition] To own my own Restaurant;

SHEPPARD, JOSEPH: [b] 9/1/92 Bradford; [home] Clayton, W. Yorks; [p]

Dylan; [sisters] Katie & Emma; [school] Clayton Village Primary; [fav sub] Maths & Science; [hobbies] Cricket, Football & Lego; [ambition] To be a Policeman or play professional Cricket;

SHEPPARD, KAYLEIGH: [b] 25/5/92 Brighton; [home] Denton, E. Sussex; [p] Martin & Tracy; [sister[Chloe; [school] Denton; [fav sub] Science & History; [hobbies] Swimming; [pets] Hamster (Chocolate);

SHEPPERSON, EMILY: [b] 5/2/91 Ipswich; [home] Worlingworth, Suffolk; [p] Wendy & Robert; [school] Dennington Primary; [fav sub] Art & I.C.T.; [hobbies] Making things; [pets] Rabbits (Amber & Violet); [ambition] To visit Australia and swim with Dolphins;

SHERGOLD, BEN: [b] 21/1/89 Exeter; [home] Appledore, N. Devon; [p] Mandy Blundell; [brothers] Samuel & Macgowan; [school] Cullompton Community College; [fav sub] Art; [hobbies] Building & Nintendo; [pets] Pure White Cat (Anno); [ambition] To do well at school and become a Vet:

SHINN, ANDREA: [b] 28/9/87 Cambridge; [home] Cambridge, Cambs; [p] Alan & Kathy; [sister] Kerry & Jennie; [school] St Bede's; [fav sub] Maths & German; [hobbies] Dancing; [pets] 2 Rabbits; [ambition] To be a Singer;

SHORT, CHANAH: [b] 2/6/89 Taunton; [home] Taunton, Som; [p] Diane & Wayne; [school] Halcon Community; [fav sub] English; [hobbies] Reading & WWF; [ambition] To write historical fiction & non-fiction;

SHORT, SARAH: [b] 17/3/93 Aylesbury; [home] Aylesbury, Bucks; [p] Steve & Christine; [brother] Ryan; [sister] Stacey; [school] William Harding Combined; [fav sub] Art; [hobbies] Running, Gym & First Aid; [pets] Hamster;

SIDDERS, DANIEL ANTHONY: [b] 22/8/92 Hastings; [home] Hastings, East Sussex; [p] Anthony & Donna; [brothers] Jamie & Charlie; [school] Hollington Primary; [fav sub] Art & PE; [hobbies] Football & Tennis; [ambition] To go on an Aeroplane and to play football for Arsenal;

SILAY, KAAN: [b] 18/12/90 Stockport; [home] Buxton, Derbys; [p] Audrey & Özer; [brother] Zeki; [school] Buxton Junior; [fav sub] Physical Education; [hobbies] Rugby, Football & Cricket; [pets] Dog (Bonnie) & Fish (Sammy); [ambition] To play professional Rugby or Cricket;

SIMMONS, THOMAS: [b] 8/9/91 St Albans; [home] Harpenden, Herts; [p] Craig & Vivien; [brother] David; [sister] Amy; [school] St Nicholas CofE JMI; [fav sub]

Art & Music; [hobbies] Football; [ambition] To be a professional Sportsman or an Artist;

SIMPSON, LIANNE: [b] 25/7/86 Ipswich; [home] Ipswich, Suffolk; [p] Debbie & Paul; [brother] Liam; [school] Beacon Hill; [fav sub] English; [hobbies] Reading, Music (listening & watching); [pets] Dogs (George & Maddie); [ambition] To look after children;

SIMS, MICHAELA JADE: [b] 25/4/92 Southampton; [home] Hordle, Hants; [p] Hazel & Guy; [brother] William; [school] New Milton Junior; [fav sub] PE, Games & English; [hobbies] Swimming, Rugby & Football; [pets] Dog & 1 Fish; [ambition] To be an Archaeologist or a Clothes Designer;

SINCLAIR, FIONA ANN: [b] 30/12/89 Welwyn Garden City; [home] East Worlington, Devon; [p] David & Debra; [sister] Laura Jane; [school] East Worlington Primary; [fav sub] Art & R.E.; [hobbies] Pony, Hamster, Dogs & Cats; [ambition] To be a Teacher;

SINGLETON, VICKY: [b] 27/8/89 Rochford; [home] Rayleigh, Essex; [p] Jackie & Rob; [sister] Lauren; [school] Sweyne Park; [fav sub] Drama; [hobbies] Judo & Swimming; [ambition] To be a Teacher;

SINNOTT, DAVID: [b] 16/11/90 Preston; [home] Goosnargh, Lancs; [p] Julie & Chris; [brother] Graeme; [sister] Lisa; [school] St Francis The Hill; [fav sub] Art; [hobbies] Drawing & Swimming; [pets] 2 Dogs, Rabbit, Fish ; [ambition] To be an Author or Artist;

SWITHINBANK, ELEANOR: [b] 12/7/90 London; [home] Chiswick, London; [p] Bridget & Chris; [sister] Sophie; [school] Belmont Primary; [fav sub] Maths & Art; [hobbies] Playing Cello & Swimming; [pets] Hamster (Nibbley); [ambition] To play the Cello, making a beautiful sound;

SKINNER, KELLY: [b] 12/6/92 Ware; [home] Ware, Herts; [p] Sharon & Andy; [brothers] Barry & Shaun; [school] Christchurch Primary; [fab sub] Maths; [hobbies] Riding my Bicycle & Scooter; [pets] Dog, Budgie & Fish;

SMART, JACOB: [b] 15/1/89; [home] Braintree, Essex; [p] Jane & Alan; [brother] Nicholas; [school] Rainsford High; [fav sub] Dance; [hobbies] Dance, Drama & Music; [pets] Guinea Pig & Rabbit; [ambition] To be an Actor or a Dancer;

SMILLIE, JONATHAN: [b] 1/12/89; [home] Euxton, Lancs; [p] Craig & Angela; [brother] Grant; [school] Euxton C of E; [fav sub] PE; [hobbies] Football; [pets] Cat (Jess) & Chicken (Babs); [ambition] To be Rich;

SMITH, CARL STUART: [b] 8/7/92 Colchester; [home] Colchester, Essex; [p]

Lynette & Kevin; [brother] Craig; [sister] Tiffany; [school] Gosbecks Primary; [fav sub] Maths; [hobbies] Karate; [pets] Dog, 2 Budgies & 1 Goldfish; [ambition] To be a Fireman;

SMITH, CARLY: [b] 28/4/88 Macclesfield; [home] Macclesfield, Cheshire; [p] Keith; [brother] Lee; [school] All Hollows Catholic High; [fav sub] PE; [hobbies] Athletics; [ambition] To compete in the Olympics;

SMITH, DANIEL: [b] 28/3/90 Stevenage; [home] March, Cambs; [school] All Saints Inter Church; [fav sub] English; [hobbies] Music, Drama, Dance & Kick Boxing; [ambition] To join the RAF;

SMITH, HARRISON: [b] 30/5/91 Harlow; [home] Theydon Bois, Essex; [p] Murray & Denise; [brothers] Ross, Marshall & Connor; [sister] Abigail; [school] Theydon Bois; [fav sub] Music; [hobbies] Drums, Running, Swimming & Football; [ambition] To be in a Pop Group;

SMITH, JAMES: [b] 11/3/92 Oxford; [home] Thame, Oxon; [p] Steve & Debbie; [brother] Luke; [sister] Lindsay; [school] John Hampden; [fav sub] Art; [hobbies] Drawing; [pets] Rabbit (Prince); [ambition] To build a Theme Park;

SMITH, JOSH: [b] 29/1/90; [home] Bretforton, Worcs; [p] Phillip & Linda; [sisters] Abigail & Bethany; [school] Blackminster Middle; [fav sub] Science; [hobbies] Swimming & Playstation; [pets] Dogs (Zak & Holly), Rabbit (Buffy); [ambition] To be a famous Scientist;

SMITH, KATHRYN LOUISE: [b] 14/5/90 Redditch; [home] Offenham, Worcs; [p] David & Wendy; [brothers] Benjamin & Jack; [school] Blackminster Middle; [fav sub] English & History; [hobbies] Dancing & Netball; [pets] 2 Dogs & 2 Cats; [ambition] To be a Choreographer and to be involved in animal welfare;

SMITH, STEPHANIE: [b] 15/2/92 Hillingdon; [home] Denham, Bucks; [p] Paul & Debbie; [sister] Emily; [school] Tilehouse; [fav sub] Art; [hobbies] Art & Crafts & Rollerblading; [pets] Cat (Paddy) [ambition] To be famous;

SMITH, TOMAS: [b] 15/4/93 Yarmouth; [home] Hickling, Norfolk; [p] Ian & Judith; [sister] Holly; [school] Hickling First; [fav sub] Art; [hobbies] Building things; [pets] Goldfish; [ambition] To be a Jet Pilot;

SMYTH, OLIVER: [b] 29/10/92 Reading; [home] Tilehurst, Berks; [p] Lindsey & Keith; [sisters] Hayley & Yasmin; [school] Micklands; [fav sub] Maths; [hobbies] Football & Swimming; [pets] 2 Cats & 2 Rabbits; [ambition] To be a Policeman;

SNAPE, KIMBERLEY: [b] 14/11/91 Preston; [home] Leyland, Lancs; [p] David & Gail; [brother] George; [sister] Lucy; [school] St James CE; [fav sub] Literacy; [hobbies] Dancing, Clarinet & poetry; [pets] 2 Goldfish; [ambition] To be a Policewoman;

SOCAS, ALICIA CHARICE: [b] 14/6/92 Keighley; [home] Haworth, W. Yorks; [p] Beverley Ann; [brother] Greg; [school] Haworth Primary; [fav sub] English & Maths; [hobbies] Writing & Country Walks; [pets] Cheeta, Teddy & Lena; [ambition] To do well in everything and become a Doctor;

SOMMERLAND, JESS: [b] 4/9/91 Haworth; [home] Haworth, W. Yorks; [p] Hilary & Peter; [school] Haworth Primary; [fav sub] History; [hobbies] Painting, Warhammer, Chess & Music; [pets] Cat (Mitzi); [ambition] To write History and play in a Band;

SOMMERVILLE, HAYLEY: [b] 8/1/89 Bo'ness; [home] East Leake, Leics; [p] Scott & Bernice; [sister] Brogan; [school] Loughborough High; [fav sub] History; [hobbies] Dancing, Horse Riding & Reading; [pets] Rabbit (Fudge); [ambition] To work with animals;

SOOTHILL, LOUISE: [b] 28/6/92 Keighley; [home] Keighley, W. Yorks; [p] Brian & Julie; [sisters] Hannah & Zoë; [school] Holycroft Primary; [fav sub] Art & Poetry; [hobbies] Reading & Writing Poems; [pets] 5 Guinea Pigs; [ambition] To be a Singer & Actress;

SPALDING, ANDREA: [b] 16/11/86 Germany; [home] Mordern, Surrey; [p] Maggie; [sister] Zoe; [school] Bishopsford Community; [fav sub; [hobbies] Swimming & Reading; [pets] Border Collie (Barney); [ambition] To be an Author or Interior Designer;

SPALDING, DANIEL: [b] 29/3/88 Bromsgrove; [home] Bromsgrove, Worcs; [p] Pauline & Dennis; [brother] Matt; [sister] Claire; [school] Aston Fields Middle; [fav sub] Rugby; [pets] Dogs, Rabbit, Gerbils, Budgie & Terrapin; [ambition] To be a Pilot;

SPEER, JOSHUA: [b] 2/3/95 Hastings; [home] St Leonards, East Sussex; [p] Darren & Clare; [brothers] Zak & Ewan; [school] Hollington Primary; [fav sub] Projects; [hobbies] Making lego models; [ambition] To be a Policeman and drive a Police Jeep;

SPEER, LILY: [b] 5/12/92 Guildford; [home] Guildford, Surrey; [p] Dee & Steve; [brother] Sam; [school] Sandfield CP; [fav sub] Reading; [hobbies] Collecting & Reading; [pets] Cat (Harry); [ambition] To be a Pop Star or Vet;

SPENCE, CHARLES: [b] 23/5/91 St Albans; [home] Harpenden, Herts; [p] Duncan & Gemma; [brothers] Toby & Reuben; [school] Crabtree Junior; [fav sub] Geography & History; [hobbies] Rugby, Cycling & Reading; [pets] Cats; [ambition] To be a Cartoonist;

STAMPER, CALLUM JOHN: [b] 11/6/91 Bristol; [home] Mosterton, Dorset; [p] Iain & Cath; [brother] Rory Matthew; [school] Parrett & Axe CEVA Primary; [fav sub] Maths, Science & Sport; [hobbies] Football, Climbing & Swimming; [pets] Boxer (Snubb) & Rat (Spike); [ambition] To be a Scientist;

STARKIE, TIMOTHY J.: [b] 21/9/89 High Wycombe; [home] Ashford, Kent; [p] Linda; [brother] Edward (Twin); [sister] Sophie; [school] Great Chart; [fav sub] English; [hobbies] Swimming, Football & Reading;

STEDMAN, MICHAEL: [b] 11/10/89 Chester; [home] Cuddington, Cheshire; [p] David & Jayne; [brother] Christopher; [school] Cuddington Primary; [fav sub] PE & Maths; [hobbies] Football; [pets] Dog, Cat & Hamster; [ambition] To be a Footballer;

STEEDMAN, KERRI: [b] 6/8/92 Aylesbury; [home] Aylesbury, Bucks; [p] John & Barbara; [brother] Alex; [school] William Harding Combined; [hobbies] Dancing; [pets] Guinea Pigs (Fudge & Toffee); [ambition] To become a Nurse;

STEPHENSON, EMMA: [b] 24/2/94; [home] Fleet, Hants; [p] Graham & Debbie; [sister] Molly (Twin); [school] Fleet Infants; [fav sub] Maths & Computer; [hobbies] Trampolining & Running; [ambition] To be a Vet;

STERLING, ANDREW: [b] 18/9/93 Little Chalfont; [home] Little Chalfont, Bucks; [p] Karen & Mike; [brother] David; [sister] Emma; [school] Little Chalfont Combined; [fav sub] Maths, History & Geography; [hobbies] Football & Basketball; [pets] Dog (Sade) & Rabbit (Candy); [ambition] To be a professional Footballer or a Zoo Vet;

STERLING, KERHYS TARNYA: [b] 23/11/89; [home] Aylesbury Bucks; [p] Janine; [brother] Reuben; [school] Turnfurlong Junior; [fav sub] Design & Technology & R.E.; [hobbies] Singing, Swimming & Reading; [ambition] To swim with Dolphins in Florida, visit Disney World and then become a Doctor;

STEVEN, ROBERT: [b] 22/12/93 Camberley; [home] Fleet, Hants; [p] John & Kate; [brother] Craig; [sister] Lydia; [school] Fleet Infant; [fav sub] Maths; [hobbies] Gameboy & Making Lego Models; [ambition] To be an Astronaut;

STEVENS, JACK: [b] 5/11/89 Oxford; [home] Stawell, Som; [p] Miriam; [sister]

Charlotte; [school] Catcott Primary; [fav sub] Mathematics; [hobbies] Cycling, Football & Art; [pets] Border Collie (Sophie); [ambition] To be a Graduate at Oxford University;

STEVENSON, GEMMA: [b] 27/3/89 Burnley; [home] Padiham, Lancs; [p] Joseph & Elizabeth; [brother] Joshua; [sister] Amy-Leigh; [school] St Hilda's RC Girls High; [fav sub] Geography & PE; [hobbies] Cross Country Running & Swimming; [pets] Boxer (Lady); [ambition] To be a Nurse or an Air Hostess;

STILES-FOLEY, CAMERON: [b] 2/12/89 Fort Walton Beach, Florida; [home] Brandon, Suffolk; [p] Christopher & Linda; [sister] Paige; [school] Breckland Middle; [fav sub] PE & Science; [hobbies] Sports & playing with friends; [ambition] To be an Ice Hockey Player for the NHL and to do well at school. Also to be Happy;

STINTON, LUKE: [b] 31/10/91 Ashford; [home] Shepperton, Middx; [p] Adrian & Julie; [brother] Andrew; [school] Saxon CP; [fav sub] Art; [hobbies] Wildlife; [pets] Dog; [ambition] To work with animals;

STOCKHAM, HOLLY: [b] 24/11/89 Redditch; [home] Bromsgrove, Worcs; [p] Julia & Peter; [brother] John; [school] Aston Fields Middle; [fav sub] Maths; [hobbies] Reading, Music & Football; [pets] Rabbits (Rosie & Sooty), Dog (Max); [ambition] To be a Vet and to travel to Africa on Safari;

STOCKWELL, BRADLEY JAMES: [b] 29/1/91 Winchester; [home] Wadebridge, Cornwall; [p] Sarah & Lee; [brother] Jack; [sister] Summer; [school] Wadebridge CP; [fav sub] Maths; [hobbies] Football, Swimming & Surf Life Saving; [pets] 2 Cats & 5 Rabbits; [ambition] To be a professional Footballer;

STRINGWELL, THOMAS: [b] 12/12/88 Leeds; [home] Banbury, Oxon; [p] Christopher & Heather; [brother] Joseph; [school] Blessed George Napier; [fav sub] D.T.; [hobbies] Football, Cricket & Reading; [pets] 2 Westies (Pixie & Bonnie); [ambition] To get a good job and make a difference;

STUBLEY, JOE: [b] 10/8/92 Keighley; [home] Haworth, W. Yorks; [p] Tracey (Mum) & Ashley Bevan (Stepdad) & Duncan (Dad) & Liz Stubley (Stepmum); [sister] Sarah (10); [school] Haworth Primary; [fav sub] History; [hobbies] Fishing & Guitar; [pets] Dog (Kim), Cat (Eddie), Rabbit, Hamster & 4 Fish; [ambition] To be an RAF Engineer and a famous Classical Guitar player;

STURMEY, SAM: [b] 13/2/89 Dorchester; [home] Stourpaine, Dorset; [p] Karen Andrews; [brothers] Billy & Mark; [school] Milldown Middle; [fav sub] Design & Technology; [hobbies] Cycling & Rugby; [pets] Cat; [ambition] To become the best Rugby Player;

SUMMERS-ROLLINGSON, CHARLOTTE: [b] 13/9/89 Greenwich; [home] Chalfont St Giles, Bucks; [p] Anita Rollingson & Craig Summers; [sisters] Kate & Grace; [school] Little Chalfont Combined; [fav sub] PE; [hobbies] Netball & Swimming; [pets] Hamster (Bianca) & Rabbit (Jasper); [ambition] To be a Child Psychologist;

SUTTON, JACK: [b] 22/8/90 High Wycombe; [home] Thame, Oxon; [p] Peter & Lorraine; [brothers] Paul & Harry; [school] Aston Rowant; [fav sub] PE; [hobbies] Football; [pets] Rabbits (Bugs & Charlie) & Dog (Tooley); [ambition] To get a good job and be successful;

SUTTON, LOUISA: [b] 10/7/87 Harrow; [home] Harrow, Middx; [p] Philip & Joanne; [brother] Matthew; [school] St Joan of Arc; [fav sub] English; [hobbies] Writing, Piano & Swimming; [ambition] To have more work published and become a Journalist or Writer;

SWEENEY, MARIA: [b] 31/8/90 Croydon; [home] Croydon, Surrey; [p] John & Jane; [sister] Clare; [school] St James the Great; [fav sub] English; [hobbies] Swimming & Cycling; [ambition] To be a Vet;

SWEENEY, ROCHELLE: [b] 11/10/90 Preston; [home] Euxton, Lancs; [p] Nerina & Mark; [sister] Chloe; [school] Euxton CE Primary; [fav sub] English; [hobbies] Drama & Writing; [ambition] To have a No.1 Hit Single;

SWEENEY, ZACHARY: [b] 13/8/89 Chelmsford; [home] Chelmsford, Essex; [p] Shelley Sweeney & Robert Henry; [brother] Kane & Sheridan; [sister] Morgon; [school] Rainsford High; [fav sub] English & PE; [hobbies] Basketball, Tennis & Writing Stories; [pets] 2 Chipmunks; [ambition] To be a Story Writer and to star at Basketball;

SYDENHAM, JOANNE: [b] 29/1/89 Huntingdon; [p] Paignton, Devon; [p] Vanessa & Steve; [brother] Stephen; [sisters] Natasha, Nicola & Lianne; [school] Churston Ferres Grammar; [fav sub] Art; [hobbies] Tennis & Dancing; [pets] Dog (Prince), Cats (Billy & Tommy). Rabbits (Magic, Cassie & Thunder) & lots of Fish; [ambition] To be a professional Dancer;

SYMES, DANIEL: [b] 26/7/89 Chester; [home] Mickle Trafford, Cheshire; [p] Nick & Jacqui; [sisters] Natalie & Samantha; [school] Upton-by-Chester County High; [fav sub] Science; [hobbies] Reading, Swimming & Scouts; [ambition] Unsure;

TAYLOR, CLAIRE: [b] 22/12/88; [home] Blandford, Dorset; [p] Brian & Linda; [brother] James; [sister] Emma; [school] Milldown Middle;

TAYLOR, DAVID PAUL: [b] 17/2/91

Manchester; [home] King's Lynn, Norfolk; [p] David & Paula; [brother] Stephen; [sisters] Anna & Emily; [school] South Wootton Junior; [fav sub] English; [hobbies] Swimming & Art; [pets] 2 Collies (Shep & Sweep); [ambition] To be a Computer Programmer and an Author;

TAYLOR, KATHRYN: [b] 10/6/88 Bath; [home] Corsham, Wilts; [p] Bev & Andy; [brother] Michael; [school] Corsham; [fav sub] PE; [hobbies] Dancing & Talking; [pets] Rabbits (Titch, Saphire & Dylan); [ambition] To enjoy University and become a Psychiatrist working with people and animals;

TAYLOR, SOPHIE: [b] 4/6/90 Hampstead; [home] Radlett, Herts; [p] Giselle & Jonathan; [brothers] Harry & Elias; [school] Newberries Primary; [fav sub] Science & Art; [hobbies] Horse Riding & Swimming; [pets] Staffordshire Bull Terrier (Monty), Guinea Pig & Goldfish; [ambition] To be an Architect or Lawyer;

TAYNTON, CARA: [b] 24/1/90; [home] Thame, Oxon; [p] Edwina & Alan; [brother] Oliver; [sisters] Natalie & Lucy; [school] John Hampden; [fav sub] Art & Games; [hobbies] Swimming & Netball; [pets] Dog, Cat, Rabbit, Guinea Pig & Fish; [ambition] To travel the world and become a professional Synchronise Swimmer;

TEUNISSEN, LULA: [b] 8/10 87 Oxford; [home] Oxford, Oxon; [p] Jenny & Adrian; [school] Oxford High; [fav sub] English; [hobbies] Reading, Writing Stories, Bowling & Shopping; [pets] Rat (Ratatouille); [ambition] To be an English Teacher and to write a book;

THAKRAR, NIKITA: [b] 7/6/90 King's Lynn; [home] King's Lynn, Norfolk; [p] Uday & Meena; [brothers] Jaimin & Vishaal; [school] South Wootton Junior; [fav sub] Maths; [hobbies] Reading; [ambition] To be a Lawyer or Accountant;

THOMAS, DAVID: [b] 17/3/90 Portsmouth; [home] Mosterton, Dorset; [p] Christopher & Maria; [brother] Ben; [sister] Gemma; [school] Parret & Axe CE Primary; [fav sub] Maths; [hobbies] Golf & Computer Games; [pets] 2 Hamsters, 2 Fish & 1 Bird; [ambition] To work with computers or be a Mechanic;

THOMSON, CLAIRE: [b] 22/10/90 Poole; [home] Upton, Dorset; [p] Simon & Julia; [brother] Andrew; [school] Upton Junior; [fav sub] Literacy; [hobbies] Swimming, Reading and Saxophone; [pets] Goldfish; [ambition] To be a Writer or Poet;

THOMSON, JAMES: [b] 27/4/89 Liverpool; [home] Alsager, Cheshire; [p] Alistair & Donna; [sister] Katie; [school] Alsager; [fav sub] Drama; [hobbies] Hockey, Cricket & Computers; [ambition] To be a Writer, Doctor or Actor;

THOMPSON, ROBERT: [b] 15/11/93 Salisbury; [home] North Perrott, Som; [p] Charles & Annette; [sisters] Louise, Alice & Victoria; [school] Haselbury Plucknett Primary; [fav sub] Design & Technology; [hobbies] All Sports; [pets] Cats (Tom & Geri); [ambition] To be a Scientist or professional Sportsman;

THORP, LEE: [b] 6/8/90 Swindon; [home] Littleton Panell, Wilts; [p] Louise & Ian; [sisters] Deanna & Gemma; [school] D.A.P.S.; [fav sub] Art; [hobbies] Shooting; [pets] Dog, 3 Rabbits, Chinchilla & Ferret; [ambition] To be a Train Driver;

THORPE, ROSY: [b] 8/10/91 Brighton; [home] South Heighton, East Sussex; [p] Sophy & Mike; [brothers] Joe & Robert; [school] Denton Community; [fav sub] History; [hobbies] Music & Reading; [ambition] To be a Pop Star;

THWAITES, SHANNON KATHERINE: [b] 25/9/93 Ascot; [home] Binfield, Berks; [p] Steve & Debbi; [sisters] Caitlin & Dana; [school] Binfield C of E Primary; [fav sub] PE; [hobbies] Looking after my Rabbit; [pets] Dog (Bhaji) & Rabbit (Snowy); [ambition] To become a Vet;

TILSTON, MICHAEL: [b] 20/9/89 Southampton; [home] New Milton, Hants; [p] Elizabeth & Geoff; [brothers] David & Paul; [school] New Milton Junior; [fav sub] Maths; [hobbies] Football, other sports & Reading; [pets] 2 Cats, 17 Fish & a Rabbit; [ambition] To be a family man and an RAF Pilot;

TIMMS, JESSICA BLEU: [b] 5/4/91 Glos; [home] Whitminster, Glos; [p] Mary & Jeremy; [sister] Alice; [school] Whitminster Endowed Cof E; [fav sub] Science & History; [hobbies] Swimming & Tennis; [ambition] To be a Marine Biologist and work with Dolphins;

TITMUS, NATALIE: [b] 1/3/90 Norwich; [home] Ashford, Kent; [p] Christine & John; [school] Great Chart Primary; [fav sub] History; [hobbies] Guides, Writing & Reading; [pets] Cat (Sweep); [ambition] To swim with Dolphins and be a History Teacher and Poet;

TOCH, FLORENCE: [b] 30/7/92; [home] Keighley, W. Yorks; [p] Kate & Martin; [brother] Tomson; [school] Holycroft Primary; [fav sub] History; [hobbies] Poetry, Horse Riding, Reading, Swimming; [pets] 2 Rabbits, 2 Hamsters & 2 Fish; [ambition] To run an Animal Sanctuary;

TOFARI, MATHEOS: [b] 16/5/91 Hillingdon; [home] Denham, Bucks; [p] Lyn & Dino; [brother] Loukas; [school] Robertswood; [fav sub] English; [hobbies] Computer Tech. & Reading; [pets] Dog, Cat & Guinea Pig; [ambition] To be a Hairdresser;

TOMKINS, CASSIE: [b] 6/2/89 Beckenham; [home] Beckenham, Kent; [p] Janet & Graham; [brother] Danny; [school] Baston; [fav sub] Art & English; [hobbies] Dancing & Singing; [ambition] To be a Clothes Designer;

TOWNSEND, SOPHIE: [b] 30/9/91 Colchester; [home] Birch, Essex; [p] Sheryl & Ray; [sister] Zoë; [school] Birch CE Primary; [fav sub] Art & Craft; [hobbies] Drawing; [pets] Dog (Benson); [ambition] To study Art;

TOWNSEND, TOM: [b] 27/9/90 Plymouth; [home] Epsom Downs, Surrey; [p] Jan & Phil; [brother] Craig; [school] Warren Mead Juniors; [fav sub] PE; [hobbies] Football; [ambition] To be a Footballer;

TRAFFORD, NICHOLAS: [b] 10/9/91 Plymouth; [home] Ivybridge, Devon; [p] Jill & Steve; [brother] Daniel; [sister] Hannah; [school] Stowford Primary; [fav sub] Maths & Games; [hobbies] Football & Astronomy; [pets] Dog (Suki); [ambition] To be an Astronaut;

TRANTER, ELLIE: [b] 26/9/87 Oxford; [home] Oxford, Oxon; [p] Sally & Graham; [brother] Joe; [school] Oxford High; [fav sub] Art, Drama, Music & English; [hobbies] Writing, Performing & annoying Joe; [pets] Cats (Tortasiha & Snowy Tom); [ambition] To be an arty, drama, misical, poetry writing person;

TRESIDDER, CRAIG: [b] 9/1/91 Camborne; [home] Camborne, Cornwall; [p] Paul & Tracey; [sister] Shonna; [school] Penponds Primary; [fav sub] Writing poems & Art; [hobbies] Fishing & Football; [pets] Dog (Ferdie); [ambition] To be an Artist or Vet;

TROWARD, OLIVER: [b] 17/11/89 St Albans; [home] Harpenden, Herts; [p] Sue & Charles; [school] Crabtree; [fav sub] Maths; [hobbies] Tennis, Football & Computers; [pets] Cat (Poochy); [ambition] To work with Computers;

TUCK, GEORGE: [b] 13/5/95 Yeovil; [home] Yeovil, Som; [p] Clive & Michelle; [sister] Darcie; [school] Pen Mill Infants; [fav sub] Reading; [hobbies] Playing games & having fun; [ambition] To be a Tennis Player;

TUCK, SOPHIE: [b] 15/6/88 London; [home] Bromley, Kent; [p] June & Butch; [school] Baston; [fav sub] Singing & English; [hobbies] Singing & Swimming; [ambition] To own a Hotel or Nursing Home. I dedicate this to my Mum, Dad & Pop;

TUCKER, CHARLIE: [b] 28/8/92 Aylesbury; [home] Aylesbury, Bucks; [p] Jackie; [sisters] Hayley (16) & Rachael (13); [school] William Harding Junior; [fav sub] Art; [hobbies] Football, Basketball & Computer Games; [pets] Dog (Solly), Cats (Lily, Blossom, Sefa & Lynx); [ambition]

To play football for Man Utd;

TURNER, BETHANY: [b] 27/1/91 Worcester; [home] Bewdley, Worcs; [p] Dale & Sue; [brother] Greg; [school] St Anne's Middle; [fav sub] French; [hobbies] Reading, Netball & Brownies; [pets] Rabbit (Daisy); [ambition] To be a Teacher;

TURNER, FRANCES: [b] 1/4/94 Kingston; [home] Surbiton, Surrey; [p] Philip & Janice; [sister] Emma; [school] Tolworth Infants; [fav sub] Art; [hobbies] Drama & Swimming; [pets] Hamster (Dave); [ambition] To help animals;

TURNNIDGE, EMILY: [b] 10/10/91 Leics; [home] New Milton, Hants; [p] Lesley & Clive; [sister] Kim; [school] New Milton Junior; [fav sub] Music; [hobbies] Swimming; [pets] Guinea Pig (Hollie); [ambition] To be a Singer;

TURRELL, SAM CHRISTOPHER: [b] 8/9/93 Norwich; [home] Hickling, Norfolk; [p] Sally Butler; [brother] Ben Turrell; [sister] Katie Turrell; [school] Hickling First; [fav sub] Computers; [hobbies] Reading & Writing; [pets] Cats, Dogs & Hamster; [ambition] Lots of things;

TUTTY, RACHEL: [b] 29/3/90 Welwyn Garden City; [home] Ware, Herts; [p] Caroline & John; [brother] Thomas; [school] Christ Church; [fav sub] Design & Technology; [hobbies] Swimming, Reading & Music; [pets] 2 Cats, Dog & 4 Fish; [ambition] To go into the Guiness Book of Records;

USHER, SAM JORDAN: [b] 3/8/92 Blackpool; [home] St Annes, Lancs; [p] Nikki & Paul; [brother] Ben; [sister] Sophie; [school] Clifton; [fav sub] English; [hobbies] Football & Computers; [pets] Cats (Todd, Gabbi & Phoebe); [ambition] unknown at present;

VASS, REBECCA: [b] 25/2/92 Southampton; [home] New Milton, Hants; [p] Brian & Michelle; [brother] Andrew; [school] New Milton Junior; [fav sub] Literacy; [hobbies] Swimming; [pets] Fish; [ambition] To be a Vet;

VAUGHAN, KATIE LOUISE: [b] 19/5/86 Taunton; [home] Little Clacton, Essex; [p] Lesley & Laurence; [brother] Christian; [school] Tendring Technology College; [fav sub] English & art; [hobbies] Sewing, Reading & Judo; [pets] Dog (Basil) & 5 Cats; [ambition] To do well at school and become a Writer;

VAUGHAN, SCOTT LEE: [b] 23/6/93 Newport; [home] Risca, Gwent; [p] Alun & Susan; [brother] Nathan & Jonathan; [school] Risca Primary; [fav sub] Art & Games; [hobbies] Football & Cricket; [pets] Goldfish (Blue & Kevin); [ambition] To be a professional Footballer;

VECE, ALEX: [b] 17/1/92 Aylesbury; [home] Aylesbury, Bucks; [p] Pasq & Naomi; [brother] Daniel; [sister] Hannah; [school] Turnfurlong Junior; [fav sub] Design & Technology & Literacy; [hobbies] Playing games, Violin, Writing, Drawing, Cycling & Shopping; [pets] Hamster (Molly) & lots of Tropical Fish; [ambition] To be a Pop Star or a Poet;

VERMEULEN, SAMANTHA: [b] 9/12/89 Basingstoke; [home] [home] Sunbury-on-Thames, Middx; [p] Carole; [brother] Paul Bradley; [sister] Samantha Louise; [school] Springfield CP & moving to Thamesmead; [fav sub] Drama & Music; [hobbies] Dancing, Karate & Guides; [pets] Dog & 2 Cats; [ambition] To be a Dance Teacher;

VERTIGAN, PRUDENCE JOY ELIZABETH: [b] 9/3/90 King's Lynn; [home] Great Massingham, Norfolk; [p] Claire & Steven; [brother] Tim; [school] Gt. Massingham VC Primary; [fav sub] History; [hobbies] Gymnastics & Singing; [pets] Dog (Willow), Rabbit (Emilio), Zebra Finch (Jo) & various Frogs; [ambition] To be a Teacher & sing in a Band;

VINCENT, KATIE: [b] 19/3/86 Harwich; [home] Harwich, Essex; [p] Matthew Vincent & Tina Kingsbury; [school] Tendring Technology College; [fav sub] Drama; [hobbies] Drama, Sailing, Ski-ing, Piano, Drums & Singing; [pets] Cat (Samson), Guinea Pig (Tiberius) & Fish (Frisky); [ambition] To win an Oscar, go into Space & travel the World;

VIRGIN, CLAIR FRANCES: [b] 2/9/91 Taunton; [home] Taunton, Som; [p] Nick & Wendy; [brother] Matthew; [school] Thurlbear VA CE Primary; [fav sub] Art; [hobbies] Netball, Riding, Swimming & Reading; [pets] Hamster (Chessie); [ambition] To become a Teacher;

WAGSTAFF, EMMA-LOUISE: [b] 7/9/91 Dunfermline; [home] The Lizard, Cornwall; [p] Asha & Andrew; [brother] Daniel; [school] Landewednack; [fav sub] English; [hobbies] Horse Riding, Gymnastics, Singing & Writing; [pets] Dog, Fish & Cockatiels; [ambition] To be a Musician, Author, Pop Star or Vet;

WAINWRIGHT, JEN: [b] 22/4/86 Axbridge; [home] Axbridge, Som; [p] Helen & Joe; [sister] Frances; [school] Kings Of Wessex; [fav sub] English; [hobbies] Acting, Singing & Writing; [pets] Stupid Rabbit & 2 demented Guinea Pigs; [ambition] To be rich and famous Dahlings!!;

WAKEMAN, JODIE: [b] 4/3/89 Orpington; [home] Orpington, Kent; [p] Lynn (mum), Beryl (nan), Charles (grandad) & Mark (uncle); [brother] Charlie; [school] Baston; [fav sub] French, Swimming & Art; [hobbies] Netball, TV & Reading; [pets] Dog

(Billy), Rabbit (Flopsy) & Fish; [ambition] To be a Singer, Actor or Policewoman;

WALBRIDGE, LAUREN NATALIE: [b] 17/3/89 Dorchester; [home] Tarrant Rawston, Dorset; [p] Tim & Debbie; [brothers] Adam & Ryan; [sister] Selina; [school] Milldown Middle; [fav sub] English; [hobbies] Collecting toy monkeys; [pets] Cat (Merlin), Dogs (Aysha & Saxon; [ambition] To be a Zoo Keeper and work with Monkeys;

WALES, DOROTHY: [b] 15/8/90 Nottingham; [home] Earl Sterndale, Derbys; [p] Bob & Sarah; [school] Brassington Primary; [fav sub] English-Creative Writing; [hobbies] Cycling, Drama, Samba & Writing; [pets] Cat (Toffee); [ambition] To become a famous Writer, Actor or Singer;

WALKER, HANNAH LISA: [b] 29/2/92 Bury St Edmunds; [home] North Lopham, Norfolk; [p] Jennie & Neil; [sister] Holly Jordon; [school] St Andrews Primary; [fav sub] English; [hobbies] Ballet, Judo & Reading; [pets] Cat (Korky); [ambition] To be a Childrens Author or Illustrator;

WALKER, MATTHEW: [b] 23/1/91 Gerrards Cross; [home] Chalfont St Peter, Bucks; [p] Anne Marie; [brother] Simon; [twin sister] Alicia; [school] Robertswood; [fav sub] English & Maths; [hobbies] Collecting toys; [pets] Spaniel (Purdy) & Yorkie (Trixie); [ambition] To write books and make films;

WALKER-SHAW, NATASHA: [b] 3/3/90 Bromsgrove; [home] Bromsgrove, Worcs; [p] Karen Moore & B. Shaw & Tim Moore (step father); [sister] Mariella; [school] Aston Fields Middle; [fav sub] English; [hobbies] Horse Riding & Gymnastics; [pets] Guinea Pig, Cat, Hamster & Rabbit; [ambition] To work with animals or be a Gymnast;

WALSH, LUCY: [b] 14/9/91; [home] Adlington, Lancs; [p] John & Carol; [sister] Sophie; [school] Adlington Primary; [fav sub] Maths & Art; [hobbies] Line Dancing & Brownies; [pets] Dog (Gemma) & Guinea Pig (Rosie); [ambition] To do well at school and to look after animals;

WALTON, ALEXANDER: [b] 30/12/93 Paris; [home] Fleet, Hants; [p] Nick & Fiona; [brothers] William & Edward; [school] Fleet Infant; [fav sub] Maths; [hobbies] Football, Beavers & Gameboy; [ambition] To be an Artist or Illustrator;

WARD, KELVIN CARL: [b] 15/6/88 ; [home] Writtle, Essex; [p] Tracey Davis; [brother] David Ward; [sister] Lisa Marie Davis; [school] Hayward; [fav sub] Maths; [hobbies] Football; [pets] Dogs & Rabbits; [ambition] To be a Fireman;

WARREN, NICOLA: [b] 19/5/84

Colchester; [home] Gt Holland, Essex; [p] Audrey & John; [brother] Michael; [sister] Tracey; [school] Tendring Technology College; [fav sub] R.E.; [hobbies] Running, Dancing & Computer; [pets] Dog (Candy);

WATERS, ASHLEY: [b] 21/11/89 Greenwich; [home] Harpenden, Herts; [p] Mari & Philip; [brothers] Nicholas, Christopher & Jonathan; [school] Crabtree Junior; [fav sub] English; [hobbies] Reading, Karate, Football, Chess & Drama; [ambition] To be an Actor;

WATKINS, ALISTAIR: [b] 5/7/91 Kingston; [home] Thames Ditton, Surrey; [p] Gareth & Susan; [brother] Angus; [school] Thames Ditton Junior; [fav sub] Maths; [hobbies] Football, Tennis & Cricket; [ambition] To be a professional Footballer;

WATSON, BEN: [b] 23/10/88 Exeter; [home] Willand, Devon; [p] John & Mary; [brother] Callum; [school] Cullompton Community College; [fav sub] Drama; [hobbies] Swimming & loving my Mum; [pets] Cats (Ratsy & Mossup); [ambition] To be an Interior Designer;

WATSON, MEGAN KATE: [b] 8/6/91 Oxford; [home] Grove, Oxon; [p] Kathleen & Martin; [brother] Matthew; [school] Millbrook Primary; [fav sub] Drama & Art; [hobbies] Disco & Tap Dancing, Swimming & Violin; [pets] Guinea Pig (Alfie); [ambition] To be a Pop Star or work with animals;

WATSON, SPENCER: [b] 16/1/89 Colchester; [home] Walton-on-Naze, Essex; [p] Susan & Norman; [school] Tendring Technology College; [fav sub] Art; [hobbies] Swimming & Computer Games; [pets] Budgie & Goldfish; [ambition] To be a Cartoonist;

WATTS, ANNA: [b] 22/7/91 London; [home] Berkhamsted, Herts; [p] Bill & Hilary; [brothers] Sam & Oliver; [sister] Madeline; [school] Bridgewater; [fav sub] PE; [hobbies] Guitar & Trampoline; [ambition] To be a Poet or Guitarist;

WATTS, STUART: [b] 23/8/89 Redditch; [home] Droitwich, Worcs; [p] David & Karen; [sister] Sarah & Emily; [school] Aston Fields Middle; [fav sub] Games; [hobbies] Football & Skateboarding; [pets] 2 Cats & Tropical fish; [ambition] To travel and make money;

WEATHERALL, ZARA: [b] 5/1/88 Canterbury; [home] Canterbury, Kent; [p] Teresa; [brothers] Philip & Richard; [school] St Anselm's Catholic; [fav sub] Animals; [hobbies] Horse Riding & Tennis; [pets] Cat & Goldfish; [ambition] To be Veterinary Nurse;

WEEDON, RICHARD: [b] 14/5/86 Ipswich; [home] Ipswich, Suffolk; [p] Jeff; [brothers] David & Chris; [sisters] Lesley &

Sarah; [school] Beacon Hill; [fav sub] Maths; [hobbies] Football; [pets] Dog (Lucky); [ambition] To go to College;

WEETMAN, EDWARD: [b] 28/9/91 Redhill; [home] Redhill, Surrey; [p] Victoria & Richard; [brother] Alexander; [school] St John's Primary; [fav sub] Maths; [hobbies] Football & Swimming; [pets] Rabbit; [ambition] To be a Sports Journalist;

WEINGART, LUKE ALÒIS: [b] 4/11/92 Aylesbury; [home] Aylesbury, Bucks; [p] Nigel & Joanna; [sister] Emily; [school] William Harding Combined; [fav sub] Art; [hobbies] Cubs; [pets] Boxer Dog (Wooster); [ambition] To join the Navy;

WELDON, ROBERT: [b] 11/1/90 Southampton; [home] Barton-on-Sea, Hants; [p] Mark & Joanne; [brother] Jonathan; [school] New Milton Junior; [fav sub] Technology; [hobbies] Rugby, Tennis, Roller Hockey & Basketball; [pets] Jack Russell (Archie); [ambition] To be a professional Sportsman;

WELLS, MEGAN: [b] 22/10/93 Farnborough; [home] Beckenham, Kent; [p] Simon & Maggie; [sister] Katie; [school] St Mary's RC Primary; [fav sub] English -Literacy; [hobbies] Drawing & Reading; [ambition] To be a Teacher and do lots of travelling;

WENHAM, MATTHEW : [b] 2/5/90; [p] Michael & Caren; [sister] Lauren; [school] Cliffe Woods; [fav sub] Information Technology; [hobbies] Swimming;

WEST, NATALIE: [b] 19/3/91 Aylesbury; [home] Aylesbury, Bucks; [p] Michael & Gillian; [brother] Paul; [school] William Harding; [fav sub] History; [hobbies] Reading & Riding; [pets] Hamster & Cat; [ambition] To be a nurse or a Vet;

WEYMOUTH, THOMAS: [b] 20/3/92 Plymouth; [home] Ivybridge, Devon; [p] Jon & Tanya; [brother] Ben; [sister] Emily; [school] Stowford Primary; [fav sub] PE; [hobbies] Reading & Cycling; [ambition] To be an Author;

WHEATCROFT, CHARLOTTE: [b] 3/10/90 Derby; [home] Chorley, Lancs; [p] Jacqueline & Mitchell; [brothers] James & Daniel; [school] Euxton CE Primary; [fav sub] Biology; [hobbies] Swimming & Gymnastics; [pets] Cat (Katie); [ambition] To be a Vet specialising in big animals;

WHEATLEY, CHARLOTTE: [b] 3/7/89 Exeter; [home] Willand, Devon; [p] Beverley & Jean-Marc; [sister] Daisy; [school] Cullompton Community College; [fav sub] Drama & Gymnastics; [hobbies] Swimming & Cycling; [pets] Dog (Minstrel) & Hamster (Topsy); [ambition] To be a Gymnast;

WHEATLEY, LAURA: [b] 7/6/91 Norwich;

[home] Grove, Oxon; [p] Nick & Lisa; [brother] Daniel; [school] Millbrook; [fav sub] Maths; [hobbies] Reading, Music & Brownies; [pets] Border Collie (Josie); [ambition] To be a Teacher and do lots of acting;

WHELDON, SARA: [b] 4/9/88 Chelmsford; [home] Chelmsford, Essex; [p] Michelle & Michael; [brothers] Jake & Cameron; [school] Rainsford; [fav sub] Maths; [hobbies] Sports; [pets] Rabbit (Toffee); [ambition] To help animals and be a Vet:

WHIFFIN, MADDISON: [b] 7/4/94 Basingstoke; [home] Fleet, Hants; [p] Pete & Yvette; [sister] Demii; [school] Fleet Infants; [fav sub] Music & Art; [pets] Cat (Pebbles); [ambition] To be a Singer in a Pop Group;

WHITAKER, STEPHEN: [b] 7/5/90 Bradford; [home] Bradford, W. Yorks; [p] Stephen & Lisa; [sister] Natalie; [school] St Francis Primary; [fav sub] English & Science; [hobbies] Football & Golf; [ambition] To be an Artist;

WHITE, ALICE EVELYN: [b] 21/11/91 Chesterfield; [home] Hollingwood, Derbys; [p] Jill & Roger; [brother] Jonathan; [sister] Kathryn; [school] Hollingwood Primary; [fav sub] Mathematcis & Art; [hobbies] Dancing, Reading & Cycling; [pets] Dog (Billie) & Cat (Jarus); [ambition] To be a Primary School Teacher;

WHITE, AMANDA F.: [b] 15/9/86 Milton Keynes; [home] London; [p] Lesley; [school] Babington House; [fav sub] Drama; [hobbies] Ballet & Music; [pets] Yorkshire Terrier (Maddie); [ambition] To be a professional Dancer;

WHITE, ANTHONY: [b] 31/8/90 Hornchurch; [home] Kelvedon Hatch, Essex; [p] Peter & Linda; [brothers] Jonathan & William; [school] Kelvedon Hatch; [fav sub] Maths; [hobbies] Football; [pets] Greyhound, Budgies & Rats; [ambition] To play football for Crystal Palace;

WHITE, ANTOINETTE: [b] 15/8/89 Banbury; [home] Banbury, Oxon; [p] Mandie; [brother] Ben; [school] B.G.N. Roman Catholic; [fav sub] Textiles; [hobbies] Karate; [pets] 10 Rabbits & 1 Hamster; [ambition] To become a Vet;

WHITE, CHARLOTTE: [b] 25/7/92 Chatham; [home] Gillingham, Kent; [p] Angela & Colin; [brother] Samuel; [school] Barnsole Junior; [fav sub] English; [hobbies] Ice Skating & playing with friends; [pets] Hamster (Smokey);

WHITE, HARRY: [b] 7/10/91 Fleet; [home] Hitchin, Herts; [p] Nick & Liz; [brother] Thomas; [school] Whitehill Junior; [fav sub] Maths; [hobbies] Collecting Beano's; [ambition] To be a Dare Devil or

Police Officer;

WHITE, OLIVIA PAIGE: [b] 6/6/93 Oxford; [home] Thame, Oxon; [p] Jo & Kevin; [brother] Callum; [sisters] Natalie & Victoria; [school] John Hampden Primary; [fav sub] Science; [hobbies] Swimming; [pets] Goldfish; [ambition] To model and to be a Pop Star;

WHITE SARAH: [b] 4/6/92 Frome; [home] Frome, Som; [p] Nick & Ali; [brother] Peter; [sisters] Hannah & Becca; [school] Upton Noble; [fav sub] Art; [hobbies] Gym, Swimming & Dance; [pets] 3 Fish; [ambition] To perform on stage;

WHITEHEAD, TRISTAN: [b] 20/4/91 Buxton; [home] Buxton, Derbys; [p] Dawn & Geoff; [brother] Jason; [sister] Holly; [school] Buxton Junior; [fav sub] Maths & English; [hobbies] Football & Rollerblading; [pets] Dog (Smudge) & Hamster (Tiger); [ambition] To join the Army;

WHITEHURST, AMY: [b] 8/8/89 Hayes; [home] Keston, Kent; [p] Louise & Andrew; [sister] Sophie; [school] Baston; [fav sub] PE, English & Art; [hobbies] Gym & Running; [pets] Dog (Cara) & 16 Fish; [ambition] To be a famous Vet;

WHITFIELD, LUCY ELIZABETH: [b] 4/2/91 Cardiff; [home] Wadebridge, Cornwall; [p] John & Julie; [brothers] William & Thomas; [sister] Aimee; [school] Wadebridge Community Primary; [fav sub] Art; [hobbies] Swimming, Horse Riding & Acting; [pets] Rabbit, Dog, Cat, Guinea Pigs & Fish; [ambition] To be an Actress and travel the world;

WHITHAM, SAMANTHA: [b] 18/4/93 Shoreham by Sea; [home] South Heighton, East Sussex; [p] Sian; [school] Denton Community; [fav sub] Art; [hobbies] Horse; [pets] 2 Dogs; [ambition] To work in an Animal Hospital;

WHITTAKER, JAMIE STUART: [b] 14/7/93 Redditch; [home] Redditch, Worcs; [p] David & Susan; [brother] Aaron; [sisters] Mia & Carly; [school] Arrowcrest First; [fav sub] Art; [hobbies] Football, Cycling & Art;

WHITWOOD, RACHEL: [b] 16/5/91 Norwich; [home] Poringland, Norfolk; [p] Steve & Gayle; [school] Poringland Primary; [fav sub] Literacy; [hobbies] Gymnastics & Piano; [pets] Cat (Tilly); [ambition] To be a Vet;

WIBBERLEY, JOE: [b] 13/10/90 Chatham; [home] St Leonards East Sussex; [p] Stephen & Debra; [sister] Amy; [school] Hollington Primary; [fav sub] English; [hobbies] Tennis & Swimming; [ambition] To work with Dolphins;

WICKHAM, CHRIS: [b] 14/2/90 Aylesbury; [home] Bishopstone, Bucks; [p] Marlyn & Michael; [brother] Matthew; [school] Stone Combined; [fav sub] ICT; [hobbies] Collecting F1 Cars; [ambition] To be a Programmer;

WILCOX, MICHAEL: [b] 5/4/90 Norwich; [home] Mileham, Norfolk; [p] Margaret; [school] Mileham Primary; [fav sub] Maths; [hobbies] Football; [pets] Guinea Pig, 2 Cats, 2 Dogs & 5 Horses; [ambition] To do well in everything I do;

WILKERSON, JOANNA: [b] 28/10/93 Fleet; [sister] Kate; [school] Fleet Infant; [fav sub] Art; [hobbies] Art, Cycling & Canoeing; [pets] Guinea Pigs; [ambition] To be a Policewoman & to travel abroad;

WILLETTS, DALE MARTIN: [b] 15/4/90 Wordsley; [home] Quedgeley, Glos; [p] Kay & Karl - Stepdad Martyn; [brothers] Jonathan, Dean, Matthew & James; [school] Field Court; [fav sub] DT; [hobbies] Cycling; [ambition] To be a Policeman;

WILLIAMS, AMY: [b] 16/9/90 Redditch; [home] Hartlebury, Worcs; [p] Tina & Geoff; [sister] Emma; [school] St Anne's Middle; [fav sub] English; [hobbies] Horse Riding; [pets] Horse, 3 Ponies, Dog, 3 Cats & 2 Guinea Pigs; [ambition] To be happy and successful and to work with animals;

WILLIAMS, BEN: [b] 1/2/89 Bromsgrove; [home] Bromsgrove, Worcs; [p] Jayne & Anthony; [brothers] Neil, Anthony & Amin; [school] Aston Fields Middle; [fav sub] Films, Drawing & Cricket; [pets] Dog; [ambition] Not sure yet;

WILLIAMS, BETHAN JOSIE: [b] 23/3/93 Newport; [home] Risca, Caerphilly; [p] Ceri; [school] Risca Primary; [fav sub] Art & Language; [hobbies] Swimming, Dancing & Craft; [pets] Collie (Megan); [ambition] To work with animals in Disney's Animal Kingdom in Florida;

WILLIAMS, HAYLEY: [b] 17/5/88 Worcester; [home] Bromsgrove, Worcs; [p] Adrian & Diane; [brother] Christopher; [sister] Natalie; [school] Aston Fields Middle; [fav sub] Art; [hobbies] Piano, Clarinet & All Sports; [pets] Boxer Dog (Bronte); [ambition] To be a photographer, Architect & Actress;

WILLIAMS, SAMUEL JOHN: [b] 4/7/91 Hounslow; [home] Chalfont St Peter, Bucks; [p] Paul & Lesley; [sister] Jessica; [school] Robertswood Combined; [fav sub] Art; [hobbies] James Bond 007; [pets] Cats (Ronnie, Reggie & Jinx); [ambition] To be a Movie Producer;

WILLIAMS, STEVEN K.: [b] 5/11/91 Poole; [home] New Milton, Hants; [p] Kevin & Beverley; [brother] Philip; [school]

New Milton Junior; [fav sub] Design Technology; [hobbies] Rugby, Cricket & Fishing; [ambition] To play Rugby for Wasps and England;

WILLIAMSON, ROSS: [b] 12/1/91 Edinburgh; [home] Guildford, Surrey; [p] Alex & Christine; [sister] Erin; [school] Sandfield CP; [fav sub] Mathematics; [hobbies] Football & Athletics; [ambition] To be a professional Sportsman;

WILLMAN, HANNAH: [b] 3/10/90 Blackpool; [home] Blackpool, Lancs; [p] Catherine & Geoffrey; [brother] Joseph (6); [school] Manor Beach; [fav sub] Art; [hobbies] Swimming & Dancing; [pets] Cats; [ambition] To learn to ride a horse;

WILMOTT, SARAH MICHELLE: [b] 30/6/89 Burnley; [home] Whitewell Bottom, Lancs; [p] Deborah & Philip; [brother] Daniel Philip; [sister] Nicole Hannah; [school] St Hilda's RC Girls High; [fav sub] Art & I.T.; [hobbies] Karate, Piano, Violin Music (listening), The Internet, Neopets; [pets] Tropical Fish, Rabbit & Brother!; [ambition[To be a Pop Star;

WILSHERE, JACK: [b] 1/1/92 Stevenage; [home] Hitchin, Herts; [p] Andy & Kerry; [brother] Tom; [sister] Rosie; [school] Whitehill Junior; [fav sub] PE; [hobbies] Football; [pets] Dog (Angus) & Cat (Spice); [ambition] To be a Footballer;

WINSHIP, SHAUN: [b] 26/8/87; [home] Rayleigh, Essex; [p] Paul & Julie; [brother] David; [sisters] Sarah & Emma; [school] Sweyne Park; [fav sub] French; [hobbies] TV & Computer Games; [pets] Gerbils; [ambition] To travel;

WISE, DAVID: [b] 29/9/84 Exeter; [home] Willand, Devon; [p] Tony & Oonagh; [brother] Michael; [school] Cullompton Community College; [fav sub] P.E.; [hobbies] Football;

WISEMAN, PATRICK: [b] 21/6/89 Chatham; [home] Borden, Kent; [p] Stephanie & Thomas; [brothers] Nathan & Aaron; [sister] Melissa; [school] Borden Grammar; [fav sub] Maths; [hobbies] Hockey & Ice Skating; [pets] Dog; [ambition] To be an Accountant of join the Police Force

WOLSTENCROFT, JOE M.D.: [b] 1/6/92 Preston; [home] Lytham, Lancs; [p] Michael & Sharron; [sisters] Ella, Peta, India & Alex; [school] Clifton CP; [fav sub] Maths; [hobbies] Modelling & playing on Computers; [pets] Cat (Milly); [ambition] to be a Computer worker or a Rock Star;

WONG, MICHELLE: [b] 23/9/93 Harrow; [home] Amersham, Bucks; [p] Gary & Jo; [sister] Stephanie; [school] Little Chalfont Combined; [fav sub] Maths; [hobbies] Swimming & Dancing; [pets] Goldfish; [ambition] To

WONG, STEPHANIE: [b] 4/12/90 Harrow; [home] Amersham, Bucks; [p] Gary & Jo; [sister] Michelle; [school] Little Chalfont Combined; [fav sub] Maths & History; [hobbies] Drama; [pets] Goldfish; [ambition] To be a Scientist;

WOOD CHELSEA LEIGH: [b] 9/6/91 Germany; [home] Tidworth, Hants; [p] Matthew & Tracey; [sister] Kirsty; [school] Zouch Primary; [fav sub] Art; [pets] Dog; [ambition] To be a Singer;

WOOD, HANNAH JAYNE: [b] 25/7/93 Basildon; [home] Aylesbury, Bucks; [p] Carol & Philip; [brother] Charlie; [school] William Harding Combined Junior; [fav sub] Art; [hobbies] Swimming; [pets] Cat (Chester); [ambition] To work with animals;

WOODS, HAYLEY: [b] 5/7/91 Watford; [home] Maple Cross, Herts; [p] Tracey & Clive; [brother] Benjamin; [school] Robertswood; [fav sub] Art; [hobbies] Ballet, Animals, Swimming, Writing & Drawing; [pets] Rat & 2 Fish; [ambition] To become a Vet;

WOODS, LAUREN ADELE: [b] 15/12/94 Preston; [home] Anderton, Lancs; [p] Donna; [brother] Liam; [sister] Leanne; [school] Adlington Primary; [fav sub] Art & Maths; [hobbies] Drawing & Playing out;

WOODWARD, HOLLIE JADE: [b] 2/7/92 Plymouth; [home] Ivybridge, Devon; [p] Craig & Paula; [sister] Imogen Rose; [school] Stowford Primary; [fav sub] ICT; [hobbies] Art, Dancing & Football; [pets] Cat & 6 Fish;

WOOKEY, CHLOE LOUISE: [b] 22/9/92 Bury St Edmunds; [home] Birch, Essex; [p] Teresa Wookey & Cliff Cracknell; [brother] Samuel; [school] Birch C of E Primary; [fav sub] Science; [hobbies] Ballet, Gymnastics, Computer Club; [pets] Love Birds; [ambition] To be a Teacher;

WOOLLEY, JACK MATTHEW: [b] 23/10/93 Eastbourne; [home] Eastbourne, East Sussex; [p] Tony & Tania; [brother] Luke Jason; [school] Hampden Park Infants; [fav sub] Maths; [hobbies] Computer Games; [pets] Cats (Healy & Ebony); [ambition] To be a Maths Teacher, or own a Sweet Shop;

WORTH, JESSICA VICTORIA: [b] 16/5/90 Gloucester; [home] Quedgeley, Glos; [p] Dawn & Dean; [school] Field Court Juniors; [fav sub] Maths, Sport & Writing; [hobbies] Guides, Sport, Music & Reading; [pets] 7 Cats & 1 Hamster; [ambition] To be a Vet or a Designer;

WOZNIAK, ADAM: [b] 7/3/90 King's Lynn; [home] King's Lynn, Norfolk; [p] Stefan & Jill; [sister] Lucy; [school] South Wootton Junior;

[fav sub] History (World War Two); [hobbies] Warhammer Model Painting , Basketball, Football & Sketching; [ambition] To be a Cartoonist or Basketball Player;

WRESSELL, TAMSIN ELLEN: [b] 4/8/91 Salisbury; [home] Tidworth, Wilts; [p] Glenn & Fiona; [sister] Melissa Ann; [school] Zouch Primary; [fav sub] English; [hobbies] Looking after animals, Swimming & Reading; [pets] Rabbit (Clover) & Hamster (Sky); [ambition] To be a Poet and to swim with Dolphins;

WRIDE, BENJAMIN: [b] 23/1/90 Worcester; [home] Honeybourne, Worcs; [p] Ian & Debbie; [brother] Adam; [school] Blackminster; [fav sub] French; [hobbies] Reading & Computer Games; [pets] Dog (Badger) & Cats (Gemma, Tizzy & Mitzy); [ambition] To be a Vet;

WRIGHT, CONNER: [b] 17/7/91 Buxton; [home] Buxton, Derbys; [p] (stepdad) Alex & Maxine & (dad) Steve; [sisters] Shauni, Tiffany, Sophie & Olivia; [school] Buxton Junior; [fav sub] Maths; [hobbies] Football; [pets] Cat; [ambition] To be a Footballer and to join the Army;

WRIGHT, GEORGE: [b] 15/10/88 Canterbury; [home] Iwade, Kent; [p] Christopher & Jacqueline; [sister] Michaela; [school] Borden Grammar; [fav sub] I.T.; [hobbies] Sport & Music; [pets] 2 Cats; [ambition] Unsure yet.

WRIGHT, NAOMI: [b] 16/4/92 Keighley; [home] Haworth, W.Yorks; [p] Fiona & Graham; [brother] Paul; [school] Haworth Primary; [fav sub] English & PE; [hobbies] Reading, Dancing, Gym & Swimming; [pets] Cats (Candy & Coco); [ambition] To become a Vet;

WRIGHT, NICHOLAS: [b] 7/1/91 Yeovil; [home] Crewkerne, Som; [p] James & Sharon; [sisters] Samantha & Harriet; [school] Parrett Axe; [fav sub] Maths; [hobbies] Swimming; [pets] Dog (Ash); [ambition] To travel;

WYNNE, ZAHRA: [b] 17/5/94 London; [home] London; [p] Maryam & Carl; [school] Belmont Primary; [fav sub] Science; [hobbies] Reading; [ambition] To be an Art Teacher;

YOUNG, HOLLY: [b] 2/1/91 Dorchester; [home] Beaminster, Dorset; [p] Derek & Georgina; [sister] Zoe; [school] Parrett & Axe; [fav sub] Art; [hobbies] Pokemon & having fun; [pets] Guinea Pig;

YOUNG, ZENA K.: [b] 30/9/90 Bromsgrove; [home] Bromsgrove, Worcs; [p] Shaun & Elaine; [school] Aston Field Middle; [fav sub] Music; [hobbies] Guitar (Electric & Bass); [ambition] To become a famous Musician;

INDEX
OF
POETS

A

Abbas, Kiran 15
Abbott, Jonathan 15
Abbott, Sam 23
Abbott, Timaisha Masomi 18
Absalom, Thomas 25
Ackroyd, Jade 13
Adams, David 22
Adams, Edward 25
Adams, Jake 14
Adams, Stephen 19
Adams-Salmon, Chris 21
Africa, Zeke 20
Afshan, Sabihah 18
Aggar, Sophie 13
Ahmed, Shahanaz 16
Ainsworth, Robert 20
Akhtar, Mobeen 14
Akhter, Sabrina 18
Alalasundralingham, Suki 18
Alamdary, Sâm 20
Albrow, Nick 19
Aldrich, Murray 15
Aldridge, Matthew 16
Alexander, Craig 25
Alexander, Oliver 11
Alison, Natasha 14
Allan, Elizabeth 17
Allcock, Andrew 20
Allcock, Lizzie 19
Allen, Amber 21
Allen, Bethany 23
Allen, Daniel 23
Allen, Emily 12
Allen, Leah 25
Allen, Sarah 17
Alleyne, Seretse 12
Allmand, Felicity 19
Alps, Matthew 22
Alton, Emily 17
Amor, Maddie 23
Amos, Caroline 19
Anderson, Caroline 7
Anderson, Charlotte 8
Anderson, Dean 13
Anderson, James 15
Andrews, Eleanor 24
Andrews, Emily 14
Andrews, Richard 21
Angood, Stephen 12
Annison, Jack 16
Anstis, Emily 17
Appleby, Jemma 21
Arnold, Emma 12
Arnold-Harman, Beverley 16
Arqum, Sabah 25
Arscott, Kelly 24
Ashbrook, Vicky 23
Ashenden, Louise 21
Ashfield, Jonathan 16
Ashford, Lauren 15

Ashley, Kirie-Lea 14
Ashmead, Amy 11
Ashraf, Rizwan 23
Ashton, Sophie 12
Ashworth, Craig 24
Askew, Craig 26
Aspin, Hannah 9
Asquith-Briggs, Bradley 16
Assimakopoulos, Tasia 15
Astles, Sophie 11
Atack, Bethany 24
Atherton, Chynalouise 13
Atkins, Claire 13
Atkins, Jodie 25
Atkinson, Daniel 21
Atkinson, Joshua 15
Atkinson, Laura 22
Atkinson, Nicholas 11
Atkinson, Rachael 20
Attack, Jodie 22
Attrill, Zoe 15
Aubery, Jake 22
Aucutt, Holly 13
Austen, Ben 22
Austen, Hazel 22
Austin, Danny 14
Auton, Peter 18
Avery, Joe 23
Avron-Cotton, Luke 24
Ayrton, Abigail 23

B

Babet, Jade 43
Backhouse, Sam 40
Baggalley, Laura 53
Baghdadi, Yasser 28
Baglow, Caitlin 27
Bailey, Abigail 42
Bailey, Harriet 70
Bailey, Jack 71
Bailey, Jonathan 63
Bailey, Lauran 34
Baillie, Alice 72
Baines, Melissa 31
Baker, Alexander 52
Baker, Clare 67
Baker, Hannah 40
Baker, James 43
Baker, Joshua 63
Baker, Martin 31
Baker, Mercedes 34
Baldock, Aaron 70
Baldwin, Hannah 55
Ball, Adrian 34
Ball, Stephanie 47
Ballard, Alice 64
Balmayer, Jade 34
Bamber, Sarah 32
Bambford, Dawn 69
Bancroft, Natasha 60
Banister, Guy 51

Banks, Calli 35
Barber, Danielle 47
Barchard, Simone 39
Bardell, Freya 54
Barimani, Bardia 34
Barker, Holly 30
Barker, Lina 71
Barker, Mitchell 35
Barker, William 70
Barling, Richard 26
Barmby, Gemma 65
Barnes, Amy 43
Barnes, Kerry 71
Barnes, Richard James 46
Barnes, Steven 59
Barnett, Amelia 27
Barnett, Lucy 54
Barnett, Marcus 20
Barnett, Simon 68
Barnett, Sylvia 35
Barr, Emma 59
Barr, Polly 62
Barrett, Naomi 48
Barry, Gemma 63
Barry, Lauren 69
Bartholomew, Paul 64
Bartlett, Abigail 33
Bartlett, William 69
Barton, Becky 11
Barton, George 25
Barton, Michael 34
Barwick, Charlotte 43
Batchelor, Adam 35
Batchelor, Emily 41
Batchelor, Tom 58
Batchelor, Zoe 32
Bateman, Emma 46
Bateman, Liam 30
Bateson, Amanda 31
Batt, Zoe 63
Batten-Turner, Florence 70
Bayley, Claire 39
Beales, Felicity 50
Beamont, Helen 55
Beard, Jack 30
Beard, Jessica 47
Beardsworth, Christine 33
Beaumont, Abigail 71
Beddoe, Keren Louise 35
Beddow, Kerry 43
Beechinor, Francis 29
Beese, Annabel Sarah 27
Bell, Elizabeth 54
Bell, Sarah 44
Bellerby, Emma 26
Bellingham, Sam 42
Bellringer, Emma 63
Belsey, Anna 72
Benham, Tom 52
Benjamin, Tui 55
Bennallick, Sam 64

Bennett, Lauren 49
Bennett, Nicholas 50
Bennett, Olivia 52
Bensted, Jessica 36
Benton, Anya 55
Berrett, Lauren 52
Berry, Christopher 40
Berry, Jade 38
Berry, Jason 49
Berry, Rachel 42
Berryman, Liam 27
Best, Huey 71
Bevan, Zoe 53
Bhatt, Ashika 28
Bi, Aysha 34
Bibi, Aaliya 35
Bibi, Abida 70
Bibi, Hafsah 63
Bibi, Harrisah 40
Bibi, Maria 64
Bibi, Rukhsana 36
Bibi, Tazma 64
Bickerstaff, Sam 33
Biddell, Jenna 30
Biggs, Nicki 27
Biggs, Stephanie 28
Billingham, Samantha 49
Billington, Katie 59
Binnee, Laura 44
Binnington Barrett, Victoria .72
Bird, Jamie 48
Birks, Katie 62
Bishop-Green, George 32
Blackbrough, Hayley 42
Blacker, Adam 50
Blacker, Amy 69
Blackmore, Ellie 45
Blade, Adam 59
Blain, Jonothon 55
Blake, Sam 67
Bland, Alexander 61
Blankley, Elissa 31
Blayer, Joe 44
Blenkinsop, Matthew 32
Blighe, Sam 57
Blitz, Jamie 41
Blood, Craig 59
Blumson, Eve 45
Boden, Charlotte 57
Bogod, Isi 28
Bolden, Alex 49
Bole, Charles 74
Bole, Lawrence 53
Bolland, Alexandra 45
Bolton, Daniel 67
Bolton, Jodi 37
Bolton, Madison 68
Bolton, Oliver 38
Bond, Emily 54
Bond, Joseph 44
Bond, Mercedes 62
Bond, Samantha 60
Bone, Amy 74
Booth, Nathan 66
Boraston, Rachael 65
Boreham, Kyrie 49
Borton, Emily 54
Bostock, Eleanor 68
Boucher, Lara 56
Boud, Yazzy 72

Boughton, Josh 58
Boukhobza, Hannay 31
Boulding, Harriet 18
Boulton, Alex 50
Bourne, Michael 72
Boutell, Bryony 27
Bovington, Tom 61
Bowe, Eleanor 58
Bowers, Donna 74
Bowers, Ricky 41
Bowler, Lucinda 73
Bowles, Ryan 69
Bowling, Josephson 39
Bowsher, Sophie 36
Bowtle, Terry 56
Boyle, Eleanor 73
Bracey, Laura 38
Bradbury, Charlotte 53
Bradbury, Kimberley Jayne ..40
Bradford, Harriet 33
Bradford, Harriet 73
Bradford, Robert 37
Bradley, Heather 45
Bradley, Hollie 60
Bradley, Laura 56
Branch, Julia 59
Breakell, David 43
Breakwell, Gemma 31
Breckon, Kayleigh 61
Brennan, Katie 61
Brennan, Rachel 53
Brewster, Stephen 41
Brick, Sarah 36
Bridger, Hannah 42
Bridgewater-Bagnall, Dan ...39
Brierley, Katie 36
Briggs, James 47
Brindle, Caroline 50
Brine, Sophie 48
Bristow, Kimberley 67
Bristow-Jones, Jessica 25
Brittain, Henry 36
Brittleton, Amy 69
Broad, Freddie 51
Broadbridge, Colin 28
Broadbridge, Philip 28
Broadgate, Louisa 74
Broadhead, Thomas 67
Brock, Rachel 26
Brocklesby, Joshua 39
Brocklesby-Millard, Lenny ..62
Bronner, Tristen 54
Brooker, Samantha 57
Brooks, Timothy 69
Brough, James 61
Browes, Andrew 47
Brown, Andrew 57
Brown, Angus 73
Brown, Chloe 32
Brown, Daniel 46
Brown, Edward 65
Brown, Hannah 43
Brown, Harry 62
Brown, Henry 66
Brown, Jessica 67
Brown, Laura 37
Brown, Lucy 65
Brown, Neil 38
Brown, Nicholas 73
Brown, Nicky 58

Brown, Rebecca 66
Brown, Sarah 68
Brown, Siân 38
Brown, Stephanie 71
Brown, Steven 60
Browne, Jeremy 41
Brownfield, Kieran 10
Browning, Laura Amy 32
Browning, Sarah 57
Brownlee, Hannah 26
Bruder, Emily 56
Brunning, James 49
Brunsdon, Craig 68
Bryan, Daniel 56
Bryant, Adam 45
Bryant, Charlie-Ann 39
Buck, Michael 29
Buckingham, George 60
Bull, Sam 66
Bullard, Ria 32
Bulloch, Leah 9
Bullock, Andrew 40
Bullock, Gemma 44
Bullworthy, Chloe 33
Bulow, Bethany 45
Bundock, Daniel 52
Bungey, Joe 68
Bunker, Kassandria 51
Bunn, Martin 58
Burch, Aimèe 73
Burchmore, Kelly 37
Burge, Christopher 74
Burgess, Alec 26
Burgess, Claire 38
Burgess, Joe 37
Burgess, Lucy 65
Burgess, Sian 65
Burman, Craig 46
Burns, Darren 48
Burns, Emily 51
Burnside, Christina 37
Burr, Daniel 62
Burrell, Leah 44
Burrough, Danielle 60
Burrows, Aimee 47
Burrows, Natasha 57
Burrows, Patrick 66
Burt, Dustin Charles 48
Burton, Lisa 30
Burton, Michael 52
Buse, Leigh-Anne 30
Butcher, Denver 60
Butcher, Laura 41
Butlin, Chloe 66
Butt, Anum 46
Butt, Jason 73
Butt, Keiron 58
Butters, Charlotte 29
Byrne Stevens, Helena 43
Byrne, Anthony 56
Byrne, Matthew 50
Byrne, Niamh 51
Bysh, Victoria 38

C

Cachia, Alex 83
Cackett, John 108
Caines, Georgina 88
Caldwell, Matthew 77
Callaghan, Emily 102

Callagher, William 87
Callow, Daniel 111
Cameron, Georgina 94
Cameron, Ross 92
Campbell, Andrew 79
Campbell, Chris 88
Campbell, Isabella 82
Campbell, Michael 95
Campion, Madeline 76
Cann, Rachel 89
Cannell, Oliver 80
Cannon, Charlotte 87
Cantle, Lauren 81
Capel, Tom 111
Capon, Oliver 80
Card, Tanya 110
Carless, Ben 112
Carney, Jake 85
Carpanini, Stephanie 85
Carpenter, Elizabeth 113
Carpenter, Emma 87
Carrick, Amanda 78
Carrigan, Emma 95
Carter, Ben .74
Carter, Caroline 113
Carter, Charlotte 108
Carter, Hannah 109
Carter, Josie 107
Carter, Lauren 102
Carter, Nicola 80
Carter, Richard 113
Carter, Ryan 75
Carter, Sara 96
Catherall, Billy 82
Catnach, Vicky 102
Caton, Ami .93
Catt, Stacey 107
Cauchois, Vicky 76
Caufield, Robyn 107
Caulkett, Josephine 102
Caulton, Laurence 83
Cavanagh, Lisa 94
Cawley, Laura 110
Chaïr, Irwin-Malek 29
Challis, Melanie 87
Chalmers, Jade 92
Chamberlin, Niamh 113
Chambers, Jemma 95
Chambers, Mili'sa 94
Chambers, Rachel 101
Chan, Elizabeth 111
Chandler, Ben 108
Chandler, Daniel 92
Chandler, Kate 110
Chantler, Adam 108
Chapman, Cheire 106
Chapman, John 107
Chapman, Ria 79
Charles, Jack 82
Charlston, Ben 96
Charlton, Gemma 91
Charlton, Matthew 105
Charteris-Black, Sara 82
Chatfield, Harriet 81
Chaudhury, Iqra 101
Chaudhury, Iqrab 111
Cheek, Emily 107
Chessman, Paul 112
Chester, Emily 75
Chesters, Kelly Rose 91

Chetwood, Martin 110
Chetwynd-Hay, Eleanor 110
Cheung, Rosalie 80
Child, Matthew 81
Child, Natalie 79
Childs, Cassy 105
Chilton, Anthea 115
Chilves, Katy 79
Chippindale, Luke 87
Chisholm, Alexandra 94
Chlebowski, Loella 111
Choudary, Faryal 108
Chowdhury, Sakhawatul 89
Chowns, Danny 83
Christian, Jess 77
Chrumka, Nicholas 76
Church, Sam 80
Churchard, Beth 78
Churcher, Laura 91
Churn, Joanna 75
Ciechanowicz, Izzy 80
Cirillo, Louisa 112
Clanford, Lucy May 89
Clare, Madison 90
Clark, Adam 90
Clark, Alex .78
Clark, Anna 77
Clark, Charlie 110
Clark, Steven 105
Clark, Verity 116
Clark, Victoria 100
Clarke, Alison 85
Clarke, Amy 105
Clarke, Camilla 103
Clarke, Robert 84
Clarke, Rosie 116
Clay, James .77
Claydon-Johns, Joe 101
Clayton, James 104
Clayton, Michael 105
Clayton, Sarah 97
Clayton, Tom 100
Cleasby, Georgia 113
Clements, Elise 106
Clifton, Douglas 79
Cluskey, Daniel 78
Coates, Katie 114
Coates, Emily 94
Cobb, Charlotte 115
Cobb, Jessica 114
Cobb, Saphinna 92
Cochrane, Zoë 72
Cock, Ryan 114
Cohen, Sean 85
Cohen, Susannah 78
Coker Gordon, Nicola 106
Coker, Joshua 99
Coker, Vanessa 106
Cole, Claire 78
Cole, David 85
Cole, Elizabeth 105
Cole, Jack .104
Cole, Joshua 81
Cole, Sarah .76
Coleman, Caroline 76
Coleman, Colin 101
Coles, Charlotte 90
Coles, Kieron 115
Collett, Rebecca 116
Collie, Mark 97

Collier, Sam 83
Collings, Isabel 103
Collins, Ellis 104
Collins, Emma 81
Collins, Geoffrey 115
Collins, Jade 114
Collins, Poppy 74
Collinson, Alice 111
Collinson, Mark 117
Collop, Rosy 85
Conlan, Luke 84
Connaughton, Joe 117
Connelly-Webster, Robyn 83
Connolly, Elisha 114
Connolly, Jack 82
Connolly, Victoria 89
Constantinou, Epiphany 75
Convery, Benjamin 102
Convey, Paige 75
Conway, Nicola 104
Cook, Faye 114
Cook, Lisa .91
Cook, Natalie 92
Cooke, Esther 93
Cooke, Sophy 105
Cooke, Thomas 116
Coombs, Hannah 97
Coomes, Michael 106
Cooper, Aidan 89
Cooper, Alexander 100
Cooper, Emma 98
Coopey, Daniel 115
Copp, Natalie 92
Corbet, Tom 95
Corby, Jade 109
Cordell, Emma 79
Cordey, Lucy 84
Cornall, James 109
Cornall, Lewis 97
Coronato, Stefania 81
Corriette, Marcel 111
Cossey, Liam 107
Cottee, Romana 84
Cottle, Dorian 104
Cottle-Barker, Joshua 112
Cottrell, Benjamin 117
Cottrill, Fiona 70
Coulson, Jake 99
Coulter, Christine 90
Coupe, Helen 109
Courtney, Ben 126
Couston, Nicola 90
Couzens, Tanya 95
Coveney, Hannah 108
Cowan, Elizabeth 100
Cowan, Hannah 94
Cowan, Jamie 93
Cowburn, Lydia 116
Cowell, Elizabeth 84
Cowell, Thomas 101
Cowles, Rachel 86
Cowley, Richard 103
Cox, Beckie 93
Cox, Becky 115
Cox, Rachael 103
Coxall, Chantelle 84
Cozins, Timothy 98
Cracknell, Benjamin 106
Cracknell, Poppy 112
Cragg, Danielle 98

Cragg, Mercedes 103
Craig, Jonathan 100
Crandon, Katy 93
Craske, Sarah 116
Credland, Elizabeth 113
Crellin, David 77
Cripps, Jade 88
Cripps, Olivia 104
Crisp, Daniel 88
Crisp, James 86
Crisp, Sam .99
Crisp, Victoria 98
Cristofani, Jamie 114
Critchley, Florrie 99
Crockford, Romani 86
Croft, James 87
Cronin, Hannah 82
Cronin, John 103
Crook, George 96
Cropper, Charlotte 83
Cross, Jessica 103
Cross, Kylie 76
Cross, Laura 96
Cross, Michael 109
Cross, Tiffany 90
Crosthwaite, Ceyhan 101
Crouch, Holly 109
Crouch, Naomi 86
Croucher, Wayne 86
Crow, Lauren 97
Crowley, Rebecca 77
Crowley, Sam 86
Crowther, Simon 95
Cruse, Joe .117
Cubbon, Ian 88
Cuddy, Melissa 116
Cullen, Charlotte 75
Cullen, Rebecca 115
Culley, James 98
Cullum, Lucy 98
Cullum, Peter 97
Cummings, Phillip 102
Curland, Michael 100
Curran, Luke 114
Curzons, Neesa Marie 112
Cusens, Emily 110
Cutler, Jessica 93
Cutting, Jessica 99

D

Dabrowski, Sarah 127
Dack, Christina 129
Dagger, Toby 125
Daley, Hannah 120
Dalgado, Martin 124
Dalley, Dominic 121
Dalton-Banks, Niall 123
Danaher, Beth 129
Daniel, George 117
Daniels, Oliver 130
Darby, Hannah 126
Darby, Natasha 125
Dathan, Martin 133
Dauncey, Tom 131
Dauwalder, Kate 133
Davey, Harriet 119
Davey, Jenine 122
Davey, Joanna 129
Davey, Rosie 135
Davi, Tétévi 120

Davies, Aaron 135
Davies, Charlotte 123
Davies, Eleanor 133
Davies, Gabriella 128
Davies, Jonathan 138
Davies, Katharine 135
Davies, Kayleigh 125
Davies, Peter 118
Davies, Rebecca 121
Davies, Ryan 136
Davies, Sam 131
Davies, Stephanie 124
Davies, Thomas 119
Davies, Wayne 133
Davis, Ben .124
Davis, Callum 137
Davis, Christina 128
Davis, David 124
Davis, Kathryn 123
Davis, Lauren 131
Davis, Lindsey 132
Davis, Nick 122
Davis, Tamsin 136
Davitt, Patrick 122
Daw, Elizabeth 134
Dawson, Hannah 128
Dawson, Laura 130
Dawson, Oliver 126
Dawson, Rosie 123
Day, Alison 126
Day, Ottalie 119
Dayton, Eleanor 130
de Lange, Christiaan 139
Deacon, Adam 120
Deacon, Kayleigh 133
Deakin, Danielle 123
Deam, Alex 130
Dean, Christopher Stuart 120
Dean, Henry 117
Dean, Isabelle 118
Dean, Jonathan 131
Dean, Jordan 121
Dearnaley, William 136
Deigan, Louise 122
Denny, Juliet 118
Denyer, Marike 119
Deol, Kayleigh 138
Desmond, Hannah 137
Dewey, Laura 134
Dhanak, Ravi 127
Dharmaratne, Sachini 132
Dick, Gary .128
Dickinson, James 132
Dickson, Andrew 139
Dickson, Helen 137
Dickson, Katie 131
Dikki, Bandi 130
Dillon, Chris 121
Dimmock, Ross 139
Dimond, Jamie 126
Dingle, Jamie 125
Dingle, Joe 136
Ditchfield, Emma-Jayne 132
Dobbie, Scott 126
Dobson, Grant 134
Dobson, Jessica 134
Dodd, Harry 134
Dodson, Mark 121
Doherty, Hannah 129
Dolan, Stephen 122

Dolor, Patrice 118
Donald, Andrew 134
Donald, Hannah 122
Donnachie, Charlie 133
Donnelly, Anne-Marie 129
Donovan, Luke 119
Doonan, Christopher 116
Dore, Jacob 124
Dorme, Sarah-Jayne 132
Dormer, Jordan 117
Dos Santos, Annabel 124
Douglas, Adam 123
Douglas, Elinor 129
Douglas, Jenny 127
Douglass, Chris 137
Dowding, Rachael 134
Dowling, Michael 117
Dowling, Michaela 118
Drain, Elizabeth 136
Drake-Brockman, Sean 128
Draper, Jessica 121
Drewitt, China 136
Dring, Rebecca Louise 125
Driver, Lucy 132
Drury, Christopher 137
Drysder, Anna 118
du Boulay, Michael 138
Dubois, Michelle 136
Dudley, Shannon 135
Duerden, Samantha 135
Duffy, Richard 120
Duncan, Matthew 130
Dunleavey, Stephanie 127
Dunn, Jack 120
Dunne, Katie 135
Durodie, Marc 126
Dutson, Lana 125
Dyball, Tom 119
Dyer, Gemma 127
Dyer, Zara .138
Dymond, Rebecca 119
Dynes, Charlotte 131
Dyson, Lewis 127

E

Eames, Lauren 145
Earl, Ashley 145
Earll, Ashley 143
Earnshaw, Sammi-Marie 143
Eastaugh, Thomas 145
Easterbrook, Lereesa 139
Easton, Laura 147
Eaton, Thomas 137
Ebdon, Jane 147
Eccles, Katie 142
Eccleston, Lucinda 147
Eddy, Rebecca 141
Edens, Lisa 148
Edgar, Thomas James 141
Edmunds, Jenny 146
Edwards, Alice 143
Edwards, Charlotte 143
Edwards, Christopher 142
Edwards, Craig 148
Edwards, Josh 140
Edwards, Tim 140
Egressy, Kinga 143
Egressy, Nora 141
Ehrmann, Georgia 144
Ekers, Rebecca 146

Eley, Michael .146
Eley, Sarah-Louise 141
Elkins-Jarret, Lisa-Jane 141
Ellaby, Nicholas 138
Elliott, Devon 142
Elliott, George 145
Elliott, Nicholas 144
Elliott, Rosanna 138
Elliott, Sophie 138
Elliott, Tom .148
Ellison, Rukaya 146
Elsey, Gemma 140
Elvidge, Natasha 144
Elwell, Kirsty 146
Emery, Stephanie Louise 140
Enkel, Casey 139
Ennew, Siohban 144
Escott, James 147
Essalmi, Yasmin 140
Etere, Mica-Lee 143
Etheridge, Alex 147
Etheridge, Glen 148
Etheridge, Helen 138
Etheridge, Kirsten 137
Etherington, Danielle 144
Eu, Jean 145
Eustace, Tré .139
Evans, Aimee 141
Evans, James 140
Every, Taylor 144
Ewington, David 147
Eyre, Stephen 142

F

Fairbairn, Matthew 156
Farmilo, Aisha 152
Farquharson, Lewis 155
Faulkner, Joel 154
Fay, Thomas 148
Fear, Chris 150
Fearns, Andrew 150
Fell, Nikki 158
Fellows, Paul 155
Fenlon, Katie 156
Fenn, Jason .159
Fernandez, Danielle 157
Fernandez, Tony 148
Ferrari, Eloise 151
Ferry, Jordan 155
Feuchtwanger, Alex 157
Field, Eleanor 153
Field, Jodie .152
Fieldhouse, Katy 149
Filmer, Michelle 155
Finch, Eliza .156
Finch, James 158
Fincken, Lara 153
Finn, Matthew 150
Finney, Declan 149
Fisher, Gemma 154
Fisher, Jamie 153
Fitch, Simon 151
Fitzer, Adam 154
Fitzerald, Jack 153
Fitzpatrick, Katie 149
Flack, Theo .159
Flacks, Luke 156
Flahaut, David 157
Flahaut, Emma-Leigh 154
Flanders, Stephanie 158

Flannery, Sinead 149
Flaxman, Catherine 158
Fletcher, Jenny 159
Fletcher, Sally 159
Fletcher, Simone 157
Flight, Melissa 154
Flint, Joe 151
Ford, Charlotte 159
Forrest, Perry 146
Forsyth, Joe .158
Foster, Alice 151
Foster, Emma 159
Foster, Kayleigh 155
Foster, Ned .151
Foster, Simon 160
Fox, Abigail .156
Fox, George .149
Frais, Simon 150
Francis, Davina 153
Francis, Matthew 152
Francis, Michaela 159
Fraus, Nicola 153
Frayne, John 151
Freeman, Neal 152
French, Alexander 152
Frewer, Sarah 155
Frisby, Drew 154
Froment, Sam 148
Frost, Daniel 158
Frost, Ellen .161
Frost, Richard 149
Frost, Sophie 151
Froud, Charlotte 149
Fry, Imogen .152
Fry, Katie 159
Fuller, Claudia 155
Fuller, Rebecca 150
Fuller, Verity 153
Furness, Jim 158
Furness, Neil 157
Fysh, Matthew 150

G

Gale, Ben 178
Gallimore, David 177
Game, Emma 169
Gangaidzo, Arnold 177
Gardner, Grace 161
Gardner, Nicholas 163
Gardner, Tom 177
Garrigues, Emily 172
Garside, Neil 173
Gaskell, Laura 165
Gaskin, Chloe 170
Gaskin, Elinor 166
Gatley, Holli .173
Gawler, Stephanie 162
Gawthorpe, Michael 176
Gawthorpe, Tom 176
Gedge, Emma 169
Gellett, Chelsey-Marie 164
Gennard, Hannah 178
Gent, Naomi 161
Gerrish, Katie 167
Ghazanfar, Tayyab 165
Gibbins, Natasha 175
Gibbon, Rhys 178
Gibbons, Chloe 159
Gibbons, Grace 163
Gibbs, Amy .174

Gibbs, Molly 177
Gibbs-Barlow, Stephen 165
Gibson, Douglas 171
Gibson, Jamie 175
Giddins, Jason 174
Gifford, Kirsty 174
Gilbert, Hannah 175
Gilbert, Jessica 172
Giles, Stephanie 178
Gilgunn, Jack 160
Gill, Douglas 170
Gill, Nicholas 179
Gillett, Jamie 170
Gillies, Corrina 165
Gladden, Adam 164
Gladden, Victoria 169
Glanville, Lisa 173
Glass, Antony 168
Goddard, John 164
Godden, Ailsa 167
Godden, Michael 166
Godding, Spike 165
Godfrey, Bethany 170
Godfrey, Charlotte 171
Golding, Joshua 171
Goldup, Natasha 162
Gooch, Miriam 161
Gooch, Miriam 171
Good, Daniel 175
Gooday, Lisa 160
Goode, Georgia 169
Goodridge, Gregory 177
Goodwin, Lucy 166
Goodwin, Moss 170
Goodwin, Tom 172
Goodyear, David 167
Gorman, Hayley 176
Gornall, Sophie 173
Gosford, Kelly 162
Goss, Chloe .173
Gould, Eleanor 161
Gould, Emma 176
Gould, Jack .173
Gowler, Tom 176
Grace, Annabel 178
Gradidge, Jack 179
Gradidge, Thomas 173
Gradwell, Hannah 160
Graham, Hayley 160
Graham-Clare, Laura 166
Grainger, Bethany 176
Grange, James 174
Grant, Elliott 168
Grant, Sam .165
Grantham, Sangeeta 170
Gray, Cassie 161
Gray, Laura .163
Gray, Niall 162
Greaves, Sam 179
Green, Callum 176
Green, Daniel 169
Green, James 162
Green, Kayleigh 175
Green, Lucy .160
Green, Matt .172
Green, Meryl 177
Green, Sarah 168
Greenaway, Victoria 174
Greenhalgh, Rebecca 171
Greenwood, Katie 161

Greenwood, Liam 175
Greenwood, Melody 160
Gregory, Charlotte 162
Gregory, Lauren 172
Gregory, Paul 166
Grewal, Satpreet 163
Griffin, Connie 169
Griffin, Katie 166
Griffin, Laura 171
Griffiths, Charlie 178
Griffiths, Kieran 176
Griffiths, Sophie 164
Griggs, Amelia 167
Grimes, Hannah 164
Grimshaw, Jasmin 168
Grimshaw, Luke 177
Grimston, Lauren 160
Groves, David 177
Groves, David 179
Groves, Paul 164
Grundy, Katie 177
Grundy, Tom 179
Guerin, Laura 167
Guilfoy, Tom 167
Guille, Paul 168
Gul, Zubaida 172
Gulbrandson, Erika 175
Gulliver, Sarah 163
Gumble, Jeanie 171
Gunn, Carly 174
Gunn, Lorraine 175
Gurton, William 163
Guthrie, Jonathan 168
Guy, Nathan 174

H

Hacker, Charlotte 212
Hadjipourou, Michael 186
Haggas, Shelley 196
Hale, Michael 188
Hall, Chris .210
Hall, Dominic 200
Hall, Jess 203
Hall, Jonathan 207
Hall, Michael 213
Hall, Rebecca 188
Halls, Rebecca 185
Hamill, Natalie 185
Hamilton, Sean 191
Hammant, Tristan 209
Hampshire, Susanna 194
Hampson, Sarah 204
Hampton, Samantha 207
Hamson, George 203
Hancock, Joshua 180
Hancock, Lucy 189
Hand, Nathan 189
Handy, Russell 209
Handy, Sarah 180
Haralambous, Katie 201
Harbon, Reece 214
Harcombe, Megan 203
Hardacre, Nicky 209
Harding, Jenny 195
Harding, Mark 190
Harding, Simon 211
Harding, Thomas 198
Hardy, Alex 211
Hardy, Daniel 187
Hardy, Jennifer 190

Hardy, Sonya 192
Hare, Charlotte 209
Hare, Rebecca 211
Harkup, John 199
Harley, George 200
Harman, Charlotte 182
Harman, Rochelle 207
Harper, Jake 201
Harper, Megan 211
Harper, Rebecca 205
Harpur, Kristina 200
Harragan, Emma Louise 188
Harrington-Clark, Alyshia 197
Harris, Beverley 210
Harris, Edward 210
Harris, James 214
Harris, Luke 186
Harris, Matthew 189
Harris, Natalie 200
Harris, Rachel 184
Harris, Sam 208
Harris, Sophie 208
Harris, Stephen 200
Harrison, Conrad 180
Harrison, Hannah 191
Harrison, Lucy Elizabeth 214
Harrison, Thomas 212
Hart, Abigail 210
Hart, Chloe 210
Hartle-Ryan, Harriette 207
Hartley, Connie 212
Hartley, Freddy 209
Harvey, Jason 206
Harvey, Joanne 206
Harvey, Joshua 211
Harvey, Luke 185
Harwin, Samuel 208
Haslam, Emily 186
Hassett, Alexander 201
Hastings, Louise 195
Hastings, Naomi 184
Hatcher, Jack 197
Haughton, Chelsea 201
Havers, Catherine 206
Hawke, Stacey 199
Hawker, Alanna 201
Hawkings, Tristan 181
Hawkins, Emma 213
Hawkins, Robert 203
Hayes, Lucy 182
Hayes, Sophie 201
Hayler, Paul 198
Haynes, Ashleigh 180
Hayter, Brett 183
Haywood, Victoria 210
Hazleton, Matthew 208
Hazlett, Emma 187
Healey, Wesley 188
Hearn, Bryony 211
Heath, Simone 207
Heathcote, Aimee 185
Heathcote, Rebecca 209
Hebditch, Max 203
Hedges, Claire 207
Heels, Nathan 198
Heffer, Lauren 211
Heinz, Nadine 208
Hellings, Scott 199
Helm, Caroline 183
Helm, Mark 203

Hemming, Jessica 213
Henderson, Donna 199
Henderson, Kirsty 182
Hennessy, Richard 211
Henney, Alice 207
Herbert, Katie 192
Herd, Andrew 201
Heron, Kerry 208
Hetherington, Sarah 211
Hewett, Victoria 190
Hewish, Eleanor 186
Hewitt, Rachel 212
Hewlett, Georgia 213
Heyes, James 210
Heywood, Joe 197
Hickling, Becky 181
Hickling, James 181
Hicks, Sarah 182
Higgins, Niall 180
Higgins, Simon 207
Higham, Jake 181
Hill, Alice .178
Hill, Alison 180
Hill, Graeme 184
Hill, Hazel .189
Hill, Jade 212
Hill, Leanne 188
Hills, Claire 213
Hilsden, Lauren 182
Hilton, Greg 212
Hinckley, Laura 183
Hindley, Rachel 189
Hinks, Amy 194
Hinks, Emily 181
Hinton, Georgie 212
Hipwell, Guy 183
Hirst, Sarah 213
Hiscock, Lydia 179
Hoare, George 202
Hobbs, Camilla 193
Hobson, Francesca 192
Hobson, Matthew 214
Hodder, Simon 191
Hodgkins, Thomas Benjamin 191
Hoff, Matthew 199
Holborow, Adam 205
Holcombe, Daryl 192
Holden, Elizabeth 190
Holden, Jack 252
Holden, Philippa 182
Holland, Cassie 191
Holley, Jessica 206
Holliday, Pia 193
Holman, Ben 183
Holmes, Alistair 204
Holmes, Emily 187
Holmes, Luke 189
Holmes, Sarah 196
Holness, Adem 204
Holroyd, Emma 184
Holt, Lauren Melissa 196
Honeyman, Lise 191
Hook, James 202
Hook, Sarah 196
Hooker, Alan 185
Hoolin, Sally 192
Hooper, James 195
Hope, Katy .185
Hopes, Caitlin 198
Hopkins, David 186

Hopley, Danielle 192
Hornby, Catherine 187
Horner, Rachel 214
Horton, Ann 202
Horton, Cloey 187
Hosegood, James 205
Hosier, Ryan 205
Houlbrook, Benjamin 202
House, Ashley 199
House, Lauren 196
Houston, Jamie 187
Hovey, Stephanie 197
Howard, Shaun 199
Howard, Stephenaie 205
Howden, Jamie 199
Howe, Christopher 193
Howell, Sam 215
Howes, Caroline 194
Hows, Charlotte 200
Howse, Abigail 193
Howson, Charlotte 198
Hoyt, Ryon .183
Hughes, Gemma 194
Hughes, Jason 186
Hughes, Jonathan 206
Humm, Emma 206
Humphreys, Joshua 193
Hundley, Zoe 195
Hunt, Declan 214
Hunt, Jamie 195
Hunt, Sarah 206
Hurford, Annabel 202
Hurrisett, Jesse 190
Hurst, Jessica 177
Hussain, Asjad 205
Hussain, Dilwor 204
Hussain, Ifzah 205
Hussain, Mohsin 204
Hussain, Rizaul 205
Hussain, Sharaz 204
Hussain, Sheraz 204
Hussain, Shoaib 196
Hussain, Sobia 203
Hussain, Zobia 193
Hussein, Kerem 196
Husseini, Serene 198
Hussey, Rebecca 195
Hussey, Ryan 194
Hutchings, Samantha 194
Hutchins, Megan 213
Hutchinson, Lucy 184
Hyam, Giselle 190
Hynes, Peter 188

I

Ibrahim, Leyla 216
Ibrahim, Liban 215
Illingworth, Jordan 216
Ilott, Nicole 216
Imtiaz, Rabia 216
Ingram, Emily 215
Ingram, William 215
Innes, Mark 216
Inns, Natalie 217
Irlam, Catherine 215
Ismay, Hayley 215
Ives, Rae 216

J

Jackson, Anthony 217

Jackson, Bonnie 218
Jackson, Laura 229
Jackson, Melissa 222
Jackson, Naomi 219
Jackson, Sophie 223
Jacques, Charlotte 229
Jacques, Kellie 224
Jaeger, Natanya 219
Jain, Anmol 220
Jama, Adam 226
James, Carl .222
James, Christopher 225
James, Cory 228
James, Eleanor 222
James, Faye .220
James, Joanne 224
James, Katy 229
James, Marcus 228
James, Sienna 228
Jamieson, Henry 225
Jarrett, Jack 220
Jarvis, Adam 229
Jarvis, Ben .226
Javed, Adnaan 223
Javeleau, Hayley 225
Jeffery, Emma 221
Jeffery, Rhian 218
Jefford, Jake 227
Jelfs, Ben 223
Jenkin, Sophie 227
Jenkins, Callum 229
Jenkins, Jordan 226
Jenkinson, Chris 219
Jenner, Jason 226
Jesudason, Daniel 228
Jewsbury, Sophie 228
Johansen, David 223
Johns, Philip 225
Johnson, Anna-Louise 230
Johnson, Georgia 229
Johnson, Kallie 221
Johnson, Katherine 226
Johnson, Matthew 218
Johnson, Samantha 221
Johnson, Sarah 204
Johnson, Steven 228
Johnson, Vicky 224
Jolly, Kevin .220
Jones, Adam 224
Jones, Alex .228
Jones, Andrew 222
Jones, Annie 228
Jones, Aurea 227
Jones, Ben .224
Jones, Claire 223
Jones, Darren 223
Jones, David 221
Jones, Dominic 227
Jones, Edward 219
Jones, Eleanor 229
Jones, Ellie .225
Jones, Elliott 217
Jones, Esther 220
Jones, Gareth 217
Jones, Jordan 217
Jones, Lauren 218
Jones, Megan 227
Jones, Rachel 219
Jones, Rhiannon 219
Jones, Rhiannon 225

Jones, Ryan 226
Jones, Ryan 228
Jones, Sarah 221
Jones, Shelby 217
Jordan, Adam 222
Jordan, Chloe 222
Joseph, Ben 227
Joseph, Chloe 227
Jourdan, Alex 227
Joyce, Michael 214
Joyce, Zoë .218
Joyner, Simon 224
Juby, Clare .218
Jury, Billy 216
Jury, Philip .226
Justice, Jeil .230
Juve, Kristi .221

K

Kaczmarczyk, Katherine 237
Kahar, Krunal 231
Karadakova, Laura 230
Karamchedu, Neeha 242
Kassam, Imran 230
Kauser, Mariam 239
Kauser, Rozina 243
Kauser, Sonia 239
Kaye, Nigel .236
Kazmi, Omera 243
Keal, Steve .238
Kearton, Nicholas 237
Keech, Alex 239
Keeler, Cameron 235
Keenan, Kathryn 232
Keenlyside, Harley 238
Keens, James 240
Kelen, Joseph 233
Kellie, Jonathan 236
Kelly, Charlotte 237
Kelly, Katie .240
Kelly, Nathan 243
Kelly, Paul .241
Kelly, Rachel 232
Kelly, Raechel 231
Kelly, Sammy 243
Kember, Elizabeth 220
Kemp, Jenny 242
Kemp, Laura 232
Kemp, Megan 242
Kemp, Rebecca 236
Kendall, Louise 240
Kendall, William 239
Kenny, Nicholas 232
Kenward, Jessica 239
Kenward, Laura 239
Keohane, Abby 241
Keppel, Isabel 234
Kerin, Katthew 230
Kerr, Alastair 244
Kershaw, Natalie 242
Kessell, Emma 230
Ketley, Louise 239
Kett, Chrissy 236
Kett, Rachael 231
Kew, Rebecca 240
Khalid, Shoaib 233
Khalsa, Michael 236
Khan, Aamir 234
Khan, Shereen 236
Khanum, Mahmuda 241

Khatun, Tasmiyaha 234
Khondkar, Adib 235
Killingworth, Rosie 235
Kimpton, Stephanie 231
King, Emma 233
King, Michael 235
King, Rachel 232
King, Rebekah 242
King, Robbie 235
King, Rosie 241
King, Rupert 231
King, Sophie 238
Kingshott, Daniel 233
Kirby, Crispin 234
Kirby, Justine 235
Kirk, Jordan 241
Kirk, Louisa 234
Kite, Thomas 238
Kneebone, Laura 238
Knibbs, Emily 242
Knight, Alice 233
Knight, Andrew 243
Knight, Emma 241
Knight, Keshia 230
Knight, Matthew 237
Knight, Zoe 240
Knights, Liam 236
Knowles, Anna 242
Kocerhan, Becky 238
Koh, Alanna 237
Koh, Jeremy 237
Konche, Aydin 238
Kouhi, Nadia 233
Kozlik, Elliott 242
Kozlik, Oliver 234
Kucuk, Erol 232
Kumar, Priya 243
Kurt, Huseyin 241

L

La Bouchardiere, Rachel 251
Ladkin, Kate 245
Laher, Adam 257
Laidlaw, Louise 248
Laidlow, Rachel 256
Laity, Tristan 258
Lam, Nikki 252
Lamb, Kate 258
Lamb, Kathryn Alison 259
Lamb, Michael 247
Lambert, Rebecca 249
Lambert, Toria 246
Lambeth, Christopher 249
Lam-Moores, Chloe 259
Lampshire, Mark 251
Lander, Charlotte 254
Landragin, Rosie 244
Lands, Sara 254
Lane, Fiona 255
Langford, Billy 253
Langton, Mark 255
Large, Charlie 258
Large, Roza 258
Large, Sophie 257
Lasota, Eleanor 248
Last, Larissa 251
Lauchlan, Eliza 247
Lavis, Adam 251
Lawless, Ricky 255
Lawrence, Annie 248

Lawrence, Madeleine 254
Layzell, Kirsty 245
Lee, Dominic 255
Lee, Helen 247
Lee, Johannah 248
Lee, Matthew 258
Lee, Rachel 259
Lee, Rebecca 252
Lees, Robert 244
Legg, Phillipa 259
Lehane, Tara 249
Leigh, Rachel 249
Lennon, Conor 253
Lennon, Daniella 253
Lennon, Georgina 251
Lennon, Rebecca 243
Leonard, Tessa 250
Lester, Rachel 253
Letley, Clare 245
Levene, Rachel 245
Leverett, Kati 245
Levett, Jessica 250
Levisalles, Amaury 256
Lewin, Billy 245
Lewis, Bliss 256
Lewis, Elizabeth 253
Lewis, Ffiona 259
Lewis, Jamie 249
Lewis, Victoria 257
Leyland, William 245
Liddell, Katy 256
Lilburn, Alex 250
Lilley, Heather 251
Lilley, James 246
Lillington, Danielle 247
Lim, William 246
Limbert, Jaid 254
Limbrick, Ruby 250
Lindop, Emma 254
Lindop, Nicola 247
Lindsay, Jessica 266
Lindsell, Lucy 245
Lineker, Chloe 256
Linford, Emma 246
Linsell, Catherine 250
Liptrot, Zoe 244
Lister, Jack 246
Little, Charlotte 251
Liu, Mary 244
Lloyd, Alisha 257
Loader, Amy 257
Lock, Sophie 244
Locke, Stuart 258
Lockyear, Harriet 248
Logan, Andrew 258
Long, Sam 255
Longley, James 253
Longman, Jack 259
Longmire, Samantha 250
Lord, Heather 252
Louch, Christopher 249
Louden, Victoria 247
Lovell, Beatrice 240
Lovell, Iain 259
Lovick, Sophie 251
Lowe, Amy 258
Lowe, Tom 246
Lowings, Sarah 258
Loza, Maaia 254
Lozinski, Alexander 257

Lucas, Eleanor 237
Lucas, Lizzie 249
Lye, Craig 257
Lye, Graeme 249
Lynch, Chelsea 259
Lynch, Katy 251
Lynch, Lucy 255
Lynch, Rosie 248
Lynes, Zoe 256

M

Mace, Ryan 286
Macintosh, Robert 279
Maciocha, Kirsty 268
Macivor, Jessica 282
Mackay, Megan 286
Mackay, Rhys 284
Mackie, Saffron 272
Mackinnon, Kirsty 289
Macklin, Kayleigh 272
Macklin, Maxine 273
Macpherson, Jamie 274
Maddern, Sophie 286
Maddock, Adam 291
Madigan, Chloe 284
Maguire, Sean 286
Mahmood, Ayshia 290
Mahmood, Husna 291
Mahmood, Zeenat 282
Mahoney, Jade 272
Mahrenholz, Ella 261
Mairs, Rachel 272
Maisey-Curtis, Max 280
Majeika, Kirsty 289
Majek, Helena 290
Majid, Kiran 282
Major, Hannah 290
Major, Sam 285
Makin, Lauren 287
Makinson, Chelsey 260
Male, Rebecca 289
Maloney, Jake 279
Manaton, Sara 279
Mangan, Carys 264
Mann, Alexandra 272
Mann, Katharyn 278
Mann, Nathan 286
Manning, Connor 282
Manning, Jenna 289
Mannion, Nathalie 287
Mansfield, Ben 283
Manthorpe, Richard 261
Marcheselli, Max 272
Marcus, Georgia 277
Marks, Oliver 286
Marland-Flint, Lorna 269
Marsh, Abigail 282
Marsh, Jordan 264
Marshall, Joshua 282
Marshall, Kerri 287
Marshall, Thomas 287
Marsland, Anna 281
Martayn, Laura 290
Martin, Abbey 289
Martin, Holly 276
Martin, Jessica 286
Martindale, William 284
Martinez, Luke 283
Maskell, Danielle 283
Massey, Jaide 274

Massing, Richard 279
Masters Jordan 289
Masters, Alex 274
Matthew, Jay 287
Matthews Elena 289
Matthews, Adam 288
Matthews, Emma 290
Matthews, James 267
Matthews, Kizzy 272
Matthews, Tate 291
Mawers, Gary 273
Maxwell, James 264
May, Ricky .280
Maybury, Charlotte 270
Mayes, Rosalind 275
Maynard, Dionne 270
Mayne, Lizzie 285
Mayo, Lucy .289
McCall, Rosie 264
McCalmont, Natalie 270
McCann, Lisa 269
McCarthy, Carla 259
McCarthy, Claire 274
McCarthy, James 274
McCathie, Kirsty 266
McCatty, Grace 263
McCatty, Jordan 265
McCaully, Hannah 278
McClintock, Jean-Philippe 274
McCluskey, Alexandra Eve 260
McCluskey, Lizzie 275
McCrea, Kayleigh 277
McCulloch, Luke 270
McDougall, Hannah 267
McErlean, Rebecca 283
McFiggans, Emily 260
McGarry, Joseph 283
McGarry, Kate 265
McGoff, Calum 259
McGrath, Andrew 277
McGregor, Ashlea 288
McIlroy, Bethany 269
McIntosh, Sophie 285
McKean, William 261
McKenner, Claire 276
McKenner, Louise 260
McLean, Jack 265
McLean-Ash, Kira 276
McMahon, Adam 259
McManus, Hollie 269
McMaster, Andrew 265
McMaster, Philippa 270
McMenemy, Lianne 271
McNerney, Joseph 267
McPherson, Chanel 285
McQueen, Adam 264
McWilliams, Kitty 260
Meacher, Rachel 283
Mead, Charlotte 261
Meade, Charlie 283
Meadows, Anna 284
Meaney, Jessie 273
Medlock, Helen 273
Medlock, Richard 288
Meek, Catherine 277
Mehmet, Kim 269
Meikle, Robbie 275
Meineke, Sally 284
Meldram, Jonathan 275
Meller, Claudia 287

Mendies, Nathaniel 281
Meredith, Robyn 290
Merrell, Jessica 277
Merrison, Katy 282
Messer, Jaclyn 278
Metcalfe, Helen 281
Meteyard, Carol 279
Metson, Keeley 268
Meyer, Bailey 290
Meyer, Sarah 287
Meynell, Rebecca 280
Michalik, Daniel 282
Middlehurst, Jennifer 277
Middleton, Leigh 287
Middleton, Rhiann 288
Millard, Holly 262
Millard, Rebecca 278
Miller, Alex .273
Miller, Kathryn 274
Millest, Hannah 273
Millington, Adam 280
Mills, Amy .277
Mills, Fiona .290
Mills, James 278
Mills, Nicholas 261
Mind, Georgina 278
Mistry, Vishal 279
Mitchell, Daniel 278
Mitchell, James 283
Mitchell, Ryan 286
Mitchell, Stuart 277
Mitchell, Thomas 260
Mitchem, Sophie 262
Modak, Stephanie 267
Moffat, Peter 285
Moghal, Umar 266
Monaghan, Kate 309
Money, Suzi 276
Montague, James 261
Moody, Tom 262
Moore, Andrew 262
Moore, Charlotte 276
Moore, Craig 271
Moore, Craig 281
Moore, Isabel 283
Moore, Kimberley 268
Moore, Samantha 281
Moran, Kathryn 266
Moran, Sally 290
More, Sarah 263
Morfoot, Charles 285
Morgan, Hara 268
Morgan, Jenny 280
Morgan, Kelly 288
Morgan, Lee 285
Morley, David 264
Morris, Catherine 266
Morris, Clare 267
Morris, Hannah 288
Morris, Hannah 290
Morris, Jim .266
Morris, Rachel 267
Morris, Sanuel 270
Morrison, Alasdair 271
Morrison, Jenny 271
Morriss, Leanne 268
Mortellaro, Mirella 263
Mortimer, Sophie 260
Morton, Max 271
Moss, Spencer 268

Moynihan, Robyn 275
Mullaly, Joanne 263
Mullender, James 265
Mullett, Aaron 281
Mulvanny, Sara 271
Mumba, Nobuhle 280
Mumford, Peter 263
Mumford, Richard 266
Munday, Hannah 275
Mundy, Christopher 276
Munir, Isma .266
Murali, Madhumathi 263
Murphy, Lewis 262
Murphy, Terri 288
Murphy, Walter 285
Murray, Andrew 288
Mvubu, Sindiwe 265
Myles, Livvy 262

N
Nagle, Paul .296
Najib, Shafiya 296
Nance, Miguel 291
Napier, Kelly 292
Nardelli, Marty 298
Nares, Arthur 293
Narey, Georgia 292
Nash, Katie .296
Nay, Nicola .298
Neal, Jimmy 296
Nedd, Aron .293
Nelson, Harry 295
Nelson, Sarah 291
Ness, James 293
Newberry, Laurence 297
Newby, Lee .294
Newcomb, Tom 291
Newe, Simon 297
Newman, Mark 295
Newman, Stacey 295
Newman, Susie 296
Newton, Jack 292
Newton, Lauren 296
Newton, Lisa 299
Nicholas, Mark 292
Nicholl, David 296
Nichols, Liam Danny 291
Nicholson, Michael 294
Nicoll, Adam 294
Nightingale, James 297
Nolan, Alexandra 291
Nolan, Harriet 294
Nolan, Kirsty 292
Norchi, India 294
Norman, Charlotte 297
Norman, Rebecca 295
Norris, Tabitha 291
North, Sophie 297
Northmore, Sophie 294
Norton, Louise 295
Nott, Dominic 293
Noy, Daniel .295
Noyes, Tamsin 292
Nudd, Joshua 297
Nussbaum, Sarah 293
Nutt, Frances 293

O
O'Brien, Dan 302
O'Brien, Morwenna 301

O'Brien, Nicole 301
O'Callaghan, Craig 302
O'Connor, Anna 297
O'Gorman, Aimee 300
O'Gorman, Heather 301
O'Gorman, Kathryn 301
O'Neill, Lauren 298
O'Reilly, Meg 300
Oaten, Katie 301
Oaten, Lucie 304
Oatham, Daisy 297
Oderdall, Kerry 302
Ogley, Charlotte 299
Olang, Yvonne 301
Oldfield, Megan 298
Oldman, Rachel 312
Oliver, Joanne 299
Oliver, Jonathan 303
Oliver, Thomas 298
Oram, Alison 303
Orchard, Victoria 302
Ore, Samantha 300
Orman, Robin 299
Orme, Danielle 299
Ors, Lara 299
Orvis, Michael 300
Osborne, Conan 298
Osborne, Kelly 302
Osborne, Paige 300
Osborne, Simon 303
Otieno, James 298
Owen, Harvey 303
Owen, James 303
Owen, William 302
Owens, Michael 300

P

Pack, Tamsyn 313
Packer, Sophie 306
Padgett, Sarah 320
Page, Claire 316
Page, Georgina 325
Page, Hannah 310
Page, Rebecca 313
Pahang, Farrah 315
Paine, Laura 316
Paine, Sally 305
Painting, Andrew 326
Paish, Claire 300
Paish, Matthew 336
Palfrey, Anne-Marie 306
Palmer, Bethany 326
Palmer, Carolyne 306
Palmer, Katie 317
Palmer, Kirsty 328
Palmer-Young, Tammi 315
Pardoe, Jonathan 304
Pargin, Amanda 323
Parish, Sarah 319
Parker, Ben 309
Parker, Caitlin 304
Parker, Emily 323
Parker, Sian 319
Parkin, Stephanie 319
Parkinson, Stuart 326
Parkman, Josh 323
Parnham, Lindsay 323
Parr, Lauren 317
Parritt, James 313
Parry, Lieha 320

Parsons, Gemma 324
Parsons, Hellen 328
Parsons, Rhianne 303
Pashley, Vicki 304
Patel, Aakash 313
Patel, Bhavish 306
Paterson, James 305
Paton, Marc 321
Patrick, Michael 319
Patten, Daniel 318
Patterson, Adam 320
Patterson, Kayleigh 310
Patterson, Lauren 318
Paxford, Laura 320
Paxton, Mark 320
Pay, Olivia 318
Payne, Kyle 306
Peach, Matthew 327
Pearce, Aimee 322
Pearce, Ben 319
Pearce, Lindsey 310
Pearce, Richard 303
Pearce, Tom 308
Pearce-Slade, Toby 326
Pearson, Amanda 318
Pearson, Christopher 324
Pearson, Hayley 315
Pearson, Jack 327
Pearson, Matthew 321
Peart, Connor 316
Pease, Gracie 313
Peddle, Michael 325
Peel, Matthew 304
Pegg, Sarah 319
Pegg-Smith, Aston 326
Pemberton, Adam 323
Pendlebury, Carl 317
Penfold, Jamie 328
Pennington, James 308
Pereira, Stephanie 325
Perkins, Joshua 317
Perry, Christopher 324
Perry, Jessica 327
Perry, Sam 320
Perry, Tom 320
Petchey, Sarah 312
Petherick, Rosa 307
Pettitt, Ricci 315
Phelan, Tobie 326
Phillips, Anthony 321
Phillips, Danielle 327
Phillips, Laura 321
Phillips, Natalie 311
Phillips, Nicol 310
Phillips, Ross 324
Pickup, Imogen 324
Pierce, Jonathan 305
Pike, Rebecca 304
Pilkington, Harriet 321
Pilley, Rachel 322
Pinel, Harriet 307
Pinnington, Ryan 321
Plaskasovitis, Akis 314
Playford, Kelsey 305
Pluck, Natalie 313
Plummer, Victoria 311
Plumridge, Imogen 314
Plumridge, Sophie 314
Pocock, Hayley 322
Polden, Katherine 330

Pollard, Zoë 318
Pollitt, William 329
Pomfret, Hannah 309
Pomfret, Rebecca 309
Poole, Andrea 311
Pope, Christopher 328
Porter, Benjamin 314
Portsmouth, Adam 309
Potter, Jake 308
Potter, Joseph 308
Potter, Katherine 317
Potter, Lisa 317
Potter, Stephen 307
Poulter, Charlotte 322
Poulter, Georgina 312
Poulton, David 328
Powdrell, Matthew 328
Powell, Carla 329
Powell, Charlotte 330
Powell, Craig 314
Powell, Fred 307
Powell, Jessica 325
Powell, Karlina 315
Powell, Matthew 310
Powell, Steven' 310
Powell, Stuart 307
Powlesland, Michele 316
Pownall, Lee 311
Prangnell, Jacob 322
Preece, Sarah 308
Preedy, Alexandra 309
Prescott, Stuart 311
Preston, Ellie 315
Pretty, Mark 307
Price, Joshua 312
Price, Katie 322
Price, Lisa 305
Price, Robert 309
Prince, Alastair 308
Prince, Olivia 323
Prior, Rebecca 325
Pritchard, Carl 328
Provis-Evans, Talfryn 305
Pruitt, Astrid Victoria 314
Pryke, Jacob 328
Pugh, Rebecca 318
Pulsford, Jessica 316
Purath, Sian 312
Purchon, James 329
Purkiss, Nicola 324
Purtill, Sarah 311
Purves, Natalie 316
Pye, Jessica 324

Q

Quiggin, Nicola 455
Quill, Sam 326
Quinton, Becky 309
Quinton, Hannah 327
Quirk, Gus 327

R

Raison, Sam 334
Rajapakse, Savini 345
Ralph, Luke 338
Ralph, Tom 342
Ramm, Jessica 341
Ramsell, Gordon 337
Ramsey, Kim 332
Rance, Zoe 349

Rankin, Kathryn 338
Raschke, Alex 348
Rashis, Haris 350
Ratcliffe, Alison 330
Ratcliffe, Toby 333
Rathbone, Leanna 348
Rattue, Jenna 345
Rauss, Rhiannon 340
Rawlinson, Lewis 350
Read, Rikky 338
Read, Ruth 330
Reade, Amy 330
Reading, Daniel 345
Redgrave, James 346
Redmond, Robyn 349
Reed, Emily 334
Reed, Heather 344
Reed, Melissa 338
Reed, Natasha 341
Reed, Steven 338
Reed, Tom 343
Rees, Elena 336
Reeve, Sam 345
Regan, Thomas 335
Reid, Bianca 390
Reid, Marisa 334
Reilly, Paul 339
Rejai-Moghadam, Maryam 332
Remmington, Jason 336
Renals, Emma 345
Renwick, Kellie 342
Reynolds, Karl 335
Reynolds, Mark 349
Reynolds, Matthew 342
Reynolds, Poppy 333
Reynolds, Rachel 10
Rheeston, Josie 347
Rhodes, Catherine 342
Rice, Alex 343
Rice, Fiona 339
Rice, Rhiannon 336
Rice, Shaun 331
Richards, Ashley 348
Richards, Christopher 331
Richards, Emma 344
Richards, Poppy 336
Richards, Saffron 334
Richards, Simon 346
Richards, William 332
Richardson, Ian 325
Richardson, Jessica 349
Richardson, Jonathan 343
Richardson, Kelly 337
Richardson, Laura 348
Richardson, Lucie 334
Richardson, Sarah 350
Richardson, Taylor 350
Richardson, Tom 325
Rickard, Chloe 337
Rickey, Sarah 346
Rickman, Hannah 333
Riddle, Jemma 338
Ridley, Maxine 346
Ridley, Sian 350
Riley, Stacey 335
Ripley, Daniel 350
Risk, Bruce 351
Risley, Jack Elliot 343
Risseh, Joseph 339
Rix, Amy 329

Riza, Ersin Sami 345
Roberson, Michael 341
Roberts, Ashley 342
Roberts, Rhiannon 370
Roberts, Sarah 352
Roberts, Scott 346
Robertson, Adam 335
Robins, Alistair 345
Robinson, Ben 344
Robinson, Daniel 343
Robinson, Emma 343
Robinson, Holly 340
Robinson, Katie 325
Robinson, Laura 347
Robinson, Luke 337
Robinson, Phyllida 333
Robinson, Sally 351
Robson, Michael 341
Robson, Sally 336
Rockall, Alex 329
Rockell, Ellen 349
Rodgers, Heather 341
Roe, Xanthe 335
Rogers, Emma 350
Rogers, Fred 351
Rogers, Lewis 339
Rogers, Molly 349
Rogers, Natalie 347
Rogerson, Lori-Rose 339
Rohl, Johann 345
Rolfe, Thalia 340
Rollings, Siân 352
Rolph, Lee 342
Romsey, Emma 343
Roper, Harriet 339
Roper, Jamie 347
Rose, Alec 340
Rose, Amber 347
Rose, Edward 337
Rose, Jonathan 349
Rose, Lucie 334
Rose-Nokes, Charles 331
Rossi, Aisha 340
Row, Miles 333
Rowbottom, John 351
Rowe, Rebecca 346
Rowles, Elizabeth 333
Royal, Jodie 332
Royce, Victoria 348
Royer, Roxanne 331
Ruddock, Darcy 335
Rudge, Terry 333
Rudman, Olivia 329
Rule, Amanda 330
Rule, Henry 344
Rumbol, Joshua 339
Runnacles, Victoria 344
Rushton, Lauren 341
Russell, Eleanor 347
Russell, Lee 332
Russell, Sarah 348
Russell, Susannah 347
Rutty, Emily 344
Ryan, Christie-Leigh 340
Ryan, Eleanor 351
Ryan, Hannah 334
Rydon, Emma 337
Rymarz, Claire 331
Rymer, Laura 350
Ryrie, Julia 329

S
Sabatowski, George 356
Sabin, Hannah 379
Sach, Georgia 358
Sadler, Louise Kerry 383
Sadler, Victoria 353
Sage, Emma 378
Saleh, Mennar 385
Salim, Humza 393
Salmon, James 370
Salmon, Lorna 380
Salmon, Rebecca 357
Sambells, Dawn 363
Sambridge, Tom 370
Samples, Mark 359
Sandford, Laura 389
Sargent, Sophie 387
Satchell, Greg 389
Saunders, Louisa 365
Saunders, Matthew 370
Saunders, Tim 382
Savage, Sharnie 387
Savile, Kelly 364
Savin, Jennifer 391
Say, Laura 391
Scambler, Francesca 387
Scamell, Mark 388
Schatten, Robert 359
Schendel-Wilson, Chloe 391
Schluter, Kelly 356
Schramm, Jessica 359
Scoppie, Robert 359
Scott, Corey 384
Scott, Gemma 354
Scott, Glenn 391
Scott, Megan 351
Scott, Stephen 383
Scottow, Jack 377
Scrivener, Gillian 354
Scullion, Louise 388
Seagers, Claire 387
Seaton, Zoey 362
Segrue, Scott 375
Sehdev, Aman 363
Sehdev, Karen 356
Sellman, Nicola 378
Sellman-Leava, Joe 371
Sendall-King, Rebecca 378
Serebriakoff, Alexandra 358
Setterington, Ben 393
Seviour, Kimberley 370
Sewell, Ashleigh 393
Sewell, Camilla 371
Seymour, Reece 371
Shah, Nishi 364
Shakespeare, Harry 367
Shanks, Amber 385
Shanmugam, Ben 356
Sharp, Harriet 389
Sharp, Nancia 368
Sharp, Sally 353
Shaw, Charlotte 393
Shaw, Gregory 371
Shea, Michael 383
Shea, Naomi 354
Shears, Alexander 354
Shears, Kristy 352
Sheffield, Abbey 352
Sheldon, Tommy 389
Shellie, Zoe Michelle 387

Shelton, Lauren 361
Shepherd, Alison 357
Shepherd, Lisa 392
Shepherd, Nichola Claire 366
Sheppard, Joseph 380
Sheppard, Kayleigh 380
Shepperson, Emily 386
Shere, Claire 361
Shergold, Ben 353
Sheriff, Hayley 378
Shinn, Andrea 369
Shinn, Jenni 355
Shipley, Jacqui 367
Shippen, Zoe 371
Shirley, Emma 388
Short, Chanah 382
Short, Edward 393
Short, Sarah 366
Shoyer, Poppy 385
Sibthorpe, Kayleigh 385
Sidders, Daniel 385
Siggins, Tasha 374
Silay, Kaan 378
Simm, Rebecca 354
Simmons, Emma 379
Simmons, Thomas 367
Simpson, Brianna 355
Simpson, Jake 352
Simpson, Lee 371
Simpson, Lianne 360
Simpson, Scott 382
Sims, Laura 386
Sims, Michaela 388
Sims, Steven 367
Sinclair, Fiona 379
Singleton, Vicky 358
Singleton, Victoria 367
Sinnott, David 378
Skinner, Katie 356
Skinner, Kelly 382
Skinner, Tom 379
Skitt, Rebecca 386
Skivington, Harry 380
Sklar, Courtney 360
Slack, Laura 380
Slade, James 375
Slater, Charlotte 377
Slater, Emily 379
Slater, Katie 386
Sleeman, Lauren 356
Slight, Molly 382
Sloman, Hannah 374
Small, Jenny 375
Smart, Jacob 355
Smaylen, Katie 374
Smillie, Ellie 357
Smillie, Jonathan 364
Smith, Adam 390
Smith, Alexandra 383
Smith, Amy 375
Smith, Annabelle 366
Smith, Ben .365
Smith, Carl .379
Smith, Carly 364
Smith, Chloe 360
Smith, Daniel 375
Smith, Elizabeth 392
Smith, Frances 369
Smith, Gemma 381
Smith, Harrison 382

Smith, Hayley Susan 381
Smith, James 391
Smith, Jenni 360
Smith, Jenny 361
Smith, Jessica 361
Smith, Jolene 374
Smith, Joshua 375
Smith, Katie 366
Smith, Katie 392
Smith, Kirsty 392
Smith, Laura 365
Smith, Lizzie 380
Smith, Luke 362
Smith, Rebecca 372
Smith, Rebecca 383
Smith, Richard 360
Smith, Rosina 390
Smith, Samantha 360
Smith, Stephanie 361
Smith, Stephanie 367
Smith, Tomas 369
Smith-Brix, Robert 359
Smith-Sheerin, Cal 368
Smyth, Oliver 374
Snape, Kimberley 366
Snow, Nicola 364
Socas, Alicia 376
Somerville, Anna 355
Sommerlad, Jess 391
Sommerville, Hayley 358
Soothill, Louise 376
Southwell, Abigail 357
Spalding, Andrea 355
Spalding, Daniel 354
Sparks, Hannah 355
Sparks, James 392
Spearpoint, Rosie 372
Speer, Joshua 374
Speer, Lily .355
Spence, Charles 376
Spencer, Alex 389
Spencer, Katie-Louise 370
Spooner, Carl 363
Spriggs, Daniel 372
Stacey, Emily 351
Stafford, Sam 390
Stamper, Callum 372
Stanley, James 372
Staples, Leah 375
Stapleton, Katherine 390
Starkey, Brian 390
Starkie, Timothy 373
Staton, Samuel 376
Stedman, Michael 389
Steedman, Kerri 387
Stephens, Matt 357
Stephenson, Emma 352
Sterling, Andrew 358
Sterling, Kerhys 385
Stern-Weiner, Jamie 373
Stern-Weiner, Kate 384
Steven, Robert 362
Stevens, Jack 376
Stevens, Jack 389
Stevenson, Gemma 364
Steward, Jodi 388
Stewart, Anna 358
Stiles-Foley, Cameron 363
Stimpson, Jon 363
Stinton, Luke 383

Stirling, Claire 384
Stock, Claire 386
Stockhan, Holly 376
Stockwell, Bradley 392
Stoddart, Imogen 353
Stoddart, Natasha 391
Stojkowski, Chelsea 366
Stone, Axl 368
Storey, Joe .386
Strahan, Kim 384
Stratford, Adam 364
Stratton, Claire 377
Strike, Helen 362
Stringwell, Tom 363
Strong, Lucy 362
Stubley, Joe 389
Sturman, Katherine 373
Sturmey, Sam 361
Sturt, Isaac .377
Styles, Ashley, ...391
Subtain, Mohammed 373
Sullivan, Kayleigh 357
Sullivan, Stephanie 369
Summerhays, Andrew 392
Summers, Hayley 352
Summers-Rollingson, Charlotte 384
Sunderland, Francesca 393
Susman, Lauren 381
Sutcliffe, Alfie 377
Sutcliffe, Gilly 370
Sutcliffe, Joe 363
Sutcliffe, Oscar 376
Sutton, Chloe 381
Sutton, Henry 384
Sutton, Ian .379
Sutton, Jack 372
Sutton, Louisa 357
Sutton, Rebecca 368
Suzuki, Shogo 352
Swales, Edie 368
Swallow, Becky 377
Swan, Adam 381
Sweeney, Maria 381
Sweeney, Phoebe 390
Sweeney, Rochelle 373
Sweeney, Zachary 354
Swindell, Benjamin 373
Swithinbank, Eleanor 374
Sydenham, Joanne 369
Symes, Daniel 368
Sysum, Sean 392
Sztyber, Max 377

T
Tahir, Kinza 398
Tappin-Beachey, Chanel 402
Tarrant, Aron 405
Tarry, Emma 402
Tatum, Joanna 382
Tawney, Harry 412
Tawney, Jack 409
Tay, Alexander 408
Taylor, Charlotte 396
Taylor, Claire 395
Taylor, David 405
Taylor, David 413
Taylor, Ellen 402
Taylor, Emma 411
Taylor, Gemma 408
Taylor, Gregory 409

Taylor, Jade 407
Taylor, James 412
Taylor, Jennifer 404
Taylor, Jenny 410
Taylor, Jonathon 407
Taylor, Kathryn 406
Taylor, Kurt 411
Taylor, Lauren 410
Taylor, Lewis 406
Taylor, Luke 396
Taylor, Mark 399
Taylor, Mark 412
Taylor, Matthew 404
Taylor, Nicholas 406
Taylor, Richard 406
Taylor, Sophie 409
Taynton, Cara 411
Teahan, John 408
Tebbatt, Thomas 412
Tebble, Joanna 405
Templeton, Molly 410
Terry, Alexandra 415
Teunissen, Lula 394
Thakrar, Nikita 402
Thakrar, Roshni 413
Thakrar, Shyam 396
Thatcher, Steely 414
Thistlethwaite, Wesley 405
Thomas, Ben 399
Thomas, David 409
Thomas, Jack 401
Thomas, Jessie 401
Thomas, Lewis 400
Thompson, Charlotte 395
Thompson, Demi 412
Thompson, Elizabeth 402
Thompson, Emma 400
Thompson, Georgia 405
Thompson, Helen 398
Thompson, Robert 407
Thompson, Scott 397
Thomsett, Joe 395
Thomson, Claire 406
Thomson, James 394
Thorn, Kelly 405
Thorogood, Daniel 397
Thorp, Lee 401
Thorpe, Rosy 408
Thorpe, Zoe 396
Thould, Ben 401
Threlfall, Ben 405
Thwaites, Shannon 408
Thynne, Caroline 402
Thynne, Tom 400
Ticehurst, Karl 395
Tilbury, Warren 401
Tiley, Jack 398
Tilley, Eleanor 394
Tilston, Michael 409
Timms, Jessica 403
Tindall, Helen 399
Titmus, Natalie 8
Toch, Florence 409
Todd, Leonie 404
Tofari, Matheos 409
Tomes, Bryn 404
Tomkins, Cassie 397
Tomlinson, James 395
Tonta, Michelle 403
Toomey, William 400

Topley, Shane 394
Topliss, Naomi 398
Tosh, Justin 394
Totty, Michael 405
Tout, Jade 403
Townsend, Sarah 407
Townsend, Sophie 403
Townsend, Tom 404
Townsend, Vicky 411
Trafford, Nicholas 413
Tranter, Ellie 396
Tresidder, Craig 403
Trevelyan, Daniel 410
Trimming, Keiran 397
Trivett, Rebecca 394
Trood, Amy 393
Trow, Clair 411
Troward, Oliver 406
Tubbs, Sophie 412
Tuck, George 407
Tuck, Sophie 400
Tucker, Charlie 398
Tucker, Martin 399
Tucker, Shannon 394
Tuckett, Lisa 403
Tugwell, Anthony 404
Tunaley, Craig 398
Turczak, April 397
Turner, Andrew 397
Turner, Ben 395
Turner, Bethany 414
Turner, Ellen 410
Turner, Frances 396
Turner, Jenny 401
Turner, William 407
Turnnidge, Emily 400
Turrell, Sam 404
Tutty, Rachel 399
Twyman, Jack 399
Tyler, Sophie 407

U
Unsworth, Stuart 416
Unwin, Robert 416
Urwin, Matthew 413
Usher, Luke 413
Usher, Sam 416
Utracik, Emerson 416

V
Van Den Bergh, Cornelia 416
Van Schie, Carl 414
Van Tankeren, Antoon 414
Vancooten, Temmel 415
Vass, Rebecca 414
Vaughan, Katie 413
Vaughan, Scott 417
Veale, Sandy 415
Vece, Alexandra 417
Venn, Kelly 417
Venner, Jamie 414
Vermeulen, Samantha 417
Vertigan, Prudence 412
Vincent, Katie 415
Viner, Alastair 417
Viner, David 409
Virgin, Clair 415
Virr, Ella 416

W
Wadey, Jack 440
Wadman, Jorge 439
Wagstaff, Emma-Louise 439
Wai, Patty .443
Wainwright, Jen 423
Wakefield, Anna 435
Wakeman, Jodie 420
Walbridge, Lauren 433
Waldron, Ben 422
Waldron, Jessica 418
Wales, Dot 450
Walker, Hannah 439
Walker, Joshua 449
Walker, Lewis 441
Walker, Matthew 442
Walker, Milli 451
Walker-Shaw, Natasha 449
Wall, Jade .440
Wallace, Helen 420
Wallace, Nathan 421
Wallis, Guy 442
Walrond, Heather 450
Walsh, Hannah 455
Walsh, Kayleigh 439
Walsh, Leon 441
Walsh, Lucy 421
Walsh, Lucy 450
Walshe, Siobhan 419
Walters, Amy 455
Walters, Brett 427
Walters, Carl 439
Walton, Alexander 443
Walton, James 443
Waltrich, Marc 421
Ward, Danielle 7
Ward, James Lee 432
Ward, James 418
Ward, Jasmine 448
Ward, Kelvin 422
Ward, Sam .445
Ware, Becky 447
Ware, Samuel 441
Wark, Freya 445
Warne, Sam 415
Warnes, Ruth 439
Warren, Jessica 438
Warren, Nicola 429
Wasylyczyn, Kirsty 450
Waterfall, Simon 427
Wateridge, Paul 450
Waters, Ashley 442
Waterson, Kathryn 423
Watkins, Alistair 452
Watkins, Wendy 451
Watson, Alistair 443
Watson, Ben 420
Watson, Matty 442
Watson, Megan 442
Watson, Spencer 432
Watts, Anna 442
Watts, Stuart 426
Way, Alexander 450
Wearing, Rachel 446
Weatherall, Zara 423
Weatherseed, Eleanor 445
Webb, Charley 434
Webb, Christopher 433
Webb, George 418
Webb, Naomi 451

Webb, Oliver 448
Webb, Rebecca 430
Webb, Toby 446
Webster, Kelly 428
Webster, Matthew 437
Webster, Shanise 419
Weedon, Richard 420
Weedon, Toby 441
Weetman, Edward 445
Weingart, Luke 451
Welch, Anthony 446
Welch, Charlie 423
Weldon, Robert 448
Welham, Charlotte 449
Welling, Rebecca 434
Welling, Robert 429
Wells, Chrisopher 421
Wells, Leanne 447
Wells, Megan 444
Wenham, Matthew 446
West, Alice 449
West, Natalie 437
Westgate, Esme 446
Westley, Anna 419
Weymouth, Thomas 413
Wheatcroft, Charlotte 448
Wheatley, Charlotte 431
Wheatley, Laura 431
Wheeler, Jamey-Louise 422
Whelan, James 420
Whelan, Leanne 447
Wheldon, Sara 428
Whiffin, Maddison 452
Whitaker, Stephen 438
Whitby, Hannah 419
Whitchurch, Matthew 452
White, Alice 447
White, Amanda 421
White, Anthony 440
White, Antoinette 431
White, Charlotte 440
White, Harry 448
White, Jack 441
White, Jemma 437
White, Kimberley 448
White, Olivia 452
White, Sarah 437
White, William 427
Whitehead, Tristan 440
Whitehurst, Amy 448
Whiteley, Mark 421
Whiteway, Simon 440
Whitfield, Lucy 452
Whitham, Samantha 444
Whitmore, Anica 444
Whittaker, Carl D. 423
Whittaker, Jamie 447
Whitwood, Rachel 446
Wibberley, Joe 426
Wickert, Robyn 430
Wickett, Francesca 441
Wickham, Chris 446

Wiggins, Martin 447
Wilcock, Sammy-Jo 444
Wilcox, Michael 445
Wild, Samantha-Jo 434
Wildney, Martyn 418
Wiles, Becky 427
Wiles, Ryan 452
Wilkerson, Amanda 420
Wilkerson, Joanna 424
Wilkins, Thomas 426
Wilkinson, Nina 449
Willan, Katie 424
Willbourne, Beverley 429
Willets, Dale 426
Willett, Tasha 451
Williams, Aimee 430
Williams, Amy 438
Williams, Ben 419
Williams, Bethan 444
Williams, Daniel 437
Williams, Daniel 437
Williams, Emma 445
Williams, Hayley 433
Williams, Jordan 438
Williams, Juan 443
Williams, Lawrence 427
Williams, Michelle 426
Williams, Nicola 431
Williams, Rebecca 445
Williams, Richard 413
Williams, Samuel 444
Williams, Sarah 438
Williams, Shaun 440
Williams, Steven 426
Williamson, Ross 427
Willis, Mia 418
Willis, Natasha 180
Willis, Rachel 429
Willman, Hannah 438
Willson, Kirsty 449
Willwohl, Cassandra 423
Wilmott, Sarah 430
Wilshere, Jack 427
Wilson, Adam 433
Wilson, Amber 429
Wilson, Andrew 422
Wilson, Karen 435
Wilson, Luke 422
Wilson, Miriam 443
Winch, Sarah 438
Winchester, Chloe 438
Wing, Rebecca 443
Wingfield, Beth 418
Winship, Shaun 420
Winskill, Katherine 414
Wise, David 435
Wise, Katie 428
Wiseman, Patrick 419
Wolstencroft, Joseph 424
Wong, Michelle 437
Wong, Stephanie 433
Wood, Chelsea 432

Wood, Frances 424
Wood, Hannah 430
Wood, Meggie 425
Wood, Richard 425
Wood, Simon 436
Wooding-Jones, Tom 424
Woods, Corin 432
Woods, Hayley 424
Woods, Lauren 437
Woodward, Hollie 424
Wookey, Chloe 435
Woolhouse, Paul 425
Woolley, Jack 431
Woolsey, Katie 436
Wooltorton, Andie 421
Worrall, Thomas 428
Worth, Jessica 432
Worth, Joseph 433
Wozniak, Adam 436
Wressell, Tamsin 430
Wride, Ben 432
Wride, Charlotte 434
Wright, Conner 425
Wright, Emma 422
Wright, Fiona 428
Wright, George 423
Wright, James 436
Wright, Joanna 430
Wright, Liam 426
Wright, Maria 435
Wright, Naomi 428
Wright, Nicholas 425
Wright, Stacey 434
Wright, Susan 437
Wright, Susan 437
Wylie, Maddie 425
Wynne, Zahra 436

Y
Yan, June 451
Yearsley, Katy 453
Yellowley, Paul 455
Yellowley, Sarah 453
Yerrell, Leonie 453
Young, Alex 453
Young, Becky 454
Young, Brett 455
Young, Holly 453
Young, James 454
Young, Jamie 454
Young, Michael 455
Young, Robert 454
Young, Zena 453

Z
Zaheer, Samah 454
Zaman, Nazneen 454
Zaw, Khant 455
Zieleniewski, Francis 452
Zyla, Carly 454